Autodesk Inventor 11 for Designers

CADCIM Technologies

525 St. Andrews Drive
Schererville, IN 46375
USA
(www.cadcim.com)

Contributing Authors

Sham Tickoo

Professor
Department of Mechanical Engineering Technology
Purdue University Calumet
Hammond, Indiana
U.S.A.

Deepak Maini

Sr. CADD Engineer
CADCIM Technologies

CADCIM Technologies

Autodesk Inventor 11 for Designers
Sham Tickoo

ISBN 1-932709-17-7

Sales Manager: *Santosh Tickoo*
Marketing and Development Manager: *Archana Dhar*
Copy editor: *Pragya Katariya*
Technical Editor: *Suresh T.V.*
Cover designer: *Deepak Maini*
Cover illustration: *Created by Deepak Maini using Autodesk Inventor and Photoshop software*
Typeface: *10/12 New Baskerville Bt*

www.cadcim.com

DEDICATION

*To teachers, who make it possible to disseminate knowledge
to enlighten the young and curious minds
of our future generations*

*To students, who are dedicated to learning new technologies
and making the world a better place to live*

SPECIAL RECOGNITION

*A special thanks to Mr. Denis Cadu and the ADN team of Autodesk Inc.
for their valuable support and professional guidance to
procure the software for writing this textbook*

THANKS

*To the faculty and students of the MET department of
Purdue University Calumet for their cooperation*

To engineers of CADCIM Technologies for their valuable help

Free Teaching Resources for Faculty

The following teaching resources are available for free to faculty:

1. *Online technical support by contacting techsupport@cadcim.com.*
2. *All part files, assembly files, and drawing files used for illustrations, tutorials, and exercises in this book.*
3. *Customizable PowerPoint presentations for every chapter of the book.*
4. *Instructor's guide with answers to review questions and solution to exercises.*
5. *Course outlines.*
6. *Students projects.*

To access the web site that contains these teaching aids, please contact the author, Prof. Sham Tickoo, at the following address.

stickoo@calumet.purdue.edu
or
tickoo@cadcim.com

Free Teaching Resources for Students

Note:
These resources are available only for the users who buy the textbook from our web site www.cadcim.com or the university/college bookstores. We need proof of purchase when you request the technical support

1. Free online technical support by contacting techsupport@cadcim.com.
2. All Part, Assembly, and Drawing files used in illustrations and tutorials in this book.
3. Additional student projects.
4. Tips and Notes.

For more information, please visit www.cadcim.com

Table of Contents

Chapter 3: Editing, Extruding, and Revolving Sketches

Chapter 8: Assembly Modeling-I

Chapter 9: Assembly Modeling-II

Chapter 10: Working with Drawing Views-I

Chapter 11: Working with Drawing Views-II

Chapter 12: Presentation Module

Chapter 13: Working with Special Design Tools

Chapter 14: Working with Sheet Metal Components

Chapter 15: Introduction to Weldments

Preface

AUTODESK INVENTOR 11

Autodesk Inventor, developed by Autodesk Inc., is one of the world's fastest growing solid modeling software. It is a parametric feature-based solid modeling tool that not only unites the 3D parametric features with 2D tools but also addresses every design-through-manufacturing process. The adaptive technology of this solid modeling tool allows you to handle an extremely large assembly with tremendous ease. Based mainly on the solid modeling users' feedback, this solid modeling tool is remarkably user-friendly and it allows you to be productive from day one.

This solid modeling tool allows you to easily import the AutoCAD, AutoCAD Mechanical, and Mechanical Desktop files with an amazing compatibility. The parametric features and assembly parameters are retained when you import the Mechanical Desktop files in Autodesk Inventor.

The 2D drawing views of the components are automatically generated in the layouts. The drawing views that can be generated include orthographic view, isometric view, auxiliary view, section view, detailed view, and so on. You can use predefined drawing standard files for generating the drawing views. You can retrieve the model dimensions or add reference dimensions to the drawing views whenever you want. The bidirectional associative nature of this software ensures that any modification made in the model is automatically reflected in the drawing views. Similarly, any modification made in the dimensions in the drawing views are automatically reflected in the model.

Autodesk Inventor 11 for Designers textbook is written with an intent of helping the people who are into 3D design. This book is written with the tutorial point of view with learn-by-doing as the theme. The mechanical engineering industry examples and tutorials are used in this book to ensure that the user can relate the knowledge of this book with the actual mechanical industry designs. The salient features of the book are as follows:

- **Sheet Metal Module**
    This book includes the complete coverage of the Sheet Metal module of Autodesk Inventor. There are fifty-six pages of heavily illustrated text on Sheet Metal module that cover each and every tool of this module.

- **Tutorial approach**
    The author has adopted the tutorial point-of-view with learn-by-doing as the theme throughout the textbook. This approach guides the users through the process of creating the models in the tutorials.

- **Real-World Projects as Tutorials**

    The author has used about 55 real-world mechanical engineering projects as tutorials in this book. This enables the reader to relate the tutorials to the real-world models in the mechanical engineering industry. In addition, there are about 40 exercises that are also based on the real-world mechanical engineering projects.

- **Coverage of all Autodesk Inventor modules**

    All the modules of Autodesk Inventor are covered in this book including the **Presentation** module for animating the assemblies, the **Sheet Metal** module for creating the sheet metal components, and the **Weldment** module for creating weldments.

- **Tips and Notes**

    Additional information related to the topics is provided to the users in the form of tips and notes.

- **Learning Objectives**

    The first page of every chapter introduces in brief the topics that are covered in that chapter. This helps the users to easily refer to a topic.

- **Tools section**

    The first page of every chapter summarizes the topics that are covered in the chapter.

- **Self-Evaluation Test, Review Questions, and Exercises**

    Every chapter ends with a Self-Evaluation Test so that the users can assess their knowledge of the chapter. The answers of the Self-Evaluation Test are given at the end of the chapter. Review Questions and Exercises given at the end of each chapter can be used by the Instructors as test questions and exercises.

- **Heavily illustrated text**

    The text in this book is heavily illustrated with about 1200 line diagrams and screen capture images.

Introduction

AUTODESK INVENTOR RELEASE 11

Welcome to the world of Autodesk Inventor. If you are new to the world of three-dimensional (3D) design, then you have joined hands with thousands of people worldwide who are already working with 3D designs. If you are already using any other solid modeling tool, you will find this solid modeling tool more adaptive to your use. You will find a tremendous reduction in the time taken to complete a design using this solid modeling tool.

Autodesk Inventor is a parametric and feature-based solid modeling tool. It allows you to convert the basic two-dimensional (2D) sketch into a solid model using very simple, but highly effective modeling options. This solid modeling tool does not restrict its capabilities to the 3D solid output, but also extends them to the bidirectional associative drafting. This means that you only need to create the solid model. Its documentation, in the form of the drawing views, is easily done by this software package itself. You just need to specify the required view. This solid modeling tool can be specially used at places where the concept of **"collaborative engineering"** is brought into use. Collaborative engineering is a concept that allows more than one user to work on the same design at the same time. This solid modeling tool allows more than one user to simultaneously work on the same design.

As a product of Autodesk, this software package allows you to directly open the drawings of the other Autodesk software like AutoCAD, Mechanical Desktop, AutoCAD LT, and so on. This interface is not restricted to the Autodesk software only. You can easily import and export the drawings from this software package to any other software package and vice versa.

To reduce the complicacies of the design, this software package provides various design environments. This helps you to capture the design intent easily by individually incorporating the intelligence of each of the design environments into the design. The design environments that are available in this solid modeling tool are discussed next.

Part Module

This is a parametric and feature-based solid modeling environment and is used to create solid models. The sketches for the models are also drawn in this environment. All applicable constraints are applied to the sketch automatically while drawing. You do not need to invoke an extra command to apply them. Once the basic sketches are drawn, you can convert them into solid models using simple, but highly effective modeling options. One of the major advantages of using Autodesk Inventor is the availability of the Design Doctor. The Design

Doctor is used to calculate and describe errors, if any, in the sketch. You are also provided with the remedy for removing errors such that the sketches can be converted into features. The complicated features can be captured in this module and can later be used in other parts. This reduces the time taken to create the designer model. These features can be created using the same principles as those for creating solid models.

Assembly Module

This module helps you to create the assemblies by assembling multiple components using assembly constraints. This module supports both the bottom-up approach as well as the top-down approach of creating assemblies. This means that you can insert external components into the **Assembly** module or create the components in the **Assembly** module itself. You are allowed to assemble the components using the smart assembly constraints. All the assembly constraints can be added using a single dialog box. You can even preview the components before they are actually assembled. This solid modeling tool supports the concept of making a part or a feature in the part adaptive. An adaptive feature or a part is the one that can change its actual dimensions based upon the need of the environment.

Presentation Module

A major drawback of most solid modeling tools is their limitation in displaying the working of an assembly. The most important question asked by the customers in today's world is how to show the working of any assembly. Most of the solid modeling tools do not have an answer to this question. This is because they do not have proper tools to display an assembly in motion. As a result, the designers cannot show the working of the assemblies to their clients. In cases where it is necessary to show the animation, they have to take the help of some other software packages such as 3D Studio MAX or 3D Studio VIZ. However, keeping this problem in mind, this software package provides a module called the **Presentation** module. In this module, you can animate the assemblies created in the **Assembly** module and view their working. You can also view any interference during the operation of the assembly. The assemblies can be animated using easy steps.

Drawing Module

This module is used for the documentation of the parts or assemblies in the form of drawing views. You can also create the drawing views of the presentation created in the **Presentation** module. All parametric dimensions, added to the components in the **Part** module during the creation of the parts are displayed in the drawing views in this module.

Sheet Metal Module

This module is used to create the sheet metal component. When you invoke a sheet metal file, the sketching environment is active by default. You can draw the sketch of the base sheet in this module and then proceed to the sheet metal module to covert it into the sheet metal component.

GETTING STARTED WITH AUTODESK INVENTOR

Install Autodesk Inventor on your system and then start it by double-clicking on the Autodesk Inventor 11 shortcut icon on the desktop of your computer. This icon will be automatically created when you install the software on to your system. You can also start Autodesk Inventor by using the taskbar shortcuts. Choose the **Start** button on the lower left corner of the screen. Choose **Programs** to display the **Program** menu. In the **Program** menu, choose **Autodesk > Autodesk Inventor 11 > Autodesk Inventor 11**, as shown in Figure I-1.

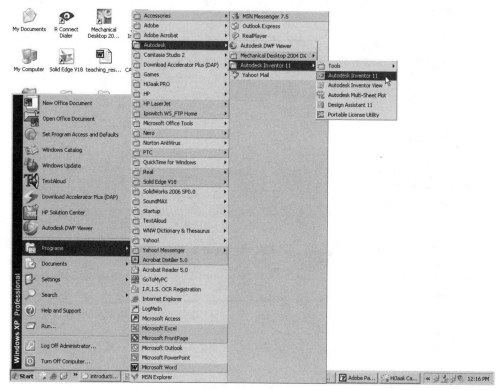

Figure I-1 *Starting Autodesk Inventor using the taskbar shortcuts*

The system will prepare to start Autodesk Inventor by loading all the required files. After loading these files, the **Open** dialog box will be displayed. Choose **New** from the **What To Do** area to display the **Default**, **English**, and **Metric** tabs for selecting a new file. Choose the **Metric** tab and then double-click on the **Standard (mm).ipt** template to open a default metric template, see Figure I-2.

A new part file with the default name of **Part1.ipt** will be opened and you can start working in this file. The initial screen appearance of Autodesk Inventor is shown in Figure I-3. This figure also displays various components of this screen.

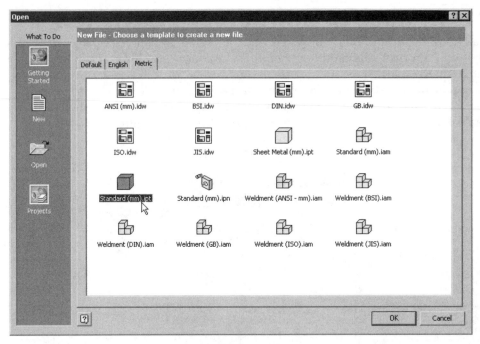

*Figure I-2 Selecting the **Standard (mm).ipt** template from the **Metric** tab*

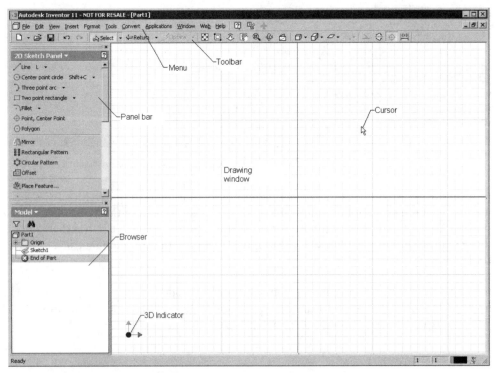

Figure I-3 Initial screen appearance of Autodesk Inventor along with the components

It is evident from Figure I-3 that the screen of Autodesk Inventor is quite user-friendly. Apart from the components shown in Figure I-3, you are also provided with various shortcut menus, which are displayed upon right-clicking the mouse. The type of the shortcut menu and its options will depend on where or when you are trying to access this menu. For example, when you are inside any command, the options displayed in the shortcut menu will be different from the options displayed when you are not inside any command. These shortcut menus will be discussed when they are used in the book.

TOOLBARS

You might have noticed that there is no command prompt in Autodesk Inventor. The complete designing process is carried out by invoking the commands from the toolbars. Therefore, Autodesk Inventor provides you with various types of toolbars while working with various design environments. This means that the toolbars available while working with the **Part**, **Assembly**, **Drawing**, **Sheet Metal**, and **Presentation** modules will be different.

Part Module Toolbars

A number of toolbars can be invoked in the **Part** module. The toolbars that will be extensively used during the designing process in this environment are described next.

Inventor Standard Toolbar

This toolbar is common to all the design environments of Autodesk Inventor. However, some of these options will not be available in all the environments. The **Inventor Standard** toolbar is shown in Figure I-4.

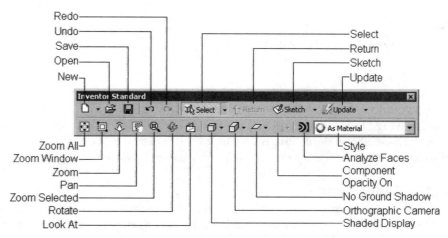

*Figure I-4 The **Inventor Standard** toolbar*

Some of the important options in this toolbar are discussed next.

Select

This tool is used to set the selection priority. When you choose the down arrow on the right of this button, three more buttons are displayed. These buttons are **Select features**, **Select faces and edges**, and **Select sketch elements**. The **Select features** button is chosen to set the selection priority to features. If this button is chosen, you can select any feature in the model. The **Select faces and edges** button is chosen to set the priority to faces and edges. If this button is chosen, you can select the faces and edges of the features. The **Select sketch elements** button is chosen to set the priority to sketched entities. If this button is chosen, you can select the entities of the sketches in the sketcher environment.

Return

This button is chosen to exit the sketching environment. Once you have finished the sketch, choose this button to proceed to the **Part** module where you can convert the sketch into a feature using the required tools. When you choose this button, the **2D Sketch Panel** panel bar is replaced by the **Part Features** panel bar.

Sketch

This button is chosen by default when you start a new file in the **Part** module and is used to draw a 2D sketch. Because the first feature in most designs is a sketched feature, you can directly start working on the sketch of the feature. Once you have completed a sketch, you can choose the **Return** button or choose the **Sketch** button again to exit the sketching environment. Whenever you need to draw the sketch for another feature, choose this button. You will be prompted to select the plane for sketching the feature. Once you define the new sketching plane, the sketching environment will be activated.

Update

This button is chosen to update the design after editing.

Style

This drop-down list is used to select the display style of the entities, features, or parts. In the sketching environment, you can select the normal or the construction option from this drop-down list. In the **Drawing** module, you can select the line or edge styles from this drop-down list. In the **Part** or the **Assembly** module, this drop-down list is replaced by the **Color** drop-down list. You can select the color for the selected models using this drop-down list.

2D Sketch Panel Toolbar

This is one of the most important toolbars in the **Part** module. All tools for creating the sketches of the parts are available in this toolbar. The **2D Sketch Panel** toolbar is shown in Figure I-5.

Tip. *In Autodesk Inventor 11, the messages and prompts are also displayed on the lower left corner of the Autodesk Inventor window.*

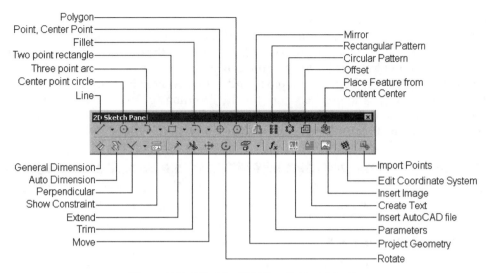

*Figure I-5 2D The **2D Sketch Panel** toolbar*

Part Features Toolbar

This is the second most important toolbar provided in the **Part** module. Once the sketch is completed, you need to convert it into a feature using the modeling commands. This toolbar provides all the modeling tools that can be used to convert the sketch into a feature. The **Part Features** toolbar along with all the buttons available in it is shown in Figure I-6.

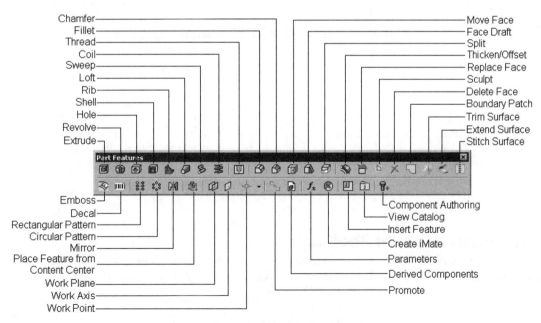

*Figure I-6 The **Part Features** toolbar*

Inventor Precise Input Toolbar

You are now aware of the fact that Autodesk Inventor does not provide you with any command prompt. Because of this, you will be restricted from entering the precise values of the sketcher entities. But this problem was foreseen and has been taken care of in Autodesk Inventor by providing you with a very important toolbar called the **Inventor Precise Input** toolbar. This toolbar is used to enter the precise values for the coordinates of the sketcher entities. This toolbar is also available in the **Drawing** and **Assembly** modules for providing the precise values. The **Inventor Precise Input** toolbar is shown in Figure I-7.

*Figure I-7 The **Inventor Precise Input** toolbar*

Sheet Metal Features Toolbar

This toolbar provides the tools that are used to create sheet metal parts. This toolbar will be available only when you are in the sheet metal environment. You can proceed to the sheet metal environment by choosing **Sheet Metal** from the **Application** menu. The **Sheet Metal Features** toolbar is shown in Figure I-8.

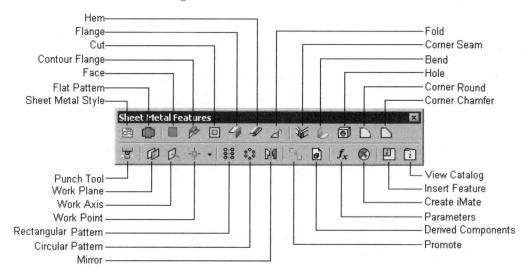

*Figure I-8 The **Sheet Metal Features** toolbar*

Assembly Module Toolbars

All the above-mentioned toolbars are also available in this environment. In addition to these toolbars, this environment also provides the **Assembly Panel** toolbar, see Figure I-9.

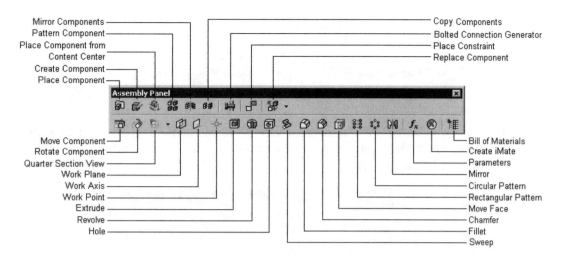

*Figure I-9 The **Assembly Panel** toolbar*

Drawing Module Toolbars

The **Inventor Standard**, **2D Sketch Panel**, and **Inventor Precise Input** toolbars are also available in this environment. In addition to these toolbars, the **Drawing** module provides you with the following two toolbars.

Drawing View Panel Toolbar

This toolbar is extensively used in the drawing environment for generating the drawing views. The **Drawing View Panel** toolbar is shown in Figure I-10

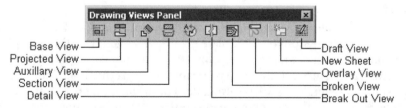

*Figure I-10 The **Drawing View Panel** toolbar*

Presentation Module Toolbar

The **Inventor Standard** toolbar is also available in this environment. In addition to this toolbar, the **Presentation** module provides you with the **Presentation Panel** toolbar, as shown in Figure I-11.

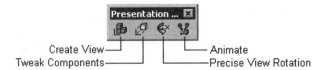

*Figure I-11 The **Presentation Panel** toolbar*

In most toolbars, you will notice that there are some buttons that have an arrow on the right. These arrows are called the down arrows. When you choose these arrows, some more related buttons will be displayed, see Figure I-12.

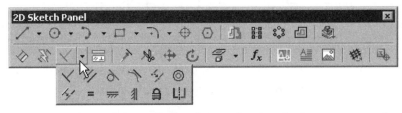

*Figure I-12 More buttons displayed upon choosing the down arrow on the right of the **Perpendicular** button*

ADDITIONAL DESIGN TOOLS

Autodesk Inventor has gone a step ahead from the other solid modeling tools in making the design intent easier. This is done by introducing the panel bar and the browser to invoke the commands or to perform an operation. Both these additional tools make the design intent a lot more easier and also appreciably reduce the time consumed in completing the design.

Panel Bars

The panel bars are generally provided on the left of the drawing window. The panel bar provides only those tools that will be required to complete the design at that step. For example, when you are in the sketching environment, at that time only the tools that are required for sketching will be available in the panel bar. Similarly, when you want to convert the sketch into a feature, at that time only the solid modeling tools will be available. This implies that the tools in the panel bar will be different for each of the designing environment of Autodesk Inventor. Figures I-13 to I-18 show the panel bars in various designing environments.

Figure I-13 The *2D Sketch Panel* panel bar

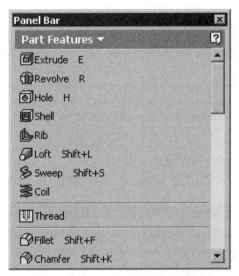

Figure I-14 The *Part Features* panel bar

*Figure I-15   The **Sheet Metal Features** panel bar*

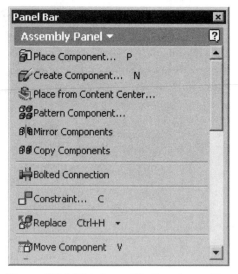

*Figure I-16   The **Assembly Panel** panel bar*

*Figure I-17   The **Drawing Views Panel** panel bar*

*Figure I-18   The **Presentation Panel** panel bar*

Browser

This is the second additional tool that is provided to make the designing process easier. The browser is also available on the left side of the drawing window and below the panel bar. It displays all the operations that were performed during the designing process in the order in which these were performed. All these operations are displayed in the form of a tree view. The contents of the browser are different for different environments of Autodesk Inventor. For example, in the **Part** module, it displays various operations that were used in creating the part. Similarly, in the **Assembly** module, it displays all the components along with the constraints that were used to assemble them.

UNITS FOR DIMENSIONS

While installing Autodesk Inventor on your system, you can specify the unit (inch or millimeter) that will be used to measure the length in the Inventor environments. If you select inch as the unit, the English standard will be followed. Similarly, if you select millimeter as the unit, the Metric standard will be followed. This book follows the millimeter unit. Therefore, it is recommended that you install Autodesk Inventor for Metric standards by selecting the unit in millimeter.

IMPORTANT TERMS AND THEIR DEFINITIONS

Before you proceed further in Autodesk Inventor, it is very important for you to understand the following terms, which are widely used in this book.

Featured-based Modeling

A feature is defined as the smallest building block that can be modified individually. In Autodesk Inventor, the solid models are created by integrating a number of these building blocks. Therefore, the models in Autodesk Inventor are a combination of a number of individual features. These features understand their fit and function properly. As a result, these can be modified, whenever required. Generally, these features automatically adjust their values, if there is any change in their surrounding. For example, a feature created by cutting right through the base feature will automatically adjust its depth, if you increase the depth of the base feature. This provides greater flexibility to the design.

Parametric Modeling

The parametric nature of a software package is defined as its ability to use the standard properties or parameters to define the shape and size of a geometry. The main function of this property is to derive the selected geometry to the new size or shape without considering its original size or shape. For example, you can derive a line of 20 mm that was initially drawn at an angle of 45° to a line of 50 mm and change its orientation to 90°. This property makes the designing process very easy. This is because now you do not need to draw the sketch to the actual dimensions that are required. You just need to draw the sketch to some relative dimensions, and then this solid modeling tool will drive it to the actual values you require.

Bidirectional Associativity

As mentioned earlier, this solid modeling tool does not restrict its capabilities to the 3D solid output. It is also capable of highly effective assembly modeling, drafting, and presentations. There exists a bidirectional associativity between all these environments of Autodesk Inventor. This means that at everytime, there exists a link between all the environments of Autodesk Inventor. This link ensures that if any modification is made in the model in any one environment, it is automatically reflected in the other environments immediately.

Adaptive

This is a new but highly effective property that is included in the designing process of this solid modeling tool. In any design, there are a number of components that can be used at various places with a small change in their shape and size. This property makes the part or the feature adapt to its environment. It also ensures that the adaptive part changes its shape and size as soon as it is constrained to the other parts. This considerably reduces the time and effort required in creating similar parts in the design.

Design Doctor

The Design Doctor is one of the most important parts of the designing process using this solid modeling tool. It is a highly effective tool to ensure that the entire design process is error free. The main purpose of the Design Doctor is to make you aware of any problem in the design. The Design Doctor works in three steps.

Selecting the Model and Errors in the Model

In this step, the Design Doctor selects the sketch, part, assembly, and so on and determines the errors in it.

Examining Errors

In this step, it examines the errors in the selected design. Each of the errors is individually examined and the required solution is provided.

Providing the Solutions for the Errors

This is the last step of the working of the Design Doctor. Once it has individually examined each of the errors, it suggests solutions for them. It provides you with a list of methods that can be utilized in order to remove the errors from the design.

Constraints

These are the logical operations that are performed on the selected design to make it more accurate or define its position with respect to the other design. There are four types of constraints in Autodesk Inventor. All these types are explained next.

Geometric Constraints

These logical operations are performed on the basic sketching entities to relate them to the standard properties like collinearity, concentricity, perpendicularity, and so on. Autodesk Inventor automatically applies these geometric constraints to the sketcher entities at the time of their creation. You do not have to use an extra command to apply these constraints on to the sketcher entities. However, you can also manually apply these geometry constraints on to the sketcher entities. There are eleven types of geometric constraints.

Perpendicular

This constraint is used to make the selected line segment normal to another line segment.

Parallel

This constraint is used to make the selected line segments parallel.

Tangent
This constraint is used to make the selected line segment or curve tangent to another curve.

Coincident
This constraint is used to make two points or a point and a curve coincident.

Concentric
Applying this constraint forces two selected curves to share the same center point. The curves that can be made concentric are arcs, circles, or ellipses.

Colinear
Applying this constraint forces two selected line segments or ellipse axes to be placed in the same line.

Horizontal
This constraint forces the selected line segment to become a horizontal line.

Vertical
This constraint forces the selected line segment to become a vertical line.

Equal
This constraint forces the selected line segments to become equal in length. It can also be used to force two curves to become equal in radius.

Smooth
This constraint forces adds a smooth constraint between a spline and another entity so that at the point of connection, the line is tangent to the spline.

Fix
This constraint fixes the selected point or curve to a particular location with respect to the coordinate system of the current sketch.

Symmetric
This constraint forces the selected sketched entities to become symmetrical about a sketched line segment, which may or may not be a center line.

Assembly Constraints
The assembly constraints are the logical operations performed on the components in order to bind them together to create an assembly. These constraints are applied to reduce the degrees of freedom of the components. There are four types of assembly constraints.

Mate
The **Mate** constraint is used to make the selected faces of different components coplanar. The model can be placed facing in the same direction or in the opposite direction. You can also specify some offset distance between the selected faces.

Angle

The **Angle** constraint is used to place the selected faces of different components at some angle with respect to each other.

Tangent

The **Tangent** constraint is used to make the selected face of a component tangent to the cylindrical, circular, or conical faces of the other component.

Insert

The **Insert** constraint forces two different circular components to share the same orientation of the central axis. It also makes the selected faces of the circular components coplanar.

Motion Constraints

The motion constraints are the logical operations performed on the components that are assembled using the assembly constraints. There are two types of motion constraints.

Rotation

The **Rotation** constraint is used to rotate one component of the assembly in relation to the other component. Both the components rotate about the specified central axis.

Rotation-Translation Constraint

The **Rotation-Translation** constraint is used to rotate the first component in relation to the translation of the second component.

Transitional Constraints

The transitional constraints are also applied on the assembled components and are used to ensure that the selected face of the cylindrical component maintains contact with the selected faces of the other component when you slide the cylindrical component.

Note
The motion and the transitional constraints are applied on the components that have already been assembled using the assembly constraints. Therefore, these constraints work along the degrees of freedom of the components that are not restricted using the assembly constraints.

Consumed Sketch

A consumed sketch is a sketch that is utilized in creating a feature using tools such as **Extrude**, **Revolve**, **Sweep**, **Loft**, and so on.

CYCLING THROUGH ENTITIES

While working on the complicated models, you have to sometimes select the entities that are not visible in the current view or are hidden behind other entities. To select these type of entities, Autodesk Inventor allows you to cycle through the entities using a cycling tool. This tool is displayed automatically when you hold the cursor at a point where more than one entity is available. You can also display the cycling tool by pressing the SPACEBAR on the keyboard. This cycling tool consists of two arrows at each end and a rectangle in between. The left arrow is used to cycle through the previous entities, the right arrow is used to cycle through the next entities, and the rectangle is used to select the highlighted entity. The current entity will be highlighted and displayed in red. Once the required entity is highlighted, move the cursor over the rectangle in the cycling tool and select it using the left mouse button. The highlighted entity will be selected and displayed in blue. Figure I-19 shows the cycling tool displayed in the sketching environment to cycle through the sketched entities. You can use this tool in all the modes and environments of Autodesk Inventor.

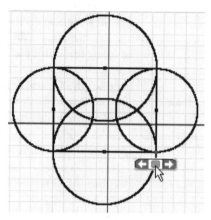

Figure I-19 Cycling through the entities

HOT KEYS

As mentioned earlier, there is no command prompt in Autodesk Inventor. However, you can still use the keys on the keyboard to invoke some tools. The keys that can be used to invoke the tools are called hot keys. Remember that the working of the hot keys will be different in different environments. All the hot keys that can be used in different environments are discussed next.

Part Module

The hot keys that can be used in the **Part** module are given next.

E	Invokes the Extrude tool
R	Invokes the Revolve tool
H	Invokes the Hole tool
SHIFT+L	Invokes the Loft tool
SHIFT+S	Invokes the Sweep tool
SHIFT+F	Invokes the Fillet tool
SHIFT+K	Invokes the Chamfer tool
SHIFT+D	Invokes the Face Draft tool
SHIFT+R	Invokes the Rectangular Pattern tool
SHIFT+O	Invokes the Circular Pattern tool
SHIFT+M	Invokes the Mirror Feature tool
]	Invokes the Work Plane tool
/	Invokes the Work Axis tool
.	Invokes the Work Point tool
Q	Invokes the Create iMate tool

The following hot keys are used in the sketching environment.

L	Invokes the Line tool
SHIFT+C	Invokes the Center point circle tool
D	Invokes the General Dimension tool
X	Invokes the Trim tool

Assembly Module

In addition to the hot keys of the part modeling tool, the following hot keys can also be used in the **Assembly** module.

P	Invokes the Place Component tool
N	Invokes the Create Component tool
C	Invokes the Place Constraint tool
CTRL+H	Invokes the Replace Component tool
SHIFT+H	Invokes the Replace All tool
V	Invokes the Move Component tool
G	Invokes the Rotate Component tool

Drawing Module

The hot keys that can be used in the **Drawing** module are given next.

A	Invokes the Baseline Dimension tool
B	Invokes the Balloon tool
D	Invokes the General Dimension tool
O	Invokes the Ordinate Dimension Set tool
F	Invokes the Feature Control Frame tool

Presentation Module

The hot keys that can be used in the **Presentation** module are given next.

T	Invokes the Tweak Components tool

In addition to these keys, you can also use some other keys for the ease of designing. Note that you will have to hold some of these keys down and use them in combination with the pointing device. These hot keys are discussed next.

F1	Help
F2	Pan Realtime
F3	Zoom Realtime
F4	Rotate
F5	Previous View
SHIFT+F5	Next View
CTRL	Command Modifiers
SHIFT	Command Modifiers
ESC	Abort the Command

COLOR SCHEME

Autodesk Inventor allows you to use various color schemes as the background color of the screen and for displaying the entities on the screen. Note that this book uses the **Presentation** color scheme with a single color background. To change the color scheme, choose **Tools > Application Options** from the menu bar; the **Options** dialog box will be displayed. Choose the **Colors** tab to display the predefined colors. Select the **Presentation** option from the **Color Scheme** list box. Next, select **1 Color** from the drop-down list in the **Background** area. Choose **Apply** and then choose **OK** to apply the color scheme to the Autodesk Inventor environment. Note that all the files you open henceforth will use this color scheme.

Chapter 1

Drawing Sketches for Solid Models

Learning Objectives

After completing this chapter, you will be able to:
- *Start a new template file for drawing sketches.*
- *Set up the sketching environment.*
- *Understand various drawing display tools.*
- *Understand the sketcher environment in the Part module.*
- *Get acquainted with the sketcher entities.*
- *Draw sketches using various sketcher entities.*
- *Delete sketched entities.*

THE SKETCHING ENVIRONMENT

Most designs that you create are a combination of sketched, placed, and work features. The placed and the work features can be created directly without creating sketches, but the sketched features require sketches. In most of the designs, the first or the base feature has to be a sketched feature. Therefore, in any design, you first need to draw the sketch of the base feature. You can add more features to the base feature later to complete the design. In the sketching environment, you will learn to draw the sketches for the base features. The same concept can also be used to add more sketched features to the base feature for completing the design. A sketch is the basic contour for the solid model. For example, consider the model shown in Figure 1-1.

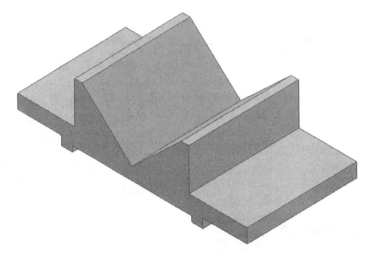

Figure 1-1 *A solid model*

This model is created using a sketched feature. The basic sketch for the sketched feature is shown in Figure 1-2. Once you have drawn the basic sketch, you need to convert it into a solid model using simple but highly effective solid modeling tools.

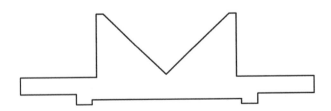

Figure 1-2 *The basic sketch for the solid model*

The sketching environment of Autodesk Inventor can be invoked at any time in the **Part** module or in the **Assembly** module. Unlike other solid modeling programs, here you just need to invoke the **Sketch** tool and specify the plane to draw the sketch; the sketching environment will be activated. Also, when you start a new file in the **Part** module, first the sketching environment will be active. You can draw a sketch in this environment and then proceed to the part modeling environment for converting the sketch into a solid model. The options in the sketching environment will be discussed later in this chapter.

STARTING A NEW FILE

The first step after you start any solid modeling tool is to start a new file. As mentioned in Introduction, when you start Autodesk Inventor, the **Open** dialog box will be displayed. The options in this dialog box are discussed next.

Getting Started

The **Getting Started** options are automatically displayed when you start Autodesk Inventor for the first time. These options are used to select various types of help topics for working in Autodesk Inventor, see Figure 1-3. You can perform tasks such as finding out the enhancements in the latest release, opening a tutorial mode that will guide you through various steps of creating solid models, browsing the help topics of Autodesk Inventor, viewing animations, and so on. You can also improve your knowledge of Autodesk Inventor using the links provided in this dialog box.

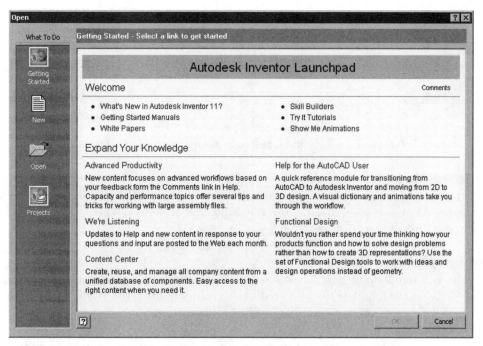

Figure 1-3 The **Getting Started** options in the **Open** dialog box

New

The options provided on choosing **New** are extensively used during the designing process using Autodesk Inventor. These options are used to select a template file for starting a design. You can select a template in the **Default**, **English**, or **Metric** standards. If you have installed Autodesk Inventor by selecting millimeter as the unit for measurement, the metric standard will be used on starting the standard template in the **Default** tab. However, if you have installed Autodesk Inventor by selecting inch as the unit for measurement, you need to select templates from the **Metric** tab, see Figure 1-4. The templates that are available on choosing the **Metric** tab are discussed next.

*Figure 1-4 Default templates displayed under the **Metric** tab of the **Open** dialog box*

.ipt Templates

Select the *.ipt* template to start a new part file for creating a solid model or a sheet metal component. When you open this file, the sketching environment will be automatically active and you can directly start drawing sketches.

.iam Templates

Select the *.iam* template to start a new assembly file for assembling various parts. Similarly, use the *Weldment.iam* template to weld two different components in the **Weldment** module.

.ipn Templates

Select the *.ipn* template to start a new presentation file for animating the assembly. The **Presentation** module marks the basic difference between Autodesk Inventor and other design tools. This module allows you to animate the assemblies created in the **Assembly** module.

For example, you can create a presentation in the **Presentation** module that shows a Drill Press Vice assembly in motion. The presentations are created using simple but highly effective tools provided in the **Presentation** module.

.idw Templates

Select the *.idw* template to start a new drawing file for generating the drawing views. You can use the drawing templates of various standards that are provided in this tab, such as ANSI, ISO, DIN, GB, JIS, and BSI.

Open

The options provided on choosing **Open** are used to open the existing files, see Figure 1-5. You can select the file to be opened from the list displayed in the dialog box. The preview of the selected file will be displayed in the preview window provided in the lower left portion of this dialog box. By default, you can open any file created using Autodesk Inventor. The reason for this is that by default, the **Files of type** drop-down list displays the **Inventor Files (*.iam;*.idw;*.ide;*.ipt;*.ipn)** option. You can also open the files created in other solid modeling programs such as AutoCAD or Pro/ENGINEER by selecting their respective options from the **Files of type** drop-down list.

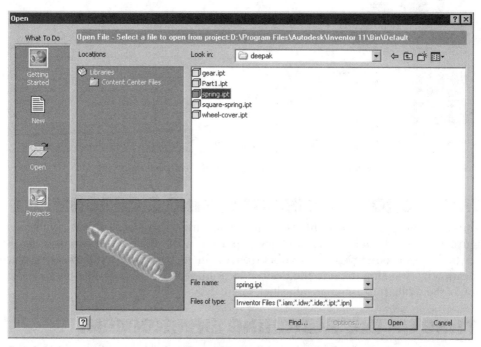

Figure 1-5 The Open File options of the Open dialog box

Projects

In Autodesk Inventor, a project defines all the files related to a design project you are working on. All the available project folders will be displayed in the upper half of the dialog box and the options of the project folder will be displayed in the lower half of the dialog box. To add another project folder to this list, choose the **New** button to display the **Inventor project wizard** dialog box. Specify the name of the project in the **Name** text box and the location in the **Project (Workspace) Folder** text box. You can also choose the **Browse for project location** button to locate the project. Next, choose **Finish**. Once you have selected the project folder, it will be added in the upper part of the dialog box and its location will also be displayed. When you select a project, the options related to it will be shown in the lower part of the dialog box. The **Open** dialog box, with various **Projects** options, is shown in Figure 1-6.

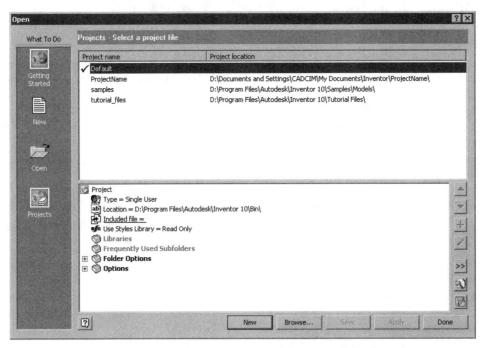

Figure 1-6 *The* **Projects** *options of the* **Open** *dialog box*

INTRODUCTION TO THE SKETCHING ENVIRONMENT

The initial screen appearance in the sketching environment of a *Standard (mm).ipt* file is shown in Figure 1-7. In addition to the toolbars displayed in the figure, you can also invoke the desired toolbar by choosing **View > Toolbar** from the menu bar. These toolbars can be placed at any location by dragging them to the desired location. You can also double-click on the blue portion of the toolbars to automatically dock them.

SETTING UP THE SKETCHING ENVIRONMENT

It is very important to first set up the sketcher environment. This has to be done before you start drawing a sketch. Setting up the sketcher environment includes modifying the grids of a drawing. It is unlikely that the designs you want to create will consist of small dimensions. You will come across a number of designs that are large. Therefore, before starting a drawing, you need to modify the grid settings. These settings will depend on the dimensions of the design. The process of modifying the grid settings of a drawing is discussed next.

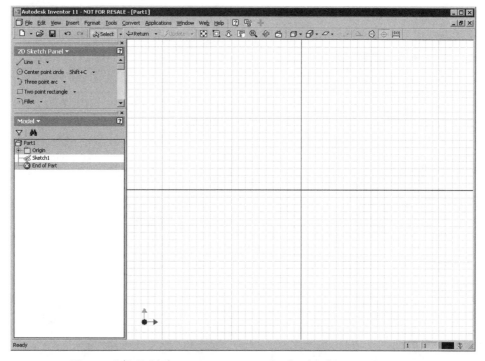

Figure 1-7 Initial screen appearance in the sketching environment

Modifying the Grid Settings of the Drawing

You must have noticed that the drawing window in the sketching environment consists of a number of light and dark lines that are drawn normal to each other. These normal lines are called grid lines. The grid is used as a reference for specifying the precise location of the entities while sketching. Based on the requirement of the sketch, you need to modify the grid settings by choosing **Tools > Document Settings** from the menu bar. When you choose this option, the **Document Settings** dialog box will be displayed. In this dialog box, choose the **Sketch** tab to display the options related to the sketching environment, see Figure 1-8. The options provided under this tab are discussed next.

Snap Spacing Area

The options under this area are used to specify the snap and grid spacing.

X
This edit box is used to specify the grid spacing in the X direction.

Y
This edit box is used to specify the grid spacing in the Y direction.

Grid Display Area

The options in this area are used to control the number of major and minor lines. The minor

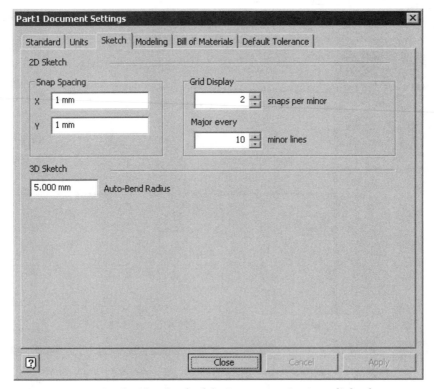

Figure 1-8 *The* **Sketch** *tab of the* **Document Settings** *dialog box*

lines are the light lines that are displayed inside the dark gray lines. The dark gray lines are called the major lines.

Snaps per minor
This spinner is used to specify the number of snap points between each minor line.

Major every minor lines
This spinner is used to specify the number of minor lines between two major lines.

Note
You will have to increase the drawing display area after increasing the grid spacing. The options to do so are discussed next.

Tip. *You can also turn off the display of the major and minor grid lines and the axes. To turn off the display, choose* **Tools > Application Options** *from the menu bar; the* **Options** *dialog box will be displayed. Choose the* **Sketch** *tab and clear the* **Grid Lines**, **Minor Grid Lines**, *and the* **Axes** *check boxes in the* **Display** *area.*

UNDERSTANDING THE DRAWING DISPLAY TOOLS

The drawing display tools are an integral part of any design software. These options are extensively used during the design process. Some of the drawing display tools in Autodesk Inventor are discussed next. The remaining ones will be discussed in later chapters.

Zoom All

Menu:	View > Zoom All
Toolbar:	Inventor Standard > Zoom All

 The **Zoom All** tool increases the drawing display area to include all the sketched entities in the current display. Pressing the HOME key also performs the same function.

Zoom Window

Menu:	View > Zoom Window
Toolbar:	Inventor Standard > Zoom Window

The **Zoom Window** tool is used to define an area to be magnified and viewed in the current drawing. The area is defined using two diagonal points of a box (called window) in the drawing window. The area inscribed inside the window will be magnified and displayed on the screen.

 Tip. *The size of the dimension text always remains constant even if you magnify the area that includes some dimensions.*

To switch to the previous view, right-click in the drawing window and then choose **Previous View** *from the shortcut menu or press the F5 key. Using this option, you can restore ten previous views in the current sketching environment*

Zoom

Menu:	View > Zoom
Toolbar:	Inventor Standard > Zoom

The **Zoom** tool is used to interactively zoom in and out of the drawing. When you choose this button, the default cursor is replaced by the arrow cursor. You can zoom into the drawing by pressing the left mouse button and dragging the cursor down. Similarly, you can zoom out of the drawing by pressing the left mouse button and then dragging the cursor up. You can exit this tool by choosing another tool or by pressing ESC. You can also choose **Done** from the shortcut menu, which is displayed on right-clicking.

 Tip. *You will need to increase the drawing display area by zooming out from the drawing using the* **Zoom** *tool after increasing the grid spacing.*

Pan

Menu:	View > Pan
Toolbar:	Inventor Standard > Pan

The **Pan** tool is used to drag the current view in the drawing window. This option is generally used to display the contents of the drawing that are outside the display area, without actually changing the magnification of the current drawing. It is similar to holding the drawing and dragging it across the drawing window.

Zoom Selected

Menu:	View > Zoom Selected
Toolbar:	Inventor Standard > Zoom Selected

When you choose the **Zoom Selected** button, you will be prompted to select the entity to zoom. The selected entity will be magnified to the maximum extent and placed at the center of the drawing window. This tool can also be invoked by pressing the END key.

SKETCHING ENTITIES

Getting acquainted with the sketching entities is an important part of learning Autodesk Inventor. A major part of the design is created using the sketcher entities. Therefore, this section can be considered as one of the most important sections of the book. In Autodesk Inventor, the sketched entities are of two types: **Normal** and **Construction**. The normal entities are used to create a feature and become a part of it, but the construction entities are drawn just for reference and support, and cannot become a part of the feature. By default, all drawn entities are normal entities. To draw construction entities, choose the **Construction** button from the **Inventor Standard** toolbar. All entities drawn after choosing the **Construction** button will be the construction entities. Clear this button by choosing it again to draw normal entities.

The sketcher entities that can be drawn in Autodesk Inventor are discussed next.

Drawing Lines

Toolbar:	2D Sketch Panel > Line
Panel Bar:	2D Sketch Panel > Line

Lines are the basic and one of the most important entities in the sketching environment. As mentioned earlier, you can draw either normal lines or construction lines. A line is defined as the shortest distance between two points. The two points are the start point and the endpoint of the line. Therefore, to draw a line, you need to define these two points. Because Autodesk Inventor is parametric in nature, you can draw the initial line of any length or at any angle by just picking the points on the screen. After drawing, you can drive the line to a new length or angle using parametric dimensions. You can also directly create the line of actual length and angle using the **Inventor Precise Input** toolbar. Both these methods of drawing the lines are discussed next.

Drawing Lines by Picking the Points in the Drawing Window

This method is very convenient for drawing lines and is extensively used while sketching. When you invoke the **Line** tool from the **2D Sketch Panel** toolbar or panel bar, the cursor (that was initially an arrow) is replaced by crosshairs with a yellow circle at the intersection. Also, at the lower left corner of the Autodesk Inventor window, you are prompted to select the start point of the line or drag off the endpoint for the tangent arc. The point of intersection of the X and Y axes (black lines among the grid lines) is the origin point. If you move the cursor close to the origin, it snaps to the origin automatically. The coordinates of the cursor location in the drawing window are displayed on the lower right corner of the Autodesk Inventor window. To start drawing the line, specify a point anywhere in the drawing window; a rubber-band line starts from that point. One end of this rubber-band line is fixed at the point you specified in the drawing window and the second end is attached to the yellow circle in the crosshairs.

Note that after specifying the start point of the line, the lower right corner of the Autodesk Inventor window displays three columns. The first column displays the coordinates of the current location of the cursor, the second column displays the current length of the line, and the third column displays the current angle of the line. Taking the reference from these columns, you can move the cursor and specify the endpoint of the line. On doing so, a line is drawn and a new rubber-band line starts. The start point of the new rubber-band line is the endpoint of the last line and you are prompted to specify the endpoint of the line. You can continue specifying the endpoints to draw continuous lines.

When you draw entities in Autodesk Inventor, the valid constraints are automatically applied to the entities. Therefore, when you draw continuous lines, the horizontal, vertical, perpendicular, and parallel constraints are automatically applied to them. The symbol of the applied constraint is displayed on the line being drawn. You can exit the **Line** tool by pressing the ESC key or by choosing another tool button. You can also right-click in the drawing window and choose **Done** from the shortcut menu. Figures 1-9 and 1-10 display the perpendicular and parallel constraints being applied to the lines when they are being drawn.

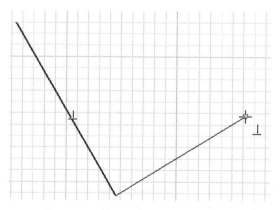

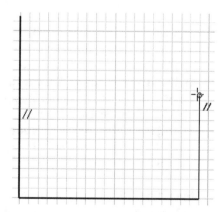

Figure 1-9 *Drawing a line with the perpendicular constraint*

Figure 1-10 *Drawing a line with the parallel constraint*

Tip. *You can turn off the automatic applications of the constraints while sketching by pressing and holding down the CTRL key while drawing the entities.*

Drawing Lines by Specifying the Exact Values

This is the second method of drawing lines in Autodesk Inventor. This method uses the **Inventor Precise Input** toolbar to define the coordinates of the start point and the endpoint of the lines. As mentioned earlier, the origin of the drawing lies at the intersection of the X and Y axes. The X and Y coordinates of this point are 0,0. Taking the reference of this point, you can draw lines. There are two methods of defining the coordinates using this toolbar. Both these methods are discussed next.

Specifying the Coordinates with Respect to the Origin

This system of defining the coordinates is also termed as the **absolute coordinate system**. In this system, the coordinates of the point are defined with respect to the origin of the drawing. By default, the origin lies at the intersection of the X and Y axes. All the points in this system are defined with respect to this origin. To define the points, you can use the following four methods.

Defining the Absolute X and Y Coordinates. In this method, you will define the X and Y coordinates of the new point with respect to the origin. To invoke this method, select the **Indicate a point location by typing X and Y values** option from the drop-down list in the **Inventor Precise Input** toolbar. The exact X and Y coordinates of the point can be entered in the **X** and **Y** edit boxes provided in this toolbar.

Defining the Absolute X Coordinate and the Angle from the X Axis. In this method, you will define the absolute X coordinate of a point with respect to the origin and the angle that this line makes with the positive X axis. The angle will be measured in the counterclockwise direction from the positive X axis. To invoke this method, select the **Specify a point using X coordinate and angle from X-axis** option from the drop-down list. The X coordinate of the new point and the angle can be defined in the respective edit boxes in the **Inventor Precise Input** toolbar.

Defining the Absolute Y Coordinate and the Angle from the X Axis. In this method you will define the absolute Y coordinate of a point with respect to the origin and the angle that this line makes with the positive X axis. To invoke this method, select the **Specify a point using Y coordinate and angle from X-axis** option from the drop-down list. The Y coordinate of the new point and the angle can be defined in the respective edit boxes in the **Inventor Precise Input** toolbar.

Specifying the Distance from the Origin and the Angle from the X Axis. In this method, you will define the distance of the point from the origin and the angle that this line makes with the X axis. To invoke this method, select the **Specify a point using distance from the origin and angle from X-axis** option from the drop-down list. The distance and the angle can be defined in the respective edit boxes.

Specifying the Coordinates with Respect to the Last Point

This system of specifying the coordinates is also termed as the **relative coordinate system**. In this type of system, the coordinates of the next point are specified with respect to the previous point. Note that this system of defining the points cannot be used for specifying the first point (the start point of the line). All the absolute coordinate methods for specifying a point with respect to the origin can also be used with respect to the last specified point by choosing the **Precise Delta** button along with the respective method. This button will be available only after you specify the start point of the first line.

Note

While drawing continuous lines, when you move the cursor close to the start point of the first line, the yellow circle changes to green and the cursor snaps to the start point. Selecting the point at this stage closes the loop and you exit the current line chain.

Restarting a Line

To restart a line, right-click and choose **Restart** from the shortcut menu. The start point of the line is canceled and you are prompted to select the start point of the line.

Drawing Circles

In Autodesk Inventor, you can draw circles using two methods. You can draw a circle by defining the center and the radius of the circle or draw a circle that is tangent to three specified lines. Both these methods of drawing the circle are discussed next.

Drawing Circles by Specifying the Center Point and the Radius

Toolbar:	2D Sketch Panel > Center point circle
Panel Bar:	2D Sketch Panel > Center point circle

This is the default method of drawing circles. In this method, you need to define the center point and the radius of the circle. To draw this type of circle, choose the **Center point circle** button; you will be prompted to select the center of the circle. As soon as you specify the center point, you will be prompted to specify a point on the circle. This point will define the circle radius. You can also specify the center and the radius using the **Inventor Precise Input** toolbar. Figure 1-11 shows a circle drawn by specifying the center and the radius.

Drawing Circles Using Three Tangent Lines

Toolbar:	2D Sketch Panel > Center point circle > Tangent circle
Panel Bar:	2D Sketch Panel > Center point circle > Tangent circle

This is the second method of drawing circles. This method draws a circle that is tangent to three selected lines. To invoke this option, choose the down arrow besides the **Center point circle** button in the **2D Sketch Panel** panel bar and then choose the **Tangent circle** button. You will be prompted to select the first, second, and third lines. As soon as you specify the three lines, a circle tangent to all three specified lines is drawn, as shown in Figure 1-12.

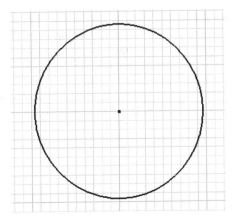

Figure 1-11 *Circle drawn using the center point and the radius of the circle*

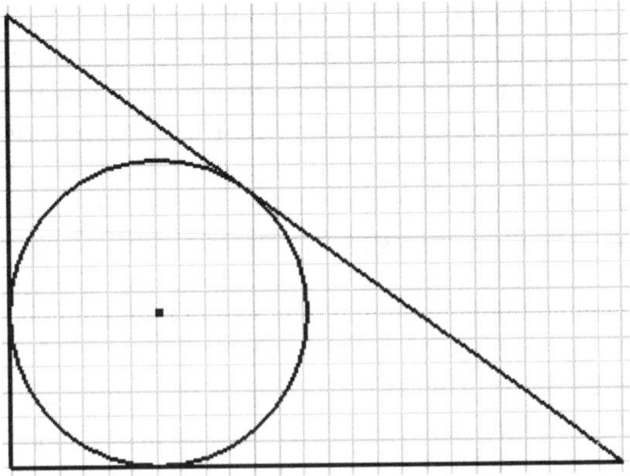

Figure 1-12 *Circle drawn using three tangent lines*

Drawing Ellipses

Toolbar:	2D Sketch Panel > Center point circle > Ellipse
Panel Bar:	2D Sketch Panel > Center point circle > Ellipse

To draw an ellipse, choose the down arrow located on the right of the **Center point circle** button in the **2D Sketch Panel** panel bar and then choose the **Ellipse** button. On doing so, you will be prompted to specify the center of the ellipse, the first axis point, and a point on the ellipse. You can also specify these points using the **Inventor Precise Input** toolbar. However, remember that you cannot use the relative options for defining the points of the ellipse. Therefore, if you use the **Inventor Precise Input** toolbar for drawing the ellipse, all the values will be specified from the origin. But you can redefine the origin by choosing the **Precise Redefine** button and placing it at the point that you want to define as the origin. Figure 1-13 shows an ellipse.

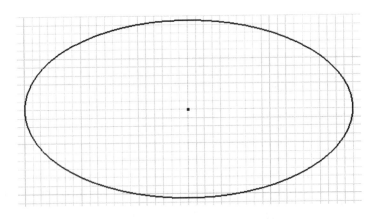

Figure 1-13 *An ellipse drawn in the sketching environment*

Drawing Arcs

Autodesk Inventor provides three methods for drawing arcs, which are discussed next.

Drawing an Arc Using Three Points

Toolbar:	2D Sketch Panel > Three point arc
Panel Bar:	2D Sketch Panel > Three point arc

This is the default method of drawing arcs. This method draws an arc using three points. The first point is the start point of the arc, the second point is the endpoint of the arc, and the third point is a point on the arc. You can define these points by specifying them in the drawing window or by using the **Inventor Precise Input** toolbar. Figure 1-14 shows an arc drawn using this method.

Drawing an Arc Tangent to an Existing Entity

Toolbar:	2D Sketch Panel > Three point arc > Tangent arc
Panel Bar:	2D Sketch Panel > Three point arc > Tangent arc

This method draws an arc that is tangent to an existing open entity. The open entity can be an arc or a line. To invoke this method, choose the down arrow located on the right of the **Three point arc** button and then choose the **Tangent arc** button. On doing so, you will be prompted to select the start point of the arc. The start point of the arc has to be the start point or the endpoint of an existing open entity. Once you specify the start point, a rubber-band arc starts from it. Note that this arc is tangent to the selected entity. Next, you will be prompted to specify the endpoint of the arc. It is very important to mention here that you cannot use the **Inventor Precise Input** toolbar to select the start point of this arc. However, you can use this toolbar to specify the endpoint of this arc. Figure 1-15 shows an arc drawn tangent to the line.

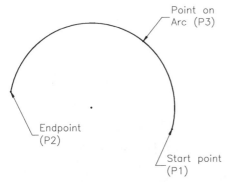

Figure 1-14 Drawing the three point arc

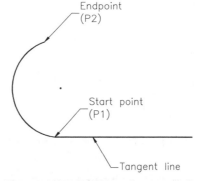

Figure 1-15 Drawing the tangent arc

Drawing Tangent/Normal Arcs Using the Line Tool

You can also draw a tangent or a normal arc when you are inside the **Line** tool. At least a line or an arc should be drawn before drawing the arc using this method. To draw the arc using the **Line** tool, draw a line or an arc and then invoke the **Line** tool. When you are prompted to select the start point of the line, move the cursor close to the point from where you want to start the tangent or normal arc; the yellow circle in the cursor turns green. Select the point at this stage. If you draw the arc in continuation with the lines, you do not need to perform this step. Next, move the cursor back to the point that you selected; the yellow circle in the cursor turns gray. Press the left mouse button and drag the mouse. Four construction lines appear at the start point displaying the normal and tangent directions. If you drag along the tangent direction, a tangent arc is drawn. But if you drag along the normal direction, an arc normal to the selected entity is drawn.

Drawing an Arc Using the Center, Start, and Endpoint of the Arc

Toolbar:	2D Sketch Panel > Three point arc > Center point arc
Panel Bar:	2D Sketch Panel > Three point arc > Center point arc

To invoke this method, choose the down arrow located on the right of the **Three point arc** button in the **2D Sketch Panel** panel bar and then choose the **Center point arc** button. This method allows you to draw an arc by specifying the center point, start point, and endpoint of the arc. On choosing this button, you will be prompted to specify the center point of the arc. Once you specify the center, you will be prompted to specify the start point and then the endpoint of the arc, see Figure 1-16. You can also use the **Inventor Precise Input** toolbar to specify these three points of the arc. As you define the center point and the start point, the radius of the arc will be automatically defined. Therefore, the third point is just used to define the arc length. If the distance between the endpoint of the arc and the center of the circle is more than the circle radius, an imaginary line is drawn from that point to the center of the arc. The point at which the arc intersects the imaginary line will then be taken as the endpoint of the arc, see Figure 1-17.

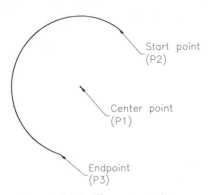

Figure 1-16 The center point arc

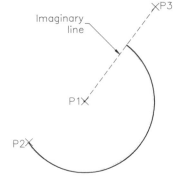

Figure 1-17 The center point arc

Drawing Rectangles

In Autodesk Inventor, rectangles can be drawn using the following two methods.

Drawing Rectangles Using the Two Opposite Corners

Toolbar:	2D Sketch Panel > Two point rectangle
Panel Bar:	2D Sketch Panel > Two point rectangle

This is the default method of drawing rectangles. This method draws a rectangle by specifying its two opposite corners. On choosing the **Two point rectangle** button, you will be prompted to specify the first corner of the rectangle. Once you specify the first corner, you are prompted to specify the opposite corner of the rectangle. Figure 1-18 shows a rectangle drawn using the **Two point rectangle** method.

Drawing Rectangles Using Three Points on a Rectangle

Toolbar:	2D Sketch Panel > Two point rectangle > Three point rectangle
Panel Bar:	2D Sketch Panel > Two point rectangle > Three point rectangle

You can invoke this method by choosing the down arrow on the right of the **Two point rectangle** button in the **2D Sketch Panel** panel bar and then choosing the **Three point rectangle** button. This method draws a rectangle using three points. The first two points are used to define the length and angle of one of the sides of the rectangle and the third point is used to define the length of the other side. On invoking this method, you will be prompted to specify the first corner of the rectangle. Once you specify it, you will be prompted to specify the second corner of the rectangle. Both these corners are along the same direction. Therefore, these points are used to define the length of one side of the rectangle. After specifying the second corner, you will be prompted to specify the third corner. This corner is used to define the length of the other side of the rectangle. Note that if you specify the second corner at a certain angle, then the resultant rectangle will also be inclined. You can also specify the three points for drawing the rectangle using the **Inventor Precise Input** toolbar. Figure 1-19 shows an inclined rectangle drawn using the **Three point rectangle** method.

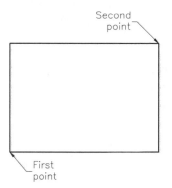

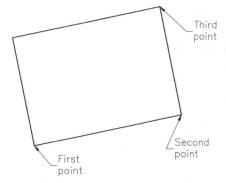

Figure 1-18 Drawing a rectangle using two points

Figure 1-19 Drawing the three point rectangle at an angle

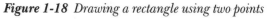

Tip. *You can move the lines by selecting them using a window or crossing and then dragging them to a new location. However, note that dragging arcs or circles will modify their radius. To move these entities, you need to select their center points and then drag them.*

You will learn more about selecting objects using a window or a crossing later in this chapter.

Drawing Polygons

Toolbar:	2D Sketch Panel > Polygon
Panel Bar:	2D Sketch Panel > Polygon

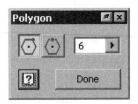

The polygons drawn in Autodesk Inventor are regular polygons. A regular polygon is a multisided geometric figure in which the length of all sides and the angle between them are the same. In Autodesk Inventor, you can draw a polygon with the number of sides ranging from 3 to 120. When you invoke the **Polygon** tool, the **Polygon** dialog box will be displayed, as shown in Figure 1-20, and you will be prompted to select the center of the polygon. The options in this dialog box are discussed next.

Figure 1-20 The **Polygon** *dialog box*

Inscribed

This is the first button in the **Polygon** dialog box and is chosen by default. This option is used to draw an inscribed polygon. An inscribed polygon is the one that is drawn inside an imaginary circle such that its vertices touch the circle. Once you have specified the polygon center, you will be prompted to specify a point on the polygon. In case of an inscribed polygon, the point on the polygon specifies one of its vertices, see Figure 1-21.

Circumscribed

This is the second button in the **Polygon** dialog box and is used to draw a circumscribed polygon. A circumscribed polygon is the one that is drawn outside an imaginary circle such that its edges are tangent to the imaginary circle. In case of a circumscribed polygon, the point on the polygon is the midpoint of one of the polygon edges, see Figure 1-22.

Number of Sides

This edit box is used to specify the number of sides of the polygon. The default value is 6. You can enter any value ranging from 3 to 120 in this edit box.

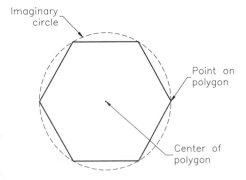

Figure 1-21 *Drawing a six-sided inscribed polygon*

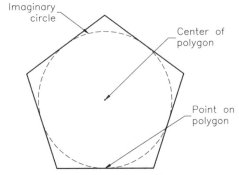

Figure 1-22 *Drawing a five-sided circumscribed polygon*

Note

The rectangles and polygons are a combination of individual lines. All the lines can be separately selected or deleted. However, when you select one of the lines and drag, the entire rectangle or polygon will be considered as a single entity. Therefore, the entire object is moved or stretched.

Placing Points/Center Points

Toolbar:	2D Sketch Panel > Point, Center Point
Panel Bar:	2D Sketch Panel > Point, Center Point

 In Autodesk Inventor, the sketched points or the hole centers are placed using the **Point, Center Point** button in the **2D Sketch Panel** toolbar. If the **Center Point** button is chosen in the **Inventor Standard** toolbar, when you invoke this tool, you will be prompted to select the hole center point and a hole center will be placed. But, if the **Center Point** button is not chosen when you invoke this tool, you will be prompted to select a sketch point; a sketched point will be placed. You can specify the point location by picking a point or by entering the value in the **Inventor Precise Input** toolbar.

 Tip. *You can redefine the origin of the current drawing while drawing an entity by placing a point at the desired origin and then relocating the origin. To relocate the origin, invoke any sketching tool and choose the **Precise Redefine** button from the **Inventor Precise Input** toolbar. Now, click on the origin of the triad and then click on the point where you want to place it. To relocate the origin back to the actual origin, choose the **Reset to Origin** button.*

Creating Fillets

Toolbar:	2D Sketch Panel > Fillet
Panel Bar:	2D Sketch Panel > Fillet

Filleting is defined as the process of rounding the sharp corners of a sketch. This is done to reduce the stress concentration in the model. Using the **Fillet** tool, you can round the corners of the sketch by creating an arc tangent to both the selected entities. The portions of the selected entities that comprise the sharp corners are trimmed when the fillet is created. When you invoke this tool, the **2D Fillet** toolbar will be displayed with the current fillet radius, see Figure 1-23, and you will be prompted to select the lines or the arcs to be filleted. If you have already created some fillets, their radius values will be stored as preset values. You can select these preset values from the list that is displayed when you choose the arrow provided on the right side of the edit box.

Figure 1-23 The 2D Fillet toolbar

You can create as many fillets of similar or different radii using the same sequence of the **Fillet** tool. If the **Equal** button in the **2D Fillet** toolbar is chosen, the dimension of the fillet is placed only on the first fillet and not on the other fillets created using the same sequence of this tool. On modifying the dimension of the first fillet, all the fillet instances are modified. To show dimensions on all fillet instances, clear the **Equal** button before creating fillets. Displaying the dimensions on all the instances of fillets make them independent and you can modify their dimensions individually by double-clicking on them. You can fillet two parallel or perpendicular lines (Figures 1-24 and 1-25), intersecting lines or arcs, nonintersecting lines or arcs, and a line and an arc.

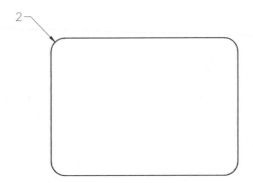

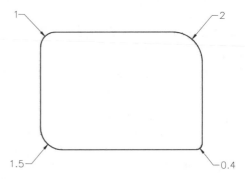

Figure 1-24 *Rectangle filleted using the same radius with the* **Equal** *button chosen*

Figure 1-25 *Rectangle filleted using different radii with the* **Equal** *button not chosen*

Creating Chamfers

Toolbar:	2D Sketch Panel > Fillet > Chamfer
Panel Bar:	2D Sketch Panel > Fillet > Chamfer

Chamfering is defined as the process of beveling the sharp corners of a sketch. This is the second method of reducing stress concentration. To chamfer the sketched entities, choose the down arrow located on the right of the **Fillet** tool in the **2D Sketch Panel** panel bar and then choose the **Chamfer** button. When you choose this button, the **2D Chamfer** dialog box is displayed, as shown in Figure 1-26, and you will be prompted to select the lines to be chamfered. The options in this dialog box are discussed next.

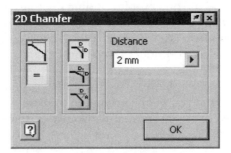

Figure 1-26 *The* **2D Chamfer** *dialog box*

Create Dimensions

The **Create Dimensions** button is chosen to show the dimensions of the chamfer on the sketch. When you chamfer two lines, the dimensions of the chamfer are shown in the sketch. If you choose this button again and clear it, the chamfer dimensions will not be displayed in the sketch when you create another chamfer.

Equal

The **Equal** button is chosen to create multiple chamfers with the same parameters. This button is enabled only if the **Create Dimensions** button is chosen.

Equal Distance

The **Equal Distance** button is chosen to create an equal distance chamfer. The distance of the vertex along the two selected edges is the same. As a result, the chamfer line created using this method is at an angle of 45-degree. The distance value is specified in the **Distance** edit box. If the **Create Dimension** button is chosen, the two dimensions of the same value are shown in the sketch, as shown in Figure 1-27.

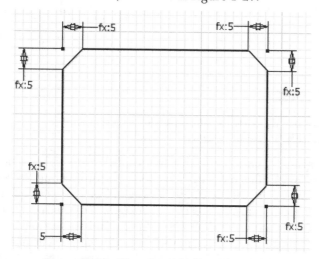

Figure 1-27 Chamfer with dimension values

Two Distances

The **Two Distances** button is chosen to create a chamfer with two different distances. The distance values are specified in the **Distance1** and **Distance2** edit boxes. The distance value specified in the **Distance1** edit box is measured along the edge selected first. Similarly, the value of **Distance2** edit box is measured along the edge selected next. Figure 1-28 shows a chamfer created by using the **Two Distances** method.

Distance and Angle

The **Distance and Angle** button is chosen to create a chamfer using a distance and an angle. The distance is specified in the **Distance** edit box and the angle in the **Angle** edit box. The specified angle is measured from the first edge selected to chamfer, see Figure 1-29.

Tip. *If multiple chamfers are created with same values, the dimension value is displayed only at the first instance. At the remaining chamfers, the dimension will be displayed as fx of the value, which means the function of the original value.*

You can also select the vertex to create a fillet or chamfer. The two entities forming the selected vertex will be filleted or chamfered using the current parameters.

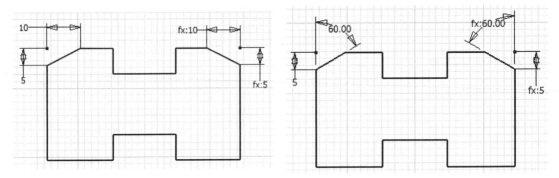

Figure 1-28 *Two distance chamfer*   **Figure 1-29** *Distance and angle chamfer*

Drawing Splines

Toolbar:	2D Sketch Panel > Line > Spline
Panel Bar:	2D Sketch Panel > Line > Spline

To draw a spline, choose the down arrow located on the right of the **Line** button in the **2D Sketch Panel** panel bar and then choose the **Spline** button. You are prompted to specify the start point of the spline or drag off for a tangent spline. After specifying the start point, you are prompted to specify the next point of the spline. This procedure will continue until you terminate the spline creation. To end the spline at the current point, double-click in the drawing window or right-click to display the shortcut menu and choose **Continue**. Note that if you choose **Done** from the shortcut menu, the spline will not be drawn. You can also end the spline creation by pressing the ENTER key.

You can undo the last drawn spline segment while you are drawing a spline. This can be done by choosing the **Back** option from the shortcut menu that is displayed when you right-click.

You can also draw a spline tangent to an existing entity. To draw the tangent spline, select the point where the spline should be tangent and then hold the left mouse button and drag it. A construction line will be drawn that displays the possible tangent directions for the spline. Drag the mouse in the required direction to draw the tangent spline. Figure 1-30 shows a spline drawn by specifying different points and Figure 1-31 shows a spline drawn tangent to an existing line.

DELETING SKETCHED ENTITIES

To delete the sketched entity, first ensure that no drawing tool is active. If it is, press the ESC key. Now, select the entity you want to delete using the left mouse button and then right-click to display the shortcut menu. In this menu, choose **Delete**. You can also press the DELETE key to delete the entities. To delete more than one entity, you can use a window or a crossing. Deleting entities using these methods are discussed next.

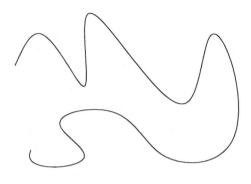

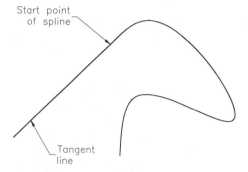

Figure 1-30 *Drawing a spline*   **Figure 1-31** *Drawing a tangent spline*

Deleting the Entities Using a Window

A window is defined as a box created by pressing and holding the left mouse button and dragging the cursor from the left to the right in the drawing window. The window has a property that all the entities that lie completely inside the window will be selected. The box defined by the window consists of continuous lines. All the selected entities will be displayed in cyan color. After selecting the entities, right-click and choose **Delete** from the shortcut menu to delete all the selected entities.

Deleting the Entities Using a Crossing

A crossing is defined as a box created by pressing and holding down the left mouse button and dragging the cursor from the right to the left in the drawing window. The crossing has a property that all entities that lie completely or partially inside the crossing or the entities that touch the crossing will be selected. The box defined by the crossing consists of dashed lines. Once the entities are selected, right-click and choose **Delete** from the shortcut menu.

> **Tip**. *You can add or remove an entity from the selection set by pressing the SHIFT or the CTRL key and then selecting the entity by using the left mouse button. If the entity is already in the current selection set, it will be removed from it. If not, it will be added to it.*

TUTORIALS

Although Autodesk Inventor is parametric in nature, in this chapter you will use the **Inventor Precise Input** toolbar to draw objects. This is to make you comfortable with the various drawing options in Autodesk Inventor. From the next chapter onwards, you will use the parametric nature of Autodesk Inventor for sizing or drawing the entities to the desired dimension values.

Note that although the sketches for the tutorials in this chapter are to be drawn on the other sketching planes, but in this chapter you will draw them on the default XY plane. In later chapters, you will learn to change the sketching plane.

Tutorial 1

In this tutorial, you will draw the sketch for the model shown in Figure 1-32. The sketch is shown in Figure 1-33. Do not dimension it as the dimensions are for reference.

(Expected time: 30 min)

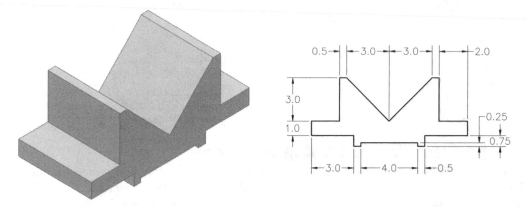

Figure 1-32 *Model for Tutorial 1*   **Figure 1-33** *Sketch of the model*

The following steps are required to complete this tutorial:

a. Start a new metric standard part file and then invoke the **Inventor Precise Input** toolbar.
b. Invoke the **Line** tool and draw the sketch by specifying the coordinates of the points in the **Inventor Precise Input** toolbar, refer to Figure 1-36.
c. Save the sketch with the name *Tutorial1.ipt* and close the file.

Starting Autodesk Inventor

1. Start Autodesk Inventor by double-clicking on its shortcut icon on the desktop of your computer. You can also choose **Start > Programs > Autodesk > Autodesk Inventor 11 > Autodesk Inventor 11** from the taskbar shortcut to start Autodesk Inventor 11; the **Open** dialog box is displayed.

2. Choose **New** from the **What To Do** area to display the **Default, English**, and **Metric** tabs. Choose the **Metric** tab to display the metric templates.

3. Double-click on the **Standard (mm).ipt** icon, as shown in Figure 1-34, to start a standard metric template; a new metric standard part file is started in the sketching environment.

   Various sketching tools are available in the **2D Sketch Panel** panel bar, see Figure 1-35. Below the **2D Sketch Panel** panel bar is the browser. The major and minor grid lines are also displayed in the drawing window, along with the X and Y axes.

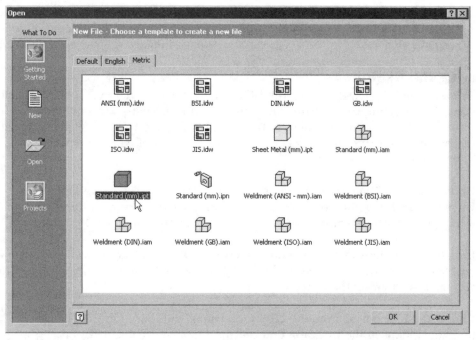

Figure 1-34 *Opening the standard metric template*

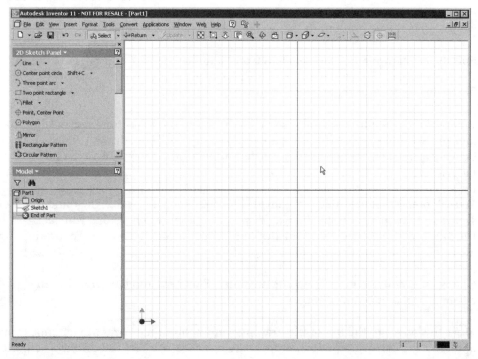

Figure 1-35 *Initial screen appearance in the* **Part** *module with the sketching environment*

Note
If you have installed Autodesk Inventor by selecting millimeter as the measurement unit, you can also open a standard metric template by selecting **Standard.ipt** *from the* **Default** *tab.*

Drawing the Sketch

As mentioned earlier, Autodesk Inventor is parametric in nature. Therefore, you can start drawing the sketch from any point in the drawing window. However, it is recommended that you initially use the **Inventor Precise Input** toolbar for specifying the points. Once you are conversant with this design tool, you can specify the points directly in the drawing window.

1. Choose **View > Toolbar > Inventor Precise Input** from the menu bar to display the **Inventor Precise Input** toolbar. Double-click on the blue portion of this toolbar to dock it. If you want, you can also leave this toolbar floating on the screen.

    Initially, the options in the **Inventor Precise Input** toolbar are not enabled. They are enabled only on invoking any sketching tool. Because all the initial settings are configured, you can start drawing the sketch.

2. Choose the **Line** button from the **2D Sketch Panel** panel bar to invoke the **Line** tool; the options in the **Inventor Precise Input** toolbar are enabled.

    When you invoke the **Line** tool, the cursor, which was initially an arrow, is replaced by the drawing cursor and a yellow circle is attached at the intersection of the crosshairs. This yellow circle is used to snap to the points in the drawing window.

3. Specify the start point of the sketch as **0** and **0** in the **X** and **Y** edit boxes of the **Inventor Precise Input** toolbar and then press ENTER. You are prompted to specify the endpoint of the line or reselect the start point to start a new line.

4. Enter **-3** in the **X** edit box and **3** in the **Y** edit box of the **Inventor Precise Input** toolbar and press ENTER to define the endpoint of the line. This draws the first line of the sketch. You are now prompted to select the endpoint of the next line or drag off to create a tangent arc.

    You will notice that the line is very small. The reason for this is that the dimensions of the sketch are very small and the drawing display area is large. Therefore, you need to modify the drawing display area using the drawing display tools. To modify the drawing display area, you can use the **Zoom** tool.

5. Choose the **Zoom** button from the **Inventor Standard** toolbar; the drawing cursor is replaced by an arrow.

6. Move the cursor to the top of the drawing window and then press the left mouse button and drag the cursor downward. Stop dragging, once you feel the display is adjusted to what you desire.

7.   Right-click to display the shortcut menu and then choose **Done** to exit the **Zoom** tool.

You will notice that line creation resumes and you are prompted to specify the endpoint of the next line.

Tip. *You can use the TAB key to shift from the* **X** *edit box to the* **Y** *edit box and vice versa in the* **Inventor Precise Input** *toolbar.*

8.   The coordinates of the remaining points in the sketch are as follows.

Point	Coordinates (X,Y)
3	-3.5,3
4	-3.5,0
5	-5.5,0
6	-5.5,-1
7	-2.5,-1
8	-2.5,-1.75
9	-2,-1.75
10	-2,-1.5
11	2,-1.5
12	2,-1.75
13	2.5,-1.75
14	2.5,-1
15	5.5,-1
16	5.5,0
17	3.5,0
18	3.5,3
19	3,3
20	0,0

9.   After specifying all these points, right-click to display the shortcut menu. In this menu, choose **Done** to exit the **Line** tool.

While specifying various points, you will notice that some of the constraints are automatically applied to the lines as you sketch them. These constraints help you in reducing the number of dimensions that are required to fully constrain the sketch.

Note
You can also force some more constraints such as equal length, collinear, parallel, and so on. The method of applying additional constraints and using them to fully constrain the sketch will be discussed in Chapter 2.

10. The final sketch for Tutorial 1 is shown in Figure 1-36.

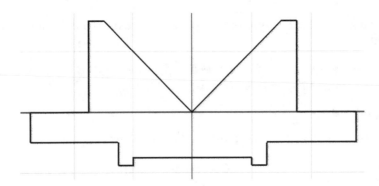

Figure 1-36 *Final sketch for Tutorial 1*

Saving the Sketch

Remember that you cannot save a sketch in the sketching environment. This is because in Autodesk Inventor, the sketching environment is just a part of the **Part** module. This environment is used only for drawing the sketches of the features. Therefore, you need to exit the sketching environment to save the sketch for further use. The sketches in the **Part** module are saved in the *.ipt* format.

1. Choose the **Return** button from the **Inventor Standard** toolbar.

    The sketching environment is closed and the part modeling environment is invoked. Notice that the **2D Sketch Panel** panel bar is replaced by the **Part Features** panel bar. This panel bar provides the options for creating features. The options under this panel bar will be discussed in later chapters.

2. Choose the **Save** button from the **Inventor Standard** toolbar; the **Save As** dialog box is displayed.

    By default, whenever you invoke the **Save As** dialog box for the first time, *\My Documents* folder is current. It is recommended that you create a new folder with the name *PersonalProject* in this folder and then create a separate folder for all chapters in the *PersonalProject* folder. The reason for creating separate folders is that you can save the tutorials of different chapters in their respective folders. This way it is easier for you to refer to the sketches or models at later stages.

3. Choose the **Create New Folder** button from the **Save As** dialog box and create a new folder with the name *PersonalProject*. This folder is created inside the *My Documents* folder.

4. Next, create a folder with the name *c01* inside the *PersonalProject* folder and make it current, as shown in Figure 1-37. Save the sketch with the name *Tutorial1.ipt* in this folder. The path for restoring this sketch at a later stage is *\PersonalProject\c01\Tutorial1.ipt*.

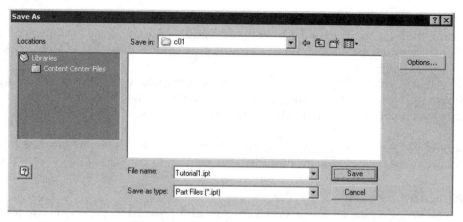

Figure 1-37 *The Save As dialog box*

5. Choose **File > Close** from the menu bar to close this file.

Tutorial 2

In this tutorial, you will draw the sketch for the model shown in Figure 1-38. The sketch is shown in Figure 1-39. Do not dimension it. The solid model and dimensions are for reference only.

(Expected time: 30 min)

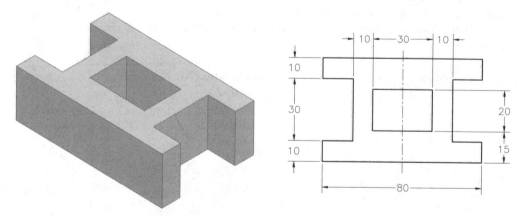

Figure 1-38 *Model for Tutorial 2*   *Figure 1-39* *Dimensioned sketch for Tutorial 2*

The following steps are required to complete this tutorial:

a. Start a new metric standard part file.
b. Draw the outer loop by specifying the coordinates of points in the **Inventor Precise Input** toolbar.
c. Draw the inner closed loop using the **Inventor Precise Input** toolbar, refer to Figure 1-40.
d. Save the sketch with the name *Tutorial2.ipt* and close the file.

Starting a New File

1. Choose the **New** button from the **Inventor Standard** toolbar to display the **Open** dialog box. Choose **New** from the **What To Do** area to display the **Default, English,** and **Metric** tabs.

    Note that if you are starting a new session of Autodesk Inventor, you do not need to choose the **New** button to invoke the **Open** dialog box. This is because the **Open** dialog box is automatically displayed when you start a new session of Autodesk Inventor.

2. Choose the **Metric** tab to display metric templates. Double-click on **Standard (mm).ipt** to start a new metric standard part file.

Drawing the Sketch

As evident in Figure 1-39, this sketch consists of two closed loops, one inside the other. When you draw nested loops and extrude them, the inner loop can be subtracted from the outer loop. Thus, the cavity is created in the model automatically when you extrude the sketch. This reduces the time and effort required in creating the inner cavity as another feature. Therefore, for this tutorial you can draw both the loops together, as shown in Figure 1-39.

Because the **Inventor Precise Input** toolbar was invoked in the previous tutorial, it is available on the screen.

1. Choose **Line** from the **2D Sketch Panel** panel bar. You are prompted to specify the start point of the line or drag off to create a tangent arc. The points and their coordinates that you need to enter in the **Inventor Precise Input** toolbar are given below.

Points	Coordinates (X,Y)
1	-40,-25
2	40,-25
3	40,-15
4	25,-15
5	25,15
6	40,15
7	40,25
8	-40,25
9	-40,15
10	-25,15
11	-25,-15
12	-40,-15
13	-40,-25

2. After specifying all these points, right-click to display the shortcut menu. Choose **Done** to exit the **Line** tool. You can also press the ESC key to exit it.

    Next, you need to draw the inner loop, which can be drawn using the **Two point rectangle** tool. The first corner of the rectangle is drawn using the absolute coordinate system. However, to specify the other corner of the rectangle, you need to use the relative coordinate system.

3. Choose the **Two point rectangle** button from the **2D Sketch Panel** panel bar; you are prompted to specify the first corner of the rectangle. Enter the first corner as **-15,-10** in the **X** and **Y** edit boxes respectively in the **Inventor Precise Input** toolbar; you are prompted to specify the opposite corner of the rectangle.

4. Enter the coordinates of the other corner of the rectangle as **15,10**. Right-click and choose **Done** from the shortcut menu. The completed sketch is shown in Figure 1-40.

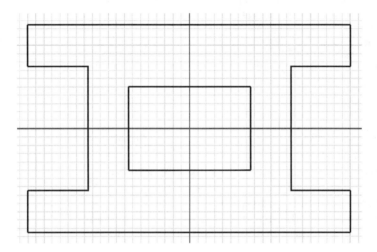

Figure 1-40 Complete sketch for Tutorial 2

Saving the Sketch

Next, you need to save the sketch. As mentioned earlier, you cannot save the sketch in the sketching environment. You need to first exit the sketching environment and then save it.

1. Choose the **Return** button from the **Inventor Standard** toolbar to exit the sketching environment.

2. Choose the **Save** button and save this sketch with the name given below.

    \PersonalProject\c01\Tutorial2.ipt

3. Choose **File > Close** from the menu bar to close this file.

Tutorial 3

In this tutorial, you will draw the sketch for the model shown in Figure 1-41. The sketch for the model is shown in Figure 1-42. Do not dimension it as these dimensions are just for reference.

(Expected time: 30 min)

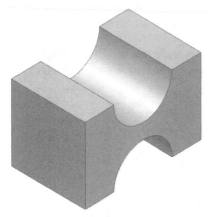

Figure 1-41 Model for Tutorial 3

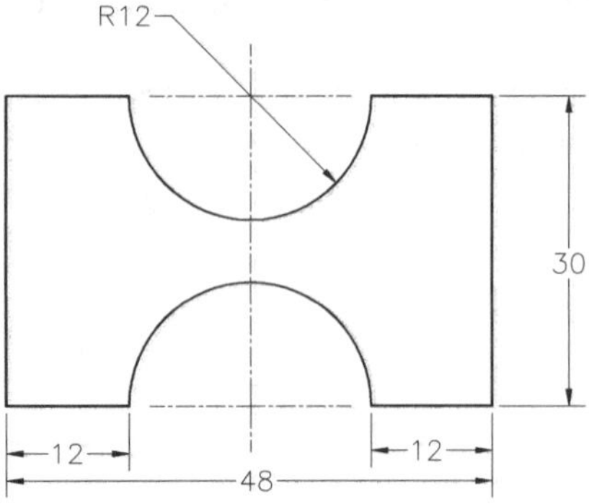

Figure 1-42 Sketch for Tutorial 3

The following steps are required to complete this tutorial:

a.   Start a new metric standard part file.
b.   Draw the sketch using the **Arc** and **Line** tools, refer to Figure 1-44.
c.   Save the sketch with the name *Tutorial3.ipt* and close the file.

Starting a New File

1.   Choose the **New** button from the **Inventor Standard** toolbar to invoke the **Open** dialog box.

2.   Start a new metric standard part file by double-clicking on **Standard (mm).ipt** in the **Metric** tab.

Drawing the Sketch

The upper arc in the sketch can be drawn by specifying the center point, start point, and the endpoint of the arc. Therefore, you will use the **Center point arc** tool to draw this arc.

1.   Choose the down arrow on the right of the **Three point arc** in the **2D Sketch Panel** panel bar and choose the **Center point arc** button.

2.   You are prompted to specify the center of the arc. Enter the coordinates of the center of the arc as **0,15** in the **Inventor Precise Input** toolbar.

3.   You are prompted to specify the start point of the arc. Specify the start point as **-12,15** in the **Inventor Precise Input** toolbar.

Next, you need to define the endpoint of the arc. The arc that is drawn when you specify the endpoint can be in the clockwise or counterclockwise direction. However, you need to define the arc in the counterclockwise direction. Move the mouse in the counterclockwise direction to a small distance. By doing this, you can define the direction in which the arc is drawn.

4. Move the mouse to a small distance in the counterclockwise direction from the start point of the arc. Now, enter the coordinates of the endpoint of the arc as **12,15** in the **Inventor Precise Input** toolbar. The upper arc is drawn.

5. Next, you need to draw the lines in the sketch. Choose **Line** from the **2D Sketch Panel** panel bar. You are prompted to specify the start point of the line.

It is evident in Figure 1-42 that the lines start from the endpoints of the arc. Therefore, you can specify the coordinates of the start point of the arc in the **Inventor Precise Input** toolbar or select the start point of the line in the drawing window.

It is recommended that you select the start point of the line in the drawing window. When you invoke any sketching tool, a yellow circle appears on the cursor. If you move the cursor close to any endpoint, the yellow circle at the end of the cursor automatically snaps to the endpoint and turns green. You will also notice that the symbol of the coincident constraint is displayed. This symbol suggests that the coincident constraint will be automatically applied to the endpoint of the arc and the start point of the line.

6. Move the cursor close to the left endpoint of the arc; the yellow circle snaps to the endpoint of the arc and turns green. When the yellow circle turn green, it indicates that the cursor has snapped to the endpoint of the arc. Press the left mouse button to select this point as the start point of the line.

Because it is easier to define the points by using the relative coordinates, it is recommended that you use the **Precise Delta** button in the **Inventor Precise Input** toolbar to draw the lines. Choose the **Precise Delta** button if it is not already chosen.

7. If the **Precise Delta** button is not chosen automatically, you need to specify the start point of the line and then choose this button. Next, press the ESC key to exit the **Line** tool. Now, invoke the **Line** tool again; the triad will be placed at the start point. Enter the coordinates of the endpoint of the line as **-12,0** in the **Inventor Precise Input** toolbar.

8. Enter the second point as **0,-30** and the third point as **12,0**.

As mentioned earlier, Autodesk Inventor provides you the option to draw tangent or normal arcs while drawing lines. This is done by dragging the cursor from the point where you want to start the arc. At this point of the sketch, you need to draw an arc normal to the last line. You can directly draw it from within the **Line** tool.

9. Move the cursor close to the right endpoint of the last line until the yellow circle snaps to that point. When the yellow circle snaps to the endpoint, it turns gray. However, because of the triad, you will not be able to view the gray circle. Now, press and hold the left mouse button down and drag the mouse through a small distance in the upward direction.

   You will notice that four imaginary lines are displayed, showing the four directions in which you can draw the arc.

10. Because you have to draw the arc normal to the line, therefore, drag the cursor in the direction of the vertical imaginary line in the upward direction to a small distance and then drag the cursor toward the right.

   You will notice that an arc normal to the last line is being drawn as you move the cursor. Remember that you need to drag the mouse upward only through a small distance and then without releasing the left button, drag the mouse toward the right. **Note that the point at which you release the left mouse button will be taken as the endpoint of the arc**. Therefore, you need to be very careful in specifying the endpoint.

   While drawing the arc by dragging the cursor, you cannot use the **Inventor Precise Input** toolbar. This is because as soon as you release the left mouse button, that point will be taken as the endpoint of the arc. Therefore, it is very difficult to define the endpoint of the arc precisely. This problem can be solved by using the **temporary tracking** option. The temporary tracking option allows you to select a point by using two different points. For example, in this case, the right endpoint of the lower arc has to be vertically in the same line as that of the right endpoint of the upper arc and horizontally in the same line as that of the start point of the lower arc. Now, imagine a vertical imaginary line drawn from the right endpoint of the upper arc and a horizontal imaginary line drawn from the start point of the lower arc. Both these imaginary lines intersect at a point, which is essentially the endpoint of the lower arc. **The temporary tracking option draws these imaginary lines for you and removes them after you have selected the point**.

11. With the left mouse button pressed to define the endpoint of the arc, drag the mouse close to the right endpoint of the upper arc. The cursor snaps to the endpoint of the arc and turns green. Now, move the cursor vertically downward.

   You will notice that a vertical imaginary line is being drawn from the right endpoint of the upper arc. You do not need to snap to the horizontal point since this point was automatically selected when you started drawing the lower arc. As you move the cursor downward, you will notice a point where both the vertical and horizontal imaginary lines intersect, see Figure 1-43. This point is the endpoint of the lower arc. The cursor will automatically snap to the point where both the imaginary lines intersect. Do not release the left mouse button until this entire process is completed.

Note
In Figure 1-43, the major and minor grid lines and triad are not displayed for a better display of the sketch and the imaginary lines.

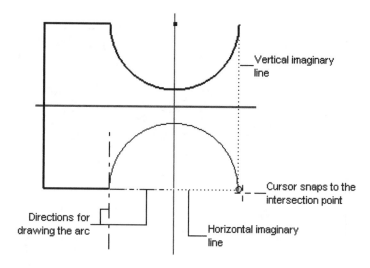

Figure 1-43 *Using of the temporary tracking option to draw an arc*

12. When the cursor snaps to the intersection point of the imaginary lines, release the mouse button to complete the lower arc.

13. Enter the coordinates of the next point as **12,0** in the edit boxes in the **Inventor Precise Input** toolbar.

14. For the next point, you can enter the coordinates in the **Inventor Precise Input** toolbar or use the temporary tracking option. To use this option, move the cursor close to the right endpoint of the upper arc. Once the cursor snaps to this point and turns green, move it horizontally toward the right. You will notice a horizontal imaginary line is being drawn. Using the left mouse button, select the point at which the vertical line meets the horizontal imaginary line. This point is the endpoint of the right vertical line.

Note
While using the temporary tracking option to draw lines, you do not need to press the left mouse button and drag it. You have to press the left mouse button only once to select the endpoint of the line after you get the intersection point of the imaginary lines.

15. Complete the sketch by snapping to the right endpoint of the upper arc as the endpoint of the next line. Right-click to display the shortcut menu and choose **Done** to exit the **Line** tool.

16. The final sketch for Tutorial 3 is shown in Figure 1-44.

Saving the Sketch

1. Choose the **Return** button in the **Inventor Standard** toolbar to exit the sketching environment.

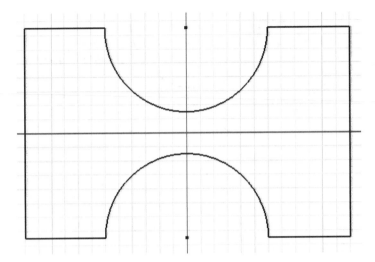

Figure 1-44 *Final sketch for Tutorial 3*

2.   Choose the **Save** button and save the sketch with the name given below.

     \PersonalProject\c01\Tutorial3.ipt

3.   Choose **File > Close** from the menu bar to close the file.

Tutorial 4

In this tutorial, you will draw the basic contour of the revolved solid model shown in Figure 1-45. The contour that you have to draw for creating this revolved solid is shown in Figure 1-46. Do not dimension the sketch as these dimensions are for reference only.

(Expected time: 30 min)

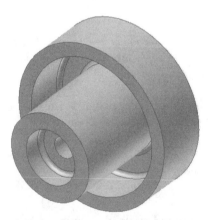

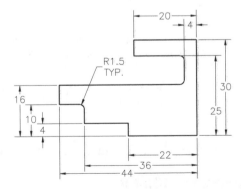

Figure 1-45 *Revolved model for Tutorial 4*   *Figure 1-46* *Sketch for the revolved model*

The following steps are required to complete this tutorial:

a. Start a new metric standard part file.
b. Invoke the **Line** tool and draw the sketch by specifying the coordinates of points in the **Inventor Precise Input** toolbar, refer to Figure 1-48.
c. Save the sketch with the name *Tutorial4.ipt* and close the file.

Starting a New File

1. Choose the **New** button from the **Inventor Standard** toolbar to display the **Open** dialog box.

2. Choose the **Metric** tab to display the standard metric templates. Double-click on **Standard (mm).ipt** to start a new metric part file.

Drawing the Sketch

1. Choose **Line** from the **2D Sketch Panel** panel bar. You are prompted to specify the start point of the line. Enter the coordinates of the start point in the **Inventor Precise Input** toolbar as **22,0**.

    You are prompted to specify the endpoint of the line. You can specify the coordinates of the next point relative to the previous point as this makes it easier to define the points. The **Precise Delta** button in the **Inventor Precise Input** toolbar is chosen automatically if you use the same session of Autodesk Inventor. However, if you use a new session, you need to chose this button to invoke this option.

2. If the **Precise Delta** button is not chosen, choose it and then press the ESC key. Now, again invoke the **Line** tool and specify the start point of the line. Enter the following coordinates of the remaining points in the **Inventor Precise Input** toolbar.

Point	Coordinates (X,Y)
2	0,30
3	-20,0
4	0,-5
5	16,0
6	0,-9
7	-40,0
8	0,-6
9	8,0
10	0,-6
11	14,0
12	0,-4
13	22,0

3. Right-click to display the shortcut menu and choose **Done** to complete the sketch. The sketch should look similar to the one shown in Figure 1-47. For your reference, the lines in the sketch are numbered.

The arcs at the end of lines 4 and 5, 5 and 6, and 8 and 9 will be created using the **Fillet** tool. This tool will draw the arcs at the point of intersection of the lines and remove the sharp corners.

4. Choose the **Fillet** button from the **2D Sketch Panel** panel bar. The **2D Fillet** toolbar is displayed with some default fillet radius. Type the value of the fillet radius in this toolbar as **1.5**. Do not press ENTER.

5. Select line 4 and then line 5; the fillet is created between these lines and the fillet radius is displayed in the sketch, see Figure 1-48.

6. Similarly, select lines 5 and 6, and then lines 8 and 9 to create the fillet between these lines. Right-click and choose **Done** to exit the **Fillet** tool after creating all the fillets.

    Because all the lines were filleted with the same radius value, the fillet radius is not displayed on the other fillets. This completes the sketch. The final sketch for Tutorial 4, after filleting, is shown in Figure 1-48.

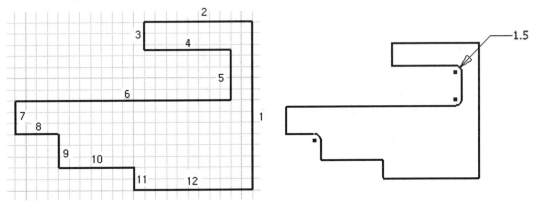

Figure 1-47 Sketch after drawing the lines   *Figure 1-48 Final sketch after filleting*

 Note
In Figures 1-47 and 1-48, the display of axes is turned off for clarity in displaying the lines of the sketch.

Saving the Sketch

1. Choose the **Return** button from the **Inventor Standard** toolbar to exit the sketching environment.

2. Choose the **Save** button and save this sketch with the name given below.

    \PersonalProject\c01\Tutorial4.ipt

3. Choose **File > Close** from the menu bar to close the file.

Self-Evaluation Test

Answer the following questions and then compare your answers with those given at the end of the chapter:

1. Most designs are a combination of sketched, placed, and work features. (T/F)

2. When you start a new file in the **Part** module, first the sketching environment will be active. (T/F)

3. You cannot turn off the display of the grid lines. (T/F)

4. You cannot draw an arc from within the **Line** tool. (T/F)

5. The two types of sketching entities that can be drawn in Autodesk Inventor are _____ and _____.

6. In the sketching environment, the _____ tool is used to place a point or a center point.

7. Filleting is defined as the process of _____ the sharp corners and sharp edges of the models.

8. You can also delete the sketched entities by pressing the _____ key.

9. The rectangles in Autodesk Inventor are drawn as a combination of _____ entities.

10. You can undo the last drawn spline segment when you are still inside the spline drawing option by choosing _____ from the shortcut menu displayed upon right-clicking.

Review Questions

Answer the following questions:

1. Generally, in most designs, the first feature or the base feature has to be the placed feature. (T/F)

2. You can also invoke the options related to the sheet metal parts from the **.ipt** file. (T/F)

3. You can change the current project directory and the project files by choosing **Projects** in the **Open** dialog box. (T/F)

4. You cannot control the display of grid lines. (T/F)

5. In Autodesk Inventor, you can save a file in the sketching environment. (T/F)

6. Using which option in the **View** menu can you invoke additional toolbars?

    (a) **Isometric**   (b) **Tools**
    (c) **Toolbars**   (d) You cannot invoke additional toolbars

7. Which one of these tabs is not available when you choose **New** from the **What To Do** area of the **Open** dialog box?

    (a) **Default**   (b) **Projects**
    (c) **Metric**   (d) **English**

8. Using which of the following drawing display options can you interactively zoom in and out of the drawing?

    (a) **Zoom All**   (b) **Pan**
    (c) **Zoom**   (d) **Zoom Window**

9. Using which key can you restore the previous view?

    (a) F5   (b) F6
    (c) F7   (d) F4

10. Which of the following drawing display options prompts you to select an entity whose magnification will be increased?

    (a) **Zoom**   (b) **Pan**
    (c) **Zoom Selected**   (d) None

Exercises

Exercise 1

Draw the basic sketch for the model shown in Figure 1-49. The sketch that you have to draw is shown in Figure 1-50. Do not dimension it as these are just for reference.

(Expected time: 30 min)

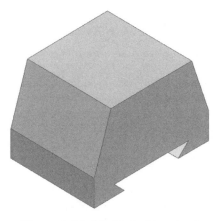

Figure 1-49 *Model for Exercise 1*

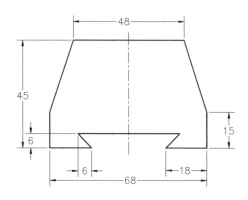

Figure 1-50 *Sketch for Exercise 1*

Exercise 2

Draw the basic sketch for the model shown in Figure 1-51. The sketch that you need to draw is shown in Figure 1-52. Do not dimension it as these dimensions are just for reference.

(Expected time: 45 min)

Figure 1-51 *Model for Exercise 2*

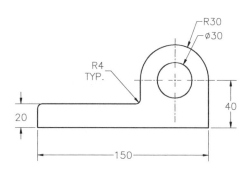

Figure 1-52 *Sketch for Exercise 2*

Note
The solid model and the dimensions in Exercises 1 and 2 are given for reference only. You do not need to dimension the sketches.

Answers to Self-Evaluation Test

1. T, **2**. T, **3**. F, **4**. F, **5**. normal, construction, **6**. **Point, Center Point**, **7**. rounding, **8**. DELETE, **9**. individual, **10**. **Back**

Chapter 2

Adding Constraints and Dimensions to Sketches

Learning Objectives

After completing this chapter, you will be able to:
- *Add geometric constraints to the sketch.*
- *View and delete constraints from the sketch.*
- *Dimension the sketch.*
- *Modify dimensions of the sketch.*
- *Measure distances, angles, loops, and areas in the sketch.*

ADDING GEOMETRIC CONSTRAINTS TO THE SKETCH

As mentioned in the Introduction, eleven types of geometric constraints can be applied to the sketched entities. Most of these constraints are automatically applied to the entities while drawing. However, sometimes you may have to apply some additional constraints. These constraints are discussed next.

Perpendicular Constraint

Toolbar:	2D Sketch Panel > Perpendicular
Panel Bar:	2D Sketch Panel > Perpendicular

The **Perpendicular** constraint forces the selected entity to become perpendicular to the specified entity. To use this constraint, choose the **Perpendicular** button from the **2D Sketch Panel** panel bar; you are prompted to select the first line or an ellipse axis. Once you select an entity, you will be prompted to select the second line or ellipse axis. The first entity becomes normal to the second entity. Figure 2-1 shows two lines before and after adding this constraint.

Parallel Constraint

Toolbar:	2D Sketch Panel > Perpendicular > Parallel
Panel Bar:	2D Sketch Panel > Perpendicular > Parallel

The **Parallel** constraint forces the selected entity to become parallel to the specified entity. The entities to which this constraint can be applied are lines and ellipse axes. To apply this constraint, choose the down arrow on the right of the **Perpendicular** button in the **2D Sketch Panel** panel bar and then choose the **Parallel** button to invoke this constraint. On doing so, you will be prompted to select the first line or ellipse axis. After you select an entity, you will be prompted to select the second line or ellipse axis. The first entity becomes parallel to the second entity. Figure 2-2 shows two lines before and after adding this constraint.

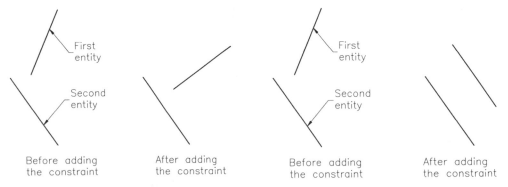

Figure 2-1 *Applying the* **Perpendicular** *constraint*   *Figure 2-2* *Applying the* **Parallel** *constraint*

Tangent Constraint

Toolbar: 2D Sketch Panel > Perpendicular > Tangent
Panel Bar: 2D Sketch Panel > Perpendicular > Tangent

The **Tangent** constraint forces the selected line segment or curve to become tangent to another curve. Choose the down arrow on the right of the **Perpendicular** button in the **2D Sketch Panel** panel bar and then choose **Tangent** to apply this constraint. On invoking this constraint, you will be prompted to select the first curve. After you select the first curve, you will be prompted to select the second curve. The curves that you can select include lines, circles, ellipses, or arcs. Figures 2-3 and 2-4 show the use of the tangent constraint.

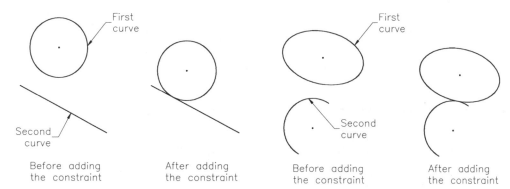

*Figure 2-3 Applying the **Tangent** constraint*   *Figure 2-4 Applying the **Tangent** constraint*

Coincident Constraint

Toolbar: 2D Sketch Panel > Perpendicular > Coincident
Panel Bar: 2D Sketch Panel > Perpendicular > Coincident

The **Coincident** constraint is used to force two points or a point and a curve to become coincident. Choose the down arrow on the right of the **Perpendicular** button in the **2D Sketch Panel** panel bar and then choose **Coincident** to apply this constraint. When you invoke this constraint, you will be prompted to select the first curve or point. Once you specify the first curve or point, you will be prompted to specify the second curve or point. Note that either the first or the second entity selected should be a point. The points include the endpoints of a line or an arc, or the center points of circles, arcs, or ellipses.

Concentric Constraint

Toolbar: 2D Sketch Panel > Perpendicular > Concentric
Panel Bar: 2D Sketch Panel > Perpendicular > Concentric

The **Concentric** constraint is used to force two curves to share the same location of the center points. The curves that can be made concentric include arcs, circles, and ellipses. When you invoke this constraint, you will be prompted to select the first arc, circle, or ellipse. After making the first selection, you will be prompted to select the second arc, circle, or ellipse.

Note
If you apply a constraint that is not required in the sketch, Autodesk Inventor will display a message box informing you that adding this constraint will over-constrain the sketch, see Figure 2-5. Over-constrained is a situation where the number of dimensions or constraints have exceeded the required number that can be applied.

Figure 2-5 Message box informing that the sketch will be over-constrained

Collinear Constraint

Toolbar:	2D Sketch Panel > Perpendicular > Collinear
Panel Bar:	2D Sketch Panel > Perpendicular > Collinear

The **Collinear** constraint forces the selected line segments or ellipse axes to be placed in the same line. When you invoke this constraint, you will be prompted to select the first line or ellipse axis. After making the first selection, you will be prompted to select the second line or ellipse axis.

Tip. *To select an ellipse axis, move the cursor close to the ellipse. Depending on whether the cursor is close to the major axis or the minor axis, it will be highlighted. When the required axis is highlighted, select it using the left mouse button.*

Horizontal Constraint

Toolbar:	2D Sketch Panel > Perpendicular > Horizontal
Panel Bar:	2D Sketch Panel > Perpendicular > Horizontal

The **Horizontal** constraint forces the selected line segment, ellipse axis, or two points to become horizontal irrespective of their original orientation. When you invoke this constraint, you will be prompted to select a line, an ellipse axis, or the first point. If you select a line or an ellipse axis, it will become horizontal. If you select a point, you will then be prompted to select a second point. The points, in this case, can also include the center points of arcs, circles, or ellipses.

Vertical Constraint

Toolbar:	2D Sketch Panel > Perpendicular > Vertical
Panel Bar:	2D Sketch Panel > Perpendicular > Vertical

The **Vertical** constraint is similar to the **Horizontal** constraint, with the difference that this constraint will force the selected entities to become vertical.

 Tip. *You can use the **Horizontal** or the **Vertical** constraint to line up arcs, circles, or ellipses in the same horizontal or vertical direction by selecting their center points.*

Equal Constraint

Toolbar:	2D Sketch Panel > Perpendicular > Equal
Panel Bar:	2D Sketch Panel > Perpendicular > Equal

The **Equal** constraint can be used either for line segments or for curves. If you select two line segments, this constraint will force the length of one of the selected line segment to become equal to the length of the other selected line segment. In case of curves, this constraint will force the radius of one of the selected curves to become equal to that of the other selected curve. Note that if the first selection includes a line, the second selection also has to be a line. Similarly, if the first selection includes a curve, the second selection also has to be a curve.

Fix Constraint

Toolbar:	2D Sketch Panel > Perpendicular > Fix
Panel Bar:	2D Sketch Panel > Perpendicular > Fix

This constraint is used to fix the orientation or location of the selected curve or point with respect to the coordinate system of the current drawing. If you apply this constraint to a line or an arc, you cannot move them from their current location. However, you can change their length by selecting one of their endpoints and then dragging it. If you apply this constraint to a circle or an ellipse, you cannot edit them by dragging. Once you apply this constraint to an entity, its color changes from black to blue.

Symmetric Constraint

Toolbar:	2D Sketch Panel > Perpendicular > Symmetric
Panel Bar:	2D Sketch Panel > Perpendicular > Symmetric

This constraint is used to force the selected sketched entities to become symmetrical about a selected sketched line segment. On invoking this constraint, you will be prompted to select the first sketched entity. Note that you can select only one entity at a time to apply this constraint. Once you have selected the first sketched entity, you will be prompted to select the second sketched entity. After doing so, you will be prompted to select the symmetry line. As soon as you select it, the second selected entity will be modified such that its distance from the line of symmetry becomes exactly equal to that of the first entity. After you have applied this constraint to one set of entities, you will again be prompted to select the first and second sketched entities. However, this time you will not be prompted to select the line of symmetry. The last line of symmetry will be automatically selected to add this constraint. Similarly, you can apply this constraint to other entities.

If the line of symmetry is different for applying the symmetric constraint to different entities in the sketch, you will have to restart the process of applying this constraint by right-clicking and choosing the **Restart** option from the shortcut menu. This is because the first symmetry line is used to apply this constraint to all the sets of entities you select. However, if you restart applying this constraint, you will be prompted to select the line of symmetry again.

Smooth Constraint

Toolbar:	2D Sketch Panel > Perpendicular > Smooth (G2)
Panel Bar:	2D Sketch Panel > Perpendicular > Smooth (G2)

 This constraint is used to apply a curvature continuity between a spline and an entity connected to it. The entities that can be selected to apply this constraint include a line, arc, or another spline. Note that these entities should be connected to the spline.

VIEWING THE CONSTRAINTS APPLIED TO A SKETCH

Toolbar:	2D Sketch Panel > Show Constraints
Panel Bar:	2D Sketch Panel > Show Constraints

You can view all constraints that are applied to the entities of a sketch by choosing the **Show Constraints** button in the **2D Sketch Panel** panel bar. When you invoke this tool and take the cursor close to any sketched entity, it will be highlighted and a box will be displayed after a pause. This box shows the symbols of all constraints that are applied to the entity. Select the entity to retain the constraint box on the screen. The number of constraints applied to the highlighted entity will also be displayed on the lower left corner of the Autodesk Inventor window. Figure 2-6 shows the constraint box displaying all the constraints applied to the lines. You can move this box by selecting it at its left end and dragging. To close this box, choose the cross (X) on the extreme right of this box.

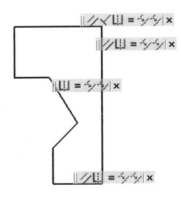

Figure 2-6 *The box showing the constraints*

If you move the cursor on a constraint in the constraint box, a red square will appear around the constraint and its position and reference will be highlighted. For example, if you take the cursor close to the perpendicular constraint, the vertical line will also be highlighted along with the horizontal line, suggesting that the horizontal line is perpendicular to the vertical line. Similarly, if you take the cursor close to the coincident constraint, the point at which this line is coincident with the vertical line will be highlighted.

 *Tip. You can also display the constraints applied to all the entities in the drawing. To display all the constraints, first make sure no tool is selected. Next, right-click to display the shortcut menu and choose **Show All Constraints**; separate boxes will be displayed showing the constraints on all the entities. Similarly, to hide all constraints, right-click and choose **Hide All Constraints** from the shortcut menu.*

DELETING GEOMETRIC CONSTRAINTS

Autodesk Inventor allows you to delete constraints applied to the selected entities. To delete the constraints, you need to first invoke the constraint box using the **Show Constraints** button. Once the constraint box is displayed, exit the **Show Constraints** tool by pressing the ESC key. Now, move the cursor over the constraint that you want to delete; a red square will appear around it. Press the left mouse button to select the constraint and then move the cursor away; the red square turns blue. Now, right-click and choose **Delete** from the shortcut menu, see Figure 2-7. The selected constraint will be deleted and will also be removed from the constraint box that is displayed on the screen. Similarly, you can delete all the unwanted constraints in the sketch.

Figure 2-7 Deleting constraints using the shortcut menu

Tip. *When you move the cursor close to the constraint in the constraint box, its references will be highlighted in the sketch. For example, if you move the cursor close to the coincident constraint, the points on which this constraint is applied will be highlighted. This allows you to confirm that the constraint selected is correct.*

ADDING DIMENSIONS TO SKETCHES

Toolbar:	2D Sketch Panel > General Dimension
Panel Bar:	2D Sketch Panel > General Dimension

After drawing the sketch and adding constraints to it, dimensioning is the next most important step in creating a design. As mentioned earlier, Autodesk Inventor is parametric in nature. The parametric nature of this software package ensures that irrespective of the original size, the selected entity is driven by the dimension value you specify. Therefore, whenever you dimension an entity, it is forced to change its size in accordance with the specified dimension value. The type of dimension that will be applied varies depending on the type of entity selected. For example, if you select a line segment, linear dimensions will be applied and if you select a circle, diameter dimensions will be applied. Note that all these types of dimensions can be applied using the same dimensioning tool. While dimensioning, you can set the priority for editing the dimension value as soon as you place it. To set this priority, choose the **General Dimension** button from the **2D Sketch Panel** panel bar and then right-click to display the shortcut menu. In this menu, choose **Edit Dimension**, see Figure 2-8. Now, as soon as you place the dimension, the **Edit Dimension** toolbar, which allows you to modify the dimensions of the entity, will be displayed, see Figure 2-9. The selected entity will be driven to the dimension value defined in this toolbar.

Figure 2-8 Setting the priority for editing the dimensions as they are placed

*Figure 2-9 The **Edit Dimension** toolbar*

You can enter a new value for the dimension or choose the button on the right of this toolbar to accept the default value.

If you do not want to edit the dimensions after you place them, invoke the **General Dimension** tool and then right-click to display the shortcut menu. Clear the check mark on the left of the **Edit Dimension** option by choosing it again. When you place a dimension now, the **Edit Dimension** toolbar will not be displayed. To edit the dimension value in this case, click on it after placing, if the **General Dimension** tool is still active. If the tool is not active, double-click on the dimension; the **Edit Dimension** toolbar will be displayed. Enter the new dimension value in this edit box.

Various dimensioning techniques available in Autodesk Inventor are discussed next.

Linear Dimensioning

Linear dimensions are defined as the dimensions that specify the shortest distance between two points. You can apply linear dimensions directly to a line or select two points or entities to apply the linear dimension between them. The points that you can select include the endpoints of lines, splines, or arcs, or the center points of circles, arcs, or ellipses. You can dimension a vertical or a horizontal line by directly selecting it. As soon as you select it, the dimension will be attached to the cursor. You can place the dimension at any desired location. If the priority for editing the dimensions is set, the **Edit Dimension** toolbar will be displayed as soon as you place the dimension. To place the dimension between two points, select the points one by one. After selecting the second point, right-click to display the shortcut menu, as shown in Figure 2-10. In this menu, choose the dimension type. If you choose **Horizontal**, the horizontal dimension will be placed between the two selected points. If you choose **Vertical**, the vertical dimension will be placed between the two selected points. If you choose **Aligned**, the aligned dimension will

Figure 2-10 Shortcut menu with the options to dimension two points

be placed between the two selected points. Figure 2-11 shows the linear dimensioning of lines and Figure 2-12 shows the linear dimensioning of two points.

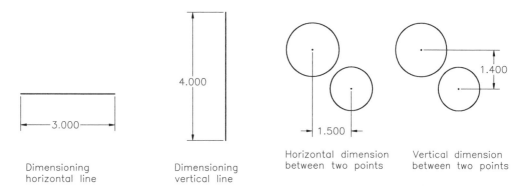

Figure 2-11 *Linear dimensioning of lines*   **Figure 2-12** *Linear dimensioning of points*

You can also apply a horizontal or vertical dimension to an inclined line, see Figure 2-13. To apply these dimensions, select the inclined line and then right-click; a shortcut menu, similar to the one shown in Figure 2-10, will be displayed. In this menu, choose **Horizontal** to place the horizontal dimension and choose **Vertical** to place the vertical dimension.

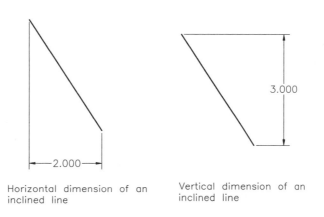

Figure 2-13 *Linear dimensioning of an inclined line*

Aligned Dimensioning

Aligned dimensions are used to dimension lines that are not parallel to the X axis or the Y axis. This type of dimensioning measures the actual distance of the aligned lines or the lines that are drawn at a certain angle. You can directly select the inclined line to apply this dimension. After selecting the inclined line, pick a point just below the line; the aligned dimension will be attached to the cursor. You can also select two points to apply the aligned dimension. The points include the endpoints of lines, splines, or arcs or the center points of arcs, circles, or ellipses. If you select two points to apply the aligned dimensions, right-click to display the shortcut menu and choose **Aligned**. Figures 2-14 and 2-15 show the aligned dimensions applied to various objects.

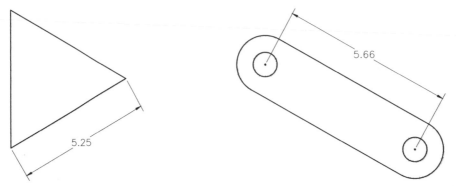

Figure 2-14 *Aligned dimension of a line*   *Figure 2-15* *Aligned dimension using two points*

Angular Dimensioning

Angular dimensions are used to dimension angles. You can select two line segments or use three points to apply the angular dimensions. You can also use angular dimensioning to dimension an arc. All these options of angular dimensioning are discussed next.

Angular Dimensioning using Two Line Segments

You can directly select two line segments to apply angular dimensions. Invoke the **General Dimension** tool and then select a line segment using the left mouse button. Instead of placing the dimension, select the second line segment. Now, place the dimension to measure the angle between the two lines. While placing the dimension, you need to be careful about the point where you place the dimension. This is because depending on the location of the dimension placement, the vertically opposite angles will be displayed. Figure 2-16 shows the angular dimension between two lines and Figure 2-17 shows the dimension of the vertically opposite angle between two lines.

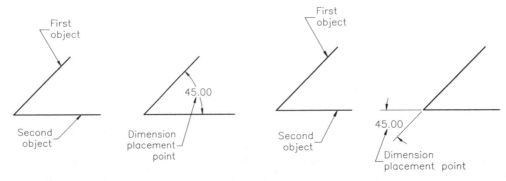

Figure 2-16 *Angular dimensioning*   *Figure 2-17* *Vertically opposite angle*

Also, depending on the location of the dimension, the major or the minor angle value will be displayed. Figure 2-18 shows the major angle dimension between two lines and Figure 2-19 shows the minor angle dimension between the same set of lines.

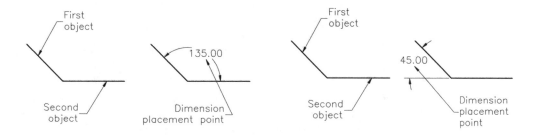

Figure 2-18 *Major angle dimension*   **Figure 2-19** *Minor angle dimension*

Angular Dimensioning using Three Points

You can also apply angular dimensions using three points. Remember that the three points should be selected in the clockwise or counterclockwise sequence. The points that can be used to apply the angular dimensions include the endpoints of lines or arcs, or the center points of arcs, circles, and ellipses. Figure 2-20 shows angular dimensioning using three points.

Angular Dimensioning of an Arc

You can use angular dimensions to dimension an arc. In case of arcs, the three points are the endpoints and the center point of the arc. Note that the points should be selected in the clockwise or counterclockwise sequence, but the center point should always be the second selection point. Figure 2-21 shows the angular dimensioning of an arc.

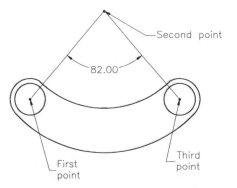

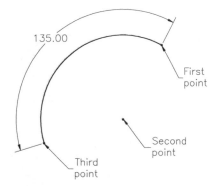

Figure 2-20 *Angular dimensioning using three points*   **Figure 2-21** *Angular dimensioning of an arc*

Tip. *After invoking the **General Dimension** tool, as you move the cursor close to the sketched entities, a small symbol will be displayed close to the cursor. This symbol displays the type of dimension that will be applied. For example, if you select a line, the linear dimensioning or aligned dimensioning symbol will be displayed. If you move the cursor close to another line after selecting the first, the symbol of angular dimensioning will be displayed. These symbols help you in determining the type of dimensions that will be applied.*

*In Autodesk Inventor, the ellipses are dimensioned as half of the major and minor axes distances. To dimension an ellipse, invoke the **General Dimension** tool and then select the ellipse. Now, if you move the cursor in the vertical direction, the axis of the ellipse along the X axis will be dimensioned in terms of its half length. Similarly, if you move the cursor in the horizontal direction, the axis of the ellipse along the Y axis will be dimensioned equal to its half length.*

Diameter Dimensioning

Diameter dimensions are applied to dimension a circle or an arc to specify its diameter. In Autodesk Inventor, when you select a circle to dimension, the diameter dimension is applied to it by default. However, if you select an arc to dimension, the radius dimension is applied to it. You can also apply the diameter dimension to an arc by invoking the **General Dimension** tool and selecting the arc. Now, right-click to display the shortcut menu, see Figure 2-22. Choose **Diameter** from this menu to apply the diameter dimension. Figure 2-23 shows a circle and an arc with diameter dimensions.

Figure 2-22 Shortcut menu to apply a diameter dimension to an arc

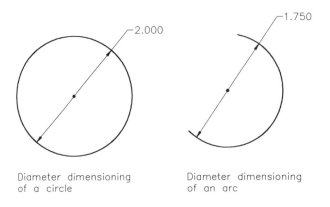

Figure 2-23 Diameter dimensioning of a circle and an arc

Radius Dimensioning

Radius dimensions are applied to dimension an arc or a circle to specify its radius. As mentioned earlier, by default, the circles will be assigned diameter dimensions and the arcs will be assigned radius dimensions. However, you can also apply the radius dimensions to a circle. To do so, invoke the **General Dimension** tool and then select the circle. Now, right-click to display the shortcut menu, as shown in Figure 2-24. Choose **Radius** from this menu to apply the radius dimension. Figure 2-25 shows an arc and a circle with radius dimensions.

Figure 2-24   Shortcut menu to apply a radius dimension to a circle

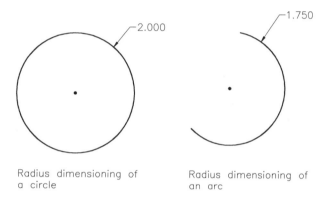

Radius dimensioning of a circle

Radius dimensioning of an arc

Figure 2-25   Radius dimensioning of a circle and an arc

Tip. *To distinguish whether the dimension applied to an arc or a circle is a radius or a diameter, try to locate the number of arrowheads in the dimension. If there are two arrowheads in the dimension and the dimension line is placed inside the circle or the arc, it is a diameter dimension. The radius dimension has one arrowhead and the dimension line is placed outside the circle or the arc.*

Linear Diameter Dimensioning

Linear diameter dimensioning is used to dimension the sketches of the revolved components. The sketch for a revolved component is drawn using simple sketcher entities. For example, if you draw a rectangle and revolve, it will result in a cylinder. Now, if you dimension the rectangle using the linear dimensions, the same dimensions will be displayed when you generate the drawing views of the cylinder. Also, the same dimensions will be used while manufacturing the component. But these linear dimensions will result in a confusing situation in manufacturing. This is because while manufacturing a revolved component, the dimensions have to be specified as the diameter of the revolved component. The linear dimensions will not be acceptable in manufacturing a revolved component. To resolve this problem, the sketches for the revolved features are dimensioned using the linear diameter dimensions. These dimensions display the distance between the two selected line segments as a diameter, that is, double the original length. For example, if the original dimension between two entities is 10 mm, the linear diameter dimension will display it as 20 mm. This is because when you revolve a rectangle with 10 mm width, the diameter of the resultant cylinder will be 20 mm. In this type of dimension, Autodesk Inventor assumes that if you select two lines, the line selected first will act as the axis of revolution for the sketch and the line selected last will result in the outer surface of the revolved feature. This means that the line selected last will be the one that will be dimensioned. But if one of the lines is a center line drawn by choosing the **Centerline** button from the **Inventor Standard** toolbar, then the centerline will be considered as the axis of revolution.

To apply linear diameter dimensions, invoke the **General Dimension** tool; you will be prompted to select the first geometry to dimension. Select the first line; you will be prompted to select the second geometry to dimension. Select the second line with reference to which you want to apply the linear diameter dimensions. If the first line you selected is a center line, the linear diameter dimension will be displayed. Else, right-click and choose **Linear Diameter** from the shortcut menu, see Figure 2-26. You will notice that the distance between the two lines is displayed as double the distance. Also, the dimension value is preceded by the **Ø** symbol, suggesting that it is a linear diameter dimension. Figures 2-27 and 2-28 show the use of linear diameter dimensioning.

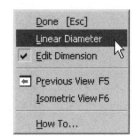

Figure 2-26 *Choosing the option for applying linear diameter dimensions*

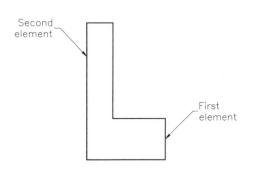

Figure 2-27 *Selecting the elements for linear diameter dimensions*

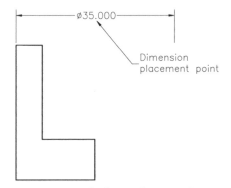

Figure 2-28 *The linear diameter dimension*

UNDERSTANDING THE CONCEPT OF FULLY CONSTRAINED SKETCHES

A fully constrained sketch is the one whose all entities are completely constrained to their surrounding using the constraints and dimensions. A fully constrained sketch cannot change its size, location, or orientation unexpectedly. Whenever you draw a sketched entity, it will be black in color. If you add dimensions and constraints to fully constrain it, the entities will turn blue. Note that while creating the base sketch in Autodesk Inventor, you need to dimension it with respect to a fixed point in order to fully constrain it. Therefore, you need to use some extra steps to fully constrain the sketch. These steps are given next.

1. Draw a sketch point at the origin. You can use the **Inventor Precise Input** toolbar to ensure that the point is placed exactly at the origin.
2. Apply the **Fix** constraint to the point.
3. Use this point to dimension the original sketch. You can add horizontal and vertical dimensions to the sketch from this point. You can also add a **Coincident** constraint between the point and the endpoints of one of the entities in the sketch.

MEASURING SKETCHED ENTITIES

Autodesk Inventor allows you to measure various parameters of the sketched entities. The parameters that you can measure are distances, angles, loops, and area. Measuring these parameters is discussed next.

Measuring Distances

Menu Bar:	Tools > Measure Distance
Shortcut Menu:	Measure > Measure Distance

Autodesk Inventor allows you to measure the length of a line segment, radius of an arc, diameter of a circle, minimum distance between two entities, or the coordinates of a point. All this can be done using the **Measure Distance** tool. On invoking this tool, the **Measure Distance** toolbar will be displayed and you will be prompted to select the first entity. The **Measure Distance** toolbar will be modified depending on the type of entities selected to be measured. The methods of measuring the distances between various entities are discussed next.

Measuring Length of a Line Segment

When you invoke the **Measure Distance** tool, the **Measure Distance** toolbar will be displayed and you will be prompted to select the first entity. If you select a line segment at this point, the **Measure Distance** toolbar will be changed to the **Length** toolbar and the length of the selected line segment will be displayed in this toolbar, see Figure 2-29.

*Figure 2-29 The **Length** toolbar displaying the length of the line*

Tip. *To restart measuring the distances, right-click to display the shortcut menu. In the shortcut menu, choose **Restart**. You will be prompted to select the first element to be measured.*

Measuring Distance Between a Point and a Line Segment

To measure the distance between a point and a line segment, invoke the **Measure Distance** tool and then select the point. The **Measure Distance** toolbar will show the X, Y, and Z coordinates of the point and you will be prompted to select the second entity. Select the line. The **Measure Distance** toolbar will be changed to the **Minimum Distance** toolbar. This toolbar will display the minimum distance between the point and the line and also the length of the line, see Figure 2-30.

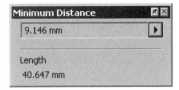

Figure 2-30 *The* **Minimum Distance** *toolbar displaying the distance between the lines*

Measuring Coordinates of a Point

To measure the coordinates of a point with respect to the current coordinate system, invoke the **Measure Distance** tool. You will be prompted to select the first element. Select the point whose coordinates you want to know. The selectable points include the endpoints of lines, arcs, or splines, center point of arcs, circles, or ellipses, or hole centers. If you select a hole center or the center point, the **Measure Distance** toolbar is changed to the **Position** toolbar and the X, Y, and Z coordinates of the selected point with respect to the current coordinate system will be displayed, see Figure 2-31. However, if you select an endpoint, the coordinates are specified in the **Measure Distance** toolbar.

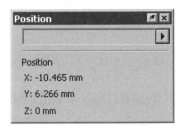

Figure 2-31 *The* **Position** *toolbar displaying the coordinates of a point/hole center*

Measuring Distance Between Two Points

To measure the distance between two points, invoke this tool and then select the first point. The **Measure Distance** toolbar will display the coordinates of the selected point and you will be prompted to select the second element. Select the second point. The **Measure Distance** toolbar will be momentarily changed to the **Minimum Distance** toolbar. This toolbar will display the distance between the two points. This toolbar will also display the coordinates of the second point. You will also notice the **Delta X**, **Delta Y**, and **Delta Z** values in this toolbar, see Figure 2-32. These values are the distances between the two selected points along the X, Y, and Z axes. Note that if you move the cursor after selecting the second point, the **Minimum Distance** toolbar will be replaced by the **Measure Distance** toolbar.

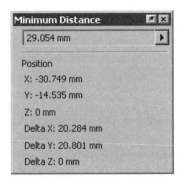

Figure 2-32 *Toolbar displaying the minimum distance between two points, coordinates of the second points, and the delta X, Y, and Z distances between the two points*

Tip. *You would have noticed that the Z coordinates or the Z distances are zero at all places. This is because by default, when you start a new drawing, the sketches are drawn in the XY plane. You can also draw the sketches on other planes. You will learn more about these sketching planes in later chapters.*

Measuring Radius of an Arc or Diameter of a Circle

You can also measure the radius of an arc or the diameter of a circle using the **Measure Distance** tool. When you invoke this tool, the **Measure Distance** toolbar will be displayed and you will be prompted to select the first element. If you select an arc, this toolbar will be momentarily changed to the **Radius** toolbar and will display the radius of the arc, see Figure 2-33. If you select a circle, this toolbar will be momentarily changed to the **Diameter** toolbar and will display the diameter of the circle, see Figure 2-34. Note that when you select an arc or a circle, you are not prompted to select the second element. This is because, you cannot calculate any value other than their radius or diameter.

*Figure 2-33 The **Radius** toolbar displaying the radius of an arc*

*Figure 2-34 The **Diameter** toolbar displaying the diameter of a circle*

Tip. *You can make sure that no sketching tool is selected by looking at the **Select** button in the **Inventor Standard** toolbar. If the **Select** button in this toolbar is chosen, this means that no sketching tool is selected. If this button is not chosen, this means that some sketching tool is active. Right-click and choose **Done** to close the sketching tool that is active. You will notice that the **Select** button is chosen automatically when you exit the sketching tool.*

Measuring Angles

Menu Bar:	Tools > Measure Angle
Shortcut Menu:	Measure > Measure Angle

To measure an angle, right-click in the drawing window and choose **Measure > Measure Angle** from the shortcut menu. The **Measure Angle** toolbar will be displayed. Using this tool, you can measure the angle between two line segments or between three points. Both these methods for measuring the angles are discussed next.

Measuring Angle Between Two lines

To measure the angle between two lines, invoke the **Measure Angle** tool. The **Measure Angle** toolbar is displayed and you will be prompted to select the first element. Select the first line. Upon doing so, you will be prompted to select the second line. The **Measure Angle** toolbar will change to the **Angle** toolbar and the angle between the selected line segments will be displayed, see Figure 2-35.

*Figure 2-35 The **Angle** toolbar displaying the angle between two lines*

Measuring Angles using Three Points

You can also measure the angle using three points. Note that the points must be selected in the clockwise or counterclockwise sequence. When you invoke this tool, you will be prompted to select the first element. If you select a point, you will be prompted to select the next point. After you select the second point, you will again be prompted to select the next point. Select the third point. Once you have selected the three points, Autodesk Inventor draws imaginary lines between the first and second points and between the second and third points. The angle between these two imaginary lines will be measured and displayed in the **Angle** toolbar, as shown in Figures 2-36 and 2-37.

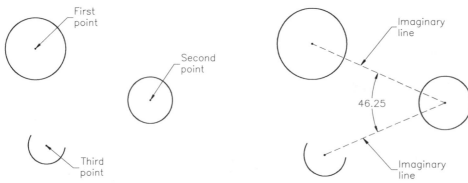

Figure 2-36 Selecting three points   *Figure 2-37 Angle between the imaginary lines*

 Tip. *Autodesk Inventor allows you to switch from one measuring tool to the other. This is done using the shortcut menu displayed upon choosing the arrow on the right of the toolbar of any measuring tools. When you choose this arrow, the shortcut menu will be displayed. The options of invoking other measuring tools will be displayed in it.*

Measuring Loops

Menu Bar:	Tools > Measure Loop
Shortcut Menu:	Measure > Measure Loop

Autodesk Inventor allows you to measure closed loops. To measure closed loops, right-click in the drawing window and choose **Measure > Measure Loop** from the shortcut menu. The **Measure Loop** toolbar will be displayed and you will be prompted to select a face or a loop. Select the loop to be measured. The **Measure Loop** toolbar will be momentarily changed to the **Loop Length** toolbar and the measurement will be displayed in it. Figure 2-38 shows the **Measure Loop** toolbar with the measurement of a loop.

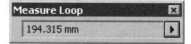

*Figure 2-38 The **Measure Loop** toolbar*

 Tip. *You can also measure the loop or the area defined by a face of an existing feature. You will learn more about features in later chapters.*

Measuring Area

Menu Bar:	Tools > Measure Area
Shortcut Menu:	Measure > Measure Area

To measure the area of closed loops, right-click in the drawing window and choose **Measure > Measure Area** from the shortcut menu. The **Measure Area** toolbar will be displayed and you will be prompted to select a face or a loop. Select the closed loop to measure the area. The **Measure Area** toolbar will change to the **Area** toolbar and the area of the loop will be displayed in it. Figure 2-39 shows the **Area** toolbar with the area of a closed loop.

Figure 2-39   The Area toolbar

TUTORIALS

This chapter onwards, you will use the parametric nature of Autodesk Inventor in drawing the sketches and creating the features. The following tutorials will explain the method of drawing sketches to some arbitrary dimensions and then driving them to the dimension values required in the model.

Tutorial 1

In this tutorial, you will draw the sketch shown in Figure 2-40. This sketch is the same as the one drawn in Tutorial 2 of Chapter 1. In this tutorial, you will not use the **Inventor Precise Input** toolbar while drawing the initial sketch. After drawing it, add the required constraints and then dimension the sketch. You will place a point at the origin and fix it at that location. Then you will dimension the sketch using this point also to fully constrain the sketch. The final sketch should be saved with the name given below.

\PersonalProject\c02\Tutorial1.ipt   (**Expected time: 30 min**)

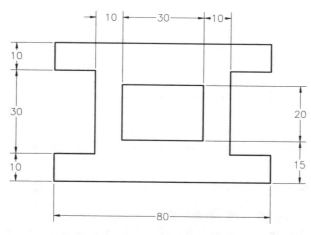

Figure 2-40   Dimensioned sketch for Tutorial 1

Before you start drawing the sketch, it is recommended that you outline the steps that will be followed to complete the tutorials. These steps are listed below.

a.   Start a new metric standard part file.
b.   Draw the initial sketch using the **Line** and **Two point rectangle** tools, refer to Figure 2-41.
c.   Add the required constraints and dimensions to complete the sketch, refer to Figure 2-43.
d.   Place a sketch point at the origin and add the **Fix** constraint to it.
e.   Dimension the sketch using this point to fully constrain it, refer to Figure 2-44.
f.   Save the sketch with the name *Tutorial1.ipt* and then close the file.

Starting Autodesk Inventor

1.   Start Autodesk Inventor by double-clicking on its shortcut icon on the desktop of your computer or by using the **Start** menu.

2.   Choose **New** in the **Open** dialog box to display the various tabs. Choose the **Metric** tab to display the metric templates. Double-click on **Standard (mm).ipt** in the **Metric** tab to start metric standard part file. By default, the sketching environment is active.

Drawing the Initial Sketch

1.   Using the **Line** tool and the **Two point rectangle** tool, draw the required sketch similar to the one shown in Figure 2-40. You do not need to draw the sketch to the exact length. Use the temporary tracking option for drawing the sketch. For your reference, all the lines in the sketch are numbered, see Figure 2-41.

Note that in this sketch, the display of the X and Y axes is turned off.

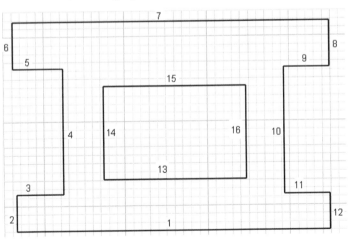

Figure 2-41 Initial sketch drawn using the sketching tools

Adding Constraints to the Sketch

It is evident in Figure 2-41 that some of the lines need to be of the same length. For example, lines 1 and 7, lines 2 and 6, lines 8 and 12, and so on need to be of the same length. One option is that you assign dimensions to all these lines. But this will increase the number of dimensions in the sketch. The other option is that you apply constraints that will force the lines to maintain an equal length.

In this case, you can apply the **Equal** constraint to all the lines that should have the same length. The **Equal** constraint will relate the length of one of the lines with respect to the other line. Now, if you dimension any one of the related lines, all other lines that are related to it are forced to acquire the same dimension value. The **Equal** constraint is applied in pairs.

1. Choose the down arrow on the right of the **Perpendicular** button in the **2D Sketch Panel** panel bar to display the other constraints. Choose **Equal** to invoke this constraint.

When you invoke this constraint, you are prompted to select the first line, circle, or arc.

 Note
*By default, the **Perpendicular** constraint will be displayed in the **2D Sketch Panel** panel bar or toolbar. However, when you select any other constraint by choosing the down arrow on the right of the **Perpendicular** constraint, the selected constraint will become active and will be displayed in the **2D Sketch Panel** panel bar or toolbar.*

2. Select line 2; the color of this line is changed to blue and you are prompted to select the second line, circle, or arc. Select line 6. The **Equal** constraint is applied to lines 2 and 6. You are again prompted to select the first line, circle, or arc. Select line 6 as the first line and then select line 8 as the second line.

If the Autodesk Inventor warning message box is displayed while applying any of these constraints, choose **Cancel** to exit that box.

3. Similarly, select lines 8 and 12, 1 and 7, 3 and 5, 5 and 9, 9 and 11, and then lines 10 and 4. This applies the **Equal** constraint to all these pairs of lines. Right-click in the drawing window and choose **Done**.

 Note
If while drawing the sketch, the vertical or horizontal constraint was not applied to any line, you need to apply it manually using the respective buttons.

Dimensioning the Sketch

Once all the required constraints are applied to the sketch, you can dimension it. As mentioned earlier, when you add dimensions to the sketch and modify their value, the entity will be forced to the dimension values you have specified.

1. Choose **General Dimension** from the **2D Sketch Panel** panel bar; you are prompted to select the geometry to be dimensioned. Select line 1.

As soon as you move the cursor close to line 1, it turns red and a small symbol is displayed, suggesting that a linear dimension will be applied to this line. It is important to modify the value of the dimensions after it is placed so that the geometries are driven to the values that you require. Therefore, after selecting line 1, right-click to display the shortcut menu. In this menu, choose **Edit Dimension**. If it is already chosen, press ESC once. This will make sure that the **Edit Dimension** toolbar is displayed when you place the dimension. This toolbar allows you to modify the dimension value.

2. Place the dimension below line 1; the **Edit Dimension** toolbar is displayed. Enter **80** as the length of line 1 in this toolbar and then choose the check mark button on the right of this toolbar.

    You will notice that the length of the line is modified to 80 units. Also, notice that the length of line 7 is also modified because of the **Equal** constraint (refer to Figure 2-43).

3. Because you are still in the **General Dimension** tool, you are again prompted to select the geometry to dimension. Select line 2 and place the dimension on the left of this line; the **Edit Dimension** toolbar is displayed. Change the length of this line in this toolbar to **10**.

    You will notice that the length of lines 6, 8, and 12 is also forced to 10 units. This is because the **Equal** constraint is applied to all these lines.

4. Select line 4 and place it along the previous dimension. Modify the dimension value to **30** in the **Edit Dimension** toolbar. Notice that the length of line 10 is also modified.

5. Select line 16 and place the dimension outside the sketch on the right side. Modify the dimension value in the **Edit Dimension** toolbar to **20**.

6. Select line 15 and place the dimension outside the sketch on the top. Modify the dimension value to **30** in the **Edit Dimension** toolbar.

7. Now, to dimension the distance between lines 4 and 14, select them one by one. Place the dimension outside the sketch on the top and then change the dimension value to **10** in the **Edit Dimension** toolbar.

8. Similarly, select lines 16 and 10 to dimension the distance between these two lines and place the dimension outside the sketch on the top. Change the dimension value to **10** in the **Edit Dimension** toolbar. You will notice that the length of lines 5, 9, 3, and 11 is automatically adjusted due to the **Equal** constraint.

9. To locate the inner rectangle vertically from the outer loop, select lines 1 and 13 and then place the dimension on the right of the sketch. Modify the dimension value in the **Edit Dimension** toolbar to **15**.

    With this, you have applied all the required constraints and dimensions to the sketch. Now, this sketch is ready to be converted into a feature. If you try to add more constraints or dimensions to this sketch, Autodesk Inventor will display an error message dialog box informing you that adding this dimension or constraint will over-constrain the sketch, see

Figure 2-42. If you still want this dimension to be displayed, choose the **Accept** button in this box. The dimension will be added as a **driven dimension**. A driven dimension is placed inside parentheses and is not used during the manufacturing process. These dimensions are used only for reference. Note that you cannot edit the value of a driven dimension.

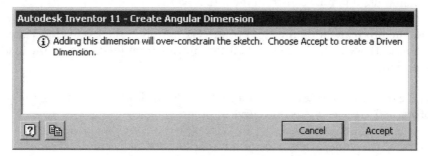

Figure 2-42 Autodesk Inventor message box

10. The sketch, after applying all dimensions and constraints, should look similar to the one shown in Figure 2-43.

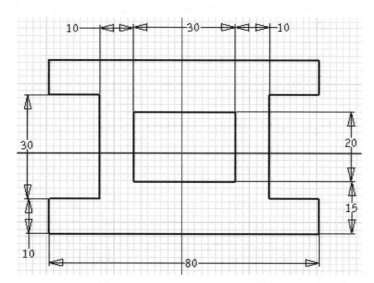

Figure 2-43 Sketch after adding dimensions

Even after adding all the dimensions, the color of the entities in the sketch is still black. This is because the sketch is not fully constrained. As mentioned in the tutorial description, you need to place a sketch point at the origin and then use it to fully constrain the sketch.

11. Using the **Inventor Precise Input** toolbar, place a sketch point at the origin.

Because you have applied the **Equal** constraint to the entities, the button of this will be displayed in the **2D Sketch Panel** panel bar instead of the default **Perpendicular** button.

12. Choose the down arrow on the right of the **Equal** button in the **2D Sketch Panel** panel bar and choose the **Fix** button. You are prompted to select a curve or a point to be fixed.

13. Select the sketch point that you placed at the origin. This will fix the point at the origin and you can now use it to fully constrain the initial sketch.

14. Choose the down arrow on the right of the **Fix** button in the **2D Sketch Panel** panel bar and choose the **Coincident** button. You are prompted to select the first curve or point.

15. Select the intersection point of line 1 and 2. This is the lower left vertex of the sketch. You are prompted to select the second curve or point.

16. Select the sketch point placed at the origin. The entire sketch shifts itself such that the lower left vertex of the sketch is now at the origin. But the sketch is not completely visible in the drawing window.

17. Choose the **Zoom All** button from the **Inventor Standard** toolbar to fit the sketch in the drawing window. You will notice that all the entities in the sketch turn blue in color, suggesting that the sketch is fully constrained. Press the ESC key to exit the **Coincident** constraint tool.

Figure 2-44 shows the fully constrained sketch for Tutorial 1.

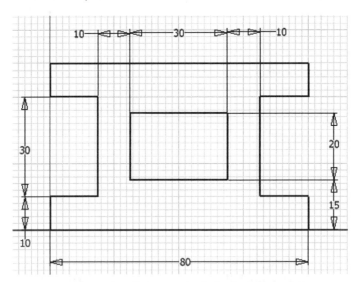

Figure 2-44 Fully constrained sketch for Tutorial 1

Saving the Sketch

1. Choose the **Return** button in the **Inventor Standard** toolbar to exit the sketching environment. You can also right-click in the drawing window and choose **Finish Sketch** from the shortcut menu to exit the sketching environment.

2. Choose the **Save** button from the **Inventor Standard** toolbar and save this sketch with the name given below.

   \PersonalProject\c02\Tutorial1.ipt

3. Choose **File > Close** from the menu bar to close the file.

Tutorial 2

In this tutorial, you will draw the sketch shown in Figure 2-45. This sketch is the same as the one that was drawn in Tutorial 4 of Chapter 1. You will not use the **Inventor Precise Input** toolbar to draw the initial sketch in this tutorial. After drawing it, apply the required constraints and dimensions to fully constrain it.   **(Expected time: 30 min)**

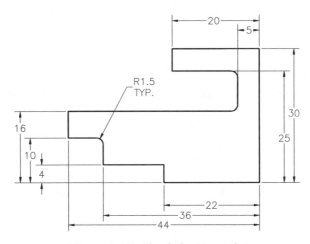

Figure 2-45 *Sketch for Tutorial 2*

The following steps are required to complete this tutorial:

a. Start a new metric standard part file and draw the initial sketch using the **Line** tool, refer to Figure 2-46.
b. Place a point at the origin and fix it using the **Fix** constraint.
c. Add linear diameter dimensions to the sketch by using the **General Dimension** tool.
d. Apply the **Coincident** relation between the fixed sketch point and the lower left vertex of the sketch to make it a fully constrained sketch, refer to Figure 2-47.
e. Add fillets and then save the sketch with the name *Tutorial2.ipt* and close the file.

Starting a New File

1. Choose the **New** button in the **Inventor Standard** toolbar and start a new metric standard part file using the **Metric** tab of the **Open** dialog box.

Drawing the Initial Sketch

1. Draw the initial sketch, as shown in Figure 2-46, using the **Line** tool.

The lines in the sketch are numbered for your reference.

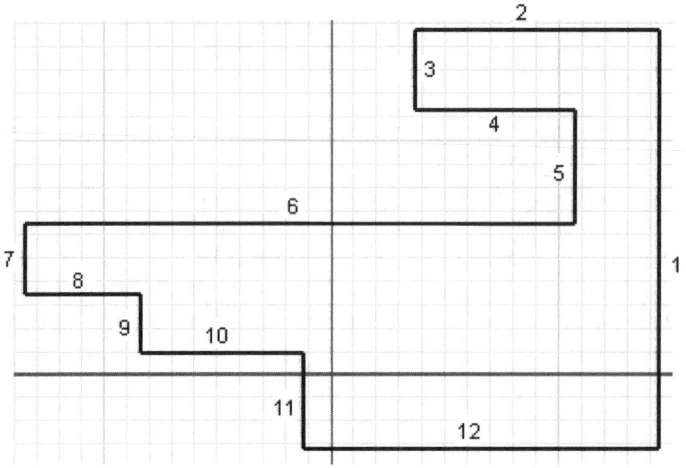

Figure 2-46 *Numbering the lines in the sketch*

2.   Place a sketched point at the origin using the **Inventor Precise Input** toolbar.

Dimensioning and Constraining the Sketch

The dimensions shown in Figure 2-45 are linear dimensions. But because the sketch is for a revolved feature, you need to add linear diameter dimensions to the sketch. It is recommended to first apply all the dimensions and then add the fillets. This is because the sketch generally changes its size after dimensioning. Before proceeding with adding dimensions to a revolved section, it is important for you to determine which line segment of the sketch will act as the revolution axis for revolving the sketch. If you refer to Figures 1-45 and 1-46 in Chapter 1, you will notice that for this model, line 12 will act as the axis for revolving the sketch. Therefore, while applying linear diameter dimensions, line 12 should be selected first.

1.   Choose **General Dimension** from the **2D Sketch Panel** panel bar; you are prompted to select the geometry to be dimensioned. Right-click to display the shortcut menu and choose **Edit Dimension**, if it is not already chosen. If it is already chosen, press the ESC key once to exit the shortcut menu.

2.   Select line 12. You are again prompted to select the geometry to be dimensioned. Select line 10 and then right-click to display the shortcut menu. In this menu, choose **Linear Diameter**.

You will notice that the dimension is displayed as the double of the actual length. Also, the dimension value is preceded by the Øsymbol, suggesting that it is a linear diameter dimension.

3.   Place the dimension on the left of the sketch. The **Edit Dimension** toolbar is displayed.

4. Figure 2-45 shows this value as 4. Because the linear diameter dimensions are placed as the double of the original length, enter **8** in the **Edit Dimension** toolbar. The vertical distance between lines 12 and 10 will be automatically adjusted to match the value entered.

5. As the **General Dimension** tool is still active, you are again prompted to select the geometry to be dimensioned. Select line 12 and then select line 8. Now, right-click to display the shortcut menu and choose **Linear Diameter**. The linear dimension is changed to the linear diameter dimension. Place the dimension on the left of the previous dimension. Modify its value in the **Edit Dimension** toolbar to **20**.

6. Select lines 12 and 6. Right-click to display the shortcut menu and then choose **Linear Diameter**. Place the dimension on the left of the previous dimension and change the value in the **Edit Dimension** toolbar to **32**.

 Tip. *Autodesk Inventor allows you to invoke the drawing display options even when any of the sketching environment tools is active. This is done using a combination of the hot keys and the left mouse button. For example, if the* **General Dimension** *tool is active, you can use the* **Pan** *option by holding the F2 key down and then pressing the left mouse button and dragging. Similarly, you can dynamically zoom in and out of the sketch by holding the F3 key down and then pressing the left mouse button and dragging.*

7. Select lines 12 and 4 and then right-click to display the shortcut menu. In this menu, choose **Linear Diameter**. Place the dimension on the right of the sketch and change the value in the **Edit Dimension** toolbar to **50**.

8. Select lines 12 and 2 and then right-click to display the shortcut menu. In this menu, choose **Linear Diameter**. Place the dimension on the right of the previous dimension and change its value in the **Edit Dimension** toolbar to **60**.

    With this, you have applied all the required linear diameter dimensions. Now, you need to add the linear dimensions.

9. Select lines 1 and 5 and then place the dimension above the sketch. Modify its value in the **Edit Dimension** toolbar to **5**.

10. Select line 2 and then place the dimension above the previous dimension. Modify its value in the **Edit Dimension** toolbar to **20**.

11. Select line 12 and then place the dimension below the sketch. Modify its value in the **Edit Dimension** toolbar to **22**.

12. Select lines 1 and 9 and place the dimension below the previous dimension. Modify its value in the **Edit Dimension** toolbar to **36**.

13. Select lines 1 and 7 and place the dimension below the previous dimension. Modify its value in the **Edit Dimension** toolbar to **44**.

Tip. *Sometimes while dimensioning the sketch, some existing dimensions move from the location where you placed them. In this case, you need to exit the **General Dimension** tool and then drag them back to their original location. To continue dimensioning, invoke the **General Dimension** tool again.*

With this, all the dimensions are added to the sketch. However, the entities in the sketch are still displayed in black, suggesting that the sketch is not fully constrained. Therefore, you need to add more dimensions or constraints. In this sketch, you will first add the **Fix** constraint to the sketched point placed at the origin and then add the **Coincident** constraint to the sketched point and the intersection point of line 11 and 12.

14. Invoke the **Fix** constraint using the **2D Sketch Panel** panel bar and select the sketch point placed at the origin to fix it at the origin.

15. Invoke the **Coincident** constraint; you are prompted to select the first curve or point. Select the intersection point of line 11 and 12. This is the lower left vertex of the sketch; you are prompted to select the second curve or point.

16. Select the sketched point placed at the origin.

    The entire sketch shifts from its original location and is relocated such that the lower left vertex of the sketch now lies at the origin.

17. Choose the **Zoom All** button from the **Inventor Standard** toolbar to fit the sketch in the drawing window. All entities in the sketch are displayed in blue, suggesting that the sketch is fully constrained. The fully constrained sketch, after adding all the dimensions, is shown in Figure 2-47.

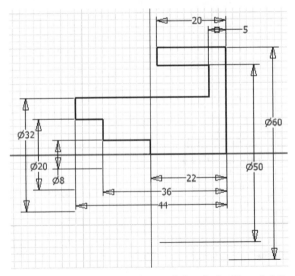

***Figure 2-47** Fully constrained sketch for Tutorial 2*

Adding Fillets to the Sketch

After dimensioning the sketch, you need to add fillets.

1. Choose the **Fillet** button from the **2D Sketch Panel** panel bar; the **2D Fillet** toolbar is displayed. Set the value of fillet in this toolbar to **1.5**. Now, select lines 8 and 9; the fillet is automatically added between these two lines and the fillet dimension is displayed.

2. Similarly, select lines 5 and 6, and lines 4 and 5 to add fillets between these lines. Exit the **2D Fillet** toolbar. The final sketch, after adding the fillets, is shown in Figure 2-48.

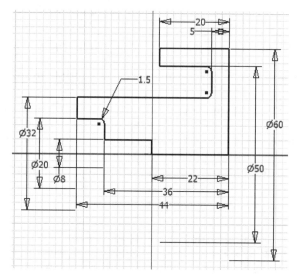

Figure 2-48   *Fully dimensioned sketch after adding fillets*

Note

*To modify the fillet radius, double-click on it. The **Edit Dimension** toolbar is displayed. Modify the value of the fillet in this edit box.*

Saving the Sketch

1. Choose **Return** from the **Inventor Standard** toolbar to exit the sketching environment.

2. Save this sketch with the name *PersonalProject\c02\Tutorial2.ipt*.

3. Choose **File > Close** from the menu bar to close the file.

Tutorial 3

In this tutorial, draw the sketch for the model shown in Figure 2-49. After drawing the sketch, add the required constraints and then dimension it. The basic dimensioned sketch that is required for the model is shown in Figure 2-50. The solid model shown in Figure 2-49 is only for your reference.   **(Expected time: 30 min)**

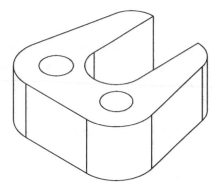

Figure 2-49 *Model for Tutorial 3*

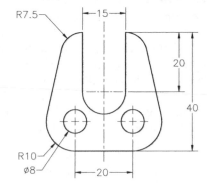

Figure 2-50 *Dimensioned sketch for the model*

The sketch shown in Figure 2-50 is a combination of multiple closed loops: the outer loop and the inner circles. As the number of loops increases, the complexity of the sketch also increases. This is because the number of constraints and dimensions in the sketch increases in case of multiple loops. Now, to draw sketches without using the **Inventor Precise Input** toolbar, it is recommended that you first draw the outer loop and then add constraints and dimensions to it. This is because once the outer loop is constrained and dimensioned, the inner circles can be easily constrained and dimensioned with reference to the outer loop.

The following steps are required to complete this tutorial:

a. Start a new metric template and draw the outer loop of the sketch, refer to Figure 2-51.
b. Add the required dimensions and constraints to the outer loop, refer to Figure 2-53.
c. Draw the inner circles and add constraints and dimensions to them, refer to Figure 2-54.
d. Finally, save the sketch with the name *Tutorial3.ipt* and close the file.

Starting a New File
1. Choose the **New** button in the **Inventor Standard** toolbar to invoke the **Open** dialog box. Choose the **Metric** tab and start a metric standard part file.

Drawing the Outer Loop
1. Using the **Line** tool, draw the outer loop of the sketch, as shown in Figure 2-51.

You can use the option of drawing the tangent arcs using the **Line** tool for drawing this sketch. This can be done by pressing the left mouse button and then dragging in the required direction. (Refer to Tutorial 3 of Chapter 1 to learn more about drawing this type of arc.)

For your reference, all the geometries in the sketch are numbered. The inner holes in the sketch will be drawn after dimensioning the outer loop.

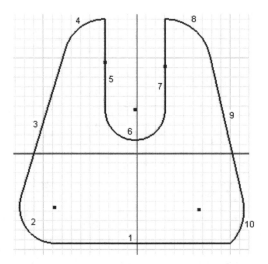

Figure 2-51 Initial sketch with numbered geometries

Adding Constraints to the Sketched Entities

As evident in Figure 2-51, some of the constraints such as tangent and equal are missing in the sketch. You need to manually add these constraints to the sketch. You can view the constraints applied on the various geometries using the **Show Constraints** tool.

1. In Figure 2-51, the tangent constraint is missing between line 1 and arc 10. To add this constraint, choose the down arrow on the right of the **Coincident** button (or the button of the constraint that was used last) in the **2D Sketch Panel** panel bar and choose **Tangent**. You are prompted to select the first curve. Select arc 10 and then select line 1 as the second curve. Similarly, add this constraint at all the places where it is missing in the sketch.

    The geometries 5 and 7, and 3 and 9 are lines and must be of equal length. Also, geometries 2 and 10, and 4 and 8 are arcs that must be of equal radii. Therefore, you need to add the **Equal** constraint between the respective pairs of all these geometries.

2. Choose the down arrow on the right of the **Tangent** button in the **2D Sketch Panel** panel bar and choose **Equal**.

3. Select line 5 as the first line and then select line 7 as the second line to apply the **Equal** constraint to them. Autodesk Inventor again prompts you to select the first entity. Select line 3 and then select line 9 to apply the **Equal** constraint to these lines.

4. You are prompted to select the first entity again. Select arc 2 and then arc 10 to apply the **Equal** constraint to these arcs.

    Applying this constraint to the arcs or circles forces their radii or diameters to be equal.

5. Similarly, apply the **Equal** constraint on arcs 4 and 8. The sketch, after applying all the constraints, is shown in Figure 2-52.

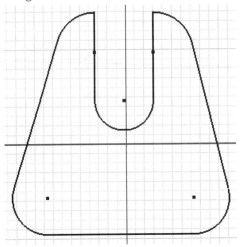

Figure 2-52 The sketch, after applying all the constraints

Note

The shape of the sketch that you have may be a little different at this stage. This is because of the difference in specifying the points while drawing the sketch. However, once all the dimensions are applied, the shape of the sketch will become similar.

Dimensioning the Sketch

1. Choose the **General Dimension** button from the **2D Sketch Panel** panel bar. Right-click to display the shortcut menu. In this menu, choose **Edit Dimension**, if it is not already chosen. If it shows the check mark, press the ESC key once to exit the shortcut menu. You are prompted to select the geometry to be dimensioned. Select line 1 and place the dimension below the sketch. Modify the value of this dimension in the **Edit Dimension** toolbar to **20**.

    As mentioned earlier, you can use a combination of hot keys and mouse buttons to modify the drawing display. At this stage, hold the F3 key down to invoke the **Zoom** tool. Press the left mouse button and drag it to modify the display. After getting the desired display, hold the F2 key down to invoke the **Pan** tool. Press the left mouse button and drag it to pan the display to the desired point.

2. As soon as you release the F2 key, the dimensioning process will resume and you will be prompted to select the geometry to dimension. Select arc 4 and place the dimension on the left of the sketch. This will place the radius dimension for the sketch. Modify the dimension value in the **Edit Dimension** toolbar to **7.5**. The size of arc 8 will also be modified because of the **Equal** constraint applied between these two entities.

3. Select arc 2 and place the radius dimension on the left of the sketch. Modify the dimension value in the **Edit Dimension** toolbar to **10**. The size of the arc 10 will also be modified due

to the **Equal** constraint applied between these two entities.

4. Select line 5 and then line 7 and place the dimension above the sketch. Modify the value of this dimension in the **Edit Dimension** toolbar to **15**.

5. Select line 7 and place the dimension on the right of the sketch. Modify the value of this dimension in the **Edit Dimension** toolbar to **20**.

6. Select the upper endpoint of line 7 and then select line 1 and place the dimension on the right of the previous dimension. Modify the value of this dimension toolbar to **40**.

    With this, all the dimensions are applied, except the horizontal dimension between the center points of arcs 4 and 6 or arcs 7 and 6. Their need depends on the constraints and dimensions assumed while drawing the sketch. If you are warned that adding any of these dimensions will over-constrain the sketch, choose **Cancel** in the message box. In this case, this dimension is already assumed.

7. Select the center point of arc 4 and then the center point of arc 6. As you have selected two points that are not horizontally or vertically aligned, you can apply horizontal, vertical, or aligned dimensions to these points. However, in this sketch, you require only the horizontal dimension. Therefore, you will use the shortcut menu.

8. Right-click and choose **Horizontal** from the shortcut menu. Place the dimension above the sketch. If the **Edit Dimension** toolbar is displayed, modify the dimension value to **7.5**. However, if the warning message box is displayed, choose **Cancel**. Try the same dimension with arcs 7 and 6. If the warning message is displayed, cancel it.

    The sketch, after adding the required dimensions, is shown in Figure 2-53. Note that the horizontal dimension between the center points of arcs was not required in this sketch and so is not displayed in Figure 2-53.

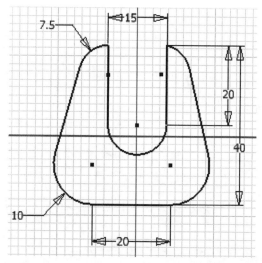

Figure 2-53 Dimensioned sketch for Tutorial 3

Drawing Circles

Once all the required dimensions and constraints are applied, you will have to draw the circles. Figure 2-50 suggests that the circles are concentric with arcs 2 and 10.

1. To draw the concentric circles, choose **Center point circle** from the **2D Sketch Panel** panel bar; you are prompted to select the center of the circle. Move the cursor close to the center of arc 2. Specify the center point when the cursor snaps to the center point of arc 2 and turns green. Now, move the cursor away from the center and specify a point to size the circle.

2. Similarly, taking the reference of the center of arc 10, draw the other circle.

Adding Constraints to the Circles

Because both circles have the same diameter, you can apply the **Equal** constraint to them. This way you have to apply a dimension to just one of them. The other circle will be automatically forced to the specified diameter value because of the **Equal** constraint.

1. Invoke the **Equal** constraint from the **2D Sketch Panel** panel bar. Select the first circle and then select the second circle to apply the **Equal** constraint.

Dimensioning the Circle

1. Choose **General Dimension** from the **2D Sketch Panel** panel bar and select the left circle. Place the dimension on the left of the sketch. Change the value of the diameter of the circle in the **Edit Dimension** toolbar to **8**.

Notice that the size of the right circle is automatically modified to match the dimension of the left circle. This is because of the **Equal** constraint applied between the two circles. The final sketch for Tutorial 3, after drawing and dimensioning the circles, is shown in Figure 2-54.

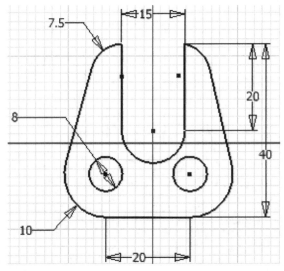

Figure 2-54 *The final dimensioned sketch for Tutorial 3*

Saving the Sketch

1. Choose the **Return** button in the **Inventor Standard** toolbar to exit the sketching environment. Save this sketch with the name given below.

   \PersonalProject\c02\Tutorial3.ipt

2. Choose **File > Close** from the menu bar to close the file.

Tutorial 4

In this tutorial, you will draw the sketch for the model shown in Figure 2-55. The dimensioned sketch is shown in Figure 2-56. After drawing, add constraints and then dimension it. The solid model is given for reference only. **(Expected time: 30 min)**

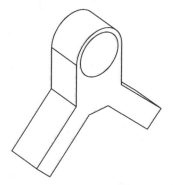

Figure 2-55 *Model for the sketch of Tutorial 4*

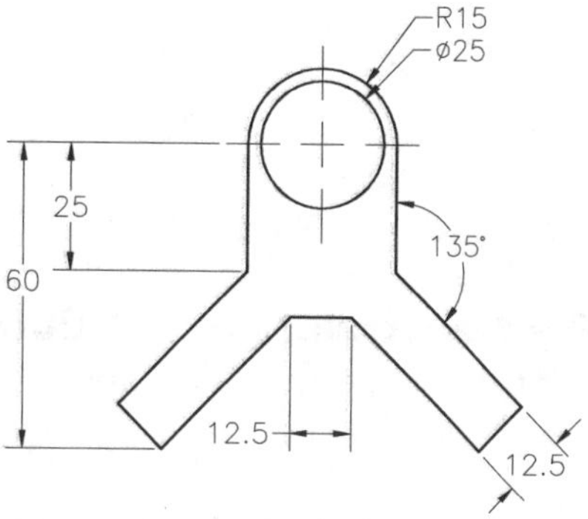

Figure 2-56 *Sketch to be drawn*

The following steps are required to complete this tutorial:

a. Start a new metric standard part file and draw the outer loop of the sketch.
b. Add the required dimensions and constraints to the sketch.
c. Add the inner circle and add the dimension to it.
d. Finally, save the sketch with the name *Tutorial4.ipt* and close the file.

Starting a New File

1. Choose the **New** button from the **Inventor Standard** toolbar to display the **Open** dialog box. Start a new metric standard part file from the **Metric** tab of this dialog box.

Drawing the Outer Loop

1. Choose **Line** from the **2D Sketch Panel** panel bar and draw the outer loop, as shown in Figure 2-57. As mentioned earlier, you should draw the inner loop after drawing and dimensioning the outer loop. This is because once the outer loop is dimensioned, you can draw the inner loop by taking the reference of the outer loop.

   You can use the option of drawing the arc from within the **Line** tool to draw the arc in the sketch. You can also use the temporary tracking option for drawing this sketch. For your reference, the geometries in the sketch are numbered, see Figure 2-57.

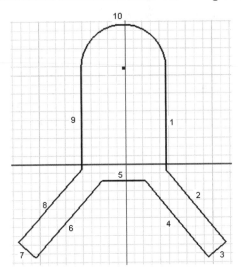

Figure 2-57 Initial sketch with the geometries numbered

Adding Constraints to the Outer Loop

1. Add the **Equal** constraint to lines 1 and 9, lines 2 and 8, lines 3 and 5, lines 5 and 7, and lines 4 and 6.

2. Add the **Perpendicular** constraint to lines 2 and 3, and lines 7 and 8.

3. Add the **Horizontal** constraint between the lower endpoints of lines 4 and 6.

Dimensioning the Outer Loop

1. Choose **General Dimension** from the **2D Sketch Panel** panel bar; you are prompted to select the geometry to dimension. Select line 9 and place the dimension on the left of the sketch. Modify the dimension value in the **Edit Dimension** toolbar to **25**.

2. Select the center of the arc and then select the lower endpoint of line 6. Place the dimension on the left of the previous dimension. Modify the dimension value in the **Edit Dimension** toolbar to **60**.

3. Select line 3 and then right-click to display the shortcut menu. Choose **Aligned** from this shortcut menu and then place the dimension below the sketch. Modify its value in the **Edit Dimension** toolbar to **12.5**.

    Notice that the length of lines 5 and 7 is also modified due to the **Equal** constraint.

4. Select lines 1 and 2 and then place the angular dimension on the right of the sketch. Modify the value of the angular dimension in the **Edit Dimension** toolbar to **135**.

5. Select arc 10 and then place the radius dimension above the sketch. Modify the value of the radius of the arc in the **Edit Dimension** toolbar to **15**.

    With this, all the required dimensions are applied to the outer loop.

Drawing the Circle

1. Choose **Center point circle** from the **2D Sketch Panel** panel bar; you are prompted to select the center of the circle.

2. Move the cursor close to the center of the arc; the cursor snaps to the center point and turns green. Select this point as the center of the circle and then move the cursor away from the center to size the circle. Specify a point to give it an approximate size.

Dimensioning the Circle

1. Choose **General Dimension** from the **2D Sketch Panel** panel bar and select the circle. Place the diameter dimension below the arc dimension. Enter the diameter of the circle as **25** in the **Edit Dimension** toolbar.

    This completes the sketch for Tutorial 4. The final dimensioned sketch is shown in Figure 2-58.

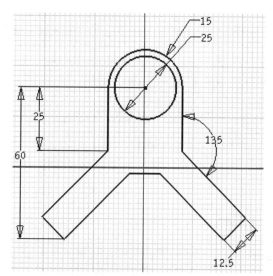

Figure 2-58 *Final dimensioned sketch for Tutorial 4*

Saving the Sketch

1. Choose the **Return** button in the **Inventor Standard** toolbar to exit the sketching environment and then save this sketch with the name given below.

    \PersonalProject\c02\Tutorial4.ipt

2. Choose **File > Close** from the menu bar to close the file.

Self-Evaluation Test

Answer the following questions and then compare your answers with those given at the end of the chapter:

1. The **Perpendicular** constraint forces the selected entity to become normal to another specified entity. (T/F)

2. The **Coincident** constraint can be applied to two line segments. (T/F)

3. The **Collinear** constraint can be applied only to line segments. (T/F)

4. If you apply a constraint that is not required in the sketch, Autodesk Inventor will display a message box informing you that adding this constraint will over-constrain the sketch. (T/F)

5. The _____ nature of Autodesk Inventor ensures that irrespective of the original size, the selected entity is driven to the dimension value you specify.

6. When you select a circle to be dimensioned, by default, the _____ dimension is applied to it.

7. The _____ dimension has one arrowhead and is placed outside the circle or the arc.

8. The _____ dimension displays the distance between two selected line segments in terms of diameter, that is, double the original length.

9. Using the _____ tool, you can measure the radius of an arc.

10. To measure the angle between three points, they must be selected either in the _____ sequence or in the _____ sequence.

Review Questions

Answer the following questions:

1. You cannot apply the **Concentric** constraint between a point and a circle. (T/F)

2. You can use the **Horizontal** or **Vertical** constraint to line up arcs, circles, or ellipses in the same horizontal or vertical direction. (T/F)

3. You can view all or some of the constraints applied to the sketch. (T/F)

4. There are twelve types of geometric constraints that can be applied additionally to the sketched entities. (T/F)

5. Linear dimensions are defined as the dimensions that define the shortest distance between two points. (T/F)

6. The situation, where the number of dimensions or constraints exceed the number that are required in the sketch, is called

    (a) Constraint   (b) Under-constrained
    (c) Over-constrained   (d) None

7. When you invoke the **Measure Distance** tool and select two lines, the **Measure Distance** toolbar changes into which of the following toolbars?

    (a) **Length**   (b) **Distance**
    (c) **Minimum Distance**   (d) Remains the same

8. Whenever you select an arc to be dimensioned, by default, which of the following types of dimensions is applied to it?

    (a) **Radius**   (b) **Diameter**
    (c) **Linear**   (d) **Linear Diameter**

9. In addition to the lines, which of the following entities can be selected to apply the **Collinear** constraint?

    (a) Arc   (b) Circle
    (c) Ellipse   (d) Ellipse axis

10. Which of the following combination of entities cannot be used to apply the tangent constraint?

    (a) Line, Line   (b) Line, Arc
    (c) Circle, Circle   (d) Arc, Circle

Exercises

Exercise 1

Draw the basic sketch for the model shown in Figure 2-59. The sketch to be drawn is shown in Figure 2-60. After drawing the sketch, add the required constraints and then dimension it.

(Expected time: 30 min)

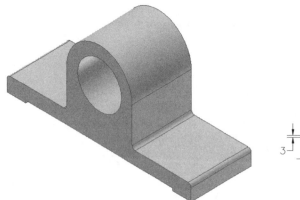

Figure 2-59 Model for Exercise 1

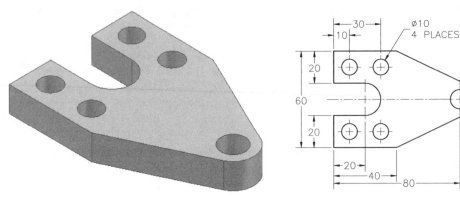

Figure 2-60 Sketch for Exercise 1

Exercise 2

Draw the basic sketch for the model shown in Figure 2-61. The sketch is shown in Figure 2-62. After drawing the sketch, add the required constraints and then dimension it.

(Expected time: 30 min)

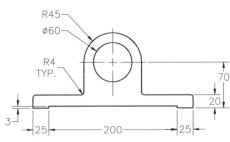

Figure 2-61 Model for Exercise 2

Figure 2-62 Sketch for Exercise 2

Exercise 3

Draw the basic sketch for the model shown in Figure 2-63. The sketch is shown in Figure 2-64. After drawing the sketch, add the required constraints and then dimension it.

(Expected time: 30 min)

Note

The solid models in Exercises 1, 2, and 3 are given for reference only.

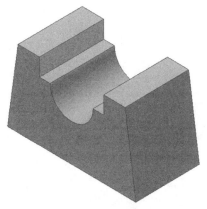

Figure 2-63 Model for Exercise 3

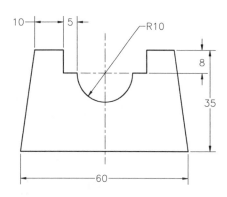

Figure 2-64 Sketch for Exercise 3

Exercise 4

Redraw the sketch for Exercise 1 of Chapter 1 without using the **Inventor Precise Input** toolbar. After drawing the sketch, add the required constraints to it and then dimension it. The dimensioned sketch is shown in Figure 2-65. **(Expected time: 30 min)**

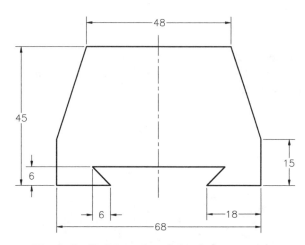

Figure 2-65 Dimensioned sketch for Exercise 4

Exercise 5

Redraw the sketch for Exercise 2 of Chapter 1 without using the **Inventor Precise Input** toolbar. After drawing the sketch, add the required constraints to it and then dimension it. The dimensioned sketch is shown in Figure 2-66. **(Expected time: 30 min)**

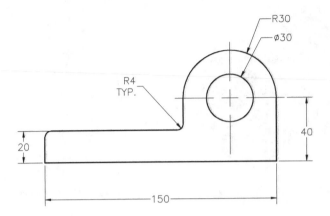

Figure 2-66 Dimensioned sketch for Exercise 5

Answers to Self-Evaluation Test

1. T, **2.** F, **3.** F, **4.** T, **5.** parametric, **6.** diameter, **7.** radius, **8.** linear diameter, **9. Measure Distance**, **10.** clockwise, counterclockwise

Chapter 3

Editing, Extruding, and Revolving Sketches

Learning Objectives

After completing this chapter, you will be able to:

- *Edit sketches using various editing tools.*
- *Create rectangular and circular patterns.*
- *Write text in the sketching environment and convert it into a feature.*
- *Insert external images, Word documents, and Excel spreadsheets in the sketching environment.*
- *Convert sketches into base features using the Extrude tool.*
- *Convert sketches into base features using the Revolve tool.*
- *Dynamically rotate the view of a model in 3D space and use the existing common views to view the model from various directions.*

EDITING SKETCHED ENTITIES

Autodesk Inventor provides you with a number of tools that can be used to edit the sketched entities. These tools are discussed next.

Extending Sketched Entities

Toolbar:	2D Sketch Panel > Extend
Panel Bar:	2D Sketch Panel > Extend

This tool is used to extend or lengthen the selected sketched entity up to a specified boundary. Therefore, to use this tool, you should have at least two entities such that when extended, they meet at a point. Taking the reference of one of the entities, the other will be extended. The entities that can be extended are lines and arcs. On invoking this tool, you will be prompted to select the curve to be extended. As you move the cursor close to the curve to be extended, the original curve will be displayed in red and the portion that will be extended will be displayed in black. While extending the arcs, the point where you select the arc will determine the side that will be extended. Figures 3-1 and 3-2 show the curves before and after extending.

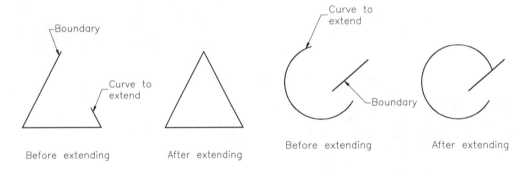

Figure 3-1 *Line before and after extending*   *Figure 3-2* *Arc before and after extending*

Trimming Sketched Entities

Toolbar:	2D Sketch Panel > Trim
Panel Bar:	2D Sketch Panel > Trim

This tool can be considered as the opposite of the **Extend** tool and is used to chop the selected sketched entity by using an edge (also called the knife edge). The knife edge, in its current form, may or may not actually intersect the entity to be trimmed. However, when extended, the knife edge must intersect the entity to be trimmed. On invoking this tool, you will be prompted to select the portion of the curve to be trimmed. As you move the cursor close to the curve, the portion to be trimmed will be displayed as a dashed red curve and the remaining curve will be displayed as a red continuous curve. You can select the side of the curve to be trimmed by selecting that side of the curve. Figure 3-3 shows the curves selected for trimming and Figure 3-4 shows the sketch after trimming the edges.

If you use this tool on an isolated entity, it will work as the **Delete** tool and delete the isolated entity.

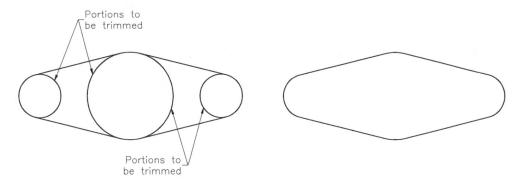

Figure 3-3 *Selecting the edges for trimming*   **Figure 3-4** *Sketch after trimming the edges*

Tip. *If you are performing editing using the **Trim** or the **Extend** tools, you can toggle between them using the shortcut menu displayed on right-clicking. The active operation has a check mark on its left. You can choose the other operation to switch to that command.*

*If you are performing the **Extend** or the **Trim** editing operation, you can also temporarily switch to the other one by just pressing the SHIFT key. For example, if the active editing operation is **Trim** and you press and hold the SHIFT key down, it will act as the **Extend** operation. When you release the SHIFT key, the original operation will resume its function of trimming.*

Offsetting Sketched Entities

| **Toolbar:** | 2D Sketch Panel > Offset |
| **Panel Bar:** | 2D Sketch Panel > Offset |

Offsetting is one of the easiest methods of drawing parallel lines, or concentric arcs and circles. You can select the entire loop as a single entity or select the individual entities to be offset. When you invoke the **Offset** tool, you will be prompted to select the curve to be offset. If you right-click at this point, a shortcut menu will be displayed, as shown in Figure 3-5.

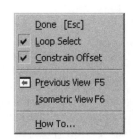

Figure 3-5 *The offset shortcut menu*

The **Loop Select** option is chosen by default, see Figure 3-5. This option allows you to select the entire loop as a single entity. However, if this option is cleared, the entire loop will be considered as a combination of individual segments and you will be allowed to select individual entities. The **Constrain Offset** option applies the constraints automatically when the loop or the individual entity is offset.

If you select the **Loop Select** option from the shortcut menu, you will be prompted to specify the offset position for the new loop immediately after selecting the original loop. If you specify the location inside the original loop, the new loop will be smaller than the original loop. If you specify the location outside the original loop, the new loop will be bigger.

In case of individual entities, once you have selected the entity to be offset, right-click to display the shortcut menu and choose **Continue**, or press the ENTER key to continue. You will be prompted to specify the location for the new entity. If the selected entity is a line segment, its length will remain the same and if it is an arc or a circle, the size of the new entity will depend on the location of the new point. Figure 3-6 shows offsetting of a loop and Figure 3-7 shows offsetting of an individual entity.

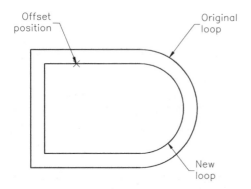

Figure 3-6 Creating a new loop by offsetting the original loop

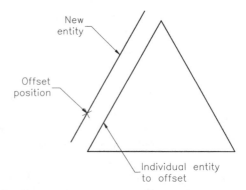

Figure 3-7 Offsetting an individual line segment to a new location

Mirroring Sketched Entities

Toolbar:	2D Sketch Panel > Mirror
Panel Bar:	2D Sketch Panel > Mirror

 The **Mirror** tool is used to create a mirror image of the selected entities. The entities are mirrored about a straight line segment. This tool is used to draw sketches that are symmetrical about a line or sketches that have some portion symmetrical about a line. When you invoke this tool, the **Mirror** dialog box will be displayed, see Figure 3-8. The **Select** button will be chosen by default and you will be prompted to select the geometries to be mirrored. You can select multiple entities to be mirrored. Once you have selected the entities, choose the **Mirror line** button; you will be prompted to select the line about which the entities should be mirrored. After selecting the mirror line, choose the **Apply** button; the selected entities will be mirrored about the mirror line. If the mirror line is at an angle, the resultant

*Figure 3-8 The **Mirror** dialog box*

entities that will be created upon mirroring will also be at an angle. After mirroring the entities, choose the **Done** button to exit this dialog box.

Figure 3-9 shows various sketched entities selected for mirroring and the mirror line that will be used to mirror the entities. Figure 3-10 shows the sketch after mirroring the entities. Figure 3-11 shows the entities selected to be mirrored about an inclined mirror line and Figure 3-12 shows the sketch after mirroring the entities.

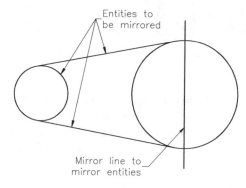

Figure 3-9 *Selecting the geometries to be mirrored about the mirror line*

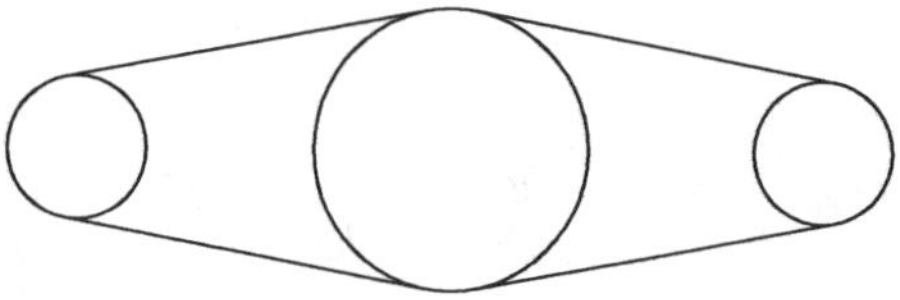

Figure 3-10 *Sketch after mirroring the geometries and deleting the mirror line*

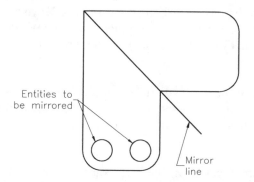

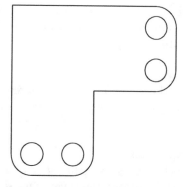

Figure 3-11 *Selecting the geometries to be mirrored about the mirror line*

Figure 3-12 *Sketch after mirroring the geometries and deleting the mirror line*

Moving Sketched Entities

Toolbar:	2D Sketch Panel > Move
Panel Bar:	2D Sketch Panel > Move

The **Move** tool is used to move one or more selected sketched entities from one specified point to the other. The points that can be used to move the entities include the sketched points/hole centers, endpoints of lines, arcs, splines, and the center points of arcs, circles, and ellipses. When you invoke this command, the **Move** dialog box will be displayed, as shown in Figure 3-13. You can also use this dialog box to create copies of the selected entities.

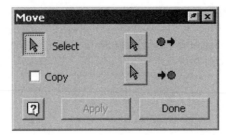

Figure 3-13 The Move dialog box

Note
*Remember that the behavior of the selected entities while moving is also governed by the constraints that are applied to them. If the selected entities are constrained with some other entities, the constrained entities will also move. However, if the other entities have a **Fix** constraint applied to them, because of which they cannot move from their location, the original entities will also not be able move.*

Move Dialog Box Options
The options provided in the **Move** dialog box are discussed next.

Select
This button is chosen to select the entities to be moved. When you invoke the **Move** tool, this button is automatically chosen. You can select more than one object using the Window or Crossing options or by selecting them one by one using the left mouse button.

Copy
This check box is selected to create a copy of the selected entities as they are moved. If this check box is selected, a copy of the selected entities will be created and placed at the destination point, keeping the original entities intact at their original location.

From Point
This button is chosen to specify the point that will act as the base point for moving the selected entities. Once you have selected all the entities to be moved, choose this button to select the point from where the movement will start.

To Point
This button is chosen to specify the destination point where the selected entities will be moved. As soon as you specify the from point for moving the entities, this button is automatically chosen in the dialog box and you will be prompted to specify the point where the selected entities will move.

Apply
This button is chosen to apply the move operation to the selected entities such that they are moved from the specified from point to the specified to point. Unless this button is chosen, the objects will not be moved from their original location. After you have applied

the move operation by choosing this button, the **Select** button is again chosen so that you can select other entities for moving.

Done
This button is chosen to exit the **Move** dialog box, thus exiting the **Move** tool.

Figures 3-14 through 3-17 show moving and copying of various sketched entities from one specified point to the other specified point.

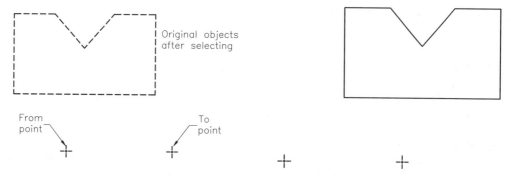

Figure 3-14 *Moving the entities using the sketch points*

Figure 3-15 *Objects after moving*

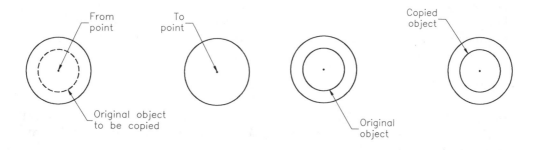

Figure 3-16 *Moving and copying the entities using the center points of circles*

Figure 3-17 *Objects after moving and copying*

Rotating Sketched Entities

Toolbar:	2D Sketch Panel > Rotate
Panel Bar:	2D Sketch Panel > Rotate

The **Rotate** tool is used to rotate the selected sketched entities about a specified center point. You can also use this tool to create a copy of the selected entities while rotating them. When you invoke this tool, the **Rotate** dialog box will be displayed, as shown in Figure 3-18.

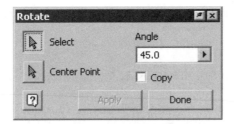

*Figure 3-18 The **Rotate** dialog box*

Rotate Dialog Box Options
The options in the **Rotate** dialog box are discussed next.

Select
This button is chosen to select the entities to be rotated. When you invoke the **Rotate** tool, the **Rotate** dialog box will be displayed and the **Select** button will be automatically chosen. You can use any object selection technique to select one or more objects.

Center Point
This button is chosen to define the base point around which the selected entities will be rotated. This point can also be referred to as the base point of rotation.

Angle
This edit box is used to define the value of the angle through which the selected entities will be rotated. You can enter the value in this edit box or choose the arrow on the right of this edit box to specify the predefined angle values. Remember that a positive angle will rotate the selected entities in the counterclockwise direction and a negative angle will rotate the selected entities in the clockwise direction.

Copy
This check box is selected to create a copy of the selected entities as they are rotated. If this check box is selected, a copy of the selected entities will be created and placed at the angle that you have specified in the **Angle** edit box. The original entities will be intact at their original location.

Apply
This button is chosen to apply the rotate operation to the selected entities. Until this button is chosen, the selected entities will not be rotated. After you apply the rotate operation by choosing this button, the **Select** button is again chosen so that you can select other entities for rotating.

Done
This button is chosen to exit the **Rotate** dialog box.

Figure 3-19 shows the rotation of the selected entities at various angles.

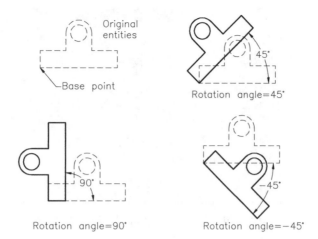

Figure 3-19 *Rotating the entities at various angles*

Tip. *You can also create a copy of the sketched entities using the shortcut menu. Select the sketched entities and right-click to display the shortcut menu. In this menu, choose* **Copy**. *Again, right-click to display the shortcut menu and choose* **Paste** *to paste the selected entities, thus creating a copy of the selected entities.*

CREATING PATTERNS

Generally, in the mechanical industry, you come across various designs that consist of multiple copies of a sketched feature arranged in a particular fashion. For example, it can be multiple grooves around an imaginary circle. It can also be along the edges of an imaginary rectangle, such as the grooves in the pedestal bearing. Drawing the sketches for such features again and again is a very tedious and time-consuming process. To avoid this lengthy process, Autodesk Inventor provides you with an option of creating patterns of the sketched entities during the sketching stage itself. The patterns are defined as the sequential arrangement of the copies of the selected entities. You can create the patterns in a rectangular fashion or a circular fashion. Both these types of patterns are discussed next.

Creating Rectangular Patterns

Toolbar:	2D Sketch Panel > Rectangular Pattern
Panel Bar:	2D Sketch Panel > Rectangular Pattern

Rectangular patterns are the patterns that arrange the copies of the selected entities in rows and columns. When you invoke this tool, the **Rectangular Pattern** dialog box will be displayed, as shown in Figure 3-20. The options provided under this dialog box are discussed next.

Geometry

This button is chosen to select the entities to be patterned. When you invoke the **Rectangular**

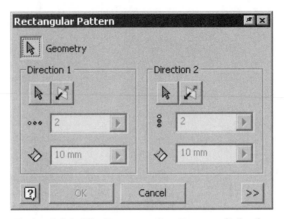

*Figure 3-20 The **Rectangular Pattern** dialog box*

Pattern tool, the **Geometry** button is automatically chosen. You can select one or more entities to be patterned using any object selecting technique.

Direction 1 Area

This area provides the option for defining the first direction of pattern creation, the number of copies to be created in this direction, and the spacing between the entities. These options are discussed next.

Direction

This is the button with an arrow and is chosen to select the first direction for arranging the items in a rectangular pattern. The other options in **Direction 1** area will be available only after you define the first direction of the pattern creation. The direction can be defined by selecting a line segment, which can be at any angle. The resultant pattern will also be created at an angle, if the line selected to specify the direction is at an angle. As you define the first direction, you can preview the pattern created using the current values in the drawing window. The pattern in the preview will be modified dynamically on changing the values in this dialog box.

Flip

This is the button available on the right of the **Direction** button and is chosen to reverse the first direction of the pattern creation. When you define the first direction using the **Direction** button, an arrow appears on the sketch. This arrow displays the direction in which the items of the pattern will be created. If you choose this button, the direction will be reversed and the arrow will point in the opposite direction.

Count

This edit box is used to specify the number of items in the pattern along the first direction. Remember that this value includes the original selected item. On increasing the value in this edit box, you can dynamically preview the increased items in the pattern in the drawing window. You can also select a predefined number of items by choosing the arrow on the right of this edit box. However, if you are using this tool for the first time in the current session of Autodesk Inventor, this arrow will not provide any value.

Spacing

This edit box is used to define the distance between the individual items of the pattern in the first direction. You can enter a value or choose the arrow on the right of this edit box to use the **Measure** or **Show Dimension** options to define this value. The **Measure** option allows you to select a line segment, the length of which will specify the distance between the individual items. The **Show Dimension** option allows you to use an existing dimension to specify the distance between the individual items of the pattern. The selected dimension will automatically appear in the edit box. You need to delete the existing value in this edit box to use the measured value.

Note
You will learn more about parameters in later chapters.

Direction 2 Area

This area provides the option for defining the second direction of the pattern creation, the number of copies to be created in this direction, and the spacing between the entities. All these options are discussed next.

Direction

This button is chosen to select the second direction for arranging the items of the rectangular pattern.

Flip

This button is available on the right of the **Direction** button and is chosen to reverse the second direction of pattern creation.

Count

This edit box is used to specify the number of items in the pattern along the second direction.

Spacing

This edit box is used to define the distance between the individual items of the pattern in the second direction. Similar to the **Spacing** edit box in the **Direction 1** area, you can directly enter a value in this edit box or use the **Measure** or the **Show Dimension** options to define this value.

Figure 3-21 shows various parameters involved in creating a rectangular pattern with three items along direction 1 and four items along direction 2.

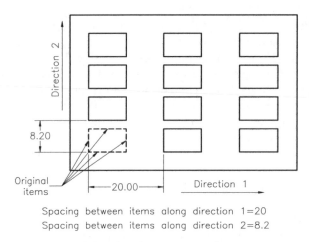

Figure 3-21 Creating a rectangular pattern

More

This button is provided on the lower right corner of the **Rectangular Pattern** dialog box. When you choose this button, this dialog box expands, providing you with more options for creating the pattern, see Figure 3-22. These options are discussed next.

*Figure 3-22 More options of the **Rectangular Pattern** dialog box*

Suppress

This button is chosen to suppress the selected item from the pattern. When you select any item of the pattern using this button, it will change into dashed lines. The items that are suppressed will be displayed on the screen, but will not participate in the feature creation when you finish the sketch. You can unsuppress these items later, if required.

Note
Editing the sketches of features will be discussed in later chapters.

Associative

This check box is selected so that all the items of the pattern are associated with each other. All the items of the associative pattern are automatically updated, if any one of the entity is modified. For example, if you modify the dimension of any of the items of the pattern, the dimensions of all the other items will also be modified. However, if you clear this check box before creating the pattern, all the items will be individual entities and you can be modify them individually.

Fitted

This option works in combination with the **Spacing** option in the **Direction 1** and **Direction 2** areas. If you select this option, the specified number of items will be created in the distances specified in the **Spacing** edit boxes in the **Direction 1** and **Direction 2** areas. Figure 3-23 shows the pattern created by clearing this check box (spacing is incremental) and Figure 3-24 shows the pattern created by selecting this check box (included spacing between all the items).

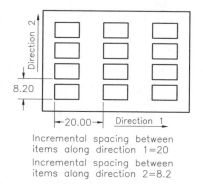

Figure 3-23 Pattern created with the **Fitted** check box cleared

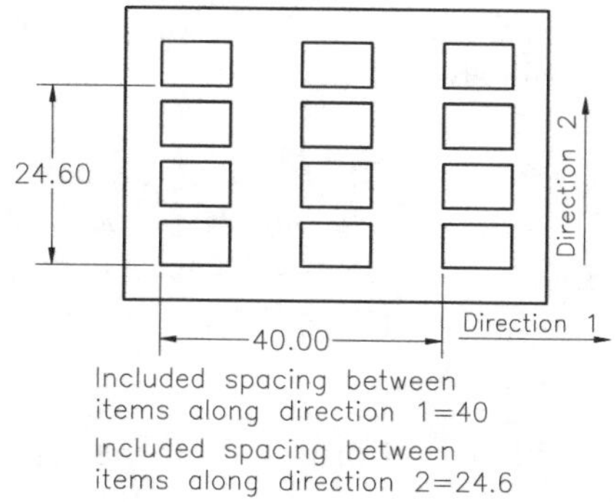

Figure 3-24 Pattern created with the **Fitted** check box selected

Creating Circular Patterns

Toolbar:	2D Sketch Panel > Circular Pattern
Panel Bar:	2D Sketch Panel > Circular Pattern

Circular patterns are the patterns created around the circumference of an imaginary circle. To create the circular pattern, you will have to define the center of that imaginary circle. When you invoke this tool, the **Circular Pattern** dialog box will be displayed, as shown in Figure 3-25. The options provided in this dialog box are discussed next.

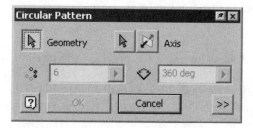

Figure 3-25 The **Circular Pattern** dialog box

Geometry

This button is chosen to select the entities to be patterned. As you select the individual entities, they turn blue, indicating that they are selected.

Axis

This is the button with an arrow and is provided on the right of the **Geometry** button. This button is chosen to select the center of the imaginary circle around which the circular pattern will be created. The points that can be used to define the center of the pattern creation are the endpoints of lines, splines, and arcs, center points of arcs, circles, and ellipses, and the points/hole centers. Most of the options in the **Circular Pattern** dialog box are enabled only after you select the axis of rotation. You can dynamically preview the pattern created using the current values. If you modify the other values in this dialog box, the preview of the pattern will also be modified.

Tip. *If you select an arc or a circle to define the axis of the circular pattern, its center will be automatically selected as the center of the circular pattern. However, this is not possible in case of an ellipse. You cannot select an ellipse to define the center of the circular pattern. You will have to select the center of ellipse.*

Flip

This is the button provided on the right of the **Axis** button and is chosen to reverse the direction of pattern creation. By default, the circular pattern will be created in the counterclockwise direction. If you choose this button, the circular pattern will be created in the clockwise direction.

Tip. *If the circular pattern is created through 360-degree, you cannot notice the difference in the changing of the direction of the pattern creation from counterclockwise to clockwise. However, if the pattern is created through an angle less than 360-degree, you will notice the difference in the changing of the direction of the pattern.*

Count

This edit box is used to specify the number of items in the circular pattern. You can enter a value in this edit box or choose the arrow provided on the right of this dialog box for using the predefined values or for using the **Measure** or **Show Dimension** options. These options are the same as those discussed in the rectangular pattern.

Angle

This edit box is used to define the angle for creating the circular pattern. You can directly enter an angle in this edit box or use the predefined values by choosing the arrow on the right of this edit box. You can also use the **Measure** or the **Show Dimension** options to define the angle. Figures 3-26 and 3-27 show the circular patterns created using various angles.

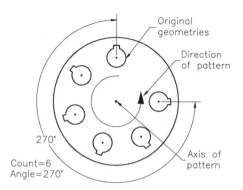

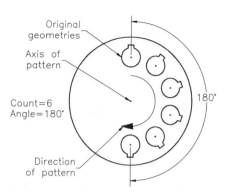

Figure 3-26 *Circular pattern with 6 items and a 270-degree angle*

Figure 3-27 *Circular pattern with 6 items and a 180-degree angle*

More

This is the button with two arrows and is provided on the lower right corner of the **Circular Pattern** dialog box. When you choose this button, the **Circular Pattern** dialog box expands, providing more options, see Figure 3-28. These options are discussed next.

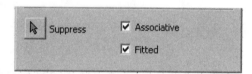

Figure 3-28 *More options of the **Circular Pattern** dialog box*

Suppress

This button is chosen to suppress the selected item from the pattern. Similar to the rectangular pattern, when you select any item of the circular pattern, it will change into dashed lines. Although the items that are suppressed will be displayed in the drawing window, they will not participate in the feature creation when you finish the sketch. However, you can unsuppress these items later, if you need them.

Associative

This check box is selected so that all the items of the pattern are associated with each other. All the items of the associative pattern are automatically updated if any one of the entity is modified. If you clear this check box before creating the pattern, all items will become individual entities and you can modify them individually.

Fitted

This option works in combination with the **Angle** edit box. If you select this option, the specified number of items will be created such that the angle specified in the **Angle** edit box defines the included angle between all the items. This check box is selected by default in the **Circular Pattern** dialog box. If you clear this check box, the angle that you specify in the **Angle** edit box will be considered as the incremental angle between each item. Figure 3-29 shows the pattern created by selecting this check box (included angle between all the items) and Figure 3-30 shows the pattern created by clearing this check box (angle is incremental).

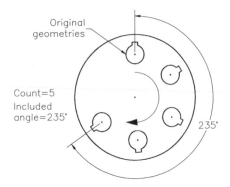

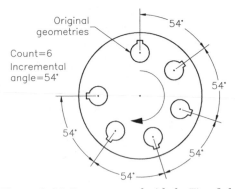

Figure 3-29 *Pattern created with the **Fitted** check box selected*

Figure 3-30 *Pattern created with the **Fitted** check box cleared*

Tip. *If you create a circular pattern through an angle of 360-degree and clear the **Fitted** check box, you will see only one item in the drawing window. This is because the incremental angle between the individual items is 360-degree and all the items will be arranged on top of each other, displaying only one copy.*

WRITING TEXT IN THE SKETCHING ENVIRONMENT

Toolbar:	2D Sketch Panel > Text
Panel Bar:	2D Sketch Panel > Text

Autodesk Inventor allows you to write text in the sketching environment. The text behaves like other sketched entities and can be converted into features using the modeling tools of Autodesk Inventor. To write the text, choose the **Text** button from the **2D Sketch Panel** panel bar; you will be prompted to select the location of the text. You can also drag a window to define the text box. Specify a point in the drawing window to start the text or press and hold the left mouse button down and drag the mouse to define a window; the **Format Text** dialog box will be displayed, as shown in Figure 3-31.

Format Text Dialog Box Options

The options in this dialog box are discussed next.

Text Justification

You can select the justification for writing the text by choosing the buttons in the upper left portion of this dialog box. The justification of a text is defined using a combination of two buttons. By default, the **Left Justification** and **Top Justification** buttons are chosen. As a result, the justification for the text is top left. You can select other justifications by choosing their respective buttons. The **Baseline Spacing** button is available only when you choose the **Single Line Text** button on the left of the **Spacing** drop-down list.

Text Box

If this button is chosen, a construction line box is placed around the text.

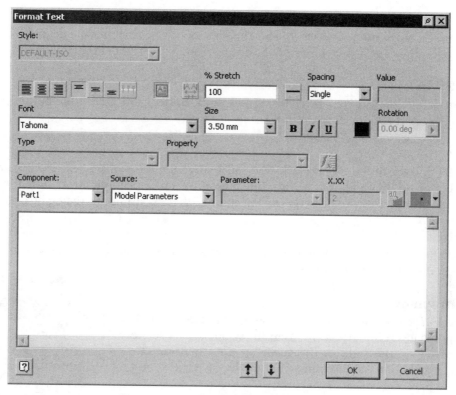

*Figure 3-31 The **Format Text** dialog box*

Fit Text

This button is available only when you choose the **Single Line Text** button and is used to fit the text in a single line inside the window that you defined by dragging the mouse.

Stretch

You can define the percentage of text stretching in the **% Stretch** edit box. The default value in this edit box is 100. As a result, there is no stretching of the text. If you enter a value more than 100, the text width will be increased. If you enter a value less than 100, the width of the text will be reduced.

Spacing

You can select the option to define the spacing between the text lines using the **Line Spacing** drop-down list. If you select the **Multiply** option from this drop-down list, the **Value** edit box will be enabled and you can enter the multiplication factor for the line spacing in this edit box.

Font

The **Font** drop-down list is located below the justification buttons. You can select the font for the text using this drop-down list.

Size

The **Size** edit box is used to specify the height of the text. You can enter the height in this edit box or select the standard values using the down arrow on the right of this edit box.

Text Style

You can define the text style by choosing the **Bold, Italics**, and **Underline** buttons on the right of the **Text Height** drop-down list.

Color

The default color of the text is black. You can change the color of the text by choosing the **Color** button on the right of the **Underline** button. When you choose this button, the **Color** dialog box is displayed. You can specify the color of the text using this dialog box.

Rotation

The **Rotation** flyout is available only when the **Text Box** button is not chosen. This flyout is used to specify the rotation angle for the text.

Insert symbol

Autodesk Inventor provides you with some standard symbols that you can insert in the text. To insert the symbols, choose the down arrow on the right of the **Insert symbol** button. The standard symbols in Autodesk Inventor are displayed, as shown in Figure 3-32.

Text Window

You can enter the text in the **Text Window**. This is the white area provided in the **Format Text** dialog box. You can also paste the text copied from some other source. The text written in this window will appear on the screen.

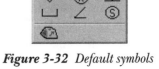

Figure 3-32 Default symbols

Zoom In/Zoom Out

 You can zoom in and out of the text in the **Text Window** by choosing the **Zoom In** and **Zoom Out** buttons provided at the bottom of this dialog box.

 Note
*The remaining options in the **Format Text** dialog box are used in the **Drawing** module and so are not discussed here.*

INSERTING IMAGES AND DOCUMENTS IN SKETCHES

Toolbar:	2D Sketch Panel > Insert Image
Panel Bar:	2D Sketch Panel > Insert Image

 The **Insert Image** tool allows you to insert the external images in the sketch. You can insert images such as JPG, BMP, PCX, TIFF, TGA, and so on. You can also insert Word documents or Excel spreadsheets using this tool. To insert an image, invoke this tool; the **Open** dialog box will be displayed, as shown in Figure 3-33.

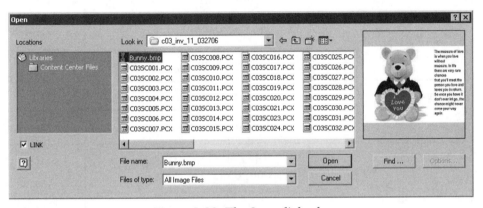

*Figure 3-33 The **Open** dialog box*

Select the image or document using this dialog box and then choose the **Open** button; the dialog box will be closed and you will be prompted to select the sketch point. The point you specify on the screen will be taken as the insertion point for the image. After inserting the image, right-click and choose **Done** from the shortcut menu to exit this tool.

Note
*You may need to modify the drawing display area using the **Zoom All** tool to display the image on the screen.*

Tip. *To modify the size of the image inserted in the sketch, drag it by holding one of its four edges. Depending on the direction in which you drag it, the size will increase or decrease. To rotate the image, hold it from one of the corners and drag. The image will be rotated in the direction in which you drag the cursor. To move the image, press and hold the left mouse button anywhere on the image and drag the cursor.*

EDITING SKETCHED ENTITIES BY DRAGGING

You can also edit the sketched entities by dragging them. Depending on the type of entity selected and the point of selection, the object will be moved or stretched. For example, if you select a circle at its center and drag, it will be moved. However, if you select the same at a point on its circumference, it will be stretched to a new size. Similarly, if you select a line at its endpoints, it will be stretched and if you select a line at a point other than its endpoints, it will be moved. Therefore, editing the sketched entities by dragging is entirely based on the selection points. The following table gives you the details of the operation that will be performed when you drag various objects.

Object	Selection point	Operation
Circle	On circumference	Stretch
	Center point	Move
Arc	On circumference	Stretch
	Center point	Move
Polygon	Any of the edges	Move
	Endpoints	Move
Single line	Any point other than the endpoints	Move
	Endpoints	Stretch
Rectangle	All lines selected together	Move
	Any one line or any endpoint	Stretch

TOLERANCES

In simple terms, tolerance is defined as the permissible variation from the actual value. Because it is an allowed variation, you can vary the dimension of the component through the specified value while manufacturing.

Adding Tolerances to the Dimensions in the Sketching Environment

In Autodesk Inventor, the tolerances are added after creating the dimensions. To add tolerance to a dimension, invoke the **Select** tool to make sure that no other drawing or dimensioning tool is active. Next, right-click on the dimension and choose **Dimension Properties** from the shortcut menu; the **Dimension Properties** dialog box will be displayed. You can use the options in the **Dimension Settings** tab of this dialog box to add tolerances, see Figure 3-34.

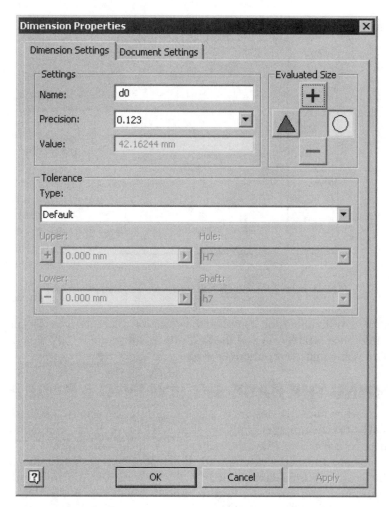

*Figure 3-34 The **Dimension Settings** tab of the **Dimension Properties** dialog box*

By default, the **Default** option is selected in the **Type** drop-down list of the **Tolerance** area. As a result, no tolerance is added to the dimension. To add tolerance, select the required tolerance type from this drop-down list. Next, specify the value of the upper and lower limits in the **Upper** and **Lower** edit boxes. If you select the fit type, you can select the values of the hole fit and the shaft fit from the **Hole** and **Shaft** drop-down lists.

Once you have defined all the tolerance values, choose the **Apply** button in the **Dimension Properties** dialog box. You will notice that the tolerance is applied to the selected dimension. Now, choose **OK** to exit this dialog box. Figure 3-35 shows a sketch with the tolerance applied to the dimensions.

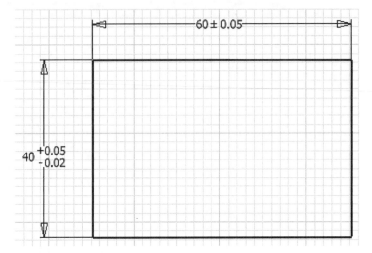

Figure 3-35 *Sketch with tolerance applied to the dimensions*

In this figure, the vertical dimension is applied the deviation tolerance type. The upper deviation value for this tolerance is 0.05 mm and the lower deviation value is 0.02 mm. The horizontal dimension in the same figure is applied the symmetric tolerance with a value of 0.05 mm.

CONVERTING THE BASE SKETCH INTO A BASE FEATURE

As mentioned earlier, any 3D design is a combination of various sketched, placed, and work features. The first feature, generally, is a sketched feature. In this chapter and in previous chapters, you have learned to draw the sketches for these base features and to dimension them. After you have finished drawing and dimensioning the sketch, choose the **Return** button on the **Inventor Standard** toolbar. On choosing this button, you will exit the sketching environment and enter the **Part** module. You will also notice that the **2D Sketch Panel** panel bar is replaced by the **Part Features** panel bar. Autodesk Inventor provides you with a number of tools such as **Extrude**, **Revolve**, **Loft**, **Sweep**, and so on to convert these base sketches into base features. However, in this chapter, you will learn the use of the **Extrude** and **Revolve** tools for converting the base sketch into a base feature. The remaining tools will be discussed in later chapters.

Tip. *You can also proceed to the **Part** module from the sketching environment by using the shortcut menu. Right-click in the graphics window and choose **Finish Sketch**.*

Note

*It is recommended that when you switch to the part modeling environment, you should change the current view to the isometric view. This is because in the isometric view, you can dynamically preview the result of the **Extrude** or the **Revolve** tools while you are defining the values in their respective dialog boxes. To change the current view to the isometric view, right-click in the graphics window and choose **Isometric View** from the shortcut menu.*

EXTRUDING THE BASE SKETCH

Toolbar:	Part Features > Extrude
Panel Bar:	Part Features > Extrude

The **Extrude** tool is one of the most extensively used tools for creating a design. Extrusion is a process of adding or removing material defined by the sketch, along the Z axis of the current sketching plane. If you create the first feature, you will be given the option of just adding the material and not removing it. This is because there is no existing feature from which you can remove the material. When you invoke this tool, the **Extrude** dialog box will be displayed. The options in the **Extrude** dialog box are discussed next.

Shape Tab

The options in this tab (Figure 3-36) are discussed next.

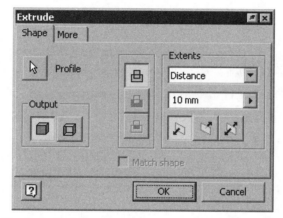

*Figure 3-36 The **Shape** tab of the **Extrude** dialog box*

Profile

This button is chosen to select the sketch to be extruded. If the sketch consists of a single loop, it will be automatically selected to be extruded when you invoke the **Extrude** tool. Also, because in this case the sketch is already selected, the **Profile** button will not be chosen. However, if the sketch consists of more than one loop, this button will be chosen and you will be prompted to select the profile you want to extrude. As you move the cursor close to one of the loops, it will be highlighted. After you have selected the sketch to be extruded, choose this button again; the preview of the resultant solid will be displayed in the drawing window. Note that if you select any of the inner loops, only that single loop will be extruded. Also, after the extrusion of one of the inner loops, the remaining loops will no more be displayed on the screen. But, if you select the profile by specifying a point inside the outer loop but outside the inner loops, the sketch will be extruded such that the resultant solid will have the inner loops subtracted from the outer loop, see Figures 3-37 and 3-38.

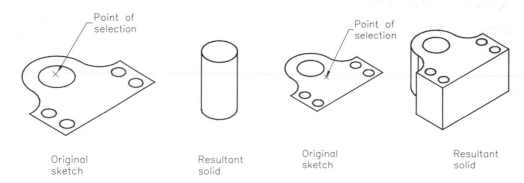

Figure 3-37 *Specifying the selection point inside the inner loop*

Figure 3-38 *Specifying the selection point between the inner and outer loops*

Tip. *To remove the closed loop that has been selected using the* **Profile** *button, hold down the SHIFT key and then select the closed loop to be removed. You will notice that the selected closed loop is no more highlighted, suggesting that it has been removed from the selection set.*

Output Area

The buttons in the **Output** area are used to specify the type of resulting feature that will be created. If you select a closed sketch to extrude, the **Solid** button is chosen automatically. As a result, a solid feature will be created. If you choose the **Surface** button, the resultant feature will be a surface and not a solid. Remember that the sketches for surface models do not need to be closed loops. If you select an open sketch to extrude, this button is chosen automatically when you invoke the **Extrude** dialog box.

Operation Area

This area is provided on the left of the **Extents** area and has three buttons. Because you are creating the first feature, only the **Join** button will be available in this area. This button is discussed next. The remaining buttons are discussed in Chapter 4.

Join

This is the first button provided in the **Operation** area. This button is chosen to create a feature by adding the material defined by the sketch.

Extents Area

You can select the method of terminating the extruded feature using the options in the drop-down list available in the **Extents** area. These options are discussed next.

Distance

By default, the **Distance** option is selected in this drop-down list. This option is used to define the extrusion depth by specifying its numeric value. The value of extrusion can be specified in the **Depth** edit box available below this drop-down list. When this

Tip. *You can dynamically modify the depth of extrusion by moving the cursor over one of the edges in the preview. The outline of the preview turns red and a double-sided arrow is displayed below the cursor. Press and hold the left mouse button down and drag the cursor to change the extrusion depth.*

termination option is selected from the drop-down list, there will be three buttons provided below the **Depth** edit box. These buttons are used to specify the direction of extrusion. The current direction will be displayed by the first button. You can reverse the direction of feature creation by choosing the second button. The third button extrudes the feature equally in both directions from the current sketch plane. This button is also called the **Mid-plane** button. For example, if the specified extrusion depth is 20 mm, the resultant feature will be created such that it is extruded 10 mm above the current sketch plane and 10 mm below the current sketch plane.

Note

*You can also select a predefined distance value or the **Measure** and the **Show Dimension** options by choosing the arrow on the right of the **Depth** edit box to specify the depth of extrusion.*

To

This is the second option in the **Distance** drop-down list and is used to define the termination of the extruded feature using a work plane, planar face, or extended face. When you select this option, all other options in the **Extents** area are removed and only the **Select surface to end the feature creation** button is displayed. If you select a plane or a face that does not intersect the extruding feature to terminate the extrusion, the **Check to terminate feature on the extended face** check box is displayed. This check box is selected to terminate the feature on the plane or the planar face as if it was extended.

From To

This is the third option in the **Distance** drop-down list. This option uses two planes to define a feature. The first plane defines the plane from which the feature will start and the second plane defines the plane for terminating the feature. When you select this option, all the remaining options in the **Extents** area are replaced by two buttons. The upper button is the **Select surface to start the feature creation** button and is used to define the plane where the feature starts. The lower button is the **Select the surface to end the feature creation** button and is used to define the plane where the feature terminates.

Note

*The methods of creating work planes will be discussed in later chapters. The **Distance** drop-down list will display more options once you have created the base feature. These options will be discussed in Chapters 4.*

More Tab

The **Taper** option in the **More** tab (Figure 3-39) is discussed next. The remaining options will be discussed in later chapters.

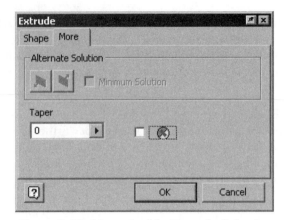

Figure 3-39 *More tab of the* **Extrude** *dialog box*

Taper

This edit box is used to define the taper angle for the resulting solid model. Taper angles are generally provided to solid models for their easy withdrawal from the molds. A negative taper angle will force the solid to taper inwards, thus creating a negative taper. A positive taper angle will force the resultant solid to taper outwards, thus creating a positive taper. When you define a taper angle, an arrow will be displayed in the preview of the solid model in the drawing window. Depending on the positive or negative value of the taper angle, this arrow will point inwards or outwards from the sketch. Figures 3-40 and 3-41 show the model created using the negative and positive taper angles.

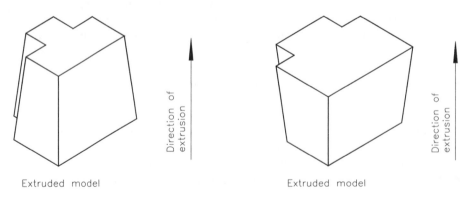

Figure 3-40 *Extruding the model with a negative taper angle*

Figure 3-41 *Extruding the model with a positive taper angle*

Figure 3-42 shows a model extruded with a positive taper angle using the **Mid-plane** option.

Tip. *You will notice that as soon as a feature is created, it is assigned a material. The default material is* **As Material***. You can also change the material of the feature. To assign a new material, select it from the drop-down list in the* **Inventor Standard** *toolbar. The selected material is applied to the model.*

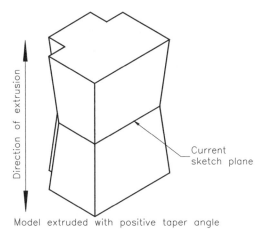

Figure 3-42 *Model extruded with a positive taper angle and using the Mid-plane button*

REVOLVING THE BASE SKETCH

Toolbar:	Part Features > Revolve
Panel Bar:	Part Features > Revolve

The **Revolve** tool is used to create circular features like shafts, couplings, pulleys, and so on. You can also use this tool for creating cut features that are circular in shape. A revolved feature is created by revolving the sketch about an axis. You can use a normal line segment, a center line, or a construction line of a sketch as the axis for revolving the sketch. When you invoke this tool, the **Revolve** dialog box will be displayed, as shown in Figure 3-43.

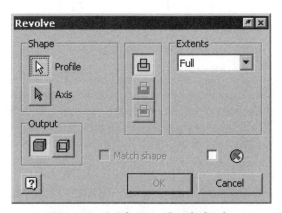

Figure 3-43 *The Revolve dialog box*

Shape Area

The buttons in this area are used to select the sketch to be revolved and the axis of revolution. These buttons are discussed next.

Profile

This button is chosen to select the sketch to be revolved. If there is only one loop in the drawing window, it will be automatically selected and the **Profile** button will not be chosen. However, if there are more than one loops, this button will be chosen and you will be prompted to select the profile to be revolved.

Axis

This button is chosen to select the axis for revolving the sketch. As mentioned earlier, you can select a line segment in the sketch as the axis for creating the revolved feature. When you select the axis, the preview of the feature that will be created using the current values will be displayed in the drawing window.

Output Area

The buttons in the **Output** area are used to specify the type of output for the revolved feature. If you choose the **Solid** button, the resulting feature will be a solid. However, if you choose the **Surface** button, the resulting feature will be a surface. The sketch for the surface may or may not be closed. But for a solid feature, the sketch needs to be closed.

Operation Area

This is the area with three buttons located on the right of the **Shape** area. While creating the base features, only one button will be enabled in this area. The remaining buttons will be enabled after you have created at least one feature. The button that is enabled is discussed next and the remaining buttons will be discussed in Chapter 4.

Join

This is the first button in the **Operation** area and is chosen to create a revolved feature by adding the material defined by the sketch. This is the option you will be using for creating the base feature.

Extents Area

The drop-down list provided under this area is used to specify the methods of termination of a revolved feature. These options are discussed next.

Full

This option is chosen to create a feature by revolving the sketch through 360-degree. This is the default option.

Angle

This option is used to terminate the revolved feature at an angle less than 360-degree. The angle of revolution can be specified in the edit box displayed below this drop-down list when you select the **Angle** option. You can use a predefined value by choosing the arrow provided on the right side of this edit box. You can also use the **Measure** and the **Show Dimensions** options to define the angle of revolution.

When you select the **Angle** option, three buttons will be displayed in this area. These buttons are used to define the direction of rotation. You can also revolve the sketch equally in both directions by choosing the **Mid-plane** button. Figures 3-44 and 3-45 show the features created by revolving the sketches through various angles.

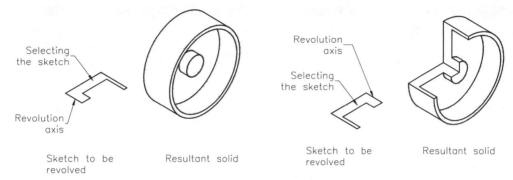

Figure 3-44 *Revolving the sketch through 360-degree*

Figure 3-45 *Revolving the sketch through 270-degree*

ROTATING THE VIEW OF A MODEL IN 3D SPACE

Autodesk Inventor provides you with an option of rotating the view of a solid model freely in 3D space. This allows you to visually maneuver around the solid model and view it from any direction. To invoke this option, choose the **Rotate** button from the **Inventor Standard** toolbar. When you choose this button, a circle will be displayed with small lines at all four quadrant points and a cross at the center of the circle. The circle is called the **rim**, the small lines at four quadrants are called **handles**, and the cross at the center is called the **center point**. Also, when you invoke this tool, the shape of the cursor changes and the new shape will depend on its current position. For example, if the cursor is inside the rim, it will show two elliptical arrows, suggesting that the model can be freely rotated in any direction. If you move the cursor close to the horizontal handles, the cursor will change to a horizontal elliptical arrow. The methods to rotate the view of a model are discussed next.

Rotating the View of a Model Freely in 3D Space

To freely rotate the view of a model, move the cursor inside the rim; the cursor will be replaced by two elliptical arrows. Select a point inside the rim and then drag it anywhere in the drawing window. The model will dynamically rotate as you drag the cursor around the drawing window.

Rotating the View of a Model Around the Vertical Axis

To rotate the view of a model around the horizontal axis, move the cursor close to one of the horizontal handles; the cursor will be replaced by a horizontal elliptical arrow. Now, select a point and drag the cursor to rotate the model along the horizontal axis.

Rotating the View of a Model Around the Horizontal Axis

To rotate the view of a model around the vertical axis, move the cursor close to one of the vertical handles; the cursor will be replaced by a vertical elliptical arrow. Now, press and drag the cursor to rotate the model along the vertical axis.

Rotating the View Around the Axis Normal To the View

To rotate the view of a model around an axis normal to the current view, move the cursor close to the rim; the cursor will be replaced by a circular arrow. Now, press and hold the left mouse button down and drag the cursor; the model will be rotated around the center point.

Figure 3-46 shows the view of a model being rotated freely in 3D space.

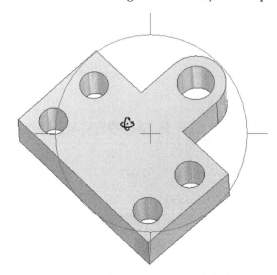

Figure 3-46 *Rotating the view of a model freely in 3D space*

To exit this tool, right-click to display the shortcut menu and choose **Done**. This shortcut menu also displays the other options that are discussed next.

Common View

If you choose this option, a cube is displayed at the center of the drawing window. All eight vertices and six faces of this cube have green arrows. You can choose any of these arrows and the model will be displayed as viewed from that direction. Figure 3-47 shows the common views that can be used to reorient the model. Once you exit the **Rotate** tool in the **Common View** mode, the next time you invoke this tool, the **Common View** mode will be invoked instead of the **Free Rotation** mode. The **Free Rotation** option replaces the **Common View** option in the shortcut menu. If you choose the **Free Rotation** option, you will again switch to the 3D rotation mode. You can also toggle between these two options using the SPACEBAR key.

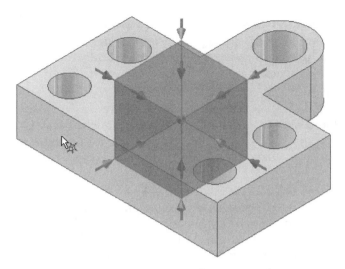

Figure 3-47 Reorienting the model using the common views

Redefine Isometric

This option is used in combination with the **Common View** option. When you choose the **Isometric View** option from the shortcut menu, the model is displayed as SE isometric view, where the direction of +X axis is considered as East. However, if you want to set the isometric view to any other view, you can use this option. Modify the viewing direction by using the **Common View** option and then choose this option from the shortcut menu. The current view will be displayed whenever you invoke the isometric view.

Previous View

When you choose this option, the view showing the previous orientation of the model will be displayed again. The **Next View** option is added to the shortcut menu when you choose this option. The **Next View** option is used to activate the view that was current before you chose the **Previous View** option. You can also invoke the previous view by pressing the F5 key and the next view by holding down the SHIFT key and then pressing the F5 key.

Isometric View

This option is chosen to reorient the model such that it is displayed in the isometric view. You can also invoke the isometric view by pressing the F6 key on the keyboard.

Note
The Pan and the Zoom options are the same as those discussed in Chapter 1, Drawing Sketches for the Solid Models.

CONTROLLING THE DISPLAY OF MODELS

Autodesk Inventor allows you to control the display of the models by setting various display modes and setting the camera type for displaying them. You can also control the display of their shadows. These options of controlling the display of the models are discussed next.

Setting Display Modes

You can set the display modes for the solid models using the buttons provided in the **Shaded Display** flyout in the **Inventor Standard** toolbar. Various display modes that you can set for the solid models are discussed next.

Shaded Display

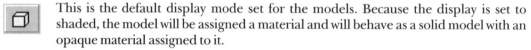 This is the default display mode set for the models. Because the display is set to shaded, the model will be assigned a material and will behave as a solid model with an opaque material assigned to it.

Hidden Edge Display

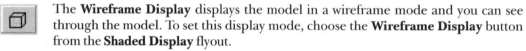 The **Hidden Edge Display** mode displays the model with a material applied to it. Also, the hidden edges of the model are displayed in light color. To change the display type, choose the arrow on the right of the **Shaded Display** button in the **Inventor Standard** toolbar; the **Shaded Display** flyout will be displayed. From this flyout, choose the **Hidden Edge Display** button.

Wireframe Display

The **Wireframe Display** displays the model in a wireframe mode and you can see through the model. To set this display mode, choose the **Wireframe Display** button from the **Shaded Display** flyout.

Setting the Camera Type

By default, the models are displayed using the orthographic camera type. You can change the camera type from the default orthographic to the perspective camera. This is done by choosing the arrow on the right of the **Orthographic Camera** button in the **Inventor Standard** toolbar. From the flyout, choose the **Perspective Camera** button to display the model using a perspective camera. Figure 3-48 shows a model using the perspective camera.

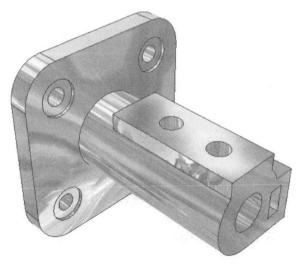

Figure 3-48 Displaying the model using the perspective camera

Setting the Shadow Options

Autodesk Inventor allows you to make your design realistic by casting their shadows. By default, the shadow option is turned off. You can cast two type of shadows using the **No Ground Shadow** flyout in the **Inventor Standard** toolbar. These two types of shadows are discussed next.

Ground Shadow

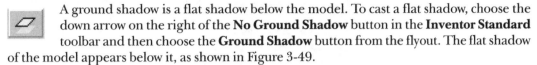 A ground shadow is a flat shadow below the model. To cast a flat shadow, choose the down arrow on the right of the **No Ground Shadow** button in the **Inventor Standard** toolbar and then choose the **Ground Shadow** button from the flyout. The flat shadow of the model appears below it, as shown in Figure 3-49.

Figure 3-49 *Model with the ground shadow*

X-Ray Ground Shadow

The X-ray ground shadow shows the features of the model. To cast this type of shadow, choose the down arrow on the right of the **No Ground Shadow** button in the **Inventor Standard** toolbar and then choose the **X-Ray Ground Shadow** button from the flyout. The flat shadow of the model appears below it. Figure 3-50 shows a model with this kind of shadow. Notice the details of the features in the shadow.

Figure 3-50 *Model with the X-ray ground shadow*

Note
You can cast shadows only below the model and not on any other plane. Also, the distance of the shadow from the model is modified as you zoom the model.

TUTORIALS

Tutorial 1

In this tutorial, you will open the sketch drawn in Tutorial 1 of Chapter 2. You will then convert this sketch into a solid model by extruding it to a distance of 20 mm. After creating the solid model, you will change its material to **Metal-Steel (Polished)** and rotate its view in 3D space using the **Rotate** tool.   **(Expected time: 30 min)**

Before you start creating the model, it is recommended that you outline the steps that will be required to complete the tutorial. The following steps are required to complete this tutorial:

a.   Save the sketch from the *c02* folder to the *c03* folder with another name.
b.   Open the sketch from the *c03* folder and extrude it to a distance of 20 mm using the **Extrude** tool, refer to Figure 3-53.
c.   Change the material of the model by using the drop-down list in the **Inventor Standard** toolbar.
d.   Rotate the model in 3D space using the **Rotate** tool, refer to Figure 3-54.

Opening the Sketch Drawn in Chapter 2

1. Start Autodesk Inventor by double-clicking on its shortcut icon on the desktop of your computer or by using the **Start** menu. The **Open** dialog box will be displayed after Autodesk Inventor is started.

2. Choose **Open** to display the **Open File - Select a file to open** option.

3. Open the *PersonalProject\c02* folder and then open the *Tutorial1.ipt* file.

When you open an existing part drawing, you are by default in the **Part** module even if the drawing is just a sketch. Also, the sketch is displayed in the isometric view, see Figure 3-51.

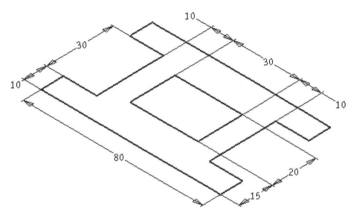

Figure 3-51 *The sketch displayed in isometric view when opened*

Saving the Sketch with Another Name

After opening the sketch, you need to first save it with another name so that the original sketch drawn in Chapter 2 is not modified. Remember that when you save the file with another name in Autodesk Inventor, a new file is created and saved, but the original file is still open. You need to close the original file and open the new file using the **Open** dialog box.

1. Choose **File > Save Copy As** from the menu bar; the **Save Copy As** dialog box is displayed.

2. Select the *PersonalProject\c03* folder from the **Save in** drop-down list.

Tip. *If you have not created the c03 folder, you can create it using the* ***Save Copy As*** *dialog box also. Select the PersonalProject folder from the* ***Save in*** *drop-down list. It will now be displayed in the* ***Save in*** *drop-down list. Choose the* ***Create New Folder*** *button and specify c03 as the name of the folder.*

3. Save the sketch with the name *Tutorial1.ipt*.

4. Now, choose **File > Close** from the menu bar to close this file. If you are prompted to specify whether or not you want to save the changes in this file, choose **No**.

5. Choose the **Open** button from the **Inventor Standard** toolbar to display the **Open** dialog box. Open the file *\PersonalProject\c03\Tutorial1.ipt*.

Extruding the Sketch

As mentioned earlier, when you open an existing part file, you are by default in the part modeling environment and the sketch is displayed in the isometric view. Sometimes when you open an existing sketch, the dimensions of the sketch are not displayed in the current view. You can use the **Zoom** tool to increase the drawing display area so that all the dimensions are displayed in the current view. Now, because you are in the part modeling environment, all the tools of this module are available in the **Part Features** panel bar.

1. Choose the **Extrude** button from the **Part Features** panel bar to invoke the **Extrude** dialog box.

Because the sketch consists of two loops, the sketch is not automatically selected. The **Profile** button in the **Shape** tab is chosen and you are prompted to select the profile to be extruded.

2. Move the cursor to a point outside the inner loop but inside the outer loop; the profile will be highlighted, as shown in Figure 3-52.

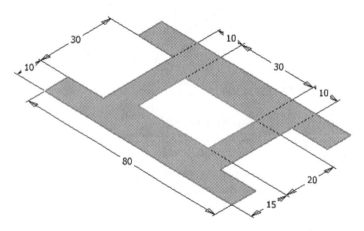

Figure 3-52 Selecting the profile to be extruded

As evident in Figure 3-52, the area inside the inner loop is not highlighted. This suggests that the selected profile, when extruded, will have a cavity in the center. This cavity is defined by the inner loop.

3. Click inside the area that is highlighted in Figure 3-52; the preview of the extruded model is displayed in the drawing window.

4. Enter **20** in the **Depth** edit box available in the **Extents** area.

You will notice that the depth of the model in the preview will be increased, as the original depth was 10 mm.

5. Choose the **OK** button to create the model and exit the **Extrude** tool. The extruded model is shown in Figure 3-53.

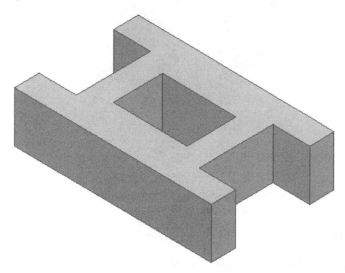

Figure 3-53 *Resulting model created by extruding the profile*

Changing the Material of the Model

When a model is created, it is applied a default material. However, as mentioned earlier, you can change this material and use one of the materials that are provided in Autodesk Inventor. Note that you do not need to select the model and then select the new material. You can directly select the required material from the drop-down list in the **Inventor Standard** toolbar and the material will be applied to the model.

1. Select **Metal-Steel (Polished)** from the drop-down list in the **Inventor Standard** toolbar; the color of the model will change to the new selected color.

Rotating the View of the Model in 3D Space

1. Choose the **Rotate** button from the **Inventor Standard** toolbar; the rim with four handles is displayed.

2. Move the cursor inside the rim and then drag it to rotate the view of the model freely in 3D space, see Figure 3-54.

3. Now, move the cursor outside the rim and drag it to rotate the model. Notice the difference between rotating the view by dragging inside the rim and dragging outside the rim.

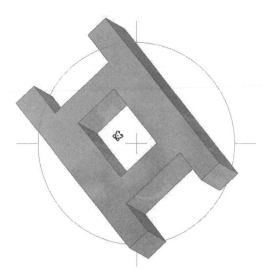

Figure 3-54 Rotating the view of the model freely in 3D space

4. Right-click to display the shortcut menu and choose **Done** to exit this tool.

5. Again, right-click and choose **Isometric View** from the shortcut menu to change the current view to isometric view.

Saving the Model

1. Choose the **Save** button in the **Inventor Standard** toolbar to save the model. Because the file is already saved once, the **Save As** dialog box is not displayed.

2. Choose **File > Close** from the menu bar to close this file.

Tutorial 2

In this tutorial, you will open the sketch drawn in Tutorial 2 of Chapter 2 and then convert it into a fully revolved model. Next, you will change the camera type to perspective and then view the model.   **(Expected time: 30 min)**

The following steps are required to complete this tutorial:

a. Open the sketch from the *c02* folder and save it in the *c03* folder.
b. Open the sketch from the *c03* folder and revolve it through an angle of 360-degree by using the **Revolve** tool.
c. Change the camera type from the **Inventor Standard** toolbar and view the model.

Opening the Sketch Drawn in Chapter 2

1. Choose the **Open** button from the **Inventor Standard** toolbar to display the **Open** dialog box.

2. Using this dialog box, open the file *\PersonalProject\c02\Tutorial2.ipt*; the sketch will be displayed in the **Part** module in the isometric view.

Saving the Sketch with Another Name

1. Choose **File > Save Copy As** from the menu bar. The **Save Copy As** dialog box is displayed.

2. Browse to the *\PersonalProject\c03* folder and save the sketch with the name *Tutorial2.ipt*.

   Because the current file is the original Chapter 2 file, you need to close it and open the Chapter 3 file.

3. Choose **File > Close** from the menu bar to close this file. Now, choose the **Open** button to display the **Open** dialog box and open the file *\PersonalProject\c03\Tutorial2.ipt*.

   The dimensions of the sketch may not be displayed completely inside the current drawing display area. You may have to increase the drawing display area using the **Zoom** and **Pan** tools to fit the dimensions in the current view, see Figure 3-55.

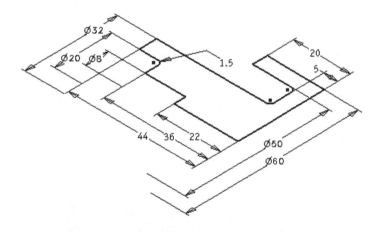

Figure 3-55 Sketch displayed in the isometric view

Revolving the Sketch

As mentioned earlier, you need an axis of revolution to revolve a profile. This axis can be a sketched line segment. In this case, the revolution axis will be the line that measures 22 mm and the sketch will be revolved about it.

1. Choose the **Revolve** button from the **Part Features** panel bar to display the **Revolve** dialog box.

Because the sketch has just one loop, it is automatically selected and highlighted. Also, the **Profile** button in the **Shape** area is not chosen. Instead, the **Axis** button is chosen.

2. Select the bottom horizontal line that measures 22 mm as the axis of revolution.

    When you move the cursor close to this line, it will be highlighted and will turn red. As soon as you select this line, the preview of the revolved model will be displayed in the drawing window.

3. Accept the default values and choose the **OK** button to complete the process of creating the revolved model.

Changing the View of the Model

The current view, in which the model is displayed, does not show the model properly. Therefore, you will have to change the view of the model.

1. Choose the **Rotate** button from the **Inventor Standard** toolbar; the rim is displayed in the drawing window.

    You will use the shortcut menu of this tool to invoke the common views for displaying the model.

2. Right-click to display the shortcut menu and choose the **Common View** option to display a cube with arrows in various directions.

3. Move the cursor close to the arrow on the upper left vertex on the left face of the cube, see Figure 3-56; the arrow turns red in color. Select this arrow.

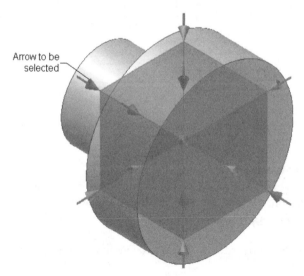

Arrow to be
selected

*Figure 3-56 Selecting the **Common View** options to reorient the model*

4. When you select this arrow, the revolved model will be reoriented and you will get a better view of the model. Right-click and choose **Done** to exit this tool.

5. Choose the **Zoom All** button from the **Inventor Standard** toolbar to modify the drawing display.

Changing the Camera Type

By default, the orthographic camera type is used to display the model. In this type of viewing, the parallel lines in the model do not meet at any point. This is the reason it is also termed as parallel viewing. The second type of camera that is available for displaying the model is perspective. In this type of viewing, the model in the drawing window is displayed exactly as it would be displayed in real 3D space. In this type of viewing, the lines in the model, when extended, meet at three points. Therefore, this type of viewing is also called the three-point perspective viewing.

1. Choose the down arrow on the right of the **Orthographic Camera** button in the **Inventor Standard** toolbar. From the flyout, choose the **Perspective Camera** button; the model will now be displayed using the perspective camera, see Figure 3-57.

Figure 3-57 Model displayed using the perspective camera

Saving the Model

1. Choose the **Save** button in the **Inventor Standard** toolbar to save the model.

2. Now, choose **File > Close** from the menu bar to close this file.

Tutorial 3

In this tutorial, you will create the model shown in Figure 3-58. Its dimensions are given in Figure 3-59. The extrusion height for the model is 10 mm. After extruding it, you will set the option of casting the X-ray ground shadow.   **(Expected time: 45 min)**

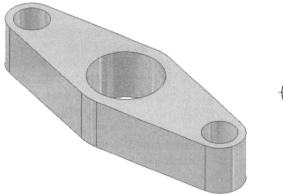

Figure 3-58 Model for Tutorial 3   *Figure 3-59 Dimensions for the model*

The following steps are required to complete this tutorial:

a. Start a new metric standard part file. Draw the sketch of the outer loop and add the constraints.
b. Draw the inner circles and add the required constraints. Dimension the complete sketch, refer to Figure 3-62.
c. Extrude the sketch to a distance of 10 mm using the **Extrude** tool, refer to Figure 3-63.
d. Choose the **X-Ray Ground Shadow** button to cast the X-ray ground shadow, refer to Figure 3-64.

Starting a New Part File

If you have installed Autodesk Inventor with millimeter as the unit of measurement, you can directly start a new metric standard part file, thus avoiding the use of the **Open** dialog box for opening a new part file. This is done using the down arrow on right of the **New** button in the **Inventor Standard** toolbar. Note that this method is not applicable for starting a metric template if you have not installed Autodesk Inventor with millimeter as the unit of measurement.

1. Choose the down arrow on the right of the **New** button in the **Inventor Standard** toolbar; a flyout is displayed with the buttons for part, assembly, drawing, and presentation files.

2. Choose the **Part** button to start a new metric part file. If Autodesk Inventor was not installed with millimeter as the measurement unit, you need to use the **Metric** tab of the **Open** dialog box to start the new metric standard part file.

Creating the Sketch of the Model

As shown in Figure 3-58, the sketch is a combination of an outer loop and three circles. First, you will create the outer loop. This outer loop will be created by drawing three circles, two at the ends and one at the center. Next, you will draw tangent lines that will join the left circle with the middle circle and the middle circle with the right circle. Finally, you will trim the unwanted portions of the circles.

1. Draw the sketch, which is a combination of three circles and tangent lines. Add the **Tangent** constraint to the lines wherever it is missing. Also, add the **Equal** constraint to all the four lines and to the circles on the left and the right. Finally, add the **Horizontal** constraint to the center points of the circles. The sketch, after drawing and adding the constraints, should look similar to the one shown in Figure 3-60.

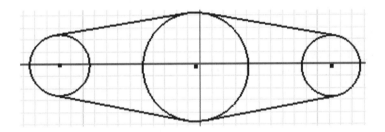

Figure 3-60 *Sketch after adding all the constraints*

Next, you need to remove the unwanted portions of the circles using the **Trim** tool.

2. Choose the **Trim** button from the **2D Sketch Panel** panel bar; you are prompted to select the portion of the curves to be trimmed.

3. Move the cursor close to the right half of the circle on the left side of the sketch.

As you move the cursor close to the circle, the circle will turn red in color and the right portion of the circle will change into dashed lines. This suggests that if you select the circle at this point, the portion displayed as dashed lines will be trimmed. In this case, the upper and lower left tangent lines will be taken as the cutting edges.

4. Specify a point on the right half of the circle that is on the left side of the sketch; the portion on the right of this circle will be trimmed. Similarly, select portions of the other circles also to trim, as shown in Figure 3-61.

5. Now, taking the center point of the trimmed arcs, draw the three circles. Add the **Equal**

constraint to the smaller circles. The sketch, after drawing the circles and applying the **Equal** constraint, should look similar to the one shown in Figure 3-62.

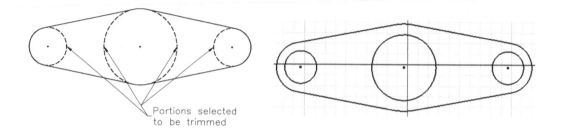

Figure 3-61 Selecting the portions to be trimmed

Figure 3-62 Sketch after creating the outer loop and the three circles

Dimensioning the Sketch

1. Add the required dimensions to the sketch. The sketch, after adding all the dimensions, should look similar to the one shown in Figure 3-63.

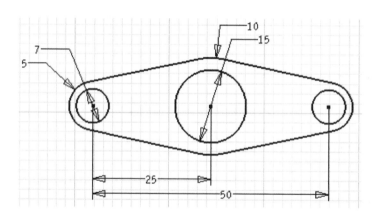

Figure 3-63 Sketch after adding dimensions

Extruding the Sketch

The sketch consists of four loops: the outer loop and the three circles. When you extrude this sketch, the three circles will be automatically subtracted from the outer loop. As a result, you will get the required model. However, this is possible only if you specify the point for selecting the profile inside the outer loop but outside all the three circles.

1. Choose **Return** on the **Inventor Standard** toolbar to exit the sketching environment.

As mentioned earlier, before proceeding to convert the sketch into a model, it is better to change the current view to the isometric view. This is because you can preview the depth of the model only if you view the model from the isometric view.

2. Right-click in the drawing window and choose the **Isometric View** option from the shortcut menu to change the current view to the isometric view.

3. Choose the **Extrude** button from the **Part Features** panel bar to invoke the **Extrude** dialog box.

Because the sketch consists of more than one loop, the **Profile** button in the **Shape** area is chosen and you are prompted to select the profile to be extruded.

4. Move the cursor to a point anywhere inside the outer loop but outside all three circles.

The profile that will be selected is highlighted. Notice that the area inside all the three circles is not shaded. This suggests that the area inside these circles will not be extruded. This is also one of the methods to cross check whether the profile selected is the one you need to extrude or not.

5. Click inside the shaded profile; the preview of the model is displayed in the drawing window.

6. Accept the default values to extrude the profile through a depth of **10 mm**.

You may need to change the camera type to parallel from the **Inventor Standard** toolbar if you use the same session of Autodesk Inventor in which you changed the camera type to perspective in Tutorial 2. The final model is shown in Figure 3-64.

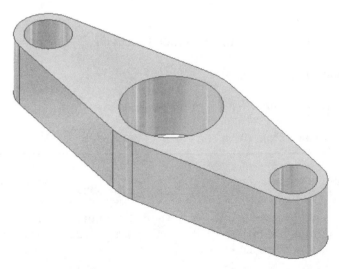

Figure 3-64 *Final model for Tutorial 3*

Casting the Shadow

Next, you need to cast the X-ray ground shadow of the model. You can cast the shadow using the tool in the **Inventor Standard** toolbar.

1. Choose the down arrow on the right of the **No Ground Shadow** button in the **Inventor Standard** toolbar; a flyout is displayed.

2. Choose the **X-Ray Ground Shadow** button from the flyout; the X-ray ground shadow is displayed, as shown in Figure 3-65.

Figure 3-65 Model with the X-ray ground shadow

Saving the Model

1. Choose the **Save** button in the **Inventor Standard** toolbar.

2. Save the model with the name:

   \PersonalProject\c03\Tutorial3.ipt

3. Choose **File > Close** from the menu bar to close the file.

Tutorial 4

In this tutorial, you will write the text shown in Figure 3-66 and then cast the shadow of the text. The font size is 5 mm and the height of extrusion of the text is 2.5 mm. Change the material of the extruded text to Zinc Chromate.   **(Expected time: 15 min)**

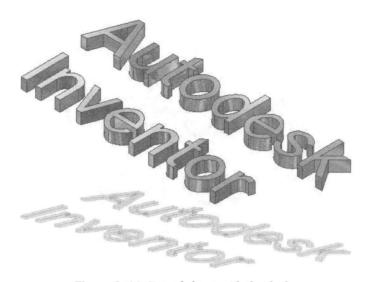

Figure 3-66 *Extruded text with the shadow*

The following steps are required to complete this tutorial:

a.   Start a new metric standard part file and write the text in the sketching environment.
b.   Extrude the text to a distance of 2.5 mm using the **Extrude** tool.
c.   Change the material of the feature to Zinc Chromate.
d.   Choose the **X-Ray Ground Shadow** button to cast the X-ray ground shadow.

Starting a New File and Writing the Text

1.   Start a new metric standard part file using the **Metric** tab of the **Open** dialog box.

2.   Using the button and flyout in the **Inventor Standard** toolbar, make sure that the option to display the shadow is turn off.

3.   Choose the **Text** button from the **2D Sketch Panel** panel bar; you are prompted to click on the location of the text.

4.   Specify a point somewhere in the drawing window; the **Format Text** dialog box is displayed.

5.   Select the **Arial** font from the **Font** drop-down list and then set the font height to 5 mm using the **Size** edit box.

6.   Enter the text **Autodesk Inventor** in the **Text Window** in two lines. Choose **OK** to exit the dialog box; the text is written and is displayed in the drawing window, as shown in Figure 3-67.

Figure 3-67 Text in the sketching environment

Extruding the Text

Next, you need to exit the sketching environment and extrude the text. But before you invoke the **Extrude** tool, you need to change the current view to isometric view.

1. Choose **Return** from the **Inventor Standard** toolbar and exit the sketching environment.

2. Right-click and choose **Isometric View** from the shortcut menu to change the current view to the isometric view.

3. Choose the **Extrude** button from the **Part Features** panel bar to invoke the **Extrude** dialog box.

   The profile button in the **Shape** tab is chosen and you are prompted to select the profile to extrude.

4. Move the cursor over the text and select it when it turns red.

5. Set the extrusion depth in the **Depth** edit box to **2.5** and choose **OK**. The text is extruded to a distance of 2.5 mm, as shown in Figure 3-68.

Changing the Material and Casting the Shadow

As mentioned earlier, the material of the feature is changed using the drop-down list in the **Inventor Standard** toolbar.

1. Select **Zinc Chromate** from the drop-down list in the **Inventor Standard** toolbar. This is the last material in this list.

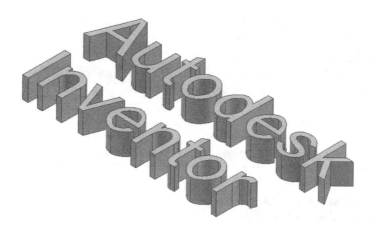

Figure 3-68 Feature created by extruding the text

The material of the text is changed to Zinc Chromate. Next, you need to cast the X-ray ground shadow.

2.   Choose the down arrow besides the **No Ground Shadow** button in the **Inventor Standard** toolbar; a flyout is displayed.

3.   Choose the **X-Ray Ground Shadow** button to cast this type of shadow below the extruded text. The final extruded text, after casting the X-ray ground shadow, is shown in Figure 3-69.

Figure 3-69 Text after changing the material and casting the shadow

Note

The distance of the feature from the shadow depends on the current zoom factor. As a result, the distance of the shadow in your drawing may be different from that shown in Figure 3-68.

Saving the Sketch

1. Choose the **Save** button from the **Inventor Standard** tool bar; the **Save As** dialog box is displayed. Save the model with the name given below.

   \PersonalProject\c03\Tutorial4.ipt

2. Choose **File > Close** from the menu bar to close the file.

Self-Evaluation Test

Answer the following questions and then compare your answers with those given at the end of this chapter:

1. The line, once drawn in Autodesk Inventor, cannot be reduced in length. You will have to delete the line and then redraw a line of smaller length. (T/F)

2. The copies of the sketched entities can be arranged along the length and width of an imaginary rectangle using the **Circular Pattern** tool. (T/F)

3. When you select the profile by using a point that is inside the outer loop but outside the inner loops, the resultant solid will have the inner closed loops subtracted from the outer closed loop. (T/F)

4. To mirror the sketched entities, you need a mirror line. (T/F)

5. The _____ option should be cleared from the shortcut menu to select only one entity to offset from a closed loop.

6. To create a copy of an existing sketched entity by rotating, select the _____ check box in the **Rotate** dialog box.

7. Autodesk Inventor allows you to create two types of patterns. These are _____ patterns and _____ patterns.

8. The _____ option allows you to select a line segment, the length of which will define the distance between the individual items.

9. The _____ angles are generally provided to solid models for their easy withdrawal from the castings.

10. If the _____ button in the **Extrude** dialog box is chosen, the resulting feature will be a surface and not a solid.

Review Questions

Answer the following questions:

1. You can invoke the **Trim** tool from within the **Extend** tool by pressing the SHIFT key. (T/F)

2. Offsetting is one of the easiest methods of drawing parallel lines or concentric arcs and circles. (T/F)

3. If you select a circle from a point on its circumference and drag, it will be moved from its location. (T/F)

4. Selecting a line at its endpoint and dragging will stretch it. (T/F)

5. The preview of a model, as it will be created after extruding or revolving, is available in the drawing window even before you exit the **Extrude** or the **Revolve** dialog box. (T/F)

6. Which one of the following tools can be used to reposition the sketched entity from one place to the other using two points?

     (a) **Move**   (b) **Rotate**
     (c) **Mirror**   (d) **Extend**

7. Which one of the following tools can be used to arrange multiple copies of the sketched entities around an imaginary circle?

     (a) **Move**   (b) **Rotate**
     (c) **Rectangular Pattern**   (d) **Circular Pattern**

8. Which one of the following options allows you to use an existing dimension to define the distance between the individual items of a pattern.

     (a) **Dimension**   (b) **Show Dimensions**
     (c) **Measure**   (d) None

9. Which one of the following check boxes is selected to ensure that all items in the pattern are automatically updated, if any one of the entities is modified.

     (a) **Associative**   (b) **Fitted**
     (c) **Suppress**   (d) None

10. Which one of the following options is added to the shortcut menu after you choose the **Previous View** option from it?

     (a) **Isometric View**   (b) **Common View**
     (c) **Pan**   (d) **Next View**

Exercises

Exercise 1

In this exercise, you will extrude the sketch drawn in Exercise 1 of Chapter 2, see Figure 3-70. The extrusion depth for the model is 15 mm.   **(Expected time: 30 min)**

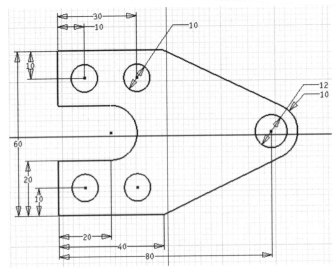

Figure 3-70 *Sketch for Exercise 1*

Exercise 2

In this exercise, you will extrude the sketch drawn in Exercise 2 of Chapter 2, see Figure 3-71. The extrusion depth for the model is 80 mm.   **(Expected time: 30 min)**

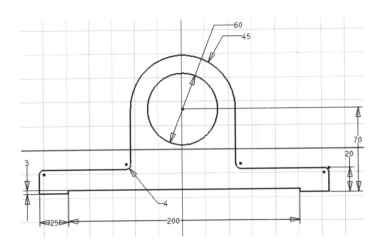

Figure 3-71 *Sketch for Exercise 2*

Exercise 3

In this exercise, you will extrude the sketch drawn in Exercise 3 of Chapter 2, see Figure 3-72. The extrusion depth for the model is 40 mm. **(Expected time: 30 min)**

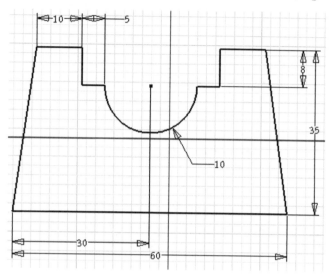

Figure 3-72 Sketch for Exercise 3

Exercise 4

In this exercise, you will extrude the sketch drawn in Exercise 4 of Chapter 2, see Figure 3-73. The extrusion depth for the model is 35 mm. **(Expected time: 30 min)**

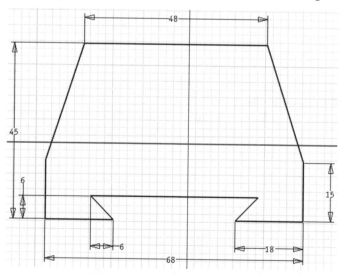

Figure 3-73 Sketch for Exercise 4

Exercise 5

In this exercise, you will extrude the sketch drawn in Exercise 5 of Chapter 2, see Figure 3-74. The extrusion depth for the model is 65 mm.   **(Expected time: 30 min)**

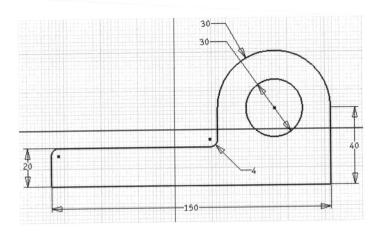

Figure 3-74 Sketch for Exercise 5

Note
When you extrude the sketches of Exercises 2, 3, 4, and 5 and change the view to isometric, the model will not be displayed as in the figures of exercises in Chapter 2. The reason is that these sketches are created on the default XY plane, which is horizontal. You will learn to draw sketches on other planes in the next chapter.

Answers to Self-Evaluation Test
1. F, **2.** F, **3.** T, **4.** T, **5. Loop Select**, **6. Copy**, **7.** Rectangular, Circular, **8. Measure**, **9.** taper, **10. Surface**

Chapter 4

Other Sketching and Modeling Options

Learning Objectives

After completing this chapter, you will be able to:

- *Create features on planes other than the default XY plane.*
- *Create work features such as work planes, work axes, and work points.*
- *Use other extrusion and revolution options for creating models.*

WHY DO YOU NEED OTHER SKETCHING PLANES?

All mechanical designs consist of a number of sketched, work, and placed features integrated together. The first feature in a model is the base feature and is generally a sketched feature. After creating the base feature, you need to add more features to it. By default, when you open a new file, the features are created on the XY plane. However, most of the times, the additional features are not created on the default plane on which the base feature is created. For example, refer to the model shown in Figure 4-1.

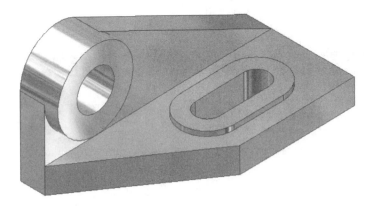

Figure 4-1 Model created by combining various features

The base feature for this model is shown in Figure 4-2. Its sketch is drawn on the XY plane. After creating it, you need to create three join features, one cut feature, and a hole feature, see Figure 4-3. Now, the cut feature and all the join features are sketched features and, therefore, you require sketching planes to draw their sketches.

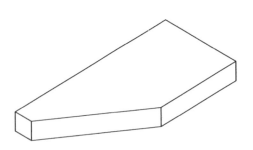

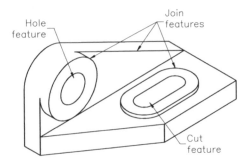

Figure 4-2 Base feature for the model   *Figure 4-3 Model after adding other features*

As evident in Figure 4-3, all these features are not created on the same plane as that of the base feature. Therefore, to draw the sketches of the sketched features, you need to define new sketching planes, which are different from the default XY plane. The method of specifying a new sketching plane is discussed next.

Defining a New Sketching Plane

In Autodesk Inventor, defining a new sketching plane is an easy process. You just need to specify the plane for drawing the sketch. The selected plane will be automatically made the current sketching plane. Once you have finished creating the base feature, choose **Sketch** from the **Inventor Standard** toolbar; you will be prompted to select the plane to create the sketch or edit an existing sketch. Select the plane to draw the sketch. When you move the cursor close to the plane, its boundary will be highlighted in red. As soon as you select the new sketching plane, the sketching environment will be activated and the grid lines will be displayed on that plane. Also, the **Part Features** panel bar will be replaced by the **2D Sketch Panel** panel bar.

Note

*Generally, when creating a feature, the isometric view is used to view the object. Now, when you define a new sketching plane to draw the sketch for the next feature, the sketching environment is activated. However, the isometric view is still the current view. Before proceeding, you need to change the current view such that you can view the new sketch plane from the top. You can change the isometric view to the plan view by choosing the **Look At** button from the **Inventor Standard** toolbar. This tool is used to reorient the view using an existing plane or sketched entity. On invoking this tool, you will be prompted to select the entity to look at. Select the new sketching plane; the view will be changed to the plan view of the selected plane. You can also use the common views to orient the sketching plane.*

WORK FEATURES

Work features are parametric features that are associated with a model. Autodesk Inventor has provided three types of work features to assist you in creating a design. The three types of work features available in Autodesk Inventor are

- **Work Planes**
- **Work Axes**
- **Work Points**

The methods of creating these work features are discussed next.

Creating Work Planes

Toolbar:	Part Features > Work Plane
Panel Bar:	Part Features > Work Plane

Work planes are similar to sketch planes and are used to draw sketches for sketched features or create placed features like holes. The reason you need work planes is that the sketch planes have some limitations. For example, it is not possible to define a sketch plane that is at some offset distance from the existing plane. Also, it is not possible to define a sketch plane that is tangent to a cylindrical feature. In such situations, you can define a work plane, which can then be selected as the sketching plane. In Autodesk Inventor, there are twelve possible combinations of creating work planes. The eleven possible combinations are discussed next and the remaining combination will be discussed in later chapters.

Note
The new work plane will be displayed on the screen as a shaded plane and will also be displayed in the browser. If required, you can turn off the display of these work planes, which is discussed later in this chapter.

Creating a Work Plane using Two Edges

This option is used to create a work plane that passes through two selected edges. Both the edges may or may not lie in the same plane. If the two edges do not lie in the same plane, the resulting work plane will be inclined, see Figures 4-4 and 4-5.

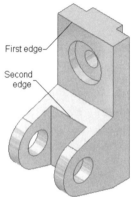

Figure 4-4 Selecting the edges to define the work plane

Figure 4-5 Resulting work plane

Tip. *You can also select work axes to define the work plane. You will learn more about work axes later in this chapter.*

Creating a Work Plane using Three Vertices

This option allows you to create a work plane using three vertices, which can be the vertices of the model or the point/hole centers. When you move the cursor close to a vertex, a yellow circle with a cross is placed on it, suggesting that the vertex is selected. Figure 4-6 shows three points selected to create the work plane and Figure 4-7 shows the resulting work plane.

Creating a Work Plane Parallel to a Plane/Planar Face and Passing through an Edge/Axis

This option allows you to create a work plane that is parallel to an existing work plane or planar face and is passing through the selected edge or axis. To create a work plane using this option, invoke the **Work Plane** tool and then select the work plane or planar face to which the resulting work plane will be parallel. Next, select the edge through which the work plane will pass; the **Angle** toolbar will be displayed. This toolbar is used to specify the angle of the resulting work plane. The default value in this toolbar is **90**. Enter **0** in the edit box. The

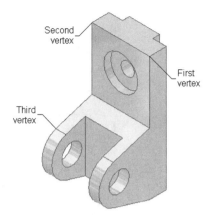

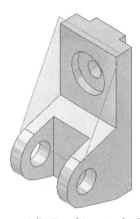

Figure 4-6 *Selecting the vertices to define the work plane*

Figure 4-7 *Resulting work plane*

resulting work plane will be parallel to the selected plane and will pass through the selected edge. Figure 4-8 shows the planar face and the edge selected for creating the work plane and Figure 4-9 shows the resulting work plane.

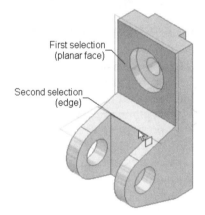

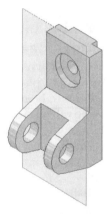

Figure 4-8 *Selecting a planar face and an edge to define the work plane*

Figure 4-9 *Resulting work plane*

Creating a Work Plane Normal to a Plane/Planar Face and Passing through an Edge/Axis

This option is used to create a work plane that is normal to an existing work plane or planar face and is passing through the selected edge or axis. To create a work plane using this option, invoke the **Work Plane** tool and select the edge through which the work plane will pass. Next, select the plane or planar face to which the new work plane will be normal. After you select the plane or planar face, the **Angle** toolbar will be displayed. The default value of the angle in this toolbar will be **90**. This value will create a work plane that is normal to the selected plane or planar face. Figure 4-10 shows the edge and the planar face selected for creating the work plane and Figure 4-11 shows the resulting work plane.

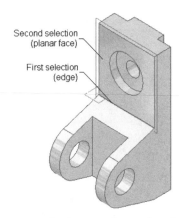

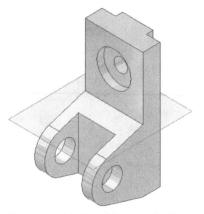

Figure 4-10 *Selecting an edge and a planar face to define the work plane*

Figure 4-11 *Resulting work plane*

Tip. *The work planes are infinite entities and the size displayed on the graphics screen is just for reference. To resize the work planes, move the cursor over one of the corners and drag the mouse when the cursor turns into a two-sided arrow. Note that the fours-sided arrow cursor will move the work plane along the same plane.*

Creating a Work Plane Passing through an Edge/Axis and at an Angle to the Selected Plane/Planar Face

This option allows you to create a work plane that passes through an edge or axis and is at an angle to an existing work plane or planar face. This option is similar to the previous options, with the only difference being that in the **Angle** toolbar, you need to set the angle at which the new work plane will be created. You can preview the work plane that will be created using the current values on the graphics screen. If you want the work plane to be rotated through a specified angle in the opposite direction, enter a negative angle value. Figure 4-12 shows the edge and the planar face selected to create the work plane and Figure 4-13 shows the work plane created at an angle of -30-degree to the selected planar face by setting the value in the **Angle** toolbar to **-30**.

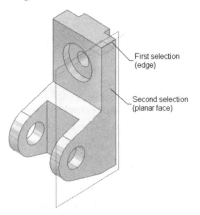

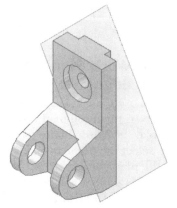

Figure 4-12 *Selecting an edge and a planar face to define the work plane*

Figure 4-13 *Resulting work plane*

Creating a Work Plane Passing through a Point and Parallel to the Selected Plane/Planar Face

This option allows you to create a work plane that passes through a specified point and is parallel to the selected plane or planar face. To define this plane, you can select the point and the plane or planar face in any sequence. You can select the point first and then select the plane or planar face to which the new work plane will be parallel. Alternatively, you can select the plane or planar face first and then the point through which the work plane will pass. Figure 4-14 shows the point and the planar face selected to define the work plane and Figure 4-15 shows the resulting work plane.

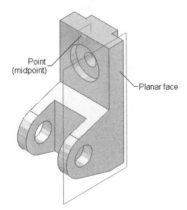
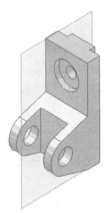

Figure 4-14 Selecting a point and a planar face to define the work plane   *Figure 4-15 Resulting work plane*

Creating a Work Plane Tangent to a Circular Feature and Parallel to a Plane/Planar Face

This option allows you to create a work plane that is tangent to the selected circular feature and is parallel to the selected plane or planar face. Figure 4-16 shows the circular feature to which the new work plane will be tangent and the planar face to which the resulting work plane will be parallel. Figure 4-17 shows the resulting work plane.

Tip. *To create a work plane tangent to a cylinder, select the cylindrical face and then select the XY, YZ, or XZ plane to which the resulting work plane should be parallel. To select the XY, YZ, or XZ planes, click on the + sign located on the left of* **Origin** *in the browser. The three default planes along with the three axes will be displayed. You can now select the required plane from the browser.*

Creating a Work Plane Tangent to a Sketched Circle

This option is used to create a work plane that is tangent to a sketched circle. Remember that you cannot create the work plane using only the circle. You need to draw a line or a centerline also from the center of the circle to the point at which the work plane should be tangent. After drawing the circle and the line or the centerline, exit the sketching environment. Next, invoke the **Work Plane** tool; you will be prompted to define the work plane by highlighting and selecting the geometry. Select the line or the centerline and then select the point of

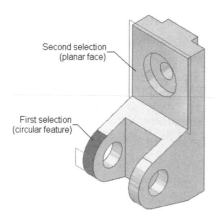

Figure 4-16 *Selecting a circular feature and a planar face to define the work plane*

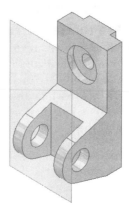

Figure 4-17 *Resulting work plane*

intersection of the line and the circle. The work plane will be created tangent to the circle and will pass through their intersection point. Also, the new work plane will be normal to the centerline, see Figures 4-18 and 4-19.

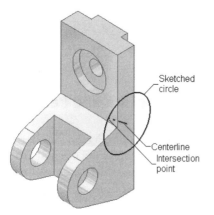

Figure 4-18 *Selecting centerline and intersection point to define the work plane*

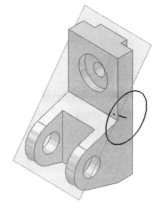

Figure 4-19 *Resulting work plane*

Tip. *You can increase or decrease the size of a work plane. To modify its size, position the cursor on one of the corners of the work plane; a two-sided arrow appears on the cursor. When this two-sided arrow appears, press the left mouse button and drag the cursor. Depending on the direction in which you drag the cursor, the size of the work plane will be modified.*

Creating a Work Plane Tangent to a Circular Face and Passing through the Selected Edge/Axis

This option allows you to create a work plane that is tangent to the selected circular face and passes through the selected edge. Figure 4-20 shows the circular face and the edge selected to create the work plane and Figure 4-21 shows the resulting work plane.

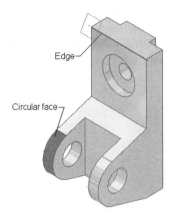
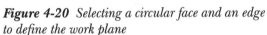

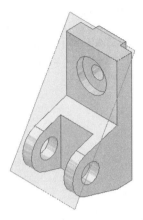

Figure 4-20 *Selecting a circular face and an edge to define the work plane*

Figure 4-21 *Resulting work plane*

Creating a Work Plane Parallel to a Plane/Planar face and at an Offset

This option is used to create a work plane that is parallel to an existing plane or planar face and is at some offset distance from the selected plane or planar face. To create this work plane, select the plane or planar face to which the resulting plane will be parallel. When the plane is highlighted, press the left mouse button and drag the cursor. As soon as you start dragging the cursor, the **Offset** toolbar will be displayed. The current offset value will be displayed in this toolbar. This value will change dynamically as you drag the plane further. You can also enter the offset value directly in this toolbar. If you enter a negative value, the work plane will be offset in the opposite direction. Figure 4-22 shows the plane selected to define the new work plane and Figure 4-23 shows the new work plane created at an offset of 30 mm.

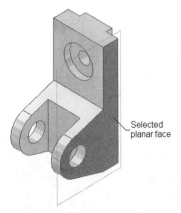

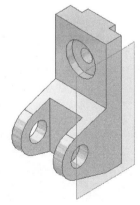

Figure 4-22 *Selecting a planar face to define the offset work plane*

Figure 4-23 *Resulting work plane*

Creating a Work Plane Normal to an Edge/Axis and Passing through a Point

This option allows you to create a work plane that is normal to the selected edge and passes through a specified point. The point can be any vertex in the model, a sketched point/hole center, or the work point. You can select the point and the edge in any sequence. Figure 4-24 shows the edge and the point selected to create the work plane and Figure 4-25 shows the resulting work plane.

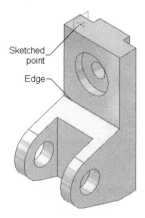

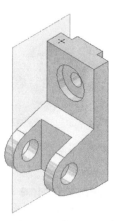

Figure 4-24 *Selecting an edge and a point to define the work plane*

Figure 4-25 *Resulting work plane*

Note

*To create more than one work feature in succession, you can turn on the option to repeat the command. To do this, invoke a work feature tool and then right-click in the graphics window. From the shortcut menu, choose the **Repeat command** option. This option ensures that the previous work feature tool is repeated until you terminate it.*

Tip. *You can modify the orientation of the coordinate system while sketching. To modify the orientation, choose **Edit Coordinate System** from the **2D Sketch Panel** panel bar; the X and Y axis appear in the drawing. Select the axis that you want to reorient; the selected axis turns blue. Now, select an edge or a work axis to orient the selected axis. You can also use the axes from the **Origin** folder in the browser to orient the coordinate system.*

*You can also select the origin of the coordinate system that is displayed when you invoke the **Edit Coordinate System** tool to relocate the origin. Select the origin and then select a vertex or a circular face to align the origin with the vertex or the center point of the circular face.*

Creating Work Axes

Toolbar:	Part Features > Work Axis
Panel Bar:	Part Features > Work Axis

Work axes are parametric axes passing through a model or feature and are used as a reference to create work planes, work points, and circular patterns. The work axis will be displayed in the model as well as in the browser and is automatically modified when you edit the feature on which you create the work axes. In Autodesk Inventor you can create a work axis using any of the following four methods:

Creating a Work Axis on a Circular Feature

This method allows you to create a work axis passing through the center of a circular feature. When you invoke the **Work Axis** tool, you will be prompted to define a work axis by highlighting and selecting the geometry. Select the circular feature; a work axis passing through the center of the circular feature will be created, see Figure 4-26.

Creating a Work Axis Normal to a Plane/Planar Face and Passing through a Point

This method allows you to create a work axis normal to a plane or planar face and passing through a specified point. After invoking this tool, select the plane to which the axis will be normal and then select the point through which the axis will pass, see Figure 4-27.

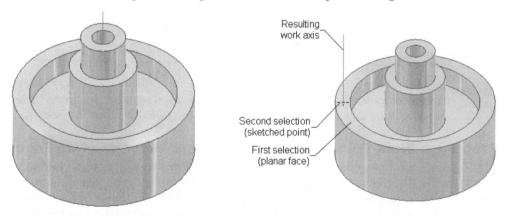

Resulting work axis

Second selection (sketched point)

First selection (planar face)

Figure 4-26 Work axis passing through the center of a circular feature

Figure 4-27 Creating work axis using a planar face and a sketched point

Creating a Work Axis Passing through the Intersection of Two Planes/ Planar Faces

This option is used to create a work axis that passes through the intersection of two planes or planar faces. If you select two planar faces that do not intersect in the model, but intersect when extended, the resulting axis will pass through the extended intersection, see Figure 4-28.

Creating a Work Axis Passing through Two Points

This option is used to create a work axis that passes through two specified points. The points that can be used are the vertices of a model, midpoints of its edges, sketched points/hole centers, or work points. Figure 4-29 shows a work axis created using the midpoints of two edges of a model.

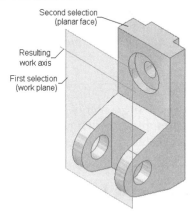

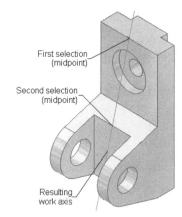

Figure 4-28 *Work axis passing through the intersection of two planes*

Figure 4-29 *Creating a work axis using the midpoints of two edges*

Creating Work Points

Toolbar:	Part Features > Work Point
Panel Bar:	Part Features > Work Point

 Work points are parametric points that can be created on an existing model and are used as an aid in creating work planes, work axes, or other features. In Autodesk Inventor, you can create a work point using the following four methods.

Creating a Work Point at a Vertex or at the Midpoint of an Edge

This option is used to create a work point at any vertex of a model or at the midpoints of its edges. Invoke this tool and then select any vertex of the model. The new work point will be created on the selected vertex. To create a work point at the midpoint of the selected edge, move the cursor close to the midpoint of the edge; the midpoint will be highlighted. You can also right-click and choose **Select Other** to cycle through various entities and select the midpoint when it is displayed. Figure 4-30 shows work points created at the vertices of the model and at the midpoints of the edges of the model.

Creating a Work Point at the Intersection of Two Edges/Axes

This option is used to create a work point at the intersection or extended intersection of two edges or axes. The edge selected for creating the work point need not necessarily be a linear edge, see Figure 4-31.

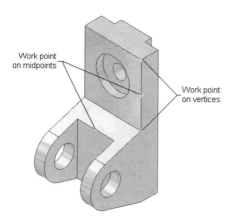

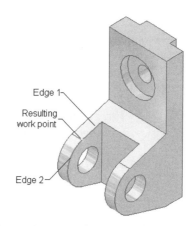

Figure 4-30 Work points on the vertices and midpoints of edges

Figure 4-31 Work point at the intersection of two edges

Creating a Work Point at the Intersection of a Plane/Planar Face and an Edge/Axis

Using this option, you can create a work point at the intersection of a plane or planar face and an edge or axis, see Figure 4-32.

Creating a Work Point at the Intersection of Three Planes/Planar Faces

Using this option, you can create a work point at the intersection of three planes or planar faces, see Figure 4-33.

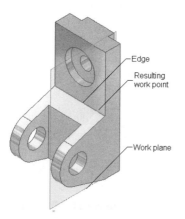

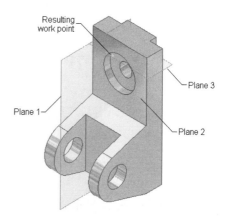

Figure 4-32 Work point at the intersection of an edge and a work plane

Figure 4-33 Work point at the intersection of three planes

Note

*If you delete the work features, the features created with reference to these work features are also deleted. If you do not want the work features to be visible on the screen, right-click on them in the browser and choose **Visibility** from the shortcut menu; the display of the selected work feature will be turned off. Choose this option again to turn the visibility on.*

Tip. *The work features can also be created in-line. The in-line features are created while you are in the process of creating some other feature. For example, while creating a work axis, if you right-click, the shortcut menu will be displayed. This shortcut menu provides the options of creating a work plane and a work point. The work plane and the work point created using this shortcut menu will be in-line work features. Note that all the in-line features are dependent on the parent features.*

OTHER EXTRUSION OPTIONS

As mentioned earlier, some of the options of the **Extrude** dialog box will not be available until you have created the base feature. Once the base feature is created, the remaining options in both the tabs of this dialog box will be available. These options are discussed next.

Shape Tab

The options in the **Shape** tab (Figure 4-34) are discussed next.

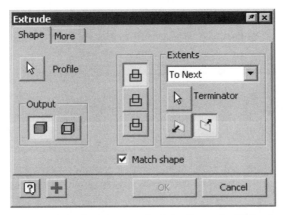

*Figure 4-34 The **Shape** tab of the **Extrude** dialog box*

Cut

This is the second button in the area on the left of the **Extents** area. This button will be available only when you are creating another feature after creating the base feature. The **Cut** option is used to create an extruded feature by removing material from the existing feature. The material that will be removed will be defined by the sketch you have drawn. Figure 4-35 shows a join feature created using a sketch and Figure 4-36 shows a cut feature created using the same sketch.

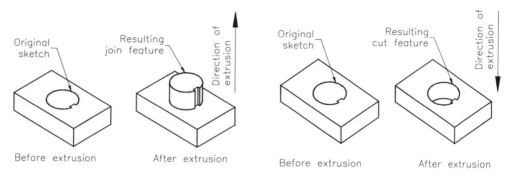

Figure 4-35 *Extruding the sketch using the* ***Join*** *option*

Figure 4-36 *Extruding the sketch using the* ***Cut*** *option*

Intersect

 This button is available below the **Cut** button and is chosen to create an extruded feature by retaining the material common to the existing feature and the sketch, see Figure 4-37.

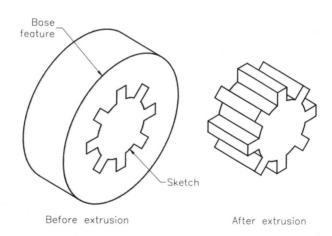

Figure 4-37 *Extruding the sketch using the* ***Intersect*** *option*

Extents Area

Once you have created the base feature, two more options will be available in the **Distance** drop-down list. These options are discussed next.

To Next

This option is used to terminate the extruded feature on the first plane or face it comes across in the specified direction. When you select this option, two buttons will be displayed in this area, which will be used to define the direction of extrusion.

Note

*The **Mid-plane** button will not be available with the **To Next** termination option. This is because you cannot select planes or planar faces in both the directions of the current sketch plane in a single attempt.*

All

The **All** option is used to create a feature by extruding the sketch through all the features that it comes across on its way to the last face of the model. You can extrude the sketch in either direction of the current sketch plane using the direction buttons in the **Extents** area. You can also extrude the sketch in both the directions of the current sketch plane by choosing the **Mid-plane** button. Note that to use this option, there should be existing feature faces in the direction in which you want to extrude the sketch.

Figure 4-38 shows a sketch drawn on an offset plane. Figures 4-39 and 4-40 show the profile extruded using the **To Next** and **All** options, respectively.

Figure 4-38 Sketch drawn on the offset plane

*Figure 4-39 Sketch extruded using the **To Next** option*

*Figure 4-40 Sketch extruded using the **All** option*

Match shape

This check box is available only when you are extruding an open sketch. If this check box is selected, the open sketch is extruded in such a way that it matches its shape while extruding. In doing so, the sketch fills with material all the features up to the last face of the model. For example, refer to the open sketch shown in Figure 4-41. This sketch is drawn at a plane offset from the bottom face of the model.

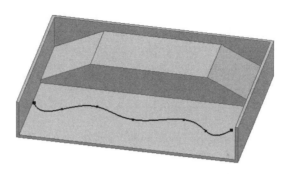

Figure 4-41 *Sketch drawn on the offset plane*

When you invoke the **Extrude** tool and select this open profile, you are allowed to extrude it in either of the two sides shown in Figures 4-42 and 4-43.

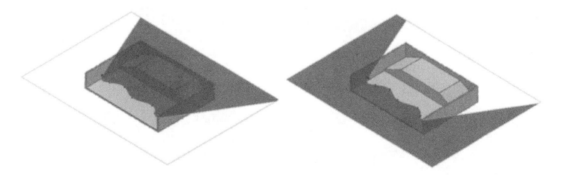

Figure 4-42 *First side for extruding the profile*   *Figure 4-43* *Second side for extruding the profile*

While selecting the side to be extruded, you need to be careful because the feature will be successful only when you extrude it in the direction in which the sketch will find faces to terminate the feature. In this case, the feature will not be created if you select the side shown in Figure 4-43. This is because the sketch cannot find any face to terminate the feature in the front direction.

After you select the side of the sketch to be extruded, you will be prompted to define the extent of the feature. You can select the type of termination from the **Distance** drop-down list and define the direction using the two buttons. If the **Match shape** check box is selected, the sketch will fill the model with the material and the feature will be created similar to that shown in Figure 4-44. But if the **Match shape** check box is cleared, the feature will be created similar to that shown in Figure 4-45. As evident in Figure 4-45, the shape of the sketch is not retained while creating the feature.

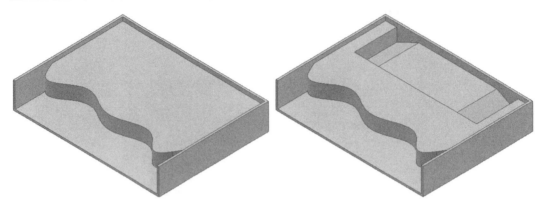

*Figure 4-44 Result with the **Match shape** check box selected*

*Figure 4-45 Result with the **Match shape** check box cleared*

More Tab

When you are creating a feature after the base feature, you can also use the remaining options of the **More** tab shown in Figure 4-46. These options are discussed next.

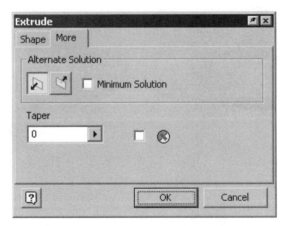

*Figure 4-46 The **More** tab of the **Extrude** dialog box*

Alternate Solution Area

The options in the **Alternate Solution** area are used in combination with the **To** and the **From To** termination options. These options are used in the extruded features that terminate on the curved faces, resulting in more than one possible solution. These options are discussed next.

Flip

The **Flip** buttons are used to reverse the direction of the extrude feature.

Minimum Solution

By default, in case of more than one solution, the extruded feature terminates at the face that is at the maximum distance from the sketch. Figure 4-47 shows the sketch and the face at which the extruded feature will terminate. Notice that the resulting feature in Figure 4-48 is created up to the face that is at the maximum distance from the sketch. However, if you select the **Minimum Solution** check box, the feature will terminate at the face that is at the minimum distance from the sketch, see Figures 4-49 and 4-50.

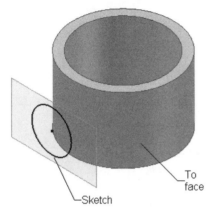

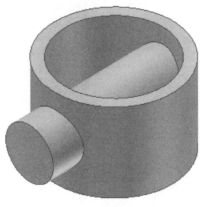

Figure 4-47 *Sketch and termination face*   *Figure 4-48* *Resulting extruded feature*

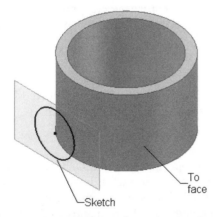

Figure 4-49 *Sketch and termination face*   *Figure 4-50* *Resulting extruded feature*

Note

In Figures 4-48 and 4-50, the visibility of work planes is turned off.

Infer iMates

This check box is selected to apply an iMate to an edge of the solid. Note that only the edge that is a full circle in shape can be selected for this purpose.

OTHER REVOLUTION OPTIONS

Most of the options in the **Revolve** dialog box were discussed in Chapter 3. The remaining options are discussed next.

Once you have created the base feature, the **Cut** and the **Intersect** buttons will also be available in the **Revolve** dialog box, see Figure 4-51. Their functions are discussed next.

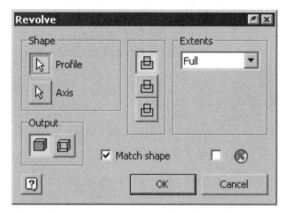

Figure 4-51 *The Revolve dialog box*

Cut

 This is the second button in the area between the **Shape** area and the **Extents** area. This button will be available only when you create another feature after creating the base feature. The **Cut** option is used to create a revolved feature by removing material from an existing feature. This material will be defined by the sketch you have drawn and the axis of revolution.

Intersect

This button is available below the **Cut** button and is used to create a revolved feature by retaining the material common to the existing feature and the sketch.

Match shape

This check box is available only when you revolve an open sketch. Similar to the **Extrude** tool, in this tool also this check box is used to revolve the open sketch in such a way that it matches its shape while extruding. In doing so, the sketch floods all the features up to the last face of the model with material. Figure 4-52 shows the open sketch and Figures 4-53 and 4-54 show the revolved feature created by selecting this check box and clearing it.

Infer iMates

This check box is selected to apply an iMate to a full circle edge of the solid feature.

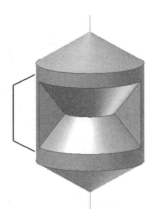

Figure 4-52 *Open sketch for the revolved feature*

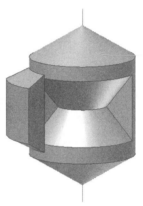

Figure 4-53 *Result with the **Match shape** check box selected*

Figure 4-54 *Result with the **Match shape** check box cleared*

THE CONCEPT OF SKETCH SHARING

Generally, while creating a design, you will frequently come across situations where you have to use a consumed sketch for creating another feature in the same plane and along the same direction of extrusion. As mentioned in Introduction, a consumed sketch is the one that has already been converted into a feature. For example, consider a case where you have to create a join feature by extruding the sketch to different distances in both the directions about the current sketch plane.

In some solid modeling programs, to use the consumed sketch, you will have to copy it to the new location. After placing the sketch, you will have to add the dimensions to locate it on its exact location. However, in Autodesk Inventor, you can directly use the same sketch by sharing it. This concept of using the consumed sketch again is termed as sharing the sketches. This concept has drawn a very distinct line between Autodesk Inventor and other solid modeling programs as it reduces the design time appreciably.

Sharing Sketches

As mentioned in Introduction, all operations that were used to create a model are displayed in the form of a tree view in the browser. All these operations will be arranged in the sequence in which they were performed. Also, once the sketch is converted into a feature, the sketch will be hidden and the feature will be displayed in the browser. For example, when you create the sketch for the base feature, the browser will display **Sketch1** below **Origin**. When this sketch is extruded and converted into the base feature, the browser will display **Extrusion1** below **Origin** and it will have a plus sign (+) located on the left. If you click on this plus sign, it will expand and will display **Sketch1**. Similarly, if you click on the plus sign of any sketched feature, it will expand and display the sketch.

To share the sketch, right-click on the sketch you want to share to display the shortcut menu, see Figure 4-55. In this shortcut menu, choose **Share Sketch**. Another sketch with the same name will be displayed in the browser. Also, the shared sketch will be displayed in the graphics window. You can now convert this sketch into a feature.

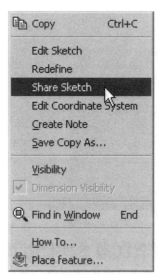

Figure 4-55 Sharing the sketch using the shortcut menu

Note

*By default, the visibility of the shared sketch is set to on. As a result, after converting into a feature, the sketch will also be displayed along with the new feature. You need to manually turn off the visibility of this sketch. This is done by using the shortcut menu that is displayed upon right-clicking on the sketch. In this shortcut menu, the **Visibility** option will have a check mark in front of it. Choose this option again to turn off the visibility. You will notice that the sketch is no more visible on the screen. Similarly, right-click on any work feature and turn off its visibility using the **Visibility** option in the shortcut menu.*

TUTORIALS

Tutorial 1

In this tutorial, you will create the model of the Standard Bracket shown in Figure 4-56a. Its dimensions are shown in Figures 4-56b through 4-56d. After creating the model, change its material to Metal-AL-6061 (Polished) and save it with the following name.

\PersonalProject\c04\Tutorial1.ipt   **(Expected Time: 30 min)**

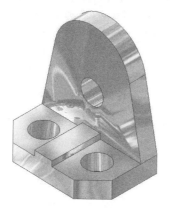

Figure 4-56a *Model for Tutorial 1*

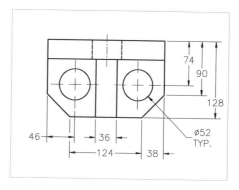

Figure 4-56b *Top view of the model*

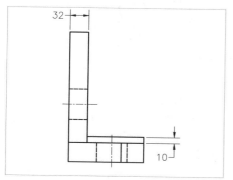

Figure 4-56c *Left-side view of the model*

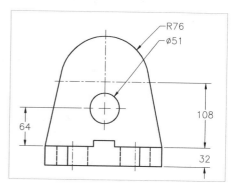

Figure 4-56d *Front view of the model*

It is clear that the model is a combination of various extruded sketched features. Also, all sketched features are created on different sketch planes. The base feature is created on the default XY plane. The remaining features are added to the base feature. Whenever you start creating a model, you need to first determine the number of features in it and then the sequence in which they will be created. The model for this tutorial consists of three features, including the base feature. The steps used to complete this model are listed next.

a. Create the base feature with two holes on the XY plane, refer to Figure 4-58.
b. Define a new sketch plane on the back face of the base feature and create the join feature with a hole, refer to Figure 4-60.
c. Define a new sketch plane on the front face of the model and create the rectangular join feature, refer to Figure 4-62.

Creating and Dimensioning the Sketch for the Base Feature

1. Start Autodesk Inventor and then start a new metric standard part file.

   As mentioned earlier, whenever you start a new part file, by default, you start sketching on the XY plane. In this tutorial, the base feature will be created on the XY plane. Therefore, you can directly start drawing the sketch when you start the new file.

2. Draw the sketch for the model using various sketching tools.

3. Add the required constraints and dimensions to the sketch to make it fully constrained, as shown in Figure 4-57.

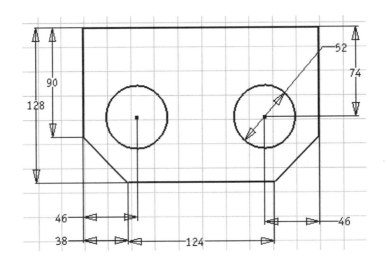

Figure 4-57 Sketch for the base feature

4. Choose the **Return** button in the **Inventor Standard** toolbar to exit the sketching environment.

Extruding the Base Sketch

As mentioned earlier, it is recommended that you change the current view to isometric view before creating the feature.

1. Press the F6 key to change the current view to isometric view.

2. Using the **Extrude** tool, extrude the sketch to a distance of 32 mm.

Because the sketch has multiple loops, you need to specify the profile that is to be extruded. Make sure you define it by specifying a point outside the circles but inside the outer loop.

3. Using the drop-down list in the **Inventor Standard** toolbar, change the material of the model to Metal-AL-6061 (Polished). Modify the drawing display area, if required. The model, after changing the material, is shown in Figure 4-58.

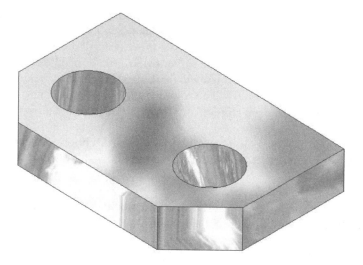

Figure 4-58 *Base feature of the model*

Creating the Feature on the Back Face of the Base Feature

To create the feature on the back face of the base feature, you first need to define the sketch plane on the back face.

1. Using the **Rotate** tool, rotate the model such that the back face of the model is visible.

2. Choose the **Sketch** button from the **Inventor Standard** toolbar; you are prompted to select the plane on which the sketch will be created.

3. Select the back face of the base feature.

    As soon as you select the back face, the sketching environment is activated and the grid lines are displayed in the drawing window. Because the current view was invoked using the **Rotate** tool, it will not be a proper view for creating the sketch. This is because the **Rotate** tool is used to arbitrarily rotate the view of the model and the rotation is not to any exact value. As a result, you need to reorient the current view using the common views.

4. Choose the **Rotate** button and then right-click to display the shortcut menu. In the shortcut menu, choose **Common View**; a cube is displayed with arrows on all the vertices and faces.

5. Select the arrow that points in the middle of the face of the cube that is parallel to the back face of the base feature; the model is reoriented such that the back face is parallel to the screen. Also, the cube is now displayed as a square. Sometimes, when the model is reoriented, the X axis of the model (displayed in red in the 3D Indicator) points vertically downward. You need to reorient the model again using the cube that is still displayed in the drawing window such that the X axis becomes horizontal.

    If you move the cursor close to any of the edges of the cube, which is a square now, you will notice that they are not actually four edges but eight. This means that each edge of the square is a combination of two edges broken by the arrow. All these eight edges are used to rotate the view of the model around the current view direction. The current view direction is normal to the screen, and so the view will be rotated about an axis normal to the screen. The direction in which the model will be rotated is displayed by a small arrow that appears on the cursor when you move it close to any of the eight edges.

6. If the X axis, in your case, points vertically downward, choose the lower right vertical edge of the square to reorient the model. If it points horizontally toward the left, you can skip this step.

    You will notice that the red arrow in the 3D Indicator has become horizontal and points toward the left, suggesting that the X axis of the model is now in the horizontal direction.

7. Right-click and choose **Done** to exit the **Rotate** tool.

    Whenever you define a sketch plane to create a sketch on a planar face, you will notice that a sketch consisting of some sketcher entities is automatically drawn. This sketch will define the contour of the planar face on which you define the sketching plane. In this case, the sketch is a rectangle defining the back face of the base feature. The entities that are used to create this sketch are called **reference geometries**. These entities can participate in feature creation but cannot be dimensioned. You can use the entire sketch or some entities of this sketch and create a feature. The entities that are not required can be deleted. However, if you do not delete these entities, they will become a part of the sketch.

8. Delete both the vertical edges of the contour and the lower horizontal edge and then create the remaining portion of the sketch, refer to Figure 4-59.

9. Add the required constraints and then dimension the sketch to make it fully constrained. The sketch, after dimensioning, should look similar to the one shown in Figure 4-59.

10. Choose the **Return** button from the **Inventor Standard** toolbar and exit the sketching environment.

Extruding the Sketch

1. Change the current view to isometric and then using the **Extrude** tool, extrude the sketch to a distance of 32 mm. You need to reverse the direction of extrusion using the second button available below the **Depth** edit box. The model, after creating the feature on the back face, should look similar to the one shown in Figure 4-60.

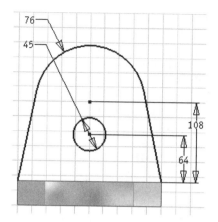

Figure 4-59 *Sketch for the feature on the back face*

Figure 4-60 *Model after creating the feature*

Creating the Sketch on the Front Face of the Base Feature

1. Choose the **Sketch** button from the **Inventor Standard** toolbar; you are prompted to select the plane on which the sketch will be created.

2. Select the front face of the base feature; the sketching environment is activated and a rectangle defining the contour of the front face will be created.

3. Choose the **Look At** button from the **Inventor Standard** toolbar and then select the front face of the base feature. Choose the **Zoom All** button to increase the drawing display area.

   The model will be reoriented such that the front face is parallel to the screen and the X axis of the model is in the horizontal direction.

4. Delete the reference geometries and draw the rectangle as the sketch for the next feature, refer to Figure 4-61. Add the **Collinear** constraint between the lower edge of the rectangle and the upper edge of the front face of the base feature.

> **Tip**. *Whenever you apply the **Collinear** constraint between one of the sketched lines and an edge, another line is created defining the linear edge selected to apply the **Collinear** constraint. It is recommended that you do not delete this line. This is because if you delete this line, the **Collinear** constraint will also be deleted along with the line.*

5. Add the required dimensions to the sketch. The sketch, after adding the dimensions and constraints, is shown in Figure 4-61.

6. Exit the sketching environment and then change the current view to isometric view.

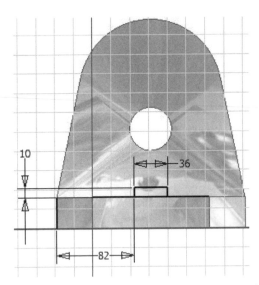

Figure 4-61 Dimensioned sketch for the feature on the front face

Extruding the Sketch

1. Choose **Extrude** from the **Part Features** panel bar to invoke the **Extrude** dialog box. Select the rectangle as the profile to be extruded.

    This feature is created using the **To** termination option from the **Distance** drop-down list in the **Extents** area.

2. Select **To** from the **Distance** drop-down list in the **Extents** area; the **Select surface to end the feature creation** button is displayed below the drop-down list. This button is chosen automatically.

3. Select the front face of the second feature as the face to terminate the current feature.

    The selected face is highlighted and turns blue. Also, the **Check to terminate feature on the extended face** check box is displayed and is selected by default. Because the current feature will terminate on the selected face, you do not need to select this check box.

4. Clear the **Check to terminate feature on the extended face** check box and then choose the **OK** button. The final model for Tutorial 1 is shown in Figure 4-62.

Saving the Model

1. Save the model with the name given below and then close the file.

    \PersonalProject\c04\Tutorial1.ipt

Note
*The holes shown in the model for Tutorial 1 can also be drawn directly using the **Hole** tool. The use of this tool will be discussed in later chapters.*

Figure 4-62 *Final model for Tutorial 1*

Tutorial 2

In this tutorial, you will create the model shown in Figure 4-63a. Its dimensions are shown in Figures 4-63b through 4-63d. After creating the model, save it with the name given below.

\PersonalProject\c04\Tutorial2.ipt   **(Expected time: 30 min)**

Before creating the model, it is important to determine the number of features in it. The model for this tutorial is a combination of a base feature and four cut features. The following steps are required to create the model:

a. Create the base feature on the YZ plane by defining a new sketch plane on it, refer to Figures 4-64 and 4-65.
b. Define a new sketch plane on the front face of the model and create the cut feature, refer to Figure 4-67.
c. Create the next cut feature by defining a new sketch plane on the back face of the model, refer to Figure 4-69.
d. Define a new sketch plane on the new face that is exposed by creating the last cut feature and create the circular cut feature, refer to Figure 4-70.
e. Create the final cut feature on the top face of the horizontal base of the first feature, refer to Figure 4-70.

Changing the Sketch Plane

The base feature for this model is an L-shaped feature. You cannot create the L-shaped base feature on the XY plane. This feature is created on the YZ plane. Therefore, you need to change the sketching plane before drawing the sketch.

1. Start a new metric standard part file. Choose the **Return** button from the **Inventor Standard** toolbar to exit the current sketching environment.

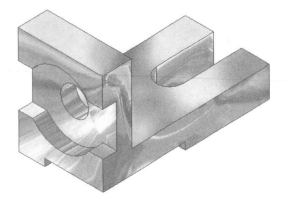

Figure 4-63a Model for Tutorial 2

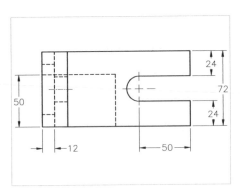

Figure 4-63b Top view of the model

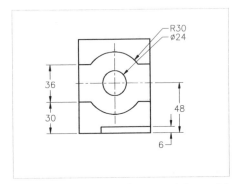

Figure 4-63c Left-side view of the model

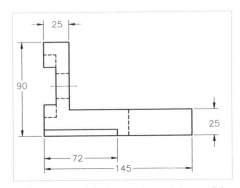

Figure 4-63d Front view of the model

This is needed to avoid drawing the sketch on the current sketching plane, which is the XY plane. It needs to be drawn on the YZ plane.

2. Change the view to the isometric view and then click on the plus sign (+) located on the left of the **Origin** folder in the browser.

   This folder expands and displays the YZ, XZ, and XY planes and the X, Y, and Z axes. The center point is also displayed.

3. Choose the **Sketch** button from the **Inventor Standard** toolbar; you are prompted to select the plane to create the sketch.

4. Select the YZ plane from the browser; the sketching environment is activated. However, the isometric view is still the current view. You need to change the current view such that the sketching plane becomes parallel to the screen.

5. Choose the **Look At** button from the **Inventor Standard** toolbar; you are prompted to select the entity to look at. Select the YZ plane from the browser.

The YZ plane will become parallel to the screen and you can draw the sketch on this plane.

Creating and Dimensioning the Sketch for the Base Feature

1. Draw the L-shaped sketch for the base feature and add the required constraints.

2. Add the dimensions to the sketch. The sketch, after adding the dimensions, is shown in Figure 4-64.

3. Choose the **Return** button from the **Inventor Standard** toolbar to exit the sketching environment. Change the current view to isometric view.

Extruding the Sketch

1. Choose the **Extrude** button from the **Part Features** panel bar to invoke the **Extrude** dialog box. Extrude the sketch to a distance of 72 mm. Use the **Mid-plane** button to extrude it.

2. Change the material of the model to Metal-AL-6061 (Polished). Choose the **Zoom All** button. The base feature is shown in Figure 4-65.

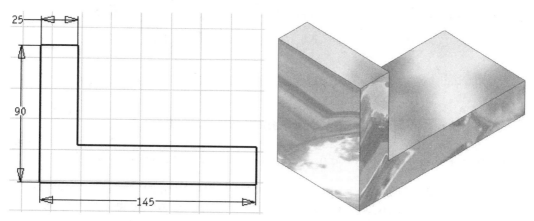

Figure 4-64   *Sketch for the base feature*   *Figure 4-65*   *Base feature*

Drawing the Sketch of the Cut Feature on the Front Face

The next feature is a rectangular cut feature and is to be created on the front face of the base feature. But before creating the feature, you need to define the sketch plane on the front face.

1. Choose the **Sketch** button from the **Inventor Standard** toolbar; you are prompted to select the sketching plane. Select the front face of the base feature; the sketching environment is activated.

2. Using the **Common View** option, reorient the model. Delete the reference geometries created when you defined the sketch plane.

3. Draw the sketch for the cut feature and then add the required constraints and dimensions to it. The dimensioned sketch is shown in Figure 4-66.

4. Choose the **Return** button from the **Inventor Standard** toolbar and then change the current view to isometric.

Creating the Cut Feature on the Front Face of the Model

1. Extrude the profile defined by the rectangle to a distance of 50 mm using the **Cut** operation. The isometric view of the model with the cut feature is shown in Figure 4-67.

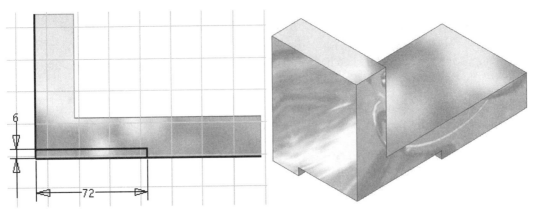

Figure 4-66 *Sketch for the cut feature*   *Figure 4-67* *Model after creating the cut feature*

Creating the Sketch for the Cut Feature on the Left Face

The next feature is the cut feature and is to be created on the left face of the model. Before creating the sketch, you need to define the sketch plane on the left face.

1. Choose the **Sketch** button from the **Inventor Standard** toolbar; you are prompted to select the plane for creating the sketch. Select the left face of the model; the sketching environment is activated.

2. Choose the **Look At** button from the **Inventor Standard** toolbar and select the left face of the model; the model will be reoriented such that the left face becomes parallel to the screen.

3. Delete all the reference geometries and then draw the sketch for the cut feature. Add the required constraints and dimension the sketch, as shown in Figure 4-68.

4. Exit the sketching environment and then change the current view to isometric.

Extruding the Sketch to Create the Cut Feature

1. Extrude the profile to a distance of 12 mm using the **Cut** operation. The model, after creating this cut feature, is shown in Figure 4-69.

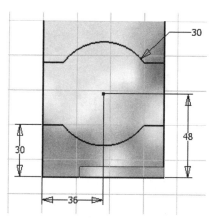

Figure 4-68 *Sketch for the cut feature*

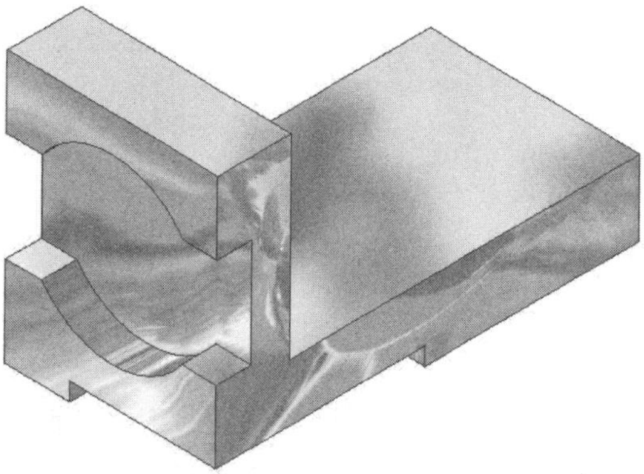

Figure 4-69 *Model after creating the cut feature*

Creating the hole

1. Define a new sketch plane on the face that is exposed after creating the last cut feature.

2. Draw the circle and then add dimensions to it, refer to Figure 4-63c for the dimensions. Extrude it using the **Cut** operation. Select the **All** option from the **Distance** drop-down list in the **Extents** area.

Creating the Last Cut Feature

1. Define a sketch plane on the horizontal face of the base feature and then reorient the model using the **Common View** options.

2. Delete all the reference geometries and then create the sketch for the cut feature, refer to Figure 4-63b for dimensions. Add the required constraints and dimensions to the sketch.

3. Extrude the sketch using the **Cut** operation. Use the **All** option from the **Distance** drop-down list in the **Extents** area. The final model for Tutorial 2 is shown in Figure 4-70.

Saving the Model

1. Save the sketch with the name given below.

   \PersonalProject\c04\Tutorial2.ipt

2. Choose **File > Close** from the menu bar to close this file.

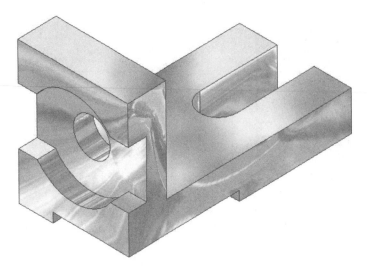

Figure 4-70 Solid model for Tutorial 2

Tutorial 3

In this tutorial, you will create the model shown in Figure 4-71a. Its dimensions are shown in Figures 4-71b through 4-71d. Change the material of the model to Metal-AL-6061 (Polished). Save the model with the name given below.

\PersonalProject\c04\Tutorial3.ipt   **(Expected time: 45 min)**

The model for this tutorial is a combination of three join features, including the base feature, and six cut features (holes). The following steps are required to create this model:

a.   Create the base feature on the YZ plane, refer to Figure 4-73.
b.   Create the next join feature on the top face of the base feature, refer to Figure 4-75.
c.   Create a work plane at an offset of 10 mm from the bottom face of the second join feature. Define a new sketch plane on this work plane and create the cylindrical join feature, refer to Figure 4-77.
d.   Create a hole in the cylindrical feature by defining a new sketch plane on the top face of the cylindrical feature, refer to Figure 4-78.
e.   Create two holes by defining a sketch plane on the left face of the model, refer to Figure 4-78.
f.   Define a new sketch plane on the top face of the groove on the top face of the model and create three holes on it, refer to Figure 4-78.

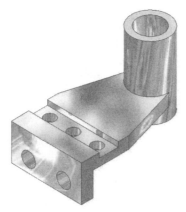

Figure 4-71a Model for Tutorial 3

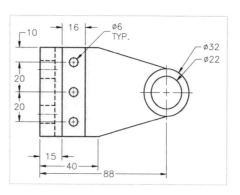

Figure 4-71b Top view of the model

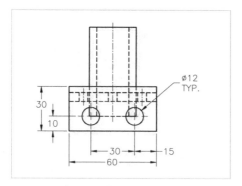

Figure 4-71c Left-side view of the model

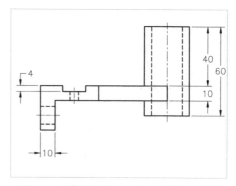

Figure 4-71d Front view of the model

Creating the Base Feature

1. Start a new metric standard part file and choose the **Return** button to exit the sketching environment.

2. Change the current view to isometric view and then click on the plus sign (+) located on the left of the **Origin** folder in the browser; the default planes, axes, and center point are displayed.

3. Choose the **Sketch** button from the **Inventor Standard** toolbar; you are prompted to select the plane to create the sketch. Select the YZ plane; the sketcher environment is activated.

4. Choose the **Look At** button from the **Standard** toolbar and then select the YZ plane from the browser; the current view will be reoriented such that the YZ plane is now parallel to the screen.

5. Create the sketch for the base feature and then add the required constraints and dimensions. The dimensioned sketch for the base feature is shown in Figure 4-72.

6. Exit the sketching environment and then change the current view to isometric. Choose the **Extrude** button from the **Part Features** panel bar; the **Extrude** dialog box will be displayed.

    Because the sketch has a single loop, it will be automatically selected.

7. Extrude the sketch to a distance of 60 mm using the **Mid-plane** option.

8. Change the material of the feature to Metal-AL-6061 (Polished). The base feature is shown in Figure 4-73.

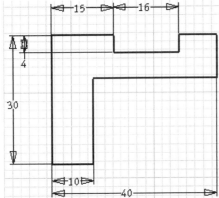

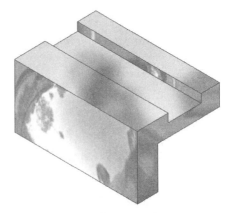

Figure 4-72 Sketch for the base feature   *Figure 4-73 Base feature*

Creating the Next Join Feature on the Top Face

1. Choose the **Sketch** button from the **Inventor Standard** toolbar and select the top face of the base feature as the new sketching plane.

2. Reorient the view using the **Common View** option. Draw the sketch for the next feature and add the required constraints and dimensions, as shown in Figure 4-74.

3. Exit the sketching environment and change the current view to isometric.

4. Extrude the sketch to a distance of 10 mm, see Figure 4-75.

Creating the Cylindrical Feature

As shown in Figure 4-71d, the cylindrical feature starts at a distance of 10 mm below the bottom face of the feature you just created. Because it is not possible to define a sketch plane at an offset, you need to define a work plane and use it to draw the sketch. As mentioned earlier, the work plane can be defined at an offset from the selected planar face. In this model, the planar face will be the bottom face of the second feature. But first, you need to change the orientation of the model such that the bottom face of the second feature is visible.

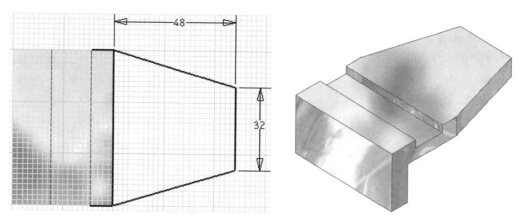

Figure 4-74 *Sketch for the second feature*   **Figure 4-75** *Model after creating the next feature*

1. Reorient the model using the **Rotate** tool such that the bottom face of the second feature is visible.

2. Choose **Work Plane** from the **Part Features** panel bar. Select the bottom face of the second feature and then drag the cursor down. As soon as you start dragging the mouse, the **Offset** toolbar is displayed. Release the left mouse button when the **Offset** toolbar is displayed.

3. Enter **10** as the offset distance in the **Offset** toolbar and press ENTER; a work plane is created at an offset of 10 mm from the bottom face of the second feature.

4. Choose the **Sketch** button from the **Inventor Standard** toolbar and select the work plane as the plane for drawing the sketch for the cylindrical feature. Reorient the model using the **Common View** option. Increase the drawing display area using the **Zoom All** tool, if required.

5. Draw a circle and then add the required constraints and dimensions to it, see Figure 4-76.

6. Exit the sketching environment and then change the current view to isometric.

7. Extrude the sketch to a distance of 60 mm in the upward direction. Increase the drawing display area.

    After extruding the sketch, you will notice that the work plane is still visible in the drawing window. Because the work plane is not required, you need to turn off its visibility. This is done using the browser.

8. Right-click on **Work Plane1** in the browser to display the shortcut menu.

    In the shortcut menu, there will be a check mark in front of the **Visibility** option. This suggests that the work plane is visible in the drawing window.

9.   Choose the **Visibility** option in the shortcut menu; the check mark is cleared and the work plane is no more displayed. Figure 4-77 shows the model after turning off the visibility of the work plane and changing the view to isometric.

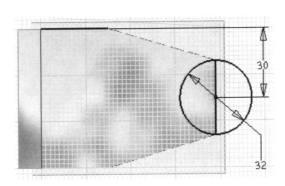

Figure 4-76 Sketch for the cylindrical feature

Figure 4-77 Model after creating the cylindrical feature

Creating the Remaining Cut Features

1.   Create the remaining cut features by creating their respective sketches on the sketching planes. The final model, after creating all the cut features, is shown in Figure 4-78.

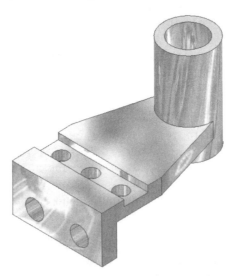

Figure 4-78 Final model for Tutorial 3

Saving the Model

1.   Save the model with the name given below and then close the file.

\PersonalProject\c04\Tutorial3.ipt

Self-Evaluation Test

Answer the following questions and then compare your answers with those given at the end of this chapter:

1. In mechanical designs, all features are created on the XY plane. (T/F)

2. As soon as you select a sketching plane, the sketching environment is activated. (T/F)

3. You cannot define a sketch plane on the circular face of a cylindrical feature. (T/F)

4. The visibility of the shared sketches is turned off by default. (T/F)

5. The work axes are the _____ lines passing through the model or the feature.

6. The _____ tool and the _____ option are used to reorient the model such that the selected plane becomes parallel to the screen.

7. While defining a work plane, when you select a planar face or plane and start dragging it, the _____ toolbar is displayed.

8. The features that are created while you are inside the process of creating some other feature are called _____ features.

9. When you select the **To Next** option in the **Extrude** dialog box, the _____ button will not be provided along with the two direction buttons.

10. The _____ planes are not visible on the screen, whereas the _____ planes are visible on the screen as well as in the browser.

Review Questions

Answer the following questions:

1. Whenever you open a new file, by default you start drawing in the XY plane. (T/F)

2. You can create a work plane tangent to a cylinder by selecting the cylindrical face and then the XY, YZ, or XZ plane to which the resulting work plane should be parallel. (T/F)

3. You can create a work axis on a cylindrical feature by directly selecting it. (T/F)

4. The **All** option in the **Distance** drop-down list of the **Extents** area in the **Extrude** dialog box cannot be combined with the **Join** operation. (T/F)

5. A consumed sketch can be used again for creating another feature. (T/F)

6. Which of the following features is not a work feature?

    (a) Work Line   (b) Work Axis
    (c) Work Plane   (d) Work Point

7. How many planes are displayed when you click on the plus sign on the left of the **Origin** folder in the browser?

    (a) 2   (b) 3
    (c) 4   (d) 1

8. Which one of the following options of the shortcut menu is used to turn off the display of the work features?

    (a) **Display**   (b) **Show**
    (c) **Visible**   (d) **Visibility**

9. Which of the following operations is used to create a feature by retaining the material common to the existing feature and the sketch?

    (a) **Cut**   (b) **Join**
    (c) **Intersect**   (d) None

10. In Autodesk Inventor, you can create a work axis using how many methods?

    (a) Four   (b) Five
    (c) Six   (d) Three

Exercises

Exercise 1

Create the model shown in Figure 4-79. Its dimensions are also given in the same figure. Save the model with the name given below.

\PersonalProject\c04\Exercise1.ipt   **(Expected time: 45 min)**

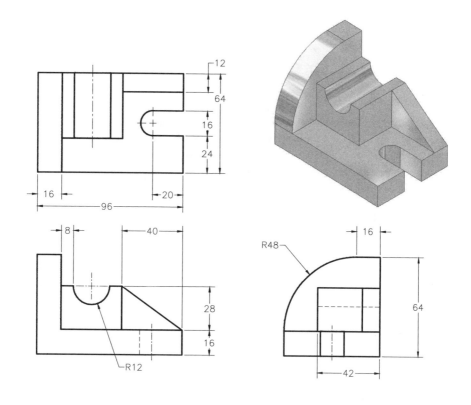

Figure 4-79 *Model for Exercise 1 and its dimensions*

Exercise 2

Create the model shown in Figure 4-80. Its dimensions are given in Figures 4-81a and 4-81b. Save the model with the name given below.

\PersonalProject\c04\Exercise2.ipt   **(Expected time: 30 min)**

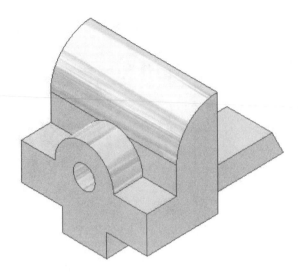

Figure 4-80 *Solid model for Exercise 2*

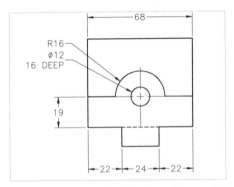

Figure 4-81a *Left-side view of the model*

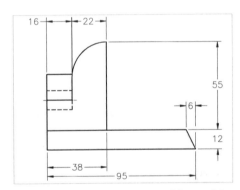

Figure 4-81b *Front view of the model*

Exercise 3

Create the model shown in Figure 4-82. Its dimensions are also given in the same figure. Save the model with the name given below.

  \PersonalProject\c04\Exercise3.ipt   **(Expected time: 30 min)**

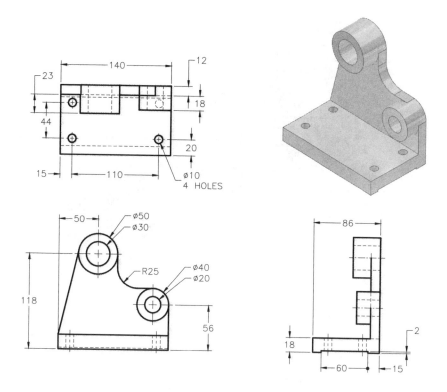

Figure 4-82 *Model for Exercise 3 and its dimensions*

Exercise 4

Create the model shown in Figure 4-83. Its dimensions are given in the views shown in Figure 4-84. After creating the model, save it with the name *\PersonalProject\c04\Exercise4.ipt*.

(Expected time 45 min)

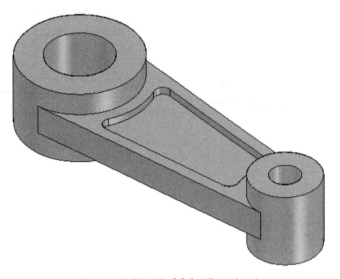

Figure 4-83 *Model for Exercise 4*

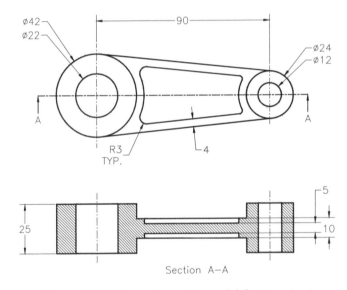

Figure 4-84 *Dimensions of the model for Exercise 4*

Chapter 5

Advanced Modeling Tools-I

Learning Objectives

After completing this chapter, you will be able to:
- *Use the Hole tool for creating various types of holes.*
- *Fillet edges of a model.*
- *Chamfer edges of a model.*
- *Mirror features.*
- *Create rectangular patterns of features.*
- *Create circular patterns of features.*
- *Create rib features.*
- *Thicken or offset faces or surfaces.*
- *Emboss or engrave sketched entities on a feature.*
- *Use the Decal tool to transfer an image on a feature.*

ADVANCED MODELING TOOLS

Autodesk Inventor has provided a number of advanced modeling tools to assist you in creating a design. These advanced modeling tools appreciably reduce the time taken in creating the features in the models, thus reducing the designing time. For example, to create a hole in a cylindrical feature, one option is that when you sketch the cylindrical feature, you sketch the hole at the same time. But, to edit the dimensions of the hole, you will have to edit the complete sketch. Also, if the hole is drawn along with the sketch of the cylindrical feature, it will be extruded to the same distance. However, if you want the hole to terminate before the end of the cylindrical feature, you will have to draw another sketch. But if you use the **Hole** tool, you can directly create various types of holes and control their depth along with the other parameters. The advanced modeling tools in Autodesk Inventor are listed next.

1.	**Hole**	13.	**Coil**
2.	**Fillet**	14.	**Thread**
3.	**Chamfer**	15.	**Shell**
4.	**Mirror**	16.	**Face Draft**
5.	**Rectangular Pattern**	17.	**Split**
6.	**Circular Pattern**	18.	**Boundary Patch**
7.	**Rib**	19.	**Trim and Extend Surface**
8.	**Thicken/Offset**	20.	**Stitch Surface**
9.	**Emboss**	21.	**Replace Face**
10.	**Decal**	22.	**Delete Face**
11.	**Sweep**	23.	**Move Face**
12.	**Loft**	24.	**Sculpt**

In this chapter, the first ten advanced modeling tools will be discussed. The remaining tools will be discussed in later chapters.

Tip. *To show additional toolbars, right-click on any toolbar and choose **Customize** from the shortcut menu. The **Customize** toolbar is displayed. Choose the **Toolbars** tab and then select the required toolbar from the **Toolbars** list box. Next, choose the **Show** button. The selected toolbar will be shown on the screen.*

Note
All features created using the advanced modeling tools are parametric in nature and can be modified at any time.

Creating Holes

Toolbar:	Part Features > Hole
Panel Bar:	Part Features > Hole

Holes are circular cut features that are created on an existing feature. Holes are generally provided for the purpose of accommodating fasteners in the assembly. In an assembly, other components such as bolts or shafts are inserted into holes. When you invoke this tool, the **Hole** dialog box will be displayed, as shown in Figure 5-1. You can create simple, counterbore, or countersink holes using the **Hole** tool. You can also specify whether the

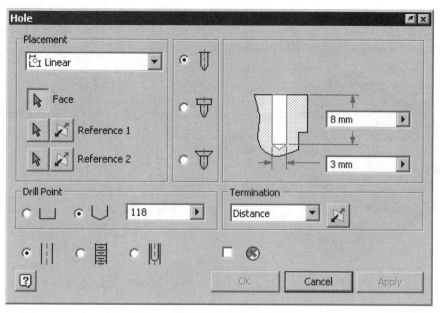

Figure 5-1 *The* **Hole** *dialog box*

hole is a simple hole, tapped hole, or clearance hole, using the options in the **Hole** dialog box. The options in this dialog box are discussed next.

Placement Area

The options in this area are used to specify the placement of the hole. These options are discussed next.

Linear

If there is no unconsumed sketch in the model, this option is selected by default in the drop-down list in the **Placement** area. This option is used to place the hole by defining its location from two linear edges in the model. When you select this option, the **Face** button will be available in this area and will be chosen. As a result, you will be prompted to select a planar face or work plane as the placement plane. As soon as you select the placement plane, the **Reference 1** button will be chosen and you will be prompted to select a linear edge to reference the dimension. On selecting the linear edge, the **Edge Dimension** toolbar will be displayed, in which you can specify the first distance. After specifying the first distance, the **Reference 2** button will be chosen and you will be prompted to select a linear edge to reference the dimension. When you select the second linear edge, the **Edit Dimension** toolbar will be displayed, in which you can modify the dimension from the second edge. Figure 5-2 shows the preview of a hole placed using two linear edges.

From Sketch

This option is used to select points/hole centers, endpoints, or center points in an unconsumed sketch to place the hole and is selected by default if there is an unconsumed sketch in the model. When you select this option, the **Centers** button will be automatically chosen in the **Placement** area. If the sketch has a hole center, it will be automatically selected to place the hole. But to use endpoints or center points, you need to select them manually. Figure 5-3 shows the preview of a hole placed as the hole center.

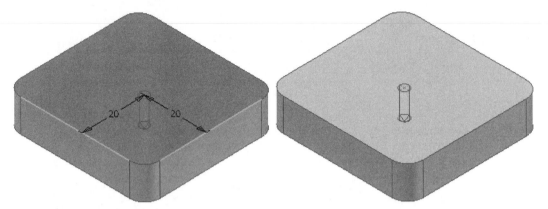

Figure 5-2 Hole placed using two linear edges   *Figure 5-3* Hole placed on a hole center

Concentric
This option is used to place the hole concentric to a circular feature in the model. When you select this option, the **Plane** button will be chosen in the **Placement** area and you will be prompted to select a planar face or work plane as the reference plane. This is the plane where the hole should be placed. After you select the placement plane, the **Concentric Reference** button will be chosen and you will be prompted to select a circular edge or cylindrical face to reference the hole center. Figure 5-4 shows the preview of a hole placed concentric to the cylindrical face of the fillet feature.

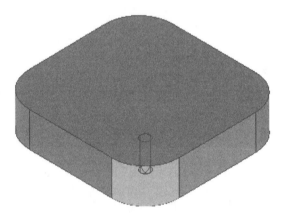

Figure 5-4 Hole placed concentric to the fillet

On Point
This option is used to place the hole on a work point. In addition to selecting the work point, you also need to select a planar face or a work plane, the normal direction of which will define the direction of the hole. You can also use an edge or an axis to define the hole direction. When you invoke this option, you will be prompted to select a work point for the hole placement. After selecting the work point, the **Direction** button will be chosen in the **Placement** area and you will be prompted to select a planar face, work plane, edge, or axis. Figure 5-5 shows the preview of a hole placed on a work point with the direction defined using the top planar face. Figure 5-6 shows the preview of the hole at the same work point but the direction is defined by the side planar face.

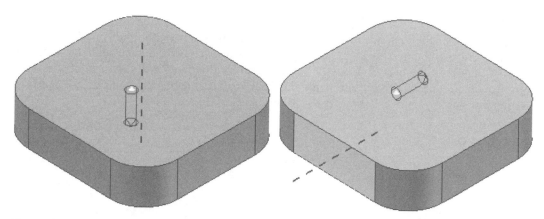

Figure 5-5 *Direction defined using the top plane*   ***Figure 5-6*** *Direction defined using the side plane*

Drilled

This is the first radio button in the area on the right of the **Placement** area. This radio button is selected by default and is used to create a drilled hole. A drilled hole is one that has a uniform diameter throughout its length. The hole diameter and depth has to be specified in the preview window on the right side of this dialog box. Figure 5-7 shows the section view of a drilled hole.

Counterbore

This radio button is available below the **Drilled** radio button and is selected to create a counterbore hole. A counterbore hole is a stepped hole and has two diameters: a bigger diameter and a smaller diameter. The bigger diameter is called the counterbore diameter and the smaller diameter is called the drill diameter. In this type of hole, you also have to specify two depths. The first depth is the counterbore depth. The counterbore depth is the depth up to which the bigger diameter will be defined. The second depth is the depth of the hole, including the counter depth. All these values are defined in the preview window on the right side of the **Hole** dialog box. Figure 5-8 shows the section view of a counterbore hole.

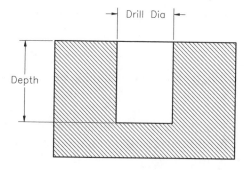

Figure 5-7 *Section view of a drilled hole*

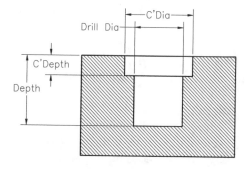

Figure 5-8 *Section view of a counterbore hole*

Countersink

This radio button is provided below the **Counterbore** radio button and is used to create a countersink hole. A countersink hole also has two diameters, but the transition between the bigger diameter and the smaller diameter is in the form of a tapered cone. You need to define the countersink diameter, drill diameter, depth of the hole, and the countersink angle. Figure 5-9 shows the sectioned view of a countersink hole.

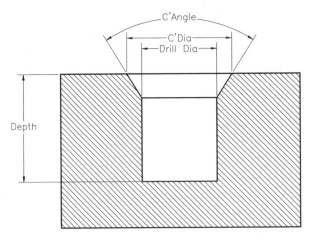

Figure 5-9 Section view of a countersink hole

Drill Point Area

The options in the **Drill Point** area are used to specify whether the end of the hole will be a flat or a tapered face. The options are discussed next.

Flat

If this radio button is selected, the end of the hole will be a flat plane.

Angle

If this radio button is selected, the end of the hole will be tapered and will converge to a point. The angle of the taper can be defined in the **Drill Point Angle** edit box provided on the right of this radio button. Figure 5-10 shows a countersink hole with a tapered end.

Termination Area

The drop-down list provided under this area is used to define the termination of the holes.

Distance

This option is used to create a hole by defining its depth up to a certain distance. The value of the depth of the hole is defined in the preview window. You can reverse the hole direction by choosing the **Flip** button below this drop-down list.

Through All

The **Through All** option is used to create a hole that is cut through all features. The hole

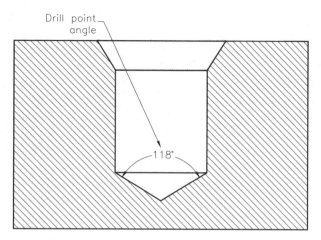

Figure 5-10 Countersink hole with a tapered end

direction can be reversed using the **Flip** button. When you select this option, the hole depth is no more displayed in the preview window because the hole will be automatically created by cutting through all the features in the specified direction.

To

The **To** option is used to terminate the hole feature at a specified plane, planar face, or an extended face. When you select this option, the **Flip** button is replaced by the **Select surface to end the feature creation** button. Using this button, you can select the face to terminate the hole feature.

Simple Hole

This check box is selected by default and is used to create simple holes.

Tapped Hole

The **Tapped Hole** radio button is selected to create threaded holes. When you select this radio button, the **Hole** dialog box expands and displays the **Threads** area, as shown in Figure 5-11. This area provides the options to create a tapped hole. These options are discussed next.

Thread Type

The **Thread Type** drop-down list is used to select the type of threads. You can select the default type of threads in this drop-down list.

Size

This drop-down list is used to select the nominal size of the threads. The designation and the class value will be different for different nominal sizes.

Designation

This drop-down list is used to specify the designation of the thread profile.

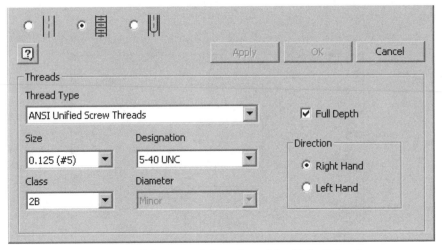

*Figure 5-11 The expanded portion of the **Hole** dialog box*

Class

The **Class** drop-down list is used to select the class of threads. Also, higher the numeric value in this drop-down list, the more accurate is the fitting.

Diameter

The **Diameter** drop-down list is used to specify whether the diameter defined for creating the threads is the major, minor, pitch, or drill diameter of the original hole. Note that you can change this value only using the **Modeling** tab of the **Document Settings** dialog box. This dialog box can be invoked by choosing **Tools > Document Settings**.

Full Depth

If the **Full Depth** check box is selected, the threads will run through the length of the hole. If this check box is not selected, you will have to specify the depth up to which the threads will be created. This depth is defined in the preview window on the right side of the **Hole** dialog box.

Direction Area

The options in the **Direction** area are used to specify the direction of the threads. These options are discussed next.

Right Hand

The **Right Hand** radio button is used to create right-handed threads. A right-handed thread enters a nut when you turn it in the clockwise direction.

Left Hand

The **Left Hand** radio button is used to create left-handed threads. A left-handed thread enters a nut when you turn it in the counterclockwise direction.

Figure 5-12 shows a hole without threads and Figure 5-13 shows a hole with threads.

Figure 5-12 *A counterbore hole without threads*   *Figure 5-13* *A counterbore hole with threads*

Clearance Hole

The **Clearance Hole** radio button is selected to create clearance holes for accommodating standard fasteners. When you select this radio button, the **Hole** dialog box expands and displays the **Fastener** area, as shown in Figure 5-14.

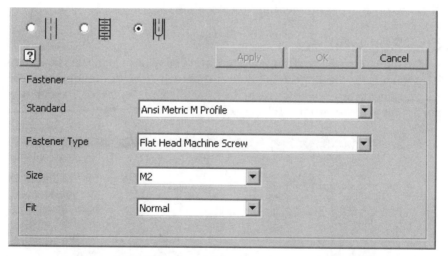

Figure 5-14 *The expanded portion of the* **Hole** *dialog box*

This area provides the options to create a tapped hole. These options are discussed next.

Standard
The **Standard** drop-down list is used to select the standard of the fastener to be accommodated in the hole.

Fastener Type
The **Fastener Type** drop-down list is used to select the type of fastener to be accommodated in the hole.

Size
This drop-down list is used to select the size of the fastener.

Fit
This drop-down list is used to specify the type of hole fit.

Infer iMates
This check box is selected to create an iMate on the hole feature.

Creating Fillets

Toolbar:	Part Features > Fillet
Panel Bar:	Part Features > Fillet

In Autodesk Inventor, you can add fillets or rounds using the **Fillet** tool. Fillets are generally used to apply curves on the interior edges of a model and result in concave surfaces by adding material. Rounds are generally used to apply curves on the exterior edges and result in convex surface by removing the material.

From this release onward, you can create three types of fillets: edge fillets, face fillets, and full round fillets. All these types of fillets are discussed next.

Creating Edge Fillets
To create edge fillets, invoke the **Fillet** tool; the **Fillet** dialog box will be displayed, as shown in Figure 5-15. By default, the **Edge Fillet** button is chosen close to the top left corner of this dialog box. As a result, the options to create the edge fillet are displayed. The options available under various tabs to create an edge fillet are discussed next.

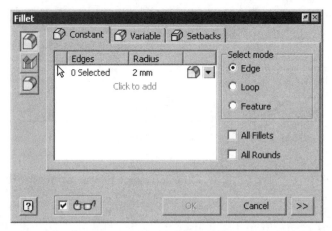

*Figure 5-15 The options in the **Constant** tab to create the edge fillets*

Constant Tab
The options under this tab are used to fillet the selected edges such that they have a constant radius throughout their length. However, different edges can have a different fillet radius.

Edges

When you invoke the **Fillet** tool, the **Fillet** dialog box will be displayed and you will be prompted to select an edge to be blended. The number of edges you select will be displayed under this column. However, note that all the edges selected will have the same fillet radius. If you want to specify a different fillet radius to some edges, click on the text **Click to add**; another row will be added. Now, if you select an edge, it will be displayed in the second row. The second row can be assigned a different fillet radius.

Radius

You can specify the fillet radius for the selected edges in this column. Different rows can have different radii.

Continuity

This drop-down list is available on the right of the **Radius** column in the list box. You can select the option to apply a tangent continuity or smooth continuity by selecting the options in this drop-down list.

Select Mode

The options under this area are used to set the priorities of selection for filleting.

Edge. If the **Edge** radio button is selected, you can select the individual edges of a model for filleting. As you move the cursor close to any of the edges, it will be highlighted.

Loop. The **Loop** radio button is used to select all the edges of a face of the model. To use this option, move the cursor close to an edge of the face; all its edges will be highlighted. Click at this stage to select all the edges of the face. Remember that edges selected using this option will have the same fillet radius.

Feature. If the **Feature** option is selected, all edges in the selected feature will be selected for filleting. In this case also, all the selected edges will be applied the same fillet radius.

All Fillets

The **All Fillets** check box is selected to apply the fillet to all the interior edges of a model. Note that the fillet radius will be the same at all places. Figure 5-16 shows a model with fillets.

All Rounds

The **All Rounds** check box is selected to apply the rounds to all the exterior edges of a model. All the exterior corners will also be curved if you select this check box. The radius for all the rounds will be the same. Figure 5-17 shows a model with rounds.

Enable/Disable feature preview

This check box is selected to enable or disable the preview of the fillet feature. If this check box is selected, the preview of the fillet will be displayed in the drawing window.

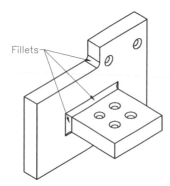

Figure 5-16 *Creating fillets*

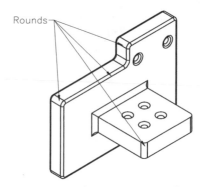

Figure 5-17 *Creating rounds*

Variable Tab

The options in the **Variable** tab (Figure 5-18) are used to fillet the selected edges such that they can be applied different radii along their length. If you select a linear or a curved edge, there will be two points on the edge, one at the start point and one at the end point. However, if you select a circular edge, no point will be defined. You can add points by specifying their desired location on the edge.

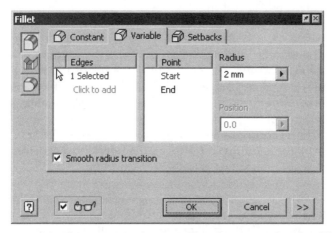

Figure 5-18 *The options in the **Variable** tab to create the edge fillets*

Edges

This column displays the number of edges selected to be filleted. You can select more edges by clicking on **Click to add**.

Point

This column displays the points selected on the edge. By default, there will be only two points, **Start** and **End**, at the start point of the edge and at the endpoint, respectively, of a linear or curved edge. To add a point, move the cursor on the edge; the preview of the point is displayed. Click to place the point. As soon as you add a point by specifying its location on the edge, it will be added in this column. Similarly, you can add as many points as required on the edge. As mentioned earlier, if you select a circular edge for adding a variable fillet, no point will be added by default. You need to add all the points manually by clicking on the edge.

Radius

The **Radius** edit box displays the radius of the point selected in the **Point** column. This edit box will not be available until you select a point in the **Point** column. To define a variable radius, select a point and then enter the value of the fillet radius in this edit box.

Position

This edit box is used to define the position of the point selected in the **Point** column. Remember that the position is defined in terms of the percentage of the selected edge. This edit box will not be available until you select a point other than the default points in the **Point** column. The length of the selected edge is taken as 1 (100 percent) and the position of the new point will be defined anywhere between 0 and 1. For example, a value of 0.5 will suggest that the point is placed at the midpoint of the edge.

Figures 5-19 and 5-20 show the variable filleting of the edges of a model.

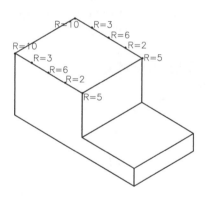
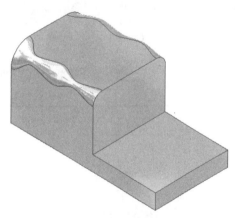

Figure 5-19 Defining the fillet radius   *Figure 5-20 Model after creating the fillet*

Smooth radius transition

This check box is selected to allow the smooth transition between all the points you have defined in the edge. If this check box is selected, there will be a smooth blending between all the points. If it is cleared, the blending will be linear, see Figure 5-21 and Figure 5-22.

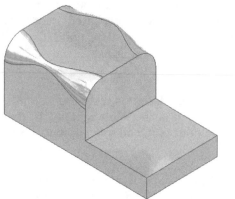

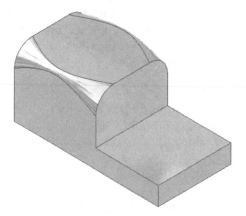

Figure 5-21 *Smooth transition*   *Figure 5-22* *Linear transition*

Setbacks Tab

The options in the **Setbacks** tab (Figure 5-23) are used to specify the setbacks of the transition between the three edges that comprise a vertex. The setback smoothly blends the transition surfaces between the selected edges and the vertex that you define to fillet. To add a setback fillet, you need to first select three edges that intersect at a corner using the **Constant** tab and then invoke the **Setbacks** tab. The options in this tab are discussed next.

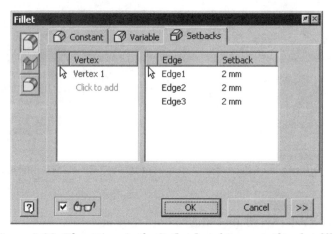

Figure 5-23 *The options in the **Setbacks** tab to create the edge fillet*

Vertex

After you have selected three edges using the **Constant** tab, invoke this tab; you will be prompted to select the common vertex to add the setback. Select the vertex common to the three selected edges. The selected vertex will be displayed in this column. You can also add more vertices by clicking on **Click to add**.

Edge

This column displays the edges common to the vertex selected in the **Vertex** column. The edge that will have the arrow in front will be highlighted in the drawing window.

Setback

This column displays the setback value for the transition along the edge selected in the **Edge** column. You can modify this value by clicking on it.

Figures 5-24 and 5-25 show the fillet created using different setback values.

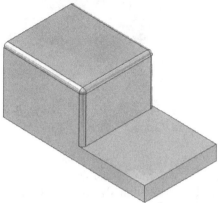 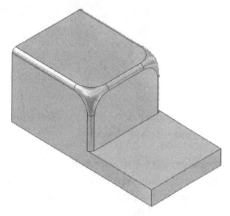

Figure 5-24 *Fillet with setback =2*   *Figure 5-25* *Fillet with setback =10*

 Note
*Using the **Setbacks** tab, you cannot set the radius of the fillet. It will be set in the **Constant** tab where you have selected the edges.*

More

This is the button with two arrows provided on the lower right corner of the **Fillet** dialog box. When you choose this button, the **Fillet** dialog box expands, providing you with more options, see Figure 5-26. All these options are discussed next.

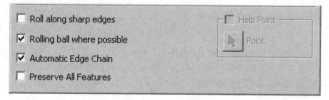

*Figure 5-26 The **More** options of the **Fillet** dialog box*

Roll along sharp edges

This check box is selected to modify the radius of the fillet in order to retain the shape and the sharpness of the edges of the adjacent faces. If this check box is cleared, the adjacent faces will extend in case the fillet radius is more than what can be adjusted in the current face. Figure 5-27 shows the fillet created with the **Roll along sharp edges** check box cleared and Figure 5-28 shows the fillet created with this check box selected.

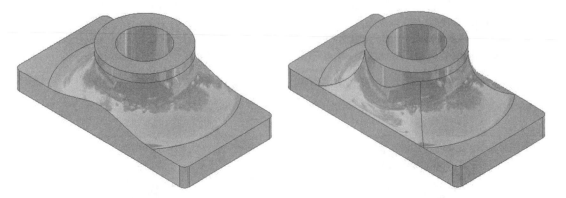

*Figure 5-27 Fillet created with the **Roll along sharp edges** check box cleared*

*Figure 5-28 Fillet created with the **Roll along sharp edges** check box selected*

Rolling ball where possible
This check box is selected to create a rolling ball fillet, wherever possible. If this check box is cleared, the transition at the sharp corners will be continuously tangent. Figure 5-29 shows the rolling ball fillet created by selecting this check box and Figure 5-30 shows the tangent fillet created by clearing it. Note that you need to select all the edges in a single fillet sequence to use this option.

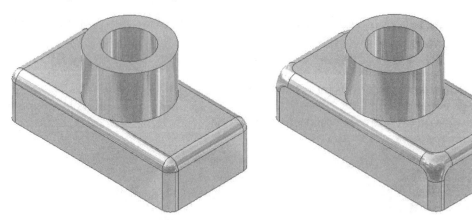

Figure 5-29 Rolling ball fillet

Figure 5-30 Tangent fillet

Automatic Edge Chain
If this check box is selected, all the tangent edges will also be selected when you select an edge to fillet. This button will be available only when no edge is selected.

Preserve All Features
This check box is selected to calculate the intersection of all the features that intersect

with the fillet. If this check box is cleared, the intersection of only the edges that are a part of the fillet will be calculated.

Creating Face Fillets

You can choose the **Face** button provided close to the top left corner of the **Fillet** dialog box to create fillet between two faces. It blends the first face with the second face. In doing so, it adds or removes the material according to the geometric conditions. It can also completely or partially remove the faces to accommodate the fillet. To create this fillet, choose the **Face Fillet** button available below the **Edge Fillet** button on the top left corner of the dialog box. When you do so, the option to create the face fillet will be displayed in the dialog box, as shown in Figure 5-31, and you will be prompted to select faces to blend. The options used to create a face fillet are discussed next.

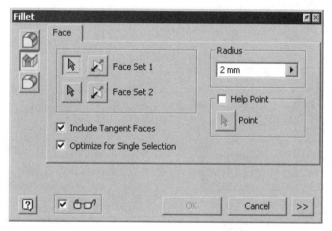

Figure 5-31 The options to create the face fillet

Face Set 1

This button is chosen by default when you choose the **Face Fillet** button and is used to select the first face to create the face fillet. You can choose the **Flip** button on the right of this button to reverse the direction in which the fillet will be created. As soon as you select the first face, it will be highlighted in blue and the **Face Set 2** button will be chosen. If you have to select multiple faces to create the fillet, you need to clear the **Optimize for Single Selection** check box available in this dialog box.

Face Set 2

This button is used to select the second face to create the face fillet. You can choose the **Flip** button on the right of this button to reverse the direction in which the fillet will be created. The face that you select as the second face to blend will be highlighted in green.

Radius Area

The edit box available in this area is used to specify the face fillet radius. If the default value specified in this edit box is valid to create the fillet, the preview of the fillet will also be displayed as soon as you select the face set 2.

Include Tangent Faces

If this check box is selected, all faces tangent to the selected face sets will also be selected to create the fillet.

Optimize for Single Selection

If this check box is selected, the **Face Set 2** button is automatically chosen when you select the first face to fillet. If this check box is cleared, you can select multiple faces.

Help Point Area

This area is available when you choose the **More** button. When you select the check box in this area, the **Point** button will be enabled. This button is used to create help points on one of the faces selected to be filleted.

Figure 5-32 shows the faces to be selected to create the face fillet and Figure 5-33 shows the resulting face fillet.

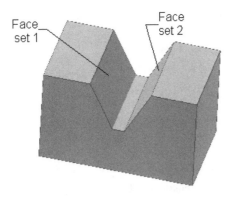

Figure 5-32 Faces selected to be filleted   *Figure 5-33 The resulting face fillet*

Creating Full Round Fillet

A full round fillet is a semicircular fillet created between two side faces that are separated by a centre face. In this case, the system determines the required radius value, based on the side faces and center face. To create this type of fillet, choose the **Full Round** button available below the **Face Fillet** button close to the top left corner of the **Fillet** dialog box. When you do so, the options for creating the full round fillet will be displayed in the dialog box, as shown in Figure 5-34, and you will be prompted to select faces to blend. The options that will be used to create a full round fillet are discussed next.

Side Face Set 1

This button is chosen by default and is used to select the first side face. As soon as you select the first side face, the **Center Face Set** button is chosen. The side face 1 is highlighted in blue.

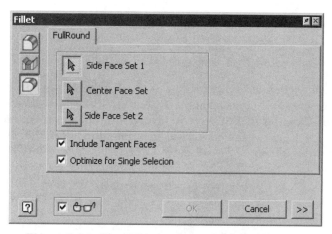

Figure 5-34 *The options to create the full round fillet*

Center Face Set

This button is chosen to specify the center face for the full round fillet. Note that this face will be removed from the fillet. As soon as you select the first side face, the **Center Face Set** button is chosen. The center face is highlighted in green.

Side Face Set 2

This button is chosen to specify the second side face. As soon as you select the second side face, the preview of the fillet will be displayed. The side face 2 is highlighted in purple.

Figure 5-35 shows the faces selected to create the full round fillet and Figure 5-36 shows the resulting fillet.

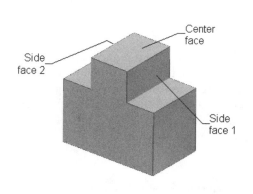

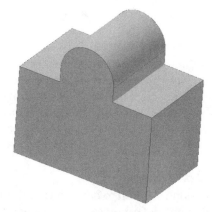

Figure 5-35 *Faces selected to be filleted*   **Figure 5-36** *The resulting face fillet*

 Note
The remaining options to create the full round fillet are the same as those discussed while creating the face fillet.

Creating Chamfers

Toolbar: Part Features > Chamfer
Panel Bar: Part Features > Chamfer

 Chamfering is defined as the process of bevelling the sharp edges of a model in order to reduce the stress concentration. In Autodesk Inventor, the chamfers are created using the **Chamfer** tool. When you invoke this tool, the **Chamfer** dialog box will be displayed, as shown in Figure 5-37, and you will be prompted to select the edges to be chamfered. The options under this dialog box are discussed next.

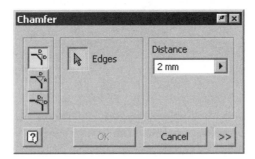

Figure 5-37 The **Chamfer** *dialog box*

Distance

This is the first button in the dialog box and is provided on the upper left corner of the **Chamfer** dialog box. This button is chosen to create a chamfer such that the distance of the selected edge is equal from both the faces. The chamfer thus created will be at a 45-degree angle. Since both the distance values are the same, therefore, there will be only one edit box in the **Distance** area. You can specify the chamfer distance in it.

Distance and Angle

This is the second method of creating chamfers. This option is used to create a chamfer by defining one distance and one angle. On choosing this button to create a chamfer, you will be prompted to select the face to be chamfered. This is the face from which the angle will be calculated. After selecting the face, you will be prompted to select the edge to be chamfered. The distance and the angle value can be specified in their respective edit boxes. These edit boxes will be displayed in the **Distance** area when you choose this button.

Two Distances

This button is chosen to create a chamfer using two different distances. The distances can be specified in the **Distance1** and **Distance2** edit boxes that are displayed in the **Distance** area when you choose this button. The face along which the distance 1 value will be calculated will be highlighted. You can select the other face by choosing the **Flip** button. This button is available below the **Edge** button.

Figure 5-38 shows the model before chamfering and Figure 5-39 shows the model after chamfering.

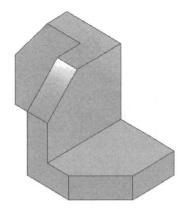

Figure 5-38 *Model before chamfering*   *Figure 5-39* *Model after chamfering*

More

This is the button with two arrows and is provided on the lower right corner of the dialog box. When you choose this button, the **Chamfer** dialog box will expand, displaying more options, see Figure 5-40. These options are discussed next.

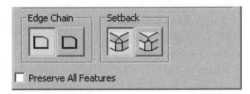

Figure 5-40 *The **More** options*

Edge Chain Area

The buttons in this area are used to set the priorities for selecting the edges to be chamfered. If you select the first button, all the edges that are tangent to the selected edge will also be selected for chamfering. If you choose the second button, the tangent edges will be ignored. These buttons will be available only when no edge is selected.

Setback Area

The buttons in this area are used to specify whether or not the setback will be applied to the model. If you choose the first button, the setback will be applied and the vertex will be flattened. However, if you choose the second button, the setback will not be applied and the vertex will be pointed. Figure 5-41 shows the chamfer created with a setback and Figure 5-42 shows the chamfer without a setback.

Note

*The **Preserve All Features** check box is the same as that discussed in the **Fillet** dialog box.*

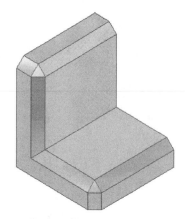

Figure 5-41 *Chamfer with a setback*

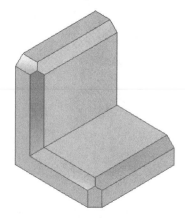

Figure 5-42 *Chamfer without a setback*

Mirroring Features and Models

Toolbar: Part Features > Mirror
Panel Bar: Part Features > Mirror

This tool is used to create a mirrored copy of selected features or to mirror the entire model using a mirror plane. The plane that can be used to mirror the features can be a planar face or a work plane. An exact replica of the selected entities will be created at a distance from the mirror plane. This distance will be equal to the distance between the original selected entities and the mirror plane. When you invoke this tool, the **Mirror** dialog box will be displayed, as shown in Figure 5-43, and you will be prompted to select the feature to be patterned. The options in the **Mirror** dialog box are discussed next.

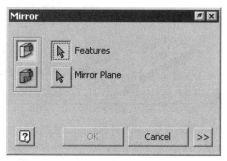

Figure 5-43 *The **Mirror** dialog box*

Mirroring Features

To mirror features, choose the **Mirror individual features** button. The **Features** button will be chosen and you will be prompted to select the feature to be patterned. Select the features that you want to mirror. Next, choose the **Mirror Plane** button and select the mirror plane about which the selected features will be mirrored; the preview of the mirrored features will be displayed. Figure 5-44 shows the features selected for mirroring and Figure 5-45 shows the model created by mirroring the features.

Mirroring Models

To mirror the entire model, choose the **Mirror the entire solid** button; the entire model will be selected and highlighted. Also, the **Mirror Plane** button will be chosen and you will be prompted to select a plane to mirror about. You can choose the **Include Work Features** button to select the work features that you want to mirror. Selecting the **Remove Original** check box

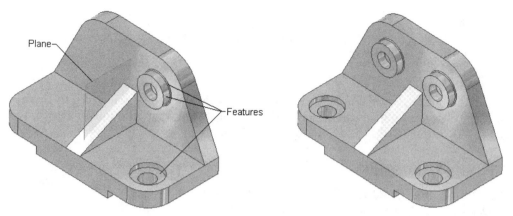

Figure 5-44 *Selecting features to be mirrored and the mirror plane*

Figure 5-45 *Model after mirroring the features and hiding the work plane*

allows you to remove the original model after mirroring. Figure 5-46 shows the model selected to be mirrored, the highlighted mirror plane, and the preview of the mirrored model. Figure 5-47 shows the mirrored model.

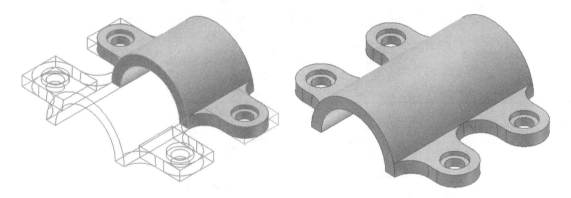

Figure 5-46 *Selecting a model to be mirrored and the mirror plane*

Figure 5-47 *Resulting model after mirroring the entire model*

More

This is the button with two arrows and is provided on the lower right corner of the **Mirror Pattern** dialog box. If you choose this button, the **Mirror Pattern** dialog box expands, providing you with more options, see Figure 5-48. These options are discussed next.

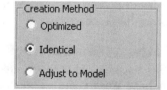

Figure 5-48 *The **More** options*

Optimized

This radio button is available only when you are mirroring the entire model. This radio button is selected to mirror the model as the direct copy of the original model.

Identical

This radio button is selected, if you want the mirrored feature to be exactly similar to the original feature, even if it intersects other features.

Adjust to Model

This radio button is available only when you mirror features and is selected if the feature to be mirrored terminates on a face of the model. In this case, the mirror feature will modify its termination such that it adjusts in the model.

Creating Rectangular Patterns

Toolbar:	Part Features > Rectangular Pattern
Panel Bar:	Part Features > Rectangular Pattern

You can use the **Rectangular Pattern** tool to create a rectangular pattern of the selected features or surfaces, or the entire model. When you invoke this tool, the **Rectangular Pattern** dialog box will be displayed, as shown in Figure 5-49.

*Figure 5-49 The **Rectangular Pattern** dialog box*

Pattern individual features

This button is chosen to create a pattern of the selected features. You can select the features using the **Features** button that is available on the right of this button.

Pattern the entire solid

This button is chosen to select the entire model to create a pattern. You can choose the **Include Work Features** button on the right of this button to select the work features that you want to include in the pattern of the model.

Direction 1/Direction 2 Area

The options in the **Direction 1** and **Direction 2** areas are similar to those discussed in the **Rectangular Pattern** dialog box in the sketching environment. The only option that are extra in these areas are the **Midplane** check boxes and the drop-down lists. These options are discussed next.

Midplane

This check box is selected to place the items symmetrically on both sides of the original feature. If there are even number of items in the pattern, the additional item is placed on the side in which the direction arrow points.

Spacing

The **Spacing** option, which is the default option, is used to specify the gap between the items in terms of the spacing between individual items.

Distance

The **Distance** option is used to specify the gap between the items in terms of the total distance between all the items along the current direction. The value entered in the **Spacing** edit box will be taken as the total distance between all the items.

Curve Length

The **Curve Length** option is used to select the length of the edge selected to define direction 1 or 2 as the distance between all the items in the array. When you select this option, the **Spacing** edit box is not enabled.

Figure 5-50 shows the hole selected for creating a rectangular pattern and Figure 5-51 shows the model after creating a rectangular pattern.

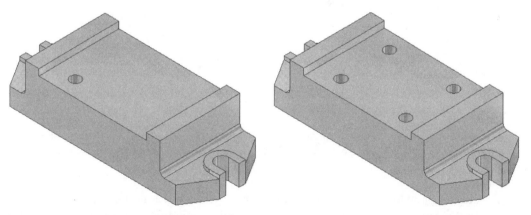

Figure 5-50 *Model before creating the pattern*   ***Figure 5-51*** *Model after creating the pattern*

When you choose the **More** button provided on the lower right corner of the dialog box, it expands and provides more options, as shown in Figure 5-52. These options are discussed next.

Direction 1/Direction 2 Area

The **Start** buttons in these areas are used to specify the start point of the path along the first or second direction. You can use this option in association with the **Curve Length** option. For

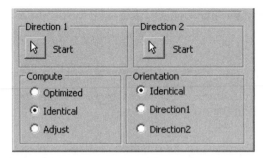

Figure 5-52 *More options of the* ***Rectangular***
Pattern *dialog box*

example, when you define the first and second directions using the edges, two green points are displayed. These points specify the start points of the path along both the directions. Now, select the **Curve Length** option and then using this button, select the endpoint of the edge that was selected to define the direction. You will notice that the preview of the rectangular pattern along the current direction is no more displayed and the value in the **Spacing** is set to 0. This is because the endpoint of the curve used to define the distance is also defined as the start point. Because the start point of the curve is the same as the endpoint, the length of the curve is forced to zero. You can change the start point back to the original point using the **Start** button to restore the placement of the items along the current direction.

Compute Area

The options under this area are discussed next.

Optimized

The **Optimized** radio button is used to create optimized pattern instances for a lesser calculation time. This option is not useful while working on complex patterns such as when the pattern instances are intersected by some other features.

Identical

The **Identical** radio button is selected, if you want the patterned features to be exactly similar to the original feature, even if they intersect other features.

Adjust

The **Adjust** radio button is selected if any of the patterned feature terminates at a face of the model. In this case, the patterned features will be modified such that they adjust in the model. But the pattern calculation time in such cases is longer.

Orientation Area

The options under this area are discussed next.

Identical

The **Identical** radio button is selected to specify the orientation of the patterned items the same as that of the original item.

Direction 1

The **Direction 1** radio button is selected to orient the items with reference to the first direction.

Direction 2

The **Direction 2** radio button is selected to orient the items with reference to the second direction.

Note

*All instances of the rectangular pattern are displayed under the heading **Rectangular Pattern** in the browser. Click on the plus sign (+) located on the left of the pattern feature in the browser to expand the tree view. You can select any of the instances and right-click and choose **Suppress** to turn off the display of that instance in the model.*

*The remaining options in the **Rectangular Pattern** dialog box are similar to those discussed under the **Rectangular Pattern** dialog box in Chapter 3.*

For a better understanding of the **Orientation** options, create a pattern only in the first direction and use a circular edge to define the first direction. Now, one by one, set the orientation to Identical and Direction 1 and notice the difference in the orientation of the items. For example, Figure 5-53 shows the preview of the rectangular pattern oriented using the **Identical** option and Figure 5-54 shows the preview of the rectangular pattern oriented using the **Direction1** option. Note that in both these options, the first direction of the pattern is defined using the circular edge.

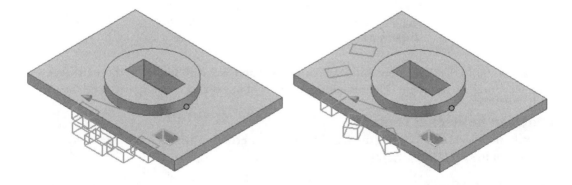

*Figure 5-53 Preview of the pattern oriented using the **Identical** option*

*Figure 5-54 Preview of the pattern oriented using the **Direction1** option*

Note

In Figures 5-53 and 5-54, the pattern is created only along one direction, which is defined by the circular edge of the cylindrical feature.

Creating Circular Patterns

Toolbar:	Part Features > Circular Pattern
Panel Bar:	Part Features > Circular Pattern

 In the Part module, you can use the **Circular Pattern** tool for arranging the selected features around an imaginary cylinder, thus creating a circular pattern. When you invoke this tool, the **Circular Pattern** dialog box will be displayed, see Figure 5-55.

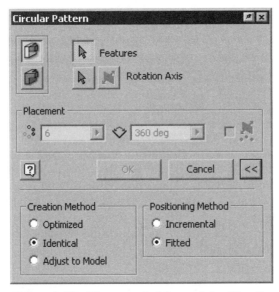

*Figure 5-55 The expanded form of the **Circular Pattern** dialog box*

Most options in the **Placement** and **Positioning Method** areas are similar to those discussed in the sketching environment. The remaining options of this dialog box are discussed next.

Pattern individual features

This button is chosen to select the features to be patterned. This button is chosen by default when you invoke this dialog box.

Pattern the entire solid

This button is chosen to pattern the entire solid. You can also select the work features to be patterned along with the solid by choosing the **Include Work Features** button.

Rotation Axis

The **Rotation Axis** button is chosen to select the axis about which the features will be arranged. The entities that can be selected as the rotation axis include a work axis or a linear edge of any face of the model. You can also select a cylindrical feature, the central axis of which will be selected as the axis of rotation.

Midplane

This check box is selected to place the items symmetrically on both sides of the original feature. If there are even number of items in the pattern, the additional item is placed on the side in which the direction arrow points.

Creation Method Area

The options under this area will be displayed, when you choose the button with two arrows provided in the lower right corner of this dialog box. These options are discussed next.

Optimized

The **Optimized** radio button is used to create optimized pattern instances for a lesser calculation time. This option is not useful while working on complex patterns such as when the pattern instances are intersected by some other features.

Identical

This radio button is selected, if you want the patterned features to be exactly similar to the original feature, even if they intersect other features.

Adjust to Model

This radio button is selected if any patterned feature terminates at a face of the model. In this case, the patterned features will be modified such that they adjust in the model.

Figure 5-56 shows a model before creating the circular pattern and Figure 5-57 shows the model after creating it. In this case, the cylindrical feature is selected for defining the axis of rotation. By doing so, you will select its central axis as the axis of rotation.

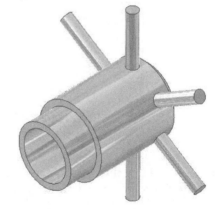

Figure 5-56 Model before creating the pattern   *Figure 5-57 Model after creating the pattern*

Creating Rib Features

Toolbar:	Part Features > Rib
Panel Bar:	Part Features > Rib

 Ribs are defined as thin wall-like structures used to bind the joints together so that they do not fail under an increased load. In Autodesk

Inventor, ribs are created using an open profile, see Figures 5-58 and 5-59.

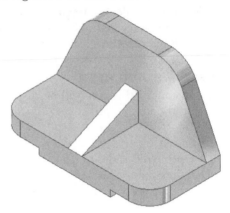

Figure 5-58 *Sketch for the rib feature*   *Figure 5-59* *The rib feature*

Remember that before invoking the **Rib** tool, you must have an unconsumed sketch. When you invoke the **Rib** tool, the **Rib** dialog box will be displayed, see Figure 5-60.

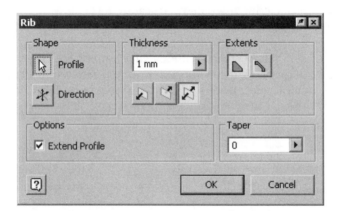

Figure 5-60 *The **Rib** dialog box*

Using this dialog box, you can create a rib or a web. A web is similar to a rib, with the only difference being that the web is an open feature. Web features are created by adding material to a specified distance. The options under this dialog box are discussed next.

Shape Area

The options under this area are used to select the profile of the rib or the web feature and the direction of the feature creation. These options are discussed next.

Profile

The **Profile** button is chosen to select the sketch of the rib or the web feature. If there is a single unconsumed sketch, it will be automatically selected when you invoke this tool.

Direction

The **Direction** button is chosen to define the direction, in which the rib or the web feature will be created. The feature can be created in a direction normal to the selected sketch or parallel to it. If you move the cursor close to the selected sketch, the directions will be displayed using green arrows. A dynamic preview of the resulting feature can also be seen along with the direction. Note that the rib feature will be successful only if it is created in the direction, in which it intersects the existing model faces.

Thickness Area

The options under this area are used to define the thickness of the rib or the web feature. The thickness is specified in the **Thickness** edit box. This area also has three buttons that are used to define the direction, in which the thickness will be applied. You can apply the thickness on either side of the sketch or equally on both sides.

Extents Area

The buttons in this area are used to specify whether the feature will be extended to the next face or to a specified distance. The two buttons in this area are discussed next.

To Next

If this button is chosen, the rib or the web feature will be created such that it merges with the next face, see Figure 5-61.

Finite

The **Finite** button is chosen to create the rib or the web feature to a specified distance, see Figure 5-62. The distance is specified in the **Extent** edit box that will be displayed in this area when you choose the **Finite** button. The direction is controlled using the **Direction** button in the **Shape** area.

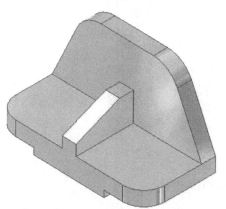

Figure 5-61 Rib created by extending the sketch to the next face

Figure 5-62 Rib created by extending the sketch to a specified distance

Extend Profile

This check box will be displayed below the **Shape** area when you select the direction to apply the thickness parallel to the sketch or choose the **Finite** button from the **Extents** area. If the sketch of the rib feature does not intersect with a face of the model, and this check box is selected, the rib feature will be extended such that it intersects the face of the model.

Taper
This edit box in this area is used to specify the taper angle for the rib. Note that you can specify the taper angle only if the rib is being created normal to the plane on which the profile of the rib is sketched.

Thickening or Offsetting the Faces of Features

Toolbar:	Part Features > Thicken/Offset
Panel Bar:	Part Features > Thicken/Offset

You can thicken a specified face or offset it using the **Thicken/Offset** tool. You can achieve the resulting output as a solid face or a surface. You can also use this tool to offset or thicken a surface. The resulting feature can be a surface or a solid face of the specified thickness. When you invoke this tool, the **Thicken/Offset** dialog box is displayed. The options provided in the various tabs of this dialog box are discussed next.

Thicken/Offset Tab
The options in the **Thicken/Offset** tab, shown in Figure 5-63, are discussed next.

*Figure 5-63 The **Thicken/Offset** tab of the **Thicken/Offset** dialog box*

Select
The **Select** button is chosen to select the face or the surface to thicken or offset. When you invoke the **Thicken/Offset** dialog box, this button is chosen by default and you are prompted to select faces.

Distance

The **Distance** edit box is used to specify the offset distance or the thickness value of the resulting feature. Note that you are also allowed to offset a selected face or a surface with a zero distance, making a copy at the same location. However, in this case, the output can only be a surface.

Filter Area

This area is above the **Output** area and it provides two radio buttons. The **Face** radio button is selected to restrict the selection to the faces of the solid models. The **Quilt** radio button is selected to restrict the selection to the surfaces only. Note that if you select the **Face** radio button, you can also select a surface. This is because a surface is also considered as a face.

Output Area

The two buttons in the **Output** area are used to specify the output of the **Thicken/Offset** tool. If you choose the **Solid** button, the resulting feature will be a solid face. If you choose the **Surface** button, the resulting feature will be a surface.

Figure 5-64 shows a surface and Figure 5-65 shows a solid face created by offsetting it surface. The offset distance is 4 mm.

Figure 5-64 *Original surface*   *Figure 5-65* *Solid face created by offsetting the surface by a distance of 4 mm*

Figure 5-66 shows the output of this tool in the form of an offset surface. The offset distance in this case also is 4 mm.

Operation Area

This is the area with three buttons and is located on the right of the **Output** area. The buttons in this area are used to specify the resulting operation that will be performed using this tool. Note that these options will not be available if the output of this tool is a surface. The three buttons in this area are **Join**, **Cut**, and **Intersect**. The functions of these buttons are the same as those discussed in the **Extrude** dialog box. The **Join** button is chosen to create a join feature, **Cut** button to create a cut feature, and **Intersect** button to

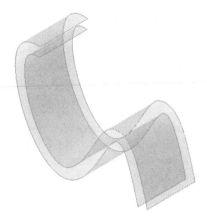

Figure 5-66 *Output in the form of a surface*

create an intersect feature. Figure 5-67 shows a feature created by offsetting the top face of the base feature using the **Join** operation. Figure 5-68 shows the feature created by offsetting the same face using the **Cut** operation.

Figure 5-67 *Offsetting the top face using the* **Join** *operation*

Figure 5-68 *Offsetting the top face using the* **Cut** *operation*

Note
As evident in Figures 5-67 and 5-68, the resulting feature is always created normal to the selected face or surface.

Direction Area
This area with three buttons is located on the right of the **Operation** area. The buttons in it are used to specify the direction, in which the resulting feature will be created.

More Tab
The options in the **More** tab, shown in Figure 5-69, are discussed next.

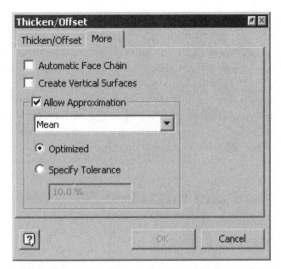

Figure 5-69 *The **More** tab of the **Thicken/Offset** dialog box*

Automatic Face Chain

This check box is used to automatically select all the tangent faces that form a chain with the selected face. To use this option, invoke the **Thicken/Offset** dialog box and then choose the **More** tab. Select this check box and then select the face using the **Select** button in the **Thicken/Offset** tab. You will notice that all the tangent faces that form a chain with the selected face are automatically selected.

Create Vertical Surfaces

This check box is used to create the vertical sides of the internal surfaces. Remember that this option is available only if the output of this tool is a surface. Also, it works only if the original face selected to be offset is a surface. Figure 5-70 shows a surface selected to be offset and Figure 5-71 shows the resulting offset surface with the side faces created by selecting the **Create Vertical Surfaces** check box. Note that the original surface selected to offset in this case is removed.

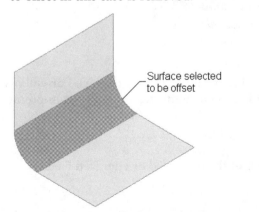

Figure 5-70 *Surface selected to be offset*

Figure 5-71 *Resulting surface with side faces*

Allow Assumptions

This check box is selected to allow Autodesk Inventor to make some assumptions if the exact thicken or offset solution of the model cannot be determined. When you select this check box, the options in this area will be enabled. The drop-down list in this area is used to specify the type of approximation to be made. You can select the **Mean**, **Never too thin**, or **Never too thick** option from this drop-down list. The **Optimized** radio button is selected to make an optimized approximation such that the minimum time is lost. Selecting the **Specify Tolerance** radio button allows you to specify the tolerance that will be used to make the approximation. If the tolerance is more, the time required to compute the feature will be increased.

Creating Embossed and Engraved Features

Toolbar:	Part Features > Emboss
Panel Bar:	Part Features > Emboss

The **Emboss** tool allows you to create an embossed or an engraved feature. This tool is generally used to emboss or engrave text on an existing feature. When you invoke this tool, the **Emboss** dialog box is displayed, as shown in Figure 5-72. The options in this dialog box are discussed next.

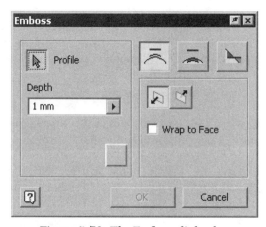

Figure 5-72 The **Emboss** dialog box

Profile

The **Profile** button is chosen to select the profile or the text to be engraved or embossed. When you invoke this dialog box, this button is chosen automatically and you are prompted to select the profile.

Depth

The **Depth** edit box is used to enter the depth of the embossed or engraved feature.

Top Face Color

The **Top Face Color** button is chosen to assign a different color for the top face of the embossed or engraved feature. When you choose this button, the **Color** dialog box will be displayed. This dialog box has a drop-down list that you can use to select a color to assign to the top face of the new feature.

Emboss from Face
The **Emboss from Face** option is used to create an embossed feature. The selected profile or text is projected on a face and then a join feature is created. The shape of the join feature is defined using the profile or text selected to be embossed. Note that the depth you define is calculated from the plane on which the feature is created and not from the sketching plane. Figure 5-73 shows a model with embossed text.

Engrave from Face
The **Engrave from Face** option is used to create an engraved feature. The selected profile or text is projected on a face and then a cut feature is created. A material equivalent to the shape of the profile or text is removed from the feature on which it is projected. Figure 5-74 shows a model with an engraved text.

Figure 5-73 *Embossed text*   *Figure 5-74* *Engraved text*

Emboss/Engrave from Plane
The **Emboss/Engrave from Plane** option is used to create an embossed as well as an engraved feature at the same time. The profile or the text is extruded in both the directions of the sketch plane. When you select this option, the **Taper** edit box appears in the **Emboss** dialog box. You can enter the taper value for the emboss/engrave feature in it. Note that when you choose this button, the **Depth** edit box is not displayed. Figure 5-75 shows a model with the embossed/engraved text.

Flip Direction
Choose the **Flip Direction** buttons to reverse the direction of the embossed or engraved features.

Wrap to Face
The **Wrap to Face** check box is selected to wrap the embossed or engraved feature around a

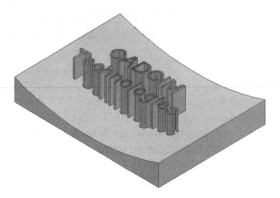

Figure 5-75 Model with embossed/engraved text

curved face, such as the face of a revolved feature. Figure 5-76 shows a bottle with an embossed text wrapped to the outer face.

Figure 5-76 Bottle with embossed text wrapped on the outer face

Transferring Images on a Feature

Toolbar:	Part Features > Decal
Panel Bar:	Part Features > Decal

 While designing a product, you may need to transfer an image to the component. The image can be the label of the company, bar code, instruction for handling the component, and so on. These images can be transferred on the feature using the **Decal** tool.

When you invoke this tool, the **Decal** dialog box is displayed, as shown in Figure 5-77. The options available in this dialog box are discussed next.

Image
The **Image** button is chosen by default when you invoke the **Decal** dialog box and is used to

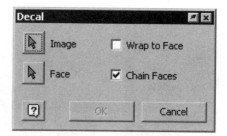

*Figure 5-77 The **Decal** dialog box*

select the image to be transferred to the feature. Note that before invoking the **Decal** tool, you need to have an image inserted using the sketching environment.

Face

The **Face** button is chosen to select the face on which the image will be transferred.

Wrap to Face

The **Wrap to Face** check box is selected to wrap the image about a circular face. This check box will not be enabled if you select a noncircular face. Figure 5-78 shows a bottle after wrapping the image on it. In this figure, the circular face of the bottle was selected as the face to transfer the image.

Figure 5-78 Image wrapped on a bottle

Chain Faces

The **Chain Faces** button is chosen to select all tangentially connected chain faces to transfer the image. Figure 5-79 shows a model with the side edges filleted and also an image. The top face of this model is selected to transfer the image. Notice that the image appears on the filleted chain faces automatically, as shown in Figure 5-80.

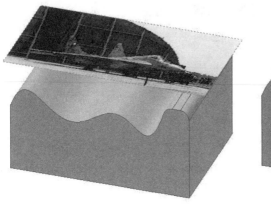

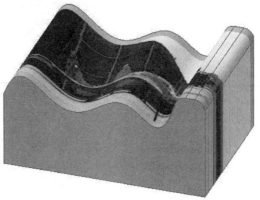

Figure 5-79 *Model and image*   *Figure 5-80* *Model after transferring the image*

TUTORIALS

Tutorial 1

In this tutorial, you will create a model of the Fixture Base shown in Figure 5-81a. Its dimensions are given in Figures 5-81b through 5-81d. After creating the model, save it with the name given below.

\PersonalProject\c05\Tutorial1.ipt   **(Expected time: 45 min)**

Before you start creating the model, it is recommended that you outline the procedure for creating it. The following steps are required to complete this tutorial:

a. Start a new part file and exit the sketching environment. Create the sketch for the base feature on the XZ plane and extrude it to a distance of 102 mm, refer to Figure 5-83.
b. Define a new sketch plane on the back face of the base feature and create the join feature, refer to Figure 5-85.
c. Create the two cylindrical features with holes on the front face of the second feature, refer to Figure 5-86.
d. Create the fillet on the base feature.
e. Using the **Hole** tool, create two counterbore holes taking the reference of the cylindrical faces of the fillets, refer to Figure 5-87.
f. Finally, draw an open sketch and convert it into a rib using the **Rib** tool to complete the model, refer to Figure 5-89.

Creating the Base Feature

As the base feature is created on the XZ plane, you need to exit the sketching environment without drawing anything. This is because if you directly start drawing the sketch in the new file, it will be created on the XY plane and not on the plane you actually want to draw on. Next, define a new sketch plane on the XZ plane for drawing the sketch.

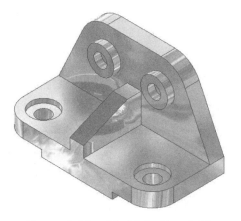

Figure 5-81a Model for Tutorial 1

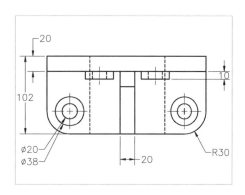

Figure 5-81b Top view of the model

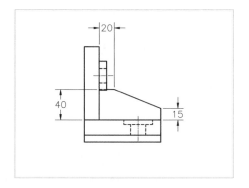

Figure 5-81c Left view of the model

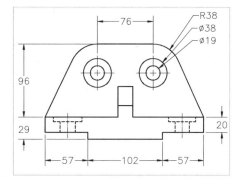

Figure 5-81d Front view of the model

1. Start a new metric standard part file and create the sketch for the base feature on the XZ plane. Add the required constraints and dimensions to it. The sketch, after adding the constraints and dimensions, is shown in Figure 5-82.

2. Exit the sketching environment and extrude the sketch to a distance of 102 mm using the **Extrude** tool to create the base feature. The base feature is shown in Figure 5-83.

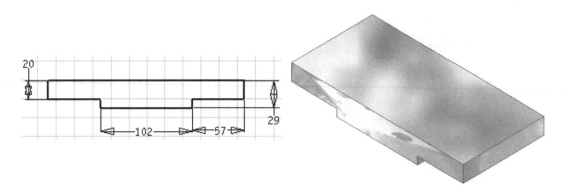

Figure 5-82 *Sketch for the base feature*   **Figure 5-83** *Base feature*

Creating a Join Feature on the Back Face of the Base Feature

1. Define a new sketch plane on the back face of the base feature. Draw the sketch for the join feature and then add the required constraints and dimensions. The sketch, after adding the constraints and dimensions, is shown in Figure 5-84.

2. Exit the sketching environment and then extrude the sketch to a distance of 20 mm. The model, after creating the join feature, is shown in Figure 5-85.

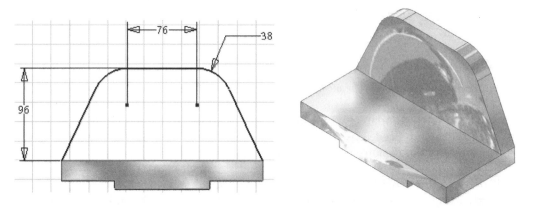

Figure 5-84 *Sketch for the join feature*   **Figure 5-85** *Model after creating the join feature*

Creating the Cylindrical Features on the Front Face of the Second Feature

To create the two cylindrical features, you can draw the sketch for both the features at the same time. Each sketch consists of two concentric circles. The reason for drawing the sketch for both the features together is that both the cylindrical features are to be extruded to the same distance.

1. Define a new sketch plane on the front face of the second feature and draw the sketch for both the cylindrical features. Extrude the sketches to a distance of 10 mm.

    While selecting the profiles for extruding, make sure that you select a point outside the inner circles but inside the outer circles. As a result, the inner circles are subtracted from the outer circles when you extrude them, thus creating the holes. The model, after creating the cylindrical features, is shown in Figure 5-86.

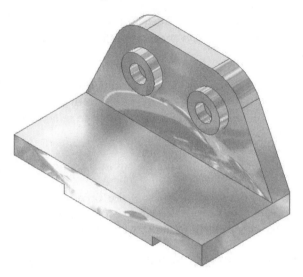

Figure 5-86 *Model after creating the cylindrical features*

Creating Fillets

The vertical edges of the front face of the base feature need to be filleted so that you can use the cylindrical faces of fillets to define the counterbore holes.

1. Choose **Fillet** from the **Part Features** panel bar; the **Fillet** dialog box is displayed. The **Constant** tab is active and you are prompted to select the edges to be blended.

2. Select the outer left and outer right vertical edges on the front face of the base feature.

    As soon as you select the edges, the **Edges** column displays 2 selected and the preview of the fillet is displayed on the model with the default radius value, which is 2 mm.

3. Click on the default radius in the **Radius** column to edit the radius value and change this value to **30**. You will notice that the fillet in the preview of the model has also increased. Choose the **OK** button to exit the **Fillet** dialog box.

Creating Counterbore Holes

As mentioned earlier, in Autodesk Inventor, holes can be created concentric to cylindrical faces. To create the two counterbore holes, you need to use the cylindrical faces of the fillet.

Because you can create only one hole at a time, you will create one of the holes and then apply it. Without closing the **Hole** dialog box, you will create the other hole.

1. Choose the **Hole** button from the **Part Features** panel bar to invoke the **Hole** dialog box.

2. Select the **Counterbore** radio button from the area on the right of the **Placement** area.

3. Select **Concentric** from the drop-down list in the **Placement** area; the **Plane** button is chosen in the **Placement** area and you are prompted select planar face or work plane for the placement plane.

4. Select the top planar face of the base feature as the face to place the hole; the preview of the counterbore hole with the current values is displayed. Also, the **Concentric Reference** button is automatically chosen and you are prompted to select circular edge or cylindrical face to reference hole center.

5. Select the cylindrical face of the fillet on the right; the preview of the hole is relocated.

6. Select **Through All** from the drop-down list in the **Termination** area. Modify the value of the counterbore diameter in the preview window to **38**. Similarly, modify the value of the bore diameter to **20** and counterbore depth to **6**.

7. Choose the **Apply** button to create the hole but retain the **Hole** dialog box.

8. Similarly, using the options already set in the **Hole** dialog box, create a hole concentric to the fillet on the left.

9. Choose **Done** to exit the **Hole** dialog box. The model, after creating the holes, is shown in Figure 5-87.

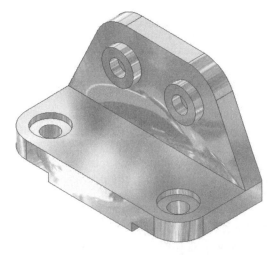

Figure 5-87 *Model after creating the fillets and the holes*

Creating the Rib Feature

The rib feature is created in the center of the model. Therefore, you need to define an offset work plane in the center on which the rib feature will be created.

1. Create a work plane at an offset from the right face of the base feature. The offset distance should be -108 mm. The negative value will ensure that the work plane is created inside the model. Choose this work plane as the sketching plane.

> **Tip**. *If the sketch plane is defined inside the model, the sketched entities are hidden by the faces of the model that are between the user and the sketch. Therefore, it is sometimes difficult to dimension such sketches. To avoid this confusing situation, Autodesk Inventor provides you with an option of temporarily slicing the portion of the model that is in between the user and the sketch. The model will be restored as soon as you exit the sketching environment. To slice the model, right-click in the drawing window and choose* **Slice Graphics** *from the shortcut menu.*

2. Draw the open sketch for the rib feature and then add the required constraints and dimensions to it. The sketch, after adding dimensions and constraints, is shown in Figure 5-88.

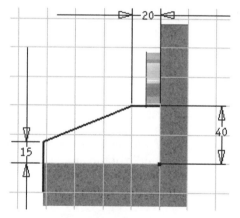

Figure 5-88 Sketch for the rib feature

When you apply the **Coincident** constraint between the lines in the sketch and the edges of the model, the lines defining the edges will be drawn. Make sure these lines are not selected when you select the sketch for the rib feature.

3. Exit the sketching environment and choose the **Rib** button from the **Part Features** panel bar to display the **Rib** dialog box; you are prompted to select the path. Select the open profile.

4. Choose the **Direction** button and move the cursor below the sketch. Click when the green arrow points downward. Set the value in the edit box in the **Thickness** area to 20 mm. Choose **OK** to exit the **Rib** dialog box. The final model, after creating all the features, is shown in Figure 5-89.

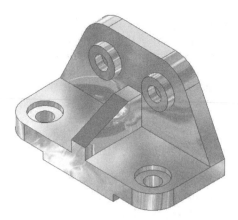

Figure 5-89 *Final model for Tutorial 1*

5.   Save the model with the name *PersonalProject**c05**Tutorial1.ipt* and close the file.

Tutorial 2

In this tutorial, you will create a model of the Pivot Base shown in Figure 5-90a. Its dimensions are given in Figures 5-90b through 5-90d. Save the model with the following name:

*PersonalProject**c05**Tutorial2.ipt*   **(Expected time: 45 min)**

The model for this tutorial is a combination of a number of join and cut features. Also, it has a rib feature and two holes. As shown in Figure 5-85a, the rib and the join feature on the right face of the model are the same as those on the left face. You will create both these features on the right of the model and then mirror them on the other side using a work plane that will be defined in the middle of the model.

The following steps are required to complete this tutorial:

a.   Create the base feature on the XZ plane, refer to Figure 5-91.
b.   Create the second feature on the back face of the base feature, refer to Figure 5-92.
c.   Create another join feature on the front face of the second feature, refer to Figure 5-93.
d.   Create the cut feature on the third feature, refer to Figure 5-94.
e.   Create a rib and a join feature on the right of the model, refer to Figure 5-95.
f.   Mirror the rib and the join feature on the left of the model, refer to Figure 5-96.
g.   Create a hole on the top face of the base feature, refer to Figure 5-97.

Creating the Base Feature

1.   Start a new metric part file and then change the sketching plane to the XZ plane.

2.   Draw the sketch for the base feature on the XZ plane. Extrude the sketch to a distance of 96 mm. The base feature of the model is shown in Figure 5-91.

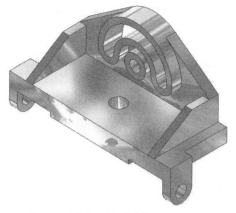

Figure 5-90a Model for Tutorial 2

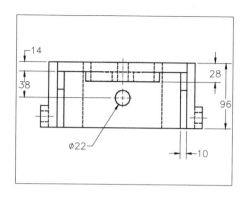

Figure 5-90b Top view of the model

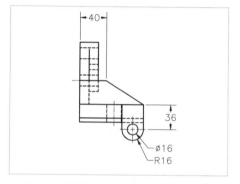

Figure 5-90c Left view of the model

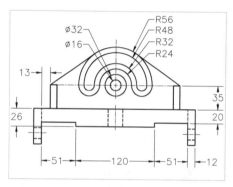

Figure 5-90d Front view of the model

Creating a Join Feature on the Back Face of the Base Feature

1. Specify a new sketch plane on the back face of the base feature and draw the sketch for the next feature on it. Extrude the sketch to a distance of 14 mm, see Figure 5-92.

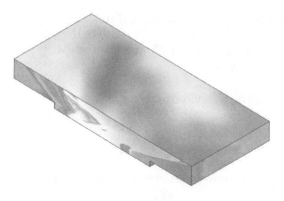

Figure 5-91 Base feature

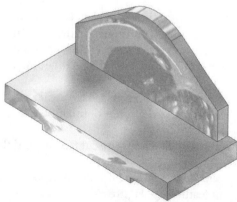

Figure 5-92 Model after creating the join feature

Creating the Join Feature on the Front Face of the Second Feature

1. Define a new sketch plane on the front face of the second feature.

2. Draw two disjoint sketches for the join feature. Extrude both the sketches to a distance of 14 mm. The model, after creating the join feature, is shown in Figure 5-93. Note that because both the sketches are extruded together, they will be displayed as a single feature in the browser.

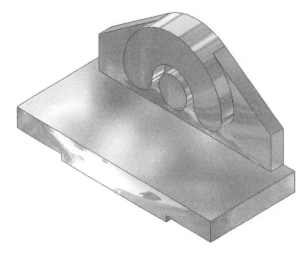

Figure 5-93 Join feature on the front face of the second feature

Creating the Cut Feature

Next, you need to create a cut feature that will remove the material from the previous feature. You can draw the two disjoint sketches for the cut feature at the same time and extrude them using the **Cut** operation. As both the sketches are to be extruded through the model, you can select both of them together while selecting the profile for creating the cut feature.

1. Define a new sketch plane on the front face of the semicircular feature.

    When you define the sketch plane on the semicircular feature, a sketch defining the semicircular feature will be drawn. Offset this sketch inside and then delete the original sketch. Since you used a reference entity to draw the inner sketch, you need to specify just one dimension value, that is the radius of any of the arcs.

    Note that the reference sketch will not be drawn on the cylindrical feature. This is because the sketch plane is not defined on it.

2. Draw the sketch for the cut feature and the circle for the hole.

3. Extrude the sketch and the circle using the **Cut** operation through the model to create the cut feature, see Figure 5-94.

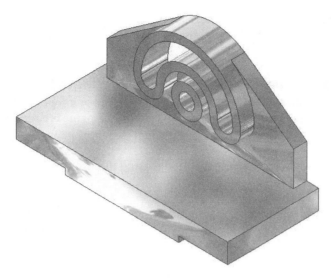

Figure 5-94 *Model after creating the cut feature*

Creating the Rib Feature

The sketch for the rib will be created on a sketch plane defined on the right face of the second feature. The sketch will be extruded toward the left to create the feature.

1. Define a new sketch plane on the right face of the second feature and draw the sketch of the rib feature. Add the required dimensions and constraints to the sketch.

2. Exit the sketching environment and choose the **Rib** button from the **Part Features** panel bar. The **Rib** dialog box is displayed and you are prompted to select the sketch for the rib feature.

3. Select the open sketch; all the other options in this dialog box are enabled. Enter **10** as the value in the edit box in the **Thickness** area. Choose the **Direction** button and move the cursor below the sketch. Click when the green arrow points in the downward direction.

4. Choose the second button in the **Thickness** area to extrude the feature toward the left side; the preview of the rib feature is displayed showing the sketch extruded toward the left of the sketch.

5. Choose **OK** to exit the **Rib** dialog box; the rib feature is created.

Creating the Join Feature on the Right Face of the Base Feature

1. Define a new sketch plane on the right face of the base feature.

2. Draw the sketch for the next feature. Draw a circle inside the sketch so that when extruded, the hole is automatically created. Add the required constraints and dimensions to it.

3. Extrude the sketch to create the feature. Make sure that you select the profile using a point inside the outer loop but outside the circle. The model, after creating the feature, is shown in Figure 5-95.

Mirroring Features on the Other Side of the Model

The second set of rib and join feature is created by mirroring them on the other side of the model. The features are mirrored using an offset work plane created in the center of the model.

1. Create an offset work plane inside the model using the right face of the base feature. The offset distance is -111 mm.

2. Choose the **Mirror Feature** button from the **Part Features** panel bar to display the **Mirror Pattern** dialog box. You are prompted to select the features to be patterned. Select the rib feature and the feature created on the right face of the base feature.

3. Choose the **Mirror Plane** button and select the offset work plane as the mirror plane. The preview of the mirrored features is displayed. Choose **OK** to exit this dialog box.

4. Right-click on the work plane in the browser to display the shortcut menu. Choose the **Visibility** option again to turn off the visibility of the work plane. The model, after mirroring the features, is shown in Figure 5-96.

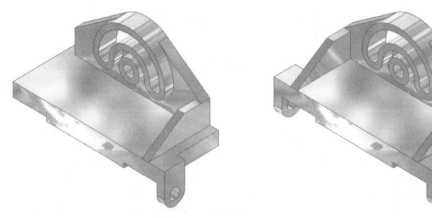

Figure 5-95 *After creating the rib and join features*   *Figure 5-96* *Model after mirroring the features*

Creating the Hole on the Top Face of the Base Feature

1. Choose the **Hole** button from the **Part Features** panel bar to invoke the **Hole** dialog box.

2. Select **Linear** from the drop-down list in the **Placement** area; the **Face** button is chosen and you are prompted to select a planar face or work plane.

3. Select the top planar face of the base feature. Next, select the left vertical edge on the top face of the base feature and then modify the value to **88**, refer to Figure 5-97.

 Tip. *You can also choose the right arrow on the right of the **Edit Dimension** toolbar to measure the length of an edge before entering the dimension value. You can use this option to determine the value you need to enter.*

4. Similarly, select the upper horizontal edge on the top face of the base feature and modify the value to **41**, as shown in Figure 5-97.

5. Select **Through All** from the drop-down list in the **Termination** area.

6. Set the value of the diameter of the hole in the preview window to **22**; the diameter of the hole in the preview also increases automatically. Choose the **OK** button. The final model for Tutorial 2 is shown in Figure 5-98.

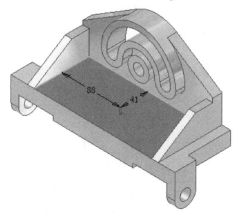

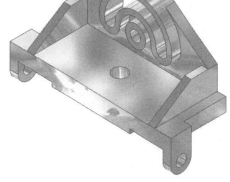

Figure 5-97 Final model for Tutorial 2   *Figure 5-98* Final model for Tutorial 2

7. Save the model with the name *\PersonalProject\c05\Tutorial2.ipt* and then close the file.

Tutorial 3

In this tutorial, you will create the model shown in Figure 5-99a. Its dimensions are given in Figure 5-99b and Figure 5-99c. After creating the model, save it with the name given below.

\PersonalProject\c05\Tutorial3.ipt   (**Expected time: 30 min**)

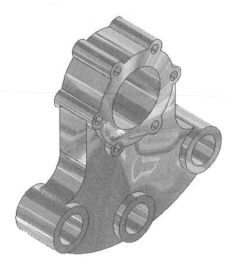

Figure 5-99a *Model for Tutorial 3*

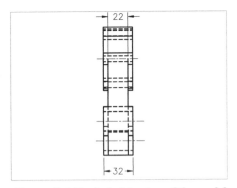

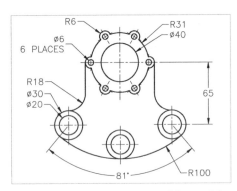

Figure 5-99b *Left-side view of the model*   *Figure 5-99c* *Front view of the model*

The following steps are required to create this model:

a. Create the sketch for the base feature on the YZ plane and extrude it midplane, refer to Figure 5-100.
b. Create the second feature on the YZ plane and extrude it midplane, refer to Figure 5-101.
c. Create one of the holes on the front face of the second feature and then create a circular pattern of this hole, refer to Figures 5-102 and 5-103.
d. Create the cylindrical join feature and then create a hole in it, refer to Figure 5-104.
e. Create the circular pattern of the last join feature and the hole, refer to Figure 5-105.
f. Finally, create the central hole, refer to Figure 5-106.

The base feature of this model will be created on the YZ plane. Also, all features in this model will be extruded using the **Mid-plane** option. This is because all features are extended equally from the front face and the back face of the base feature.

Creating the Base Feature

The base feature for this model will be created on the YZ plane. Therefore, you need to exit the sketching environment of the new file and then define a new sketch plane on the YZ plane.

1. Start a new metric standard part file and then change the sketching plane to the YZ plane. Draw the sketch for the base feature.

2. Add the required constraints and dimensions to it. Exit the sketching environment and then extrude the sketch to a distance of 22 mm using the **Mid-plane** option. The base feature of the model is shown in Figure 5-100.

Creating the Next Join Feature

Because the last feature was created on the YZ plane and was extruded using the **Mid-plane** option, you can create the other features also in the same plane and extrude them using the **Mid-plane** option.

1. Choose the **Sketch** button from the **Inventor Standard** toolbar; you are prompted to select the plane or planar face to create the sketch. Select the YZ plane from the browser.

   The sketching environment is activated. But because the sketch is drawn inside the model, it is hidden by the faces that lie between the sketch and the user. Therefore, you need to slice the model.

2. Right-click in the drawing window to display the shortcut menu and choose **Slice Graphics** from it.

3. Draw the central circle and then add the required dimensions and constraints to it.

4. Next, draw one of the smaller circles. Trim the unwanted portion of the bigger and smaller circles and then add the dimensions and constraints to the sketch.

Tip. *If the coordinate system and the origin is not aligned properly with the model, choose* **Edit Coordinate System** *from the* **2D Sketch Panel** *panel bar; the coordinate system appears. Now, select the outer edge of the lowest curved feature. The origin of the current coordinate system will be aligned to the center of the lowest curved feature.*

5. Using the **Circular Pattern** tool, create six instances of the trimmed smaller circle.

Tip. *If you create a circular pattern of the smaller circle without trimming it first, you cannot trim it after the pattern. This is because Autodesk Inventor does not allow you to trim the instances that are created using the* **Circular Pattern** *tool.*

6. Finally, trim the unwanted portions of the sketch.

7. Exit the sketching environment and then extrude the sketch to a distance of 32 mm using the **Mid-plane** option. The model, after creating the next feature, is shown in Figure 5-101.

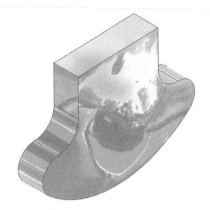
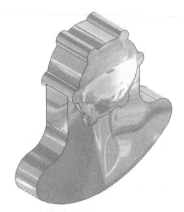

Figure 5-100 *Base feature of the model*   *Figure 5-101* *Model after creating the next feature*

Creating the Hole Pattern

Next, you need to create six holes cutting through the previous feature. Instead of creating all the holes, you can create one of them and then create a circular pattern of the holes. To create the pattern, you need to create one hole by defining the sketch plane on the front face of the previous feature.

1. Choose the **Hole** button from the **Part Features** panel bar; the **Hole** dialog box is displayed. Select **Concentric** from the drop-down list in the **Placement** area.

2. Select the front planar face of the second feature as the plane to place the hole and then select one of the six semicircular features

3. Select **Through All** from the drop-down list in the **Termination** area.

4. Modify the value of the diameter of the hole in the preview window to **6**. Choose **OK** to exit the dialog box and create the hole. The model, after creating one of the holes, is shown in Figure 5-102.

5. Choose the **Circular Pattern** button from the **Part Features** panel bar to display the **Circular Pattern** dialog box; you are prompted to select the feature to be patterned.

6. Select the hole. Next, choose the **Rotation Axis** button and select the outer cylindrical face of the second join feature.

As soon as you select the cylindrical face to specify the rotation axis, an axis is displayed passing through its center and the preview of the hole pattern is displayed on the model. A copy of the hole will be displayed on each of the semicircular features.

7. Accept the default values and choose **OK** to exit this dialog box and create the hole pattern. The model, after creating the hole pattern, is shown in Figure 5-103.

 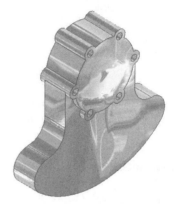

Figure 5-102 *Model after creating the hole*   ***Figure 5-103*** *Model after creating the hole pattern*

Creating the Cylindrical Join Feature

The cylindrical join feature is also created on the YZ plane and is extruded using the **Mid-plane** option.

1. Define a new sketch plane on the YZ plane and then slice the graphics. Draw the circle as the sketch for the cylindrical join feature. Add the required constraints and dimensions to the sketch.

2. Exit the sketching environment and then extrude the circle to a distance of 32 mm using the **Mid-plane** option.

Creating the Hole in the Join Feature

1. Choose the **Hole** button from the **Part Features** panel bar; the **Hole** dialog box is displayed. The **Concentric** option is automatically selected in the drop-down list in the **Placement** area.

2. Select the front face of the previous feature and then select the cylindrical face of the same feature to place the hole.

3. Select **Through All** from the drop-down list in the **Termination** area, if not already selected.

4. Modify the value of the diameter of the hole in the preview window to **20**. Choose **OK** to exit the dialog box and create the hole. The model, after creating the hole on the join feature, is shown in Figure 5-104.

Creating Circular Patterns

1. Choose the **Circular Pattern** button from the **Part Features** panel bar; the **Circular Pattern** dialog box will be displayed and you are prompted to select the feature to be patterned.

2. Select the cylindrical join feature and the hole to pattern; both the features are displayed with a blue outline.

3. Choose the **Rotation Axis** button and select the bottom cylindrical face of the base feature to define the axis of rotation for the pattern.

   The preview of the pattern with six items arranged through an angle of 360-degree is displayed on the model. But because the pattern shown in the preview is not the required pattern, you need to modify the values.

4. Enter **3** in the **Occurrence Count** edit box and **81** in the **Occurrence Angle** edit box under the **Placement** area.

5. Accept the other default values and choose **OK** to create the circular pattern. The model, after creating the pattern, is shown in Figure 5-105.

 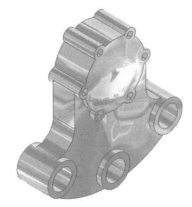

Figure 5-104 *Model after creating the hole on the join feature*

Figure 5-105 *Model after creating the circular pattern of the join feature and the hole*

Creating the Central Hole

1. Choose the **Hole** button from the **Part Features** panel bar; the **Hole** dialog box will be displayed.

   The **Concentric** option is automatically selected in the drop-down list in the **Placement** area.

2. Select the front face of the second feature and then select the cylindrical face of the same feature to place the hole.

3. Select **Through All** from the drop-down list in the **Termination** area, if not already se-
    lected.

4. Modify the value of the diameter of the hole in the preview window to **40**.

5. Choose **OK** to exit the dialog box and create the hole. The final model for Tutorial 3 is
    shown in Figure 5-106.

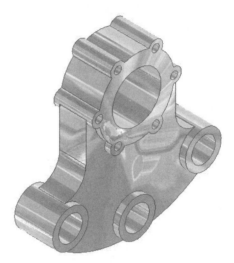

Figure 5-106 Final model for Tutorial 3

5. Save the model with the name *\PersonalProject\c05\Tutorial3.ipt* and close the file.

Tutorial 4

In this tutorial, you will create the bottle and then write text on the upper circular face of the
bottle, as shown in Figure 5-107. The wall thickness of the bottle is 1 mm. Next, you will transfer
an external image on the bottle as shown in the same figure. You can select any image available
on your computer to be transferred to the bottle. The dimensions of the bottle are shown in
Figure 5-108. **(Expected time: 30 min)**

The following steps are required to complete this tutorial:

a. Create the bottle by revolving a sketch drawn on the XZ plane, refer to Figure 5-109.
b. Write the text such that it can be wrapped on the upper circular face of the bottle, refer
    to Figure 5-110.
c. Emboss the text on the bottle such that it is wrapped to it, refer to Figure 5-111.
d. Insert an image in the sketching environment and then transfer it to the bottle such that it
    is wrapped around it, refer to Figure 5-113.

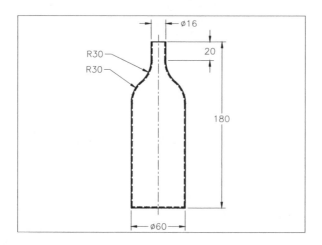

Figure 5-107 *Bottle with an image and text wrapped on it*

Figure 5-108 *Dimensions of the bottle*

Creating the Bottle

1. Start a new metric template file and then exit the sketching environment.

2. Define a new sketch plane on the XZ plane and draw the sketch of the bottle. You can draw the outline of the bottle and then offset it to a distance of 1 mm to create a hollow bottle. Join the edges to create a closed sketch.

3. Add the required constraints and linear diameter dimensions.

4. Exit the sketching environment and then revolve the sketch to create the bottle. Change the material of the bottle to Metal-AL-6061 (Polished). The bottle is shown in Figure 5-109.

Embossing Text on the Bottle

Next, you need to write a text and emboss it on the bottle. The text is written on a work plane created tangent to the outer face of the bottle and parallel to the YZ plane.

1. Create a work plane tangent to the bottle and parallel to the YZ plane. The plane needs to be created in front of the bottle and not at the back of it.

2. Select the new work plane as the sketching plane and then write the text in the sketching environment. The text that you need to write is **CADCIM Technologies**. The text height is 3.5 mm. After writing the text, select it and drag it such that it is in front of the neck of the bottle, see Figure 5-110.

Figure 5-109 *Bottle created on the XZ plane*

Figure 5-110 *Partial view of the bottle displaying the location of the text*

 Tip. *If the text that you write is written in the reverse direction, you need to flip the normal of the work plane. Exit all the tools and then select the work plane. Right-click on it and choose **Flip Normal** from the shortcut menu.*

3. Exit the sketching environment and then choose the **Emboss** button from the **Part Features** panel bar; the **Emboss** dialog box is displayed and you are prompted to select the profile.

4. Select the text and then choose the **Top Face Color** button below the **Depth** edit box; the **Color** dialog box is displayed. Select **Gold Metallic** from the drop-down list available in the **Color** dialog box. Exit this dialog box.

5. Select the **Wrap to Face** check box; the **Face** button appears below this check box. Choose this button, if not already chosen, and select the neck of the bottle on which you need to

wrap the text. Choose **OK** to exit the dialog box. A partial view of the bottle, after wrapping the text on it, is shown in Figure 5-111.

Figure 5-111 *Partial view of the bottle after wrapping the text*

Wrapping the Image on the Bottle

When you insert an image in the sketching environment, it does not become a part of the Inventor file. It remains an external image. As a result, whenever you open a file, in which you have inserted an image, Autodesk Inventor looks for the folder in which the image is stored. Therefore, it is recommended that you copy the image in the current folder and then insert in the sketching environment.

1. Copy any external image on your computer to the current folder and then select the tangent work plane created earlier as the sketching plane.

2. In the sketching environment, use the **Insert Image** tool to insert an external image. You may need to resize and relocate the image such that its size and location is close to that shown in Figure 5-112.

3. Exit the sketching environment and then choose the **Decal** button from the **Part Features** panel bar; the **Decal** dialog box is displayed and you are prompted to select the image.

4. Select the image inserted in the sketching environment. Next, select the face of the bottle to transfer the image.

5. Select the **Wrap to Face** check box and then choose **OK** to exit the dialog box. The image is wrapped on the bottle. The final bottle, after wrapping the text and the image, is shown in Figure 5-113.

Figure 5-112 *Image inserted in the sketching environment*

Figure 5-113 *Final model of the bottle*

6.   Save the model with the name *\PersonalProject\c05\Tutorial4.ipt* and then close the file.

Self-Evaluation Test

Answer the following questions and then compare your answers with those given at the end of this chapter:

1.   The hole created using the **Hole** tool is parametric in nature. (T/F)

2.   You can remove any entity from the current selection set by pressing the SHIFT key and then selecting the entity once again. (T/F)

3.   You can create both fillets and rounds using the same **Fillet** dialog box. (T/F)

4.   You can mirror the entire model or selected features. (T/F)

5.   The diameter of the holes is defined in the _____ of the **Hole** dialog box.

6.   _____ is defined as the process of bevelling the sharp edges of the model in order to reduce the area of stress concentration.

7.   The rib feature is created using an _____ sketch.

8.   The _____ radio button is selected in the **Mirror Pattern** dialog box to create a mirrored feature exactly similar to the original feature, even if they intersect other features.

9.   _____ are defined as the thin wall-like structures used to bind the joints together so that they do not fail under an increased load.

10. A _____ hole is a stepped hole with a bigger and a smaller diameter.

Review Questions

Answer the following questions:

1.   In Autodesk Inventor, you can create holes only on the points/hole centers. (T/F)

2.   In the Part module, you can use the **Circular Pattern** tool for arranging the selected features around the circumference of an imaginary circle. (T/F)

3.   The chamfer created using the **Distance** button will be at a 45-degree angle. (T/F)

4.   The options in the **Variable** tab are used to fillet the selected edges by applying different radius values along the length of the edge. (T/F)

5.   You can use the options in the **Hole** dialog box to create a tapped hole. (T/F)

6.   Which of the following is not a type of hole?

     (a) Counterbore   (b) Countersink
     (c) Countercut   (d) Drilled

7.   Which one of the following tabs provides you with an option of creating a flat base hole?

     (a) **Type**   (b) **Options**
     (c) **Size**   (d) **Thread**

8.   How many edges are used to define the setback for a vertex?

     (a) 2   (b) 3
     (c) 1   (d) 4

9.   Which check box is displayed in the **Rib** dialog box when you select the direction of applying a thickness parallel to the sketch or choose the **Finite** button from the **Extents** area?

     (a) **Extend Profile**   (b) **Clear Profile**
     (c) **Trim Profile**   (d) **None**

10. How many type of methods are provided for creating a chamfer?

     (a) 2   (b) 3
     (c) 1   (d) 4

Exercises

Exercise 1

Create the model shown in Figure 5-114a. Its dimensions are given in Figures 5-114b and 5-114c. Save this model with the name \PersonalProject\c05\Exercise1.ipt.

(Expected time: 45 min)

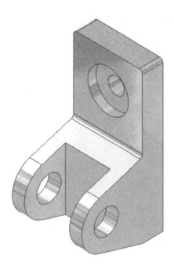

Figure 5-114a Model for Exercise 1

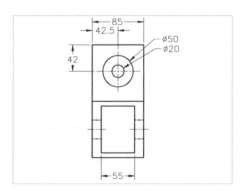

Figure 5-114b Left-side view of the model

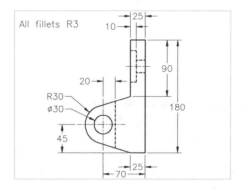

Figure 5-114c Front view of the model

Exercise 2

Create the model shown in Figure 5-115a. Its dimensions are given in Figures 5-115b through 5-115d. Save it with the name \PersonalProject\c05\Exercise2.ipt.

(Expected time: 45 min)

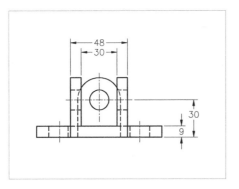

Figure 5-115a Model for Exercise 2

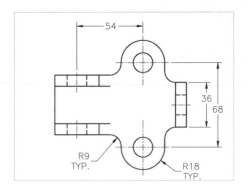

Figure 5-115b Top view of the model

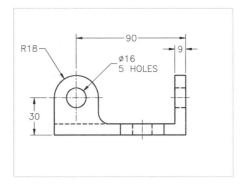

Figure 5-115c Left-side view of the model

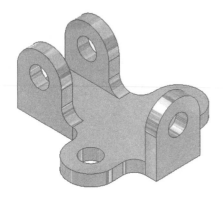

Figure 5-115d Front view of the model

Answers to Self-Evaluation Test

1. T, **2.** T, **3.** T, **4.** T, **5.** preview window, **6.** Chamfering, **7.** open, **8. Identical, 9.** Ribs, **10.** counterbore

Chapter 6

Editing Features and Adding Automatic Dimensions to Sketches

Learning Objectives

After completing this chapter, you will be able to:
- *Edit features in a model.*
- *Update the model after editing.*
- *Edit sketches of the sketched features.*
- *Suppress features.*
- *Unsuppress features.*
- *Delete features.*
- *Copy features.*
- *Redefine the sketching plane of a feature.*
- *Assign different color to a face of a feature.*
- *Add automatic dimensions to the sketches.*

CONCEPT OF EDITING FEATURES

Editing is one of the most important part of designing. Most of the designs require editing, either during creation or after creation. As mentioned earlier, Autodesk Inventor is a feature-based solid modeling tool. As a result, the model created in Autodesk Inventor is a combination of various features integrated together. All these features are individual components and can be edited separately. This property gives this solid modeling software a cutting edge over the other non-feature-based solid modeling tools. For example, Figure 6-1 shows a cylindrical part with six countersink holes created at some pitch circle diameter (PCD).

Now, in case you have to edit the features such that the number of holes is to be increased to eight and the countersink holes are to be changed into counterbore holes, you just need to perform two editing operations. The first editing operation will open the **Holes** dialog box where you can modify the countersink holes to counterbore holes. You can specify the various parameters for the counterbore hole in this dialog box. When you exit this dialog box, all the six countersink holes will be modified into counterbore holes. The second editing operation will open the **Circular Pattern** dialog box. In this dialog box, you can change the number of instances to eight, see Figure 6-2.

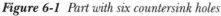

Figure 6-1 *Part with six countersink holes*   *Figure 6-2* *Modified part with counterbore holes*

Similarly, you can also edit work features or the sketches of the sketched features. The features created using the work features will be modified automatically when you edit the work features. For example, if you have created a feature on a work plane that is at an offset of 100 mm, the feature will be automatically repositioned if you change the offset value of the work plane. In Autodesk Inventor, all the editing operations are performed using the browser.

Editing Features of a Model

As mentioned earlier, all editing operations will be performed using the browser. To edit a feature, select it in the browser; the selected feature will be highlighted in the model. Right-click on the selected feature in the browser or in the model to display the shortcut menu and choose **Edit Feature** from it, see Figure 6-3. Depending on the feature selected for editing, the corresponding dialog box will be displayed. For example, if you right-click on an

Figure 6-3 *Editing a feature using the browser*

extruded feature, the **Extrude** dialog box will be displayed. Also, the feature selected to edit is highlighted in bold in the browser. The dialog box will also have the sequence number of the feature. This means that if you right-click on the fifth extruded feature in a model to display the shortcut menu and choose **Edit Feature**, the **Extrude : Extrusion5** dialog box will be displayed, see Figure 6-4.

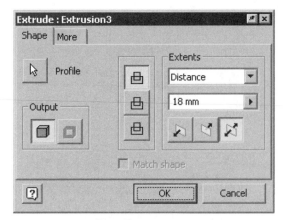

Figure 6-4   *The **Extrude : Extrusion5** dialog box for editing an extruded feature*

You can perform the required editing operation using this dialog box. These include reselecting the sketch to be extruded, modifying the taper angle, changing the type of operation, and so on. Similarly, if you right-click on a hole feature and choose **Edit Feature** from the shortcut menu, the **Holes : Holes#** dialog box will be displayed, as shown in Figure 6-5.

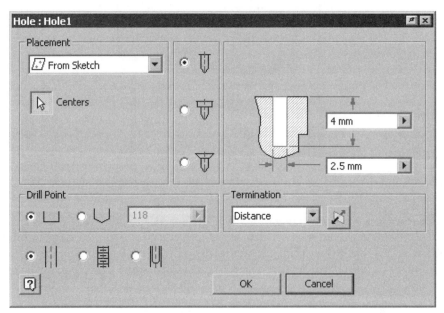

Figure 6-5   *The **Holes : Hole1** dialog box for editing the hole feature*

You can also edit a hole feature by double-clicking on it in the browser. All the dimensions related to the hole will be displayed on the model. Double-click on the diameter dimension and the **Hole Dimensions** dialog box will be displayed. The options in this dialog box will be available depending on whether the hole is drilled, countersink, or counterbore. Figure 6-6 shows the **Hole Dimensions** dialog box for a counterbore hole.

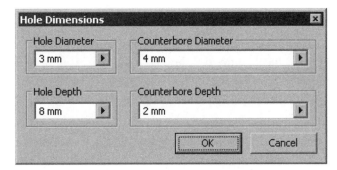

Figure 6-6 The **Hole Dimensions** dialog

Tip. *You can also display the dimensions of a feature on the model by double-clicking on the feature in the browser.*

*When you choose the option of displaying the dimensions of the feature for editing, the dimensions will be retained on the screen even after the editing operation is over. To clear these dimensions from the screen, choose **Update** from the **Inventor Standard** toolbar or select another feature from the browser.*

Updating Edited Features

If you edit a feature using the browser, you do not have to update the feature to view the effect of the editing operation. This is because as soon as you exit the editing operation, the feature will be automatically updated. However, if you modify the feature using dimensions, you will have to update the feature manually. Until the feature is updated after editing, it will not display the modified values. The features can be modified by choosing the **Update** button in the **Inventor Standard** toolbar. This button will be activated when you modify the dimensions of any of the features.

Dynamically Editing Features Using 3D Grips

This is a new concept added in the recent releases of Autodesk Inventor. Using this tool, you can dynamically edit extruded, revolved, or swept features. To invoke this editing tool, right-click on the feature in the browser or in the drawing window and choose **3D Grips** from the shortcut menu; the original sketch of the feature is displayed with dimensions and the feature is displayed in wireframe. You will notice that small circles are displayed on all faces of the model, except for the face that lies on the sketching plane. These small circles will also be displayed on all the edges that are along the normal direction of the sketching plane, see Figure 6-7. This figure shows a rectangular block after invoking 3D grips.

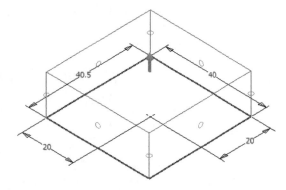

Figure 6-7 Editing of a block using 3D grips

To edit the feature, move the cursor over the circle on any face or edge. If you move the cursor over the circle on a face, an arrow normal to the face will be displayed on the circle. Press and hold the left mouse button at that point and then drag the cursor; the feature will be resized along the normal of that face. Figure 6-8 shows the model shown in Figure 6-7 being resized normal to the front face. The value by which the feature will be resized is displayed on the right of the cursor.

If you move the cursor on the circles displayed on the edges of the feature and drag, the feature will be simultaneously modified along the X and Y axis direction of the sketch, as shown in Figure 6-9. The values by which the feature will be resized along the X and Y axes are displayed on the right of the cursor.

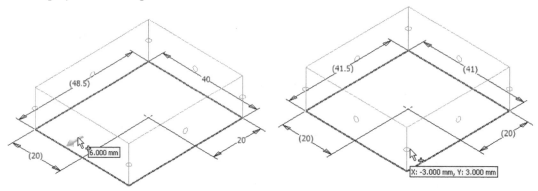

Figure 6-8   *Resizing the feature normal to a plane*   *Figure 6-8*   *Resizing the feature using an edge*

After dynamically editing the feature using 3D grips, right-click in the model and choose **Done** from the shortcut menu. The model will be updated only after you choose **Done**.

Dynamically Moving or Rotating Features

This is also a new concept added in the previous release of Autodesk Inventor. This tool allows you to dynamically move and rotate extruded, revolved, or swept features. To do this, right-click on an extruded, revolved, or a swept feature in the browser and choose **Move Feature**. If you select the base feature, the **3D Move / Rotate** dialog box will be displayed, as shown in Figure 6-9 and a triad will be displayed on the model, as shown in Figure 6-10. If you select any other feature, right-click and choose **Triad Move** to invoke this dialog box.

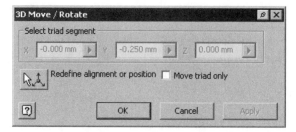

Figure 6-9   *The **3D Move / Rotate** dialog box*

Depending on where you click on the triad, you can move or rotate the model. The details of using this triad to move or rotate the model are discussed next.

Moving the Selected Feature

The triad allows you to move the feature along the direction of a specified axis in a specified plane, or in 3D. The methods of moving a feature using these three options are discussed next.

Moving Along the Direction of a Selected Axis

To move the feature along the direction of a specified axis, move the cursor over the arrowhead of that axis of the triad; it will be highlighted in red, as shown in Figure 6-11. Make sure you do not move the cursor over the axis because that will rotate the model. Select the arrowhead when it is highlighted; the edit box of the selected direction will be enabled in the **3D Move / Rotate** dialog box. You can enter the exact value in it and choose **OK**. You can also drag the mouse to move the feature in the selected direction and then right-click and choose **OK (3D Move/Rotate)** from the shortcut menu.

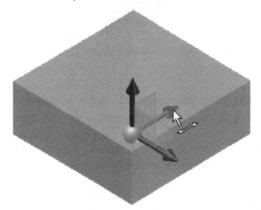

Figure 6-10 *Triad displayed on the model*   *Figure 6-11* *Selecting the Y axis to move the feature*

Tip. *You can modify the default snap value while dynamically moving or rotating the feature or while editing the feature using 3D grips. To do this, choose **Tools > Document Settings**; the **Document Settings** dialog box will be displayed. Choose the **Modeling** tab and modify the values in the **Distance Snap** and **Angle Snap** edit boxes.*

Moving in a Selected Plane

To move the feature in a specified plane, select one of the planes displayed in the triad, as shown in Figure 6-12; the related edit boxes will be enabled in the **3D Move / Rotate** dialog box. You can enter the exact values of moving in these edit boxes or drag the mouse to move the feature dynamically in the selected plane. Next, choose **OK** from the dialog box to execute the editing operation.

Tip. *If you have made an incorrect selection in the triad for moving or rotating the feature, you can right-click and choose **Redefine** from the menu bar to make the selection again.*

Moving Freely in 3D Space

To move the feature in 3D space, select the sphere of the triad, as shown in Figure 6-13; the edit boxes of all three axes will be enabled in the **3D Move / Rotate** dialog box. You can enter the exact values of moving in these edit boxes or drag the mouse to move the feature dynamically in 3D space and then choose **OK** from the dialog box.

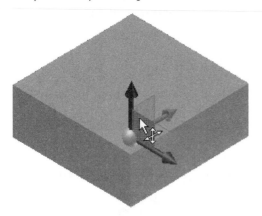

Figure 6-12 Selecting a plane to move the feature   *Figure 6-13*   Selecting sphere to move the feature freely in 3D space

Rotating the Selected Feature

You can rotate the selected feature around any of the three axes of the triad. To rotate the feature, move the cursor over any one of the triad axes; the axis will be highlighted in red, as shown in Figure 6-14. Select the axis at this stage; the related area will be displayed in the **3D Move / Rotate** dialog box. You can enter the exact value of rotation in the edit box or drag the mouse to rotate the feature dynamically. Choose **OK** from the dialog box to complete the editing operation. Figure 6-15 shows a model with the top cut feature at its default orientation and Figure 6-16 shows the same model after rotating the feature.

Figure 6-14 Selecting an axis to rotate the feature

Editing Sketches of Features

Autodesk Inventor also provides you with the flexibility of editing sketches of the sketched feature. You can add additional entities to the sketch or remove some of the entities from the sketch. Once you have made the necessary changes, you just have to update the sketched feature using the **Update** button in the **Inventor Standard** toolbar. However, you have to make sure that the sketch after editing remains a closed loop. In case the sketch is not a closed loop, the **Autodesk Inventor 11 - Exit Sketch Mode** dialog box will be displayed. It will give an error message that the loop could not be repaired after editing.

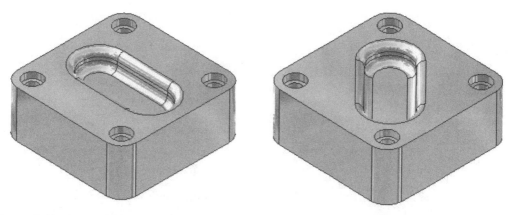

Figure 6-15 *Original orientation of the feature*   *Figure 6-16* *Feature after rotation*

To edit the sketch of a sketched feature, right-click on the sketch in the browser to display the shortcut menu. In this shortcut menu, choose **Edit Sketch**; the sketching environment will be activated. Once you have made the necessary changes, choose the **Update** button from the **Inventor Standard** toolbar.

Redefining the Sketching Plane of a Sketched Feature

Sometimes, you may need to relocate a feature drawn on one of the planes to another plane. For example, you may need to relocate a cylinder drawn on the XY plane to YZ plane. Autodesk Inventor allows you to relocate the features on the other planes by redefining the sketching plane. After redefining it, the necessary changes in the orientation of the model are automatically made. For example, a cylinder drawn on the XY plane stands vertically. However, the same cylinder drawn on the YZ plane lies horizontally.

To redefine the sketching plane of a sketched feature, click on the + sign located on the left of the sketched feature in the browser; the name of the sketch of that feature will appear below it in the browser. Right-click on the sketch and choose **Redefine** from the shortcut menu, as shown in Figure 6-17. You will be prompted to select a work plane or planar face to redefine the sketch. Select the new work plane or planar face for the sketched feature; the sketch of the feature will be relocated on the new plane and the model will reorient, based on the new parameters. Also, all the features created with reference to the current features will be updated automatically.

Figure 6-17 *Redefining the sketching plane of a sketched feature*

Figure 6-18 shows a model with the base feature created on the XY plane. Figure 6-19 shows the model after redefining the sketching plane of the base feature to the YZ plane. Notice that the base feature and all the other features in the model are reoriented based on the new sketching plane.

Figure 6-18 *Base feature created on the XY plane*   *Figure 6-19*   *Model after redefining the sketching plane of the base feature to YZ plane*

Note
If one or more features of a model are not resolved after you redefine the sketching plane, a message box will be displayed informing about the features that are not resolved.

SUPPRESSING FEATURES

Sometimes, there may be a situation where you want some of the features should not show up in the drawing views of the model or in the printout of the model. In any of the nonfeature-based solid modeling tools, you will have to either delete the feature or create it after taking the printout. However, in Autodesk Inventor, you can simply suppress the feature that you do not want. Once the feature is suppressed, it will neither be displayed in the drawing views nor in the printout of the model. Remember that the features are not deleted, they are temporarily turned off. Note that all the features that are dependent on the feature that you select are also suppressed. To suppress a feature, right-click on it in the browser and then choose **Suppress Features** from the shortcut menu, see Figure 6-20.

Note
All the features that are suppressed will be displayed in light gray color in the browser. Also, they will have a line that will strike through the name of the feature in the browser.

Figure 6-20 *Shortcut menu to suppress a feature*

UNSUPPRESSING THE SUPPRESSED FEATURES

The suppressed features can be resumed using the browser. Right-click on the suppressed feature in the browser to display the shortcut menu. In this shortcut menu, choose **Unsuppress Features**; the selected feature will be displayed in the model again.

Tip. *If after generating the drawing views of the current model, you suppress any feature in the model, it will not be displayed in the drawing views. Similarly, as soon as you unsuppress the feature, it will be displayed in the drawing views.*

MOVING FACES OF A SOLID

Toolbar:	Part Features > Move Face
Panel Bar:	Part Features > Move Face

One of the enhancements in the previous release of Autodesk Inventor is its ability to let you move the selected faces in a model. This option is extensively used when you edit a model imported in Autodesk Inventor. This is because an imported model is displayed as a base feature. To move the faces, choose the **Move Face** button from the **Part Features** panel bar; the **Move Face** dialog box will be displayed, as shown in Figure 6-21.

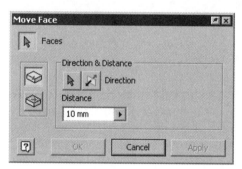

Figure 6-21 The **Move Face** *dialog box*

When you invoke the **Move Face** dialog box, the **Faces** button is chosen by default and you are prompted to select a face to be moved. You can use this dialog box to move faces using the **Direction Distance** or **Planar Move** method. Both these methods are discussed next.

Moving Faces Using the Direction Distance Method

This is the default method of moving selected faces. This is the reason, the **Direction Distance** button, available below the **Faces** button, is chosen by default. If you select a planar face to be moved, it will be moved in the direction of its normal, by default. If you want to change the direction, choose the **Direction** button from the **Direction & Distance** area and select an edge to define the direction. You can also choose the **Flip** button to reverse the direction of movement. Figure 6-22 shows the face of the rectangular cut feature being moved in the direction of the normal of that face.

Moving Faces Using the Planar Move Method

This method allows you to move the selected faces in a specified plane. The distance of the movement is defined using two points. To invoke this method, select the planes to be moved and then choose the **Planar Move** button below the **Direction Distance** button; the **Plane** button will be automatically chosen in the **Direction & Distance** area. Select the plane in which you want to move the selected face; the **Points** button will be automatically chosen and you will be prompted to select the first point. Select a point to specify the start point of the movement. Next, you will be prompted to select the second point. On specifying the second point, the preview of the resulting movement will be displayed, as shown in Figure 6-23.

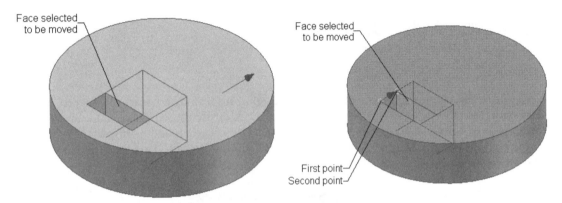

*Figure 6-22 Preview of a face being moved using the **Direction Distance** method*

*Figure 6-23 Preview of a face being moved using the **Planar Move** method*

If you try to move faces that have a partial circular cut feature in between, as shown in Figure 6-24, the faces will be moved only to the distance at which the partial circle becomes a full circle. If you try to specify the movement value more than this distance, an error message will be displayed and the faces will not be moved. Figure 6-25 shows the cut feature that has now become almost of full circle.

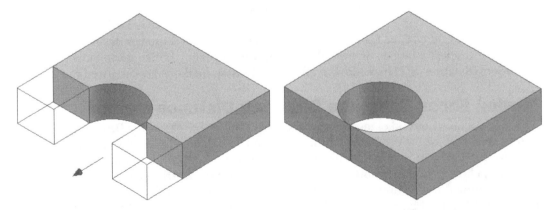

Figure 6-24 Faces selected to be moved

Figure 6-25 Partial circular cut feature changed to a circular cut feature by moving faces

DELETING FEATURES

The unwanted feature can be deleted from the model using the browser. Right-click on the feature to be deleted in the browser; a shortcut menu is displayed. Choose the **Delete** option in it; the **Delete Features** dialog box will be displayed. This dialog box will prompt you to specify whether or not you want to delete the dependent features and sketches. The options that you can select for deleting include the sketch of the feature, the dependent sketches and features, and the dependent work features. The options that are not applicable to the selected feature will not be enabled in this dialog box. For example, if you delete a feature that does not have any work feature created with reference to it, the last option in the **Delete Features** dialog box will not be enabled.

COPYING AND PASTING FEATURES

Autodesk Inventor allows you to copy and paste a sketch-based feature from the current file to any file or at some other place in the same file. However, the method of copying a feature in Autodesk Inventor is different from that in the other solid modeling tools. To copy a feature, right-click on its name in the browser and choose **Copy** from the shortcut menu. Note that this option will be available only for the sketch-based features. Now, to paste the feature in another file, open it. Else open any other existing file. Right-click in the drawing window to display the shortcut menu and then choose **Paste** from it. The **Paste Features** dialog box will be displayed, as shown in Figure 6-26, and the dynamic preview of the feature will be displayed in the drawing window.

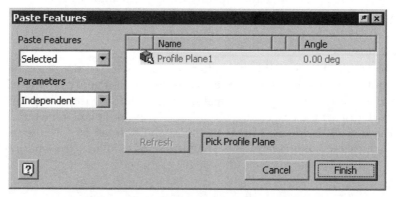

*Figure 6-26 The **Paste Features** dialog box*

By default, the feature will be attached to any planar face in the model. However, you can attach the feature to the desired face using the options in the **Paste Features** dialog box. The options under this dialog box are discussed next.

Paste Features

This drop-down list is used to select the option for pasting the features. By default, only the selected feature will be pasted and the features that are dependent on the selected features will not be pasted. This is because by default, the **Selected** option in this drop-down list is selected. However, if you want to paste all the dependent features also, select **Dependent** from this drop-down list.

Parameters

This drop-down list is used to select whether the parameters of the feature should be independent or dependent. You can select the required option from this drop-down list.

Name

This column displays the plane on which the feature will be pasted. When you invoke this dialog box, by default the feature will be temporarily pasted on any plane. As you move the mouse on any plane, the feature will be temporarily pasted on that plane. You can view all this in the dynamic preview of the feature on the model. Once you select the plane on which the feature should be pasted, the dynamic preview will fix to that plane. Until you select the plane to paste the feature, an icon will be displayed on the left of the profile plane in this column. This icon will display an arrow on the face of a box. This suggests that you have not selected the plane for placing the feature. When you select the plane, this icon is replaced by a box that has a check mark, suggesting that the plane for placing the feature has been selected. In case you want to change the plane for the feature placement, click on **Profile Plane** in this column.

Angle

This column is used to rotate the pasted feature through an angle by specifying the angle in it. The preview of the feature will be dynamically rotated through the specified angle.

Refresh

The **Refresh** button will be available only after you have selected the plane for pasting the feature. This button is chosen to refresh the feature such that it adjusts to the selected plane. For example, if a feature has a dependent feature that is cut using the **All** option, the preview of the model will display the cut feature extending beyond the plane on which the feature is pasted, see Figure 6-27. However, when you choose the **Refresh** button, the cut feature will be adjusted such that it is not extended beyond the selected plane, see Figure 6-28.

Finish

The **Finish** button is used to paste the feature on the selected face. The paste operation will be completed only after you choose this button. Figure 6-29 shows a model before copying the feature and Figure 6-30 shows the model after copying the original cut feature and the dependent cut feature on two different planes.

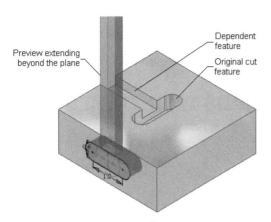

Figure 6-27 *Preview of the dependent cut feature extending beyond the selected plane*

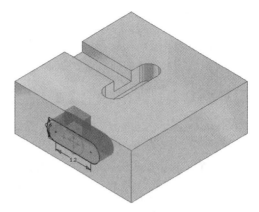

Figure 6-28 *Preview of the dependent cut feature adjusted to fit the plane*

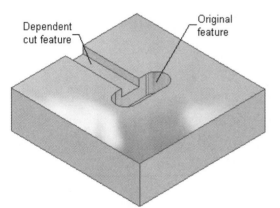

Figure 6-29 *Model with the original cut feature and dependent cut feature*

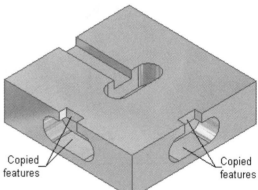

Figure 6-30 *Cut features copied on two different faces of the model*

ASSIGNING DIFFERENT COLOR TO A FACE OR FEATURE

Sometimes, you may need to represent a face of a model differently from the other for the presentation purpose. Autodesk Inventor allows you to do this by assigning a different color to the selected face of a feature. The remaining feature will have the color of the model, but the selected face can be assigned a different color. To assign a different color to a face, right-click on the face in the drawing window. A shortcut menu is displayed. Select **Properties** from the shortcut menu; the **Face Properties** dialog box is displayed. This dialog box has a drop-down list that provides various colors. The default color of the selected face is **As Feature**. This suggests that the color of the face is that of the original feature. To assign a different color, select the desired color from the drop-down list and then choose **OK**. The dialog box will be closed and the selected color will be assigned to the selected face.

Similarly, to assign a different color to a feature, right-click on it in the browser to display the shortcut menu. From the shortcut menu, choose **Properties** to display the **Feature Properties** dialog box and select the required color from the **Feature Color Style** drop-down list.

ADDING AUTOMATIC DIMENSIONS TO SKETCHES

Toolbar:	2D Sketch Panel > Auto Dimension
Panel bar:	2D Sketch Panel > Auto Dimension

 The auto dimensions are the dimensions that are added automatically to the sketch by Autodesk Inventor. Note that you cannot apply all the dimensions required in the sketch using only the automatic dimensions. These dimensions are used in association with the general dimensions to fully constrain the sketch. In Autodesk Inventor, the automatic dimensions are added using the **Auto Dimension** tool. When you invoke this tool, the **Auto Dimension** dialog box is displayed, as shown in Figure 6-31.

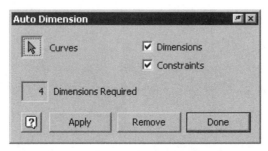

Figure 6-31 The **Auto Dimension** dialog box

The options under this dialog box are discussed next.

Curves

The **Curves** button is chosen to select the sketch for applying the automatic dimensions. By default, the complete sketch is selected to be dimensioned. As a result, all the entities in the sketch are dimensioned. However, if you want to add automatic dimensions to some selected entities, choose this button and then select the entities from the graphics screen. The selected entities will be highlighted in blue. Choose the **Apply** button to apply the automatic dimensions to the sketch.

Dimensions Required

The **Dimensions Required** box will display the number of dimensions that are required in the sketch. You cannot modify the value in this box. When you select the sketch and apply the automatic dimensions using the **Apply** button, the number of dimensions that are still required to fully constrain the sketch will be displayed in this box.

      Tip. *You can use this tool to verify if the sketch you have drawn is fully constrained or not. After adding all the dimensions and constraints, invoke this tool. If the dialog box shows 0 dimensions required, the sketch will be fully constrained.*

Dimensions

The **Dimensions** check box is selected to apply automatic dimensions to the sketch. If this check box is cleared, the dimensions will not be applied to the sketch.

Constraints

The **Constraints** check box is selected to also apply the constraints to the sketch while applying the automatic dimensions. If this check box is cleared, the constraints will not be applied.

Apply

The **Apply** button is chosen to apply the automatic dimensions to the selected sketch. Invoke the **Auto Dimension** dialog box and then choose this button to add the dimensions. Note that until this button is chosen, the automatic dimensions will not be applied to the sketch.

Remove

The **Remove** button is chosen to remove the automatic dimensions from the sketch.

Done

The **Done** button is chosen to exit the **Auto Dimension** dialog box.

PROJECTING ENTITIES IN THE SKETCHING ENVIRONMENT

Autodesk Inventor allows you to project the edges of an existing feature to a sketching plane while drawing the sketches. The projected edges are converted into sketched entities and can be used as a part of the sketch. You can project the selected edge or face of a feature, or project the part of the model that is cut by the sketching plane. Note that since the projected entities are reference entities, you cannot dimension them. Both these options of projecting the entities are discussed next.

Projecting Edges or Faces

| Toolbar: | 2D Sketch Panel > Project Geometry |
| Panel bar: | 2D Sketch Panel > Project Geometry |

You can project the selected edges or faces to a sketching plane by choosing **Project Geometry** from the **2D Sketch Panel** panel bar. When you invoke this tool, you will be prompted to select an edge, vertex, work geometry, or sketch geometry to be projected. If you move the cursor over a face, it will be highlighted with a red outline. Similarly, if you move the cursor over an edge, it will be highlighted in red. Select the geometry to be projected, it will be projected on the current sketch plane as a sketched entity. Figure 6-32 shows a model in which a sketch plane is defined in the center of the model. Figure 6-33 shows the model after projecting the spline edge.

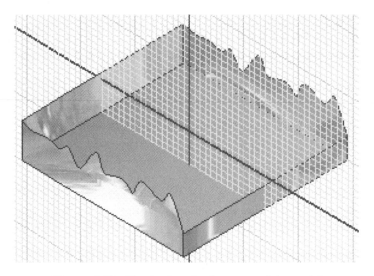

Figure 6-32 *Sketch plane in the center of the model*

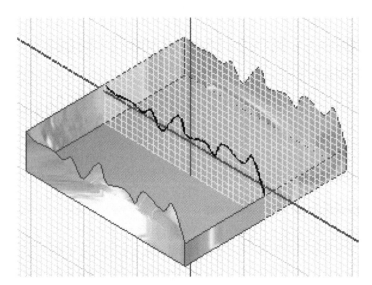

Figure 6-33 *After projecting the spline edge*

Projecting Cutting Edges

Toolbar:	2D Sketch Panel > Project Geometry > Project Cut Edges
Panel bar:	2D Sketch Panel > Project Geometry > Project Cut Edges

The cutting edges are those that define the contour of the model that is created when you define a sketching plane on a face of a model or inside the model. When you define a sketching plane inside the model, it cuts the model, thus forming cutting edges. You can project these cutting edges by choosing **Project Cut Edges** from the **Project Geometry** flyout in the **2D Sketch Panel** panel bar. As soon as you choose this button, the edges that are cut by the sketching plane are projected. Figure 6-34 shows a model and the sketching plane cutting through it and Figure 6-35 shows the sketch after projecting the cutting edges.

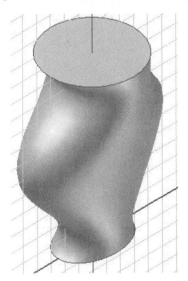

Figure 6-34 *Sketch plane in the center of the model*

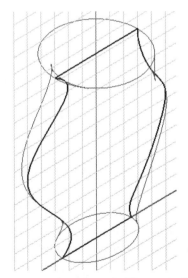

Figure 6-35 *After projecting the cutting edges*

Note

*The models shown in Figures 6-34 and 6-35 are created using the **Loft** tool. This tool is discussed in the next chapter.*

TUTORIALS

Tutorial 1

In this tutorial, you will create a model of the Gear-shifter link shown in Figure 6-36a. Its dimensions are shown in Figures 6-36b through 6-36d. After creating the model, save it with the name given below.

\PersonalProject\c06\Tutorial1.ipt   **(Expected time: 45 min)**

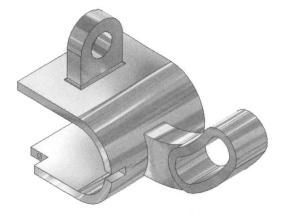

Figure 6-36a Model for Tutorial 1

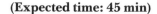
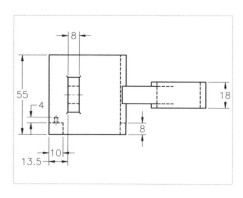

Figure 6-36b Top view of the model

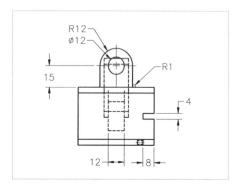

Figure 6-36c Left-side view of the model

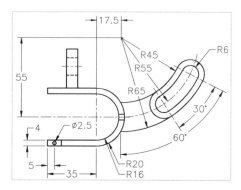

Figure 6-36d Front view of the model

Before you start creating the model, it is recommended that you outline the procedure for creating it. The following steps are required to complete this tutorial:

a. Create the base feature, which is a reverse C-like feature. Its sketch will be created on the XZ plane and extruded using the **Mid-plane** option, see Figure 6-37.
b. Define a new sketch plane on the XZ plane and add the curved features on the circular face of the base feature, refer to Figure 6-39.
c. Again, define a new sketch plane on the XZ plane and draw the sketch for the third feature. Extrude this feature also using the **Mid-plane** option, refer to Figure 6-41.

d. Define a new sketch plane on the front face of the third feature and draw the sketch for the cut feature. Extrude this sketch using the **Cut** operation, refer to Figure 6-42.

e. Suppress all features, except the base feature, and then define a work plane at an offset of 17.5 mm from the left face of the base feature. Draw the sketch for the feature on the top face of the base feature and extrude it using the **Mid-plane** option, refer to Figure 6-43.

f. Suppress the last feature and create the slots and hole on the front face of the base feature, refer to Figure 6-44.

g. Finally, unsuppress all features to complete the model, refer to Figure 6-45.

Creating the Base Feature

1. Start a new metric standard part file and then draw the sketch for the base feature on the XZ plane.

2. Exit the sketching environment and then extrude the sketch to a distance of 55 mm using the **Mid-plane** option. The base feature of the model is shown in Figure 6-37.

Figure 6-37 Base feature of the model

Creating the Curved Features

As the base feature was created on the XZ plane and was extruded using the **Mid-plane** option, you can create the sketch for the curved features also on the same plane and then extrude it to the required distance using the **Mid-plane** option.

1. Select the XZ plane as the plane for creating the sketch for the curved feature. Create the sketch for the feature and then add the required constraints and dimensions to it. The sketch for the curved feature, after applying all the dimensions and constraints, is shown in Figure 6-38.

2. Exit the sketching environment and then extrude the sketch to a distance of 12 mm using the **Join** operation. Use the **Mid-plane** option for creating the feature. The model in the isometric view is shown in Figure 6-39.

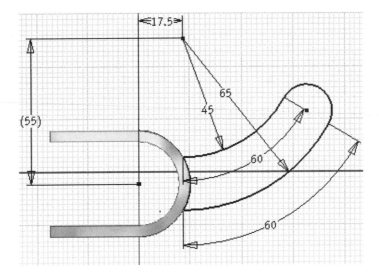

Figure 6-38 Sketch for the curved feature

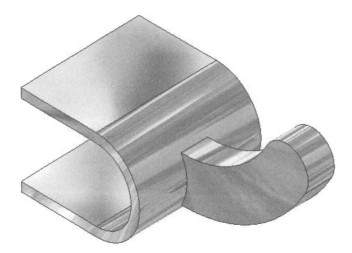

Figure 6-39 Feature created after extruding the sketch

3. Using the same sketching plane, draw the sketch for the third feature, which is also a join feature, as shown in Figure 6-40. You can draw the sketch and then apply the **Concentric** and **Equal** constraints to the sketch and the existing feature.

4. Exit the sketching environment and then extrude the sketch to a distance of 18 mm using the **Join** operation and the **Mid-plane** option, see Figure 6-41.

5. Specify a new sketch plane on the front face of the second join feature and then create the sketch for the cut feature. You can offset and dimension the reference entities to create the sketch of the cut feature.

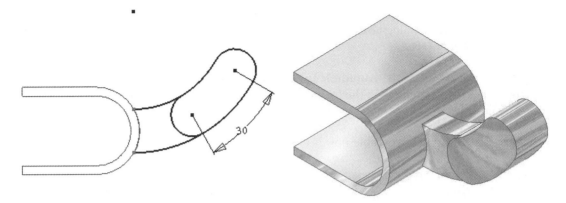

Figure 6-40 *Sketch for the next join feature in the wireframe display*

Figure 6-41 *Model after creating the second join feature*

6.   Extrude the sketch using the **Cut** operation and the **All** option to create the cut feature.

7.   The model after creating the cut feature is shown in Figure 6-42.

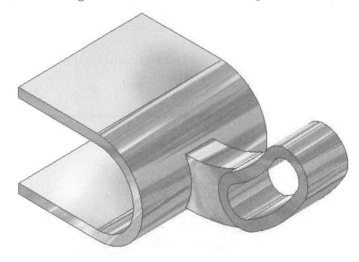

Figure 6-42 *Model after creating the cut feature*

Suppressing Features

As mentioned earlier, in a complex model, it is better to suppress the features that are not required for creating the other features. Once all the features are created, you can unsuppress the suppressed features. In Autodesk Inventor, the features are suppressed using the browser.

1.   Right-click on **Extrusion2** in the browser to display the shortcut menu.

2.   In the shortcut menu, choose **Suppress Features**.

You will notice that the second feature is no more visible. Also, the **Autodesk Inventor 11 - Suppress Feature** dialog box is displayed and the third feature and the cut feature is still visible on the model.

3. Choose **Accept** from the **Autodesk Inventor 11 - Suppress Feature** dialog box. Now, right-click on **Extrusion3** in the browser and then choose **Suppress Features** to suppress the join feature and the cut feature.

The only feature that is visible now is the base feature of the model.

Creating the Fifth Feature

The fifth feature is also a join feature and is created on an offset work plane. This work plane will be offset from the left face of the base feature to a distance of -17.5 mm. The negative value will make sure that the work plane is offset inside the model.

1. Define a new work plane at an offset of -17.5 mm from the left face of the base feature. Create the sketch for the join feature. Create the circle inside the sketch so that the hole is also created at the same time when you extrude the sketch.

2. Extrude the sketch to a distance of 8 mm using the **Join** operation and the **Mid-plane** option. If the **Autodesk Inventor** warning window appears, choose **Accept**.

3. Create a fillet of 1 mm radius. The model after creating the join feature and the fillet, is shown in Figure 6-43.

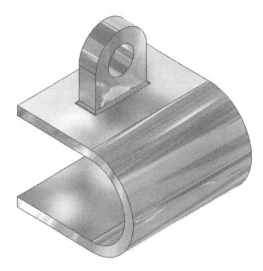

Figure 6-43 Model after creating the fifth feature and the fillet

Suppressing the Previous Feature

1. Right-click on **Extrusion5** in the browser to display the shortcut menu. Choose **Suppress**

Features from this menu; the fillet feature will also be suppressed because it is dependent on the join feature. The only feature that will be visible will be the base feature.

Creating the Slots and the Hole

Next, slots will be created on the front face of the base feature. Because both the slots will be cut to the same distance, you can draw the sketch for both the slots together and then extrude them using the **Cut** operation.

1. Define a new sketch plane on the front face of the base feature.

2. Draw the sketch for both the cut features and then extrude them to a distance of 8 mm using the **Cut** operation.

3. Create a drilled hole of 2.5 mm diameter on the face exposed by the slot on the left side. The depth of the hole is 4 mm. The model, after creating the slots and the hole, is shown in Figure 6-44.

Figure 6-44 Model after creating the cut and hole feature

Note
*The viewing direction of Figure 6-44 is changed using the **Common View** options.*

Unsuppressing the Features

Once all the features of the model are created, you can unsuppress the suppressed features and save the model. As mentioned earlier, all the suppressed features will be displayed in light gray color and will have a line that strikes through their names in the browser.

1. Right-click on **Extrusion2** in the browser and choose **Unsuppress Features** from the shortcut menu.

2. If Autodesk Inventor encounters any error while updating the features, the **Autodesk Inventor 11 - Unsuppress Feature** dialog box will be displayed. Choose **Accept**, if this dialog box is displayed. The second feature, which was the join feature, is unsuppressed.

3. Similarly, unsuppress the remaining suppressed features. Choose **Accept** in the **Autodesk Inventor 11 - Unsuppress Feature** dialog box whenever it is displayed. The final solid model of the Gear-shifter link, after unsuppressing all the suppressed features, is shown in Figure 6-45.

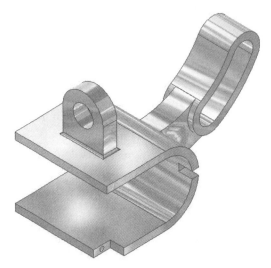

Figure 6-45 Final solid model of the Gear-shifter link

Saving the Model

1. Save the model with the name *PersonalProject\c06\Tutorial1.ipt* and close the file.

Tutorial 2

In this tutorial, you will create the model shown in Figure 6-46a. Its dimensions are shown in Figures 6-46b through 6-46d. After creating the model, save it with the name *PersonalProject\c06\Tutorial2.ipt*   **(Expected time: 45 min)**

Before you start creating the model, it is recommended that you outline the procedure for creating it. The steps required to complete this tutorial are listed next.

a. Create the base feature on the XZ plane, refer to Figure 6-47. The sketch for the base feature consists of a square with fillets on all the four corners.

b. On the front face of the base feature, create the counterbore holes by using the center points of fillets as the center of holes, refer to Figure 6-48.

c. Suppress the holes and create the cylindrical join feature on the front face of the base feature.

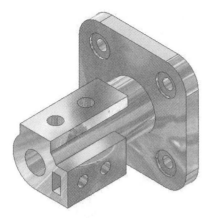

Figure 6-46a *Model for Tutorial 2*

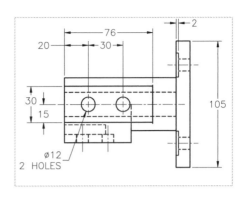

Figure 6-46b *Top view of the model*

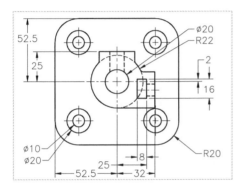

Figure 6-46c *Left-side view of the model*

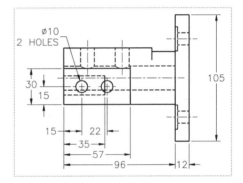

Figure 6-46d *Front view of the model*

d. Add two rectangular join features to the cylindrical feature and create the rectangular cut feature on one of the rectangular join feature, refer to Figure 6-50.

e. Finally, create all drilled holes by defining the sketch plane on the required planes. Once all the features are created, unsuppress the holes on the base feature, refer to Figure 6-51.

Creating the Base Feature

1. Start a new metric part file and then draw the sketch for the base feature on the XZ plane.

The sketch for the base feature will be a square of side 105 mm and with all four corners filleted with a radius of 20 mm.

2. Exit the sketching environment and extrude the sketch to a distance of 12 mm. The base feature of the model is shown in Figure 6-47.

Creating the Holes

The base feature has four counterbore holes. You can create these four holes concentric to the cylindrical faces of the fillet. You can also create one of the holes and then create a rectangular pattern for creating the remaining three holes.

1. Invoke the **Hole** tool and create the four counterbore holes using the **Concentric** placement option. Refer to Figure 6-46c for dimensions. The model, after creating the counterbore holes, is shown in Figure 6-48.

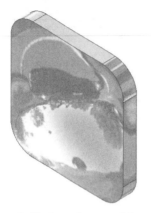

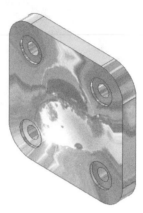

Figure 6-47 *Base feature of the model*

Figure 6-48 *Model after creating the counterbore holes*

Suppressing the Holes

Because you created four individual holes, the browser will display four hole operation with names **Hole1**, **Hole2**, **Hole3**, and **Hole4**. For this reason, you need to select all four holes and suppress them.

1. Press and hold the SHIFT key down and select all four holes from the browser.

2. Right-click on the selected holes in the browser to display the shortcut menu. In the shortcut menu, choose **Suppress Features**; all four holes are no more visible on the model. The only feature that is visible is the base feature.

Creating the Cylindrical and Rectangular Join Features

1. Define a new sketch plane on the front face of the base feature and then draw a circle that will define the sketch for the cylindrical feature. Extrude the circle to a distance of 96 mm.

2. Define a new sketch plane on the front face of the cylindrical feature and then create one of the rectangular join features. Similarly, create the other rectangular join feature, as shown in Figure 6-49.

Creating the Cut Feature and Holes

1. Define a new sketch plane on the front face of the cylindrical feature and then create the rectangular cut feature.

2. One by one, create holes on the faces of the rectangular join features. The model, after creating the holes and the cut feature, is shown in Figure 6-50.

 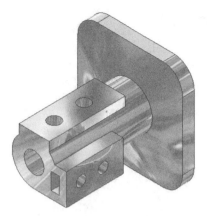

Figure 6-49 Model after creating the join features *Figure 6-50* After creating the cut feature and holes

Unsuppressing the Counterbore Holes

1. From the browser, select all the holes created on the base feature. Right-click on the selected holes and choose **Unsuppress Features** from the shortcut menu; all counterbore holes will now be displayed on the base feature. The final model for Tutorial 2 is shown in Figure 6-51.

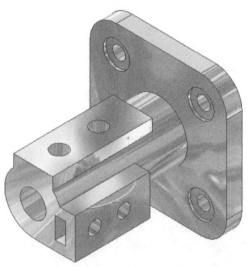

Figure 6-51 Final model for Tutorial 2

2. Save the model with the name *\PersonalProject\c06\Tutorial2.ipt* and close the file.

Tutorial 3

In this tutorial, you will create the model of the Body of the Butterfly Valve assembly, shown in Figure 6-52a. Its dimensions are shown in Figures 6-52b through 6-52d. After creating the model, modify the 175 mm dimension of the curved feature on the top face to 200 mm. The dimensions of the remaining five instances should also change automatically. Save the model with the name *\PersonalProject\c06\Tutorial3.ipt*.   **(Expected time: 45 min)**

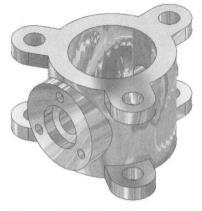

Figure 6-52a *Model for Tutorial 3*

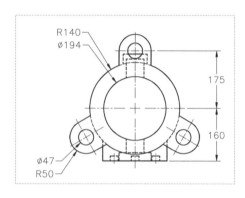

Figure 6-52b *Top view of the model*

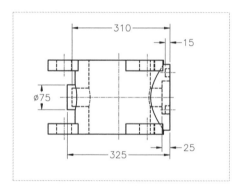

Figure 6-52c *Left-side view of the model*

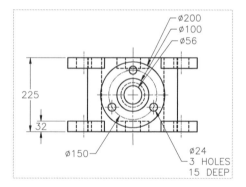

Figure 6-52d *Front view of the model*

Before you start creating the model, it is recommended that you outline the procedure for creating it. The following steps are required to complete this tutorial:

a. Create the base feature on the XY plane, refer to Figure 6-53. The sketch of the base feature consists of two circles and will be extruded using the **Mid-plane** option.
b. Define new offset work planes to create the two cylindrical join features on the cylindrical face of the base feature, refer to Figure 6-54.
c. Add the counterbore hole and three smaller holes on the front face of the second feature, refer to Figure 6-55.
d. Suppress the second and third features and then create the curved sketch feature with a hole on the top face of the model, refer to Figure 6-56.

e. Pattern the last feature using the **Circular Pattern** tool. Finally, mirror all the three instances of the circular pattern on the bottom face of the model, see Figure 6-58.

f. After creating the features, edit them as mentioned in the tutorial, see Figure 6-60.

Creating the Base Feature

1. Open a new metric part file and then create the base feature on the XY plane. Take the origin as the center of the two circles in the sketch of the base feature.

> **Tip**. *While creating the sketch for the base feature, it is recommended that you select the origin as the center of both the circles. The origin is the point at which the X and Y axes meet in the drawing window. This is because the origin is not only the point at which the X and Y axes meet in the sketching environment, but also the point at which all the three planes meet in the* **Part** *mode. Now, if the origin is selected as the center of the base feature, you can use the default XZ plane to create the offset planes. If the origin is not selected as the center of the base feature, you will have to first create a work plane tangent to the cylindrical face of the base feature. After creating a tangent work plane, you will have to use it to define the offset work plane.*

2. Extrude the sketch to a distance of 225 mm using the **Mid-plane** option.

The reason of extruding the sketch using the **Mid-plane** option is that you can use the XY plane as the plane for mirroring the features on the top face of the model to the bottom face of the model. If the base feature is not extruded using the **Mid-plane** option, you will have to create a new work plane for mirroring the features. The base feature of the model is shown in Figure 6-53.

Figure 6-53 *Base feature of the model*

Creating the Join Features on the Cylindrical Faces of the Base Feature

Since the base feature was created taking the origin as the center of the circles, you can use the XZ plane to create the offset work plane.

1. Create a new work plane at an offset of -160 mm from the XZ plane. The negative value will ensure that the work plane is created toward the front side of the base feature and not toward the back side.

2. Define a new sketch plane on **Work Plane1** and draw the sketch of the next feature using the origin of a new sketch plane as the center. Extrude it using the **To Next** extents option.

3. Similarly, define a new work plane at an offset of 325 mm from **Work Plane1**. Define a new sketch plane on **Work Plane2** and create the second join feature. The model, after creating the two join features, is shown in Figure 6-54.

Creating the Counterbore Hole and Drilled Holes on the Front Face of the Second Feature

1. Using the **Concentric** placement option, create the counterbore hole on the front face of the second feature.

2. Create one of the drilled holes on the front face of the second feature using a hole center.

3. Create a circular pattern containing three instances of the drilled holes. The model, after creating the counterbore hole and the three smaller drilled holes, is shown in Figure 6-55.

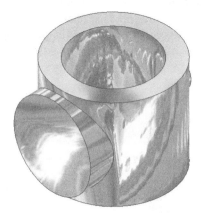   

Figure 6-54 Model after creating the join features   *Figure 6-55* Model after creating the holes

Suppressing the Features

Because the features other than the base feature are not required in creating the remaining features in the model, you can suppress them. This will reduce the complicacy of the model and it will be easier for you to create the remaining features.

1. Right-click on **Extrusion2** in the browser and choose **Suppress Features**.

You will notice that the counterbore hole and the three drilled holes are also suppressed. This is because the holes are created on the second join feature and so are dependent on it.

2. Similarly, right-click on **Extrusion3** in the browser and choose **Suppress Features**.

Creating the Join Feature on the Top Face of the Base Feature

1. Define a new sketch plane on the top face of the base feature and draw the sketch of the join feature. Include the circle in the sketch so that the hole is created automatically.

2. Extrude the sketch to a distance of 32 mm. The model, after creating the join feature on the top face of the base feature, is shown in Figure 6-56.

Creating the Circular Pattern of the Feature

1. Create a circular pattern of the feature on the top face of the base feature. The circular pattern should have three instances, as shown in Figure 6-57.

Figure 6-56 *Join feature on the top face*   ***Figure 6-57*** *After creating the circular pattern*

Mirroring the Features on the Bottom Face of the Base Feature

As the base feature was extruded using the **Mid-plane** option, you can use the XY plane for mirroring the feature on the bottom face of the base feature. This is because the base feature is extruded equally in both the directions of the XY plane.

1. Invoke the **Mirror Feature** tool and then select the join feature on the top face of the base feature and the circular pattern as the features to be mirrored.

2. Mirror the features using the XY plane as the mirror plane and choose **OK**.

Tip. *You can specify the features to be mirrored by selecting them in the drawing window or in the browser.*

Unsuppressing the Features

1. Right-click on **Extrusion2** in the browser and choose **Unsuppress Features**. The second feature as well as the holes will be unsuppressed.

2. Right-click on **Extrusion3** and then choose **Unsuppress Features** from the shortcut menu to unsuppress the third feature also. The model, after creating all the features, is shown in Figure 6-58.

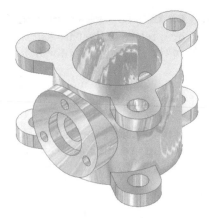

Figure 6-58 *Model after creating all the features*

Modifying the Dimensions of Feature on the Top Face of the Model

Out of the three instances of the join feature on the top face of the model and the three instances on the bottom face, only one was actually sketched. The rest were either created using the **Circular Pattern** tool or the **Mirror Feature** tool. Therefore, if you modify the original feature, the rest of the features will be automatically modified.

1. Right-click on **Extrusion4** in the browser to display the shortcut menu. In this menu, choose **Show Dimensions**, see Figure 6-59.

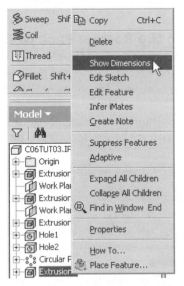

Figure 6-59 *Editing the feature using the browser*

The basic sketch of the feature will be displayed on the feature along with the dimensions. You can double-click on any dimension to display the **Edit Dimension** toolbar. This toolbar can be used to edit the selected dimension value.

2. Double-click on the 175 mm dimension to display the **Edit Dimension** toolbar and enter the dimension value as 200 mm.

    You will notice that the temporary sketch of the feature that is displayed in the drawing window is modified due to the change in the dimension value. However, the features are still not modified. This is because the features will be modified only when you choose the **Update** button from the **Inventor Standard** toolbar.

3. Choose the **Update** button from the **Inventor Standard** toolbar. All six instances of the feature will be automatically modified. The model for Tutorial 3 is shown in Figure 6-60.

Figure 6-60 *Final model after editing features*

Note

While drawing the sketch for the feature that you modified in the last step, if you do not apply the coincident constraint between the lower endpoint of the lines of the sketch and the outer circle of the base feature, the feature will be separated from the base feature when you modify it. You can also apply the concentric constraint between the arc of the sketch and the outer circle of the base feature to avoid separation.

4. Save the model with the name *\PersonalProject\c06\Tutorial3.ipt* and then close the file.

Self-Evaluation Test

Answer the following questions and then compare your answers with those given at the end of this chapter:

1. Most of the designs require editing, either during or after creation. (T/F)

2. In Autodesk Inventor, all editing operations are performed using toolbars. (T/F)

3. You can also edit a hole feature by right-clicking on it in the browser and then choosing **Show Dimensions**. (T/F)

4. You can also display the dimensions of a feature on the model by double-clicking on the feature in the browser. (T/F)

5. If you right-click on the third extruded feature in a model and choose **Edit Feature** from the shortcut menu, the _____ dialog box will be displayed.

6. The features edited using the dimensions can be updated by choosing the _____ button from the _____.

7. The features in the model can be suppressed by right-clicking on the feature and choosing _____ from the shortcut menu.

8. The _____ dialog box is used to paste the copied features in a new file.

9. The _____ button in the **Paste Features** dialog box is chosen to adjust the preview of the pasted feature on the selected plane.

10. If the feature that you select to suppress has some dependent features, they will also be _____.

Review Questions

Answer the following questions:

1. Autodesk Inventor allows you to copy the features from one file to the other. (T/F)

2. Autodesk Inventor allows you to edit the sketches of the sketched features. (T/F)

3. When you choose the option of displaying the dimensions of the feature for editing, the dimensions will be retained on the screen even after the editing operation is over. (T/F)

4. The feature to be copied can be rotated at any angle. (T/F)

5. After editing the sketch of the feature, you have to make sure the sketch is still a closed loop. (T/F)

6. You can redefine the sketching plane of a sketched feature. (T/F)

7. You can specify whether or not you want to delete the dependent sketches and features. (T/F)

8. In the **Paste Features** dialog box, you can specify whether you want to paste only the selected feature or the dependent features also. (T/F)

9. All suppressed features are displayed in light gray color in the browser. (T/F)

10. If you edit a feature using the browser, you do not need to update it to view the effect of the editing operation. (T/F)

Exercises

Exercise 1

Create the model of the Slide Bracket shown in Figure 6-61a. Its dimensions are shown in Figures 6-61b through 6-61d. After creating the model, save it with the name \PersonalProject\c06\Exercise1.ipt **(Expected time: 45 min)**

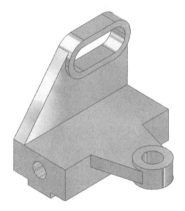

Figure 6-61a *Model for Exercise 1*

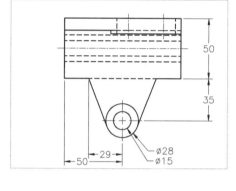

Figure 6-61b *Top view of the model*

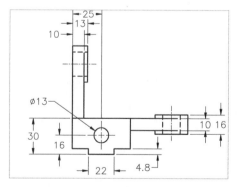

Figure 6-61c *Left-side view of the model*

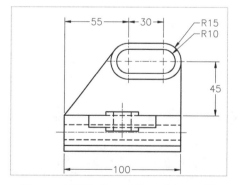

Figure 6-61d *Front view of the model*

Exercise 2

Create the model shown in Figure 6-62a. Its dimensions are shown in Figures 6-62b through 6-62d. After creating the model, save it with the name given below.

\PersonalProject\c06\Exercise2.ipt   **(Expected time: 45 min)**

Figure 6-62a *Model for Exercise 2*

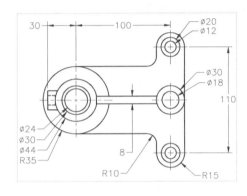

Figure 6-62b *Top view of the model*

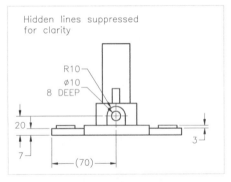

Figure 6-62c *Left-side view of the model*

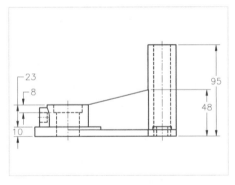

Figure 6-62d *Front view of the model*

Exercise 3

Create the model shown in Figure 6-63a. Its dimensions are shown in Figures 6-63b through 6-63d. After creating the model, save it with the name given below.

\PersonalProject\c06\Exercise3.ipt   **(Expected time: 45 min)**

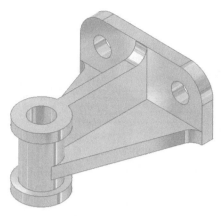

Figure 6-63a Model for Exercise 3

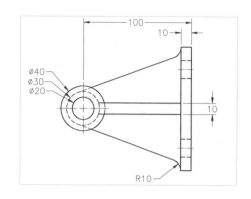

Figure 6-63b Top view of the model

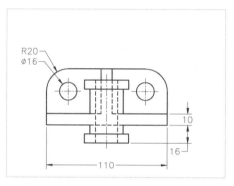

Figure 6-63c Left-side view of the model

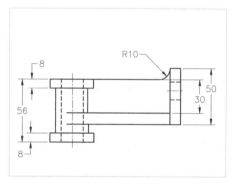

Figure 6-63d Front view of the model

Exercise 4

Create the model shown in Figure 6-64a. Its dimensions are shown in Figures 6-64b through 6-64d. After creating the model, save it with the name given below.

\PersonalProject\c06\Exercise4.ipt   (Expected time: 45 min)

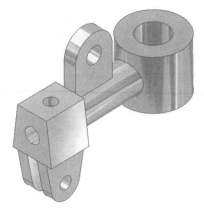

Figure 6-64a *Model for Exercise 4*

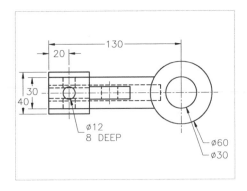

Figure 6-64b *Top view of the model*

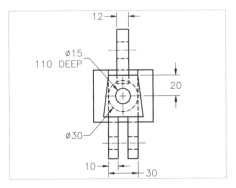

Figure 6-64c *Left-side view of the model*

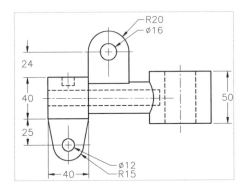

Figure 6-64d *Front view of the model*

Answers to Self-Evaluation Test

1. T, **2.** F, **3.** T, **4.** T, **5. Extrude: Extrusion3**, **6. Update, Inventor Standard** toolbar, **7. Suppress Features**, **8. Paste Features**, **9. Refresh**, **10.** suppressed

Chapter 7

Advanced Modeling Tools-II

Learning Objectives

After completing this chapter, you will be able to:
- *Create sweep features.*
- *Create lofted features.*
- *Create coils.*
- *Create internal or external threads.*
- *Create shell features.*
- *Apply drafts on the faces of a model.*
- *Split faces of a model or the complete model.*
- *Delete the selected faces of the model.*
- *Replace the selected face of a model with surfaces.*
- *Add surface patches.*
- *Stitch multiple surfaces in a single surface.*
- *Create sculpt features.*

ADVANCED MODELING TOOLS

The first few advanced modeling tools were discussed in Chapter 5, Advanced Modeling Tools-I. In this chapter, you will learn about the remaining ones.

Creating Sweep Features

Toolbar:	Part Features > Sweep
Panel bar:	Part Features > Sweep

The next advanced modeling tool is the **Sweep** tool and is used to create sweep features. A sweep feature is created when a closed sketch is swept along an open or a closed path. Therefore, to create the sweep feature, you need two unconsumed sketches: a closed sketch (called profile) and a path. It is recommended that the profile and the path used to create the sweep feature intersect at a point. If the profile does not intersect with the path, an error message is displayed and you will be informed that the profile and the path do not intersect. You will also be prompted to specify whether you want to continue. Note that the result of this kind of sweep may be different than what is required.

The path for the sweep feature is created using the usual method of creating sketches. It can be a combination of the sketcher entities such as lines, arcs, circles, splines, and ellipses. As mentioned earlier, it is recommended that the profile and the path should intersect. Therefore, after you have finished drawing the path, create a work plane normal to the path and at its start point. To create a work plane using the path, exit the sketching environment and choose **Work Plane** from the **Part Features** panel bar. Now, select the start point of the path and then select a line segment to which the resulting work plane will be normal. If the path does not have a straight line segment, then select a plane from the browser to which the resulting work plane will be parallel. Next, create the profile on that work plane. Figure 7-1 shows a profile and a 2D path and Figure 7-2 shows the resulting sweep feature.

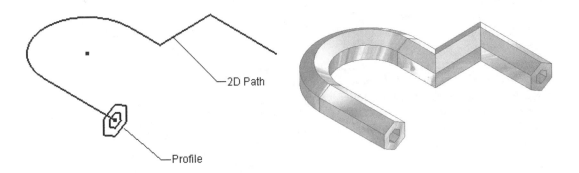

Figure 7-1 Path and profile for sweep   *Figure 7-2* Resulting sweep feature

To create the sweep feature, choose the **Sweep** button from the **Part Features** panel bar; the **Sweep** dialog box will be displayed, as shown in Figure 7-3. The options in various tabs of this dialog box are discussed next.

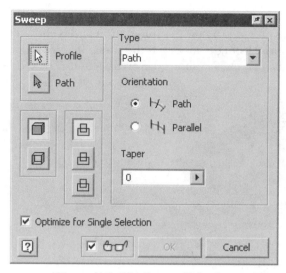

Figure 7-3 The Sweep dialog box

Shape Area

This area is available on the top left corner of the dialog box and provides the following two buttons:

Profile

The **Profile** button is chosen to select the profile for the sweep feature. Remember that the profile has to be a closed loop for creating the solid sweep feature. When you invoke the **Sweep** dialog box, the **Profile** button will be chosen by default and you will be prompted to select the profile for the sweep feature.

Path

The **Path** button is chosen to select the path for the sweep feature.

Output Area

The buttons in the **Output** area are chosen to specify the type of output of the **Sweep** tool. If the profile selected is closed, the **Solid** button is chosen by default. As a result, a solid sweep feature will be created. If you choose the **Surface** button, the resulting sweep will be a surface feature. The **Surface** button is chosen automatically, if you select an open profile.

Operation Area

This area provides the following buttons:

Join

The **Join** button is the first button provided in the area that is on the right side of the **Shape** tab. This button is chosen to create a sweep feature by adding material to the model. Figure 7-4 shows the sweep feature created using the **Join** operation.

Cut

The **Cut** button is provided below the **Join** button and is chosen to create a sweep feature by removing material from the model. If the sweep feature is the first feature, this button will not be available. Figure 7-5 shows the sweep feature created using the **Cut** operation.

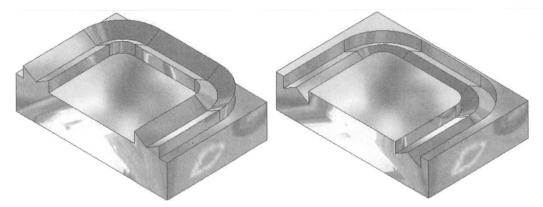

Figure 7-4 *Sweep feature created using the **Join*** *operation*

Figure 7-5 *Sweep feature created using the **Cut*** *operation*

Intersect

The **Intersect** button is provided below the **Cut** button and is used only when you have an existing feature. This means that this button will not be available if the sweep feature is the first feature in the model. This operation is used to create a sweep feature such that the material common to the profile and the existing feature is retained. The remaining material is removed from the model.

Optimize for Single Selection

If this check box is selected, the next selection step is activated automatically after you compete the first selection. For example, the **Path** button is automatically chosen as soon as you select any one sketch as the profile. If you clear this check box, you can select nested sketches as the profile.

Type Area

The options available in this area allow you to create three types of sweeps: using only path, using path and a guide curve, and using a path and a guide surface. Creating all these three types of sweeps is discussed next.

Creating Sweeps with Path Curve

By default, the **Path** option is selected from the drop-down list in the **Type** area. As a result, the option to create the sweep feature with the path curve is active. This option allows you to create a sweep feature that follows the specified path. You can specify whether the orientation of the profile will be constant to the path or parallel to the sketching plane. The options that are available when you select the **Path** option from the drop-down list are discussed next.

Path

This radio button is selected by default. It forces the profile to remain constantly oriented to the path at all points.

Parallel

This radio button forces the sketch to remain parallel to the sketching plane throughout the sweep feature.

Figure 7-6 shows the profile and the path to create the sweep feature. Figure 7-7 shows the sweep feature created with the **Path** radio button selected. As evident in this figure, the profile remains oriented to the path throughout the sweep feature. Figure 7-8 shows the sweep feature with the **Parallel** radio button selected. As evident in this figure, the profile is oriented parallel to the sketching plane throughout the sweep feature.

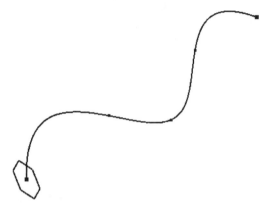

Figure 7-6 Profile and path for the sweep feature

*Figure 7-7 Sweep feature with the **Path** radio button selected*

*Figure 7-8 Sweep feature with the **Parallel** radio button selected*

Taper

This edit box is used to define the taper angle for the sweep feature. A positive taper angle will taper the sweep feature outwards and a negative taper angle will taper it inwards. Figure 7-9 shows a sweep feature with a positive taper angle and Figure 7-10 shows a sweep feature with a negative taper angle.

Creating Sweeps with Path and Guide Curves

To invoke this option, choose the **Path & Guide Rail** option from the drop-down list in the

Figure 7-9 *Sweep feature created with a positive taper angle*

Figure 7-10 *Sweep feature created with a negative taper angle*

Type area; the options in this area will be modified, as shown in Figure 7-11. These options are discussed next.

Figure 7-11 *The* ***Type*** *area with different options*

Guide Rail

This button is chosen to select the guide curve for creating the sweep feature. Figure 7-12 shows the profile, path, and guide curve for creating the sweep feature.

Profile Scaling

The radio buttons available in this area are used to specify the scaling method for the profile that is swept using a path and a guide curve. Selecting the **X & Y** radio button ensures that the sweep feature is scaled in both X and Y directions. Figure 7-12 shows the profile, path, and guide curve to create the sweep feature and Figure 7-13 shows the preview of the sweep feature with scaling in X and Y directions. Selecting the **X** radio button ensures that the sweep feature is scaled only in the X direction, as shown in the preview in Figure 7-14. Selecting the **None** radio button ensures there is no scaling in the sweep feature. However, if there is any rotation in the guide curve, it will be reflected in the sweep feature also. Figure 7-15 shows the preview of the feature with no scaling.

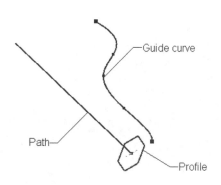

Figure 7-12 *Profile, path, and guide curve for creating the sweep feature*

Figure 7-13 *Sweep feature scaled in both X and Y directions*

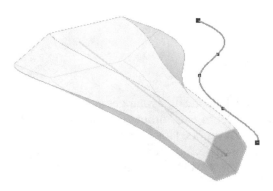

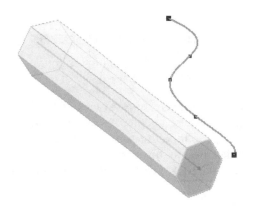

Figure 7-14 *Sweep feature scaled only in the X direction*

Figure 7-15 *Sweep feature with no scaling*

Creating Sweeps with Path and Guide Surface

To invoke this option, choose the **Path & Guide Surface** option from the drop-down list in the **Type** area; the **Guide Surface** button will be displayed in this area and you will be prompted to select the surface to control the profile twist. Figure 7-16 shows a the path and profile for a sweep feature. Figure 7-17 shows a sweep feature created using the **Path** option and Figure 7-18 shows the sweep feature with the same profile and path, but created using the **Path & Guide Surface** option with the top face of the base feature taken as the guide surface. As evident in Figure 7-17, the shape and twist of the sweep feature is controlled by the guide surface.

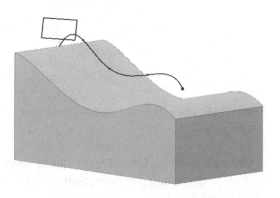

Figure 7-16 *Profile and path for the sweep feature*

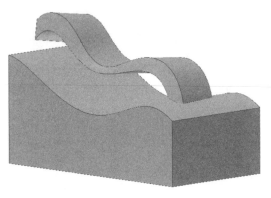

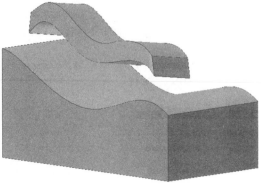

Figure 7-17 *Sweep feature created using the* ***Path*** *option*

Figure 7-18 *Sweep feature created using the* ***Path & Guide Surface*** *option*

Creating Lofted Features

Toolbar:	Part Features > Loft
Panel bar:	Part Features > Loft

Lofted features are created by blending more than one dissimilar geometries together. These geometries may or may not be parallel to each other. The sketches for the solid loft features should be closed profiles or points. However, for a surface model, the sketches can be open profiles. Figure 7-19 shows a circle, a triangle, and a point drawn on planes parallel to each other, but at some offset. Figure 7-20 shows the resulting lofted feature.

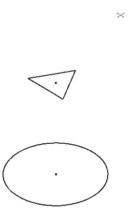

Figure 7-19 *Three dissimilar sketches drawn on parallel planes*

Figure 7-20 *Feature created after blending the sketches*

In Autodesk Inventor, lofted features are created using the **Loft** tool. When you invoke this tool, the **Loft** dialog box is displayed. The options provided in various tabs of this dialog box are discussed next.

Curves Tab

The options in the **Curves** tab (Figure 7-21) are used to select the sketches, rails, and center lines for creating the loft features. These options are discussed next.

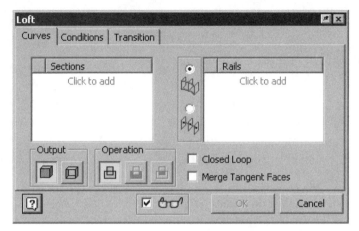

*Figure 7-21 The **Curves** tab of the **Loft** dialog box*

Sections Area

When you invoke the **Loft** dialog box, you will be prompted to select a sketch for creating the loft feature. The **Sections** area displays all the sketches that you have selected for creating the loft feature. When you select the sketches, a green arrow appears on the graphics screen showing the path for the loft feature. For example, if you select three sketches: Sketch1, Sketch2, and Sketch3 in the same sequence, two arrows will appear on the graphics screen. The first arrow will point from Sketch1 to Sketch2 and the second arrow will point from Sketch2 to Sketch3. This suggests that the resulting loft feature is a blending between Sketch1-Sketch2 and Sketch2-Sketch3.

Tip. *You can also modify the sequence in which the sketches are selected using the **Sections** area. To modify the sequence, select the sketch and drag it above or below the other sketch. The arrow direction will also change automatically in the preview of the model.*

Output Area

The options in the **Output** area are used to specify the output of the **Loft** tool. If you select closed loops to blend, the **Solid** button is chosen in this area. As a result, a solid loft feature is created. If you select the **Surface** button, the resulting loft will be a surface.

Operation Area

The options in the **Operation** area are used to specify the type of operation performed using the **Loft** tool. If this is the first feature, only the **Join** button will be available in this area. The buttons in this area are discussed next.

Join. The **Join** button is the first button in the **Operation** area and is chosen to create a loft feature by adding material to the model.

Cut. The **Cut** button is chosen to create a loft feature by removing material common to the loft and the model. This button will not be available if the loft feature is the first feature.

Intersect. The **Intersect** button is provided below the **Cut** button and is chosen to create a loft feature by retaining material common to the loft and the model. The remaining material will be removed from the model. This button will also not be available if the loft feature is the first feature.

Rails

 This is the first radio button available in the area on the right of the **Sections** area. If this radio button is selected, the **Rails** area to select rails for the loft feature will be displayed on its right. The rails are used to control the shape of the entire body of the loft. You can use open sketches as rails to control the shape of the loft. Note that the rails should intersect all the sections selected to loft. To add rails, click on **Click to add** in the **Rails** area and then select the rails. The names of the selected rails will be displayed in this area. Figure 7-22 shows the sections and rails used to create the loft feature. Figure 7-23 shows the loft feature without selecting the rails and Figure 7-24 shows the loft feature with rails.

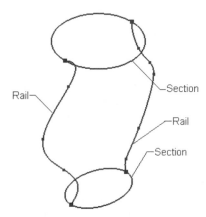

Figure 7-22 Sections and rails for loft

Figure 7-23 Loft without selecting rails

Figure 7-24 Loft with rails

Tip. *The rails used to guide the shape of the loft should intersect all the sections of the loft. If the rail does not intersect the sections, an error message will be displayed. You can make sure that the sketch of the rail intersects the section by projecting the sections on the sketching plane of rails and then adding a **Coincident** constraint between the rail and the projected sections. Make sure you convert projected entities into construction elements before exiting the sketching environment.*

Center Line

This radio button is available below the **Rails** radio button. If this radio button is selected, the **Center Line** area to select the center line for the loft feature will be displayed on its right. A center line is a curve to which the resulting loft feature will be normal at every point. The center line may or may not intersect the sections. Figure 7-25 shows the two sections that are drawn at parallel planes and the curve to be used as the center line. Figure 7-26 shows the loft feature without selecting the center line and Figure 7-27 shows the loft feature with the center line.

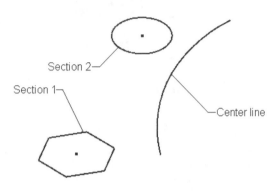

Figure 7-25 Sections and the center line for loft

Figure 7-26 Loft without selecting the center line   *Figure 7-27 Loft with center line*

Closed Loop

The **Closed Loop** check box is selected to close the loft feature by joining the end section with the start section. Figure 7-28 shows a loft feature created with this check box cleared and Figure 7-29 shows a loft feature created with this check box selected.

Merge Tangent Faces

If this check box is selected, the tangent faces are merged together and no edge is created between the tangent faces of the loft feature.

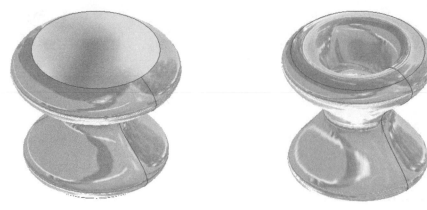

Figure 7-28 *Open-ended loft feature*   ***Figure 7-29*** *Closed-ended loft feature*

Conditions Tab

The options in the **Conditions** tab, shown in Figure 7-30, are used to control the shape of the lofted feature by applying end conditions to the sections at the two ends. The two end sections or edges selected to create the loft feature are displayed in the list box of this tab.

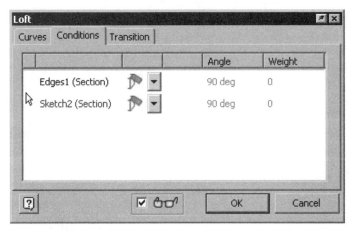

Figure 7-30 *The **Conditions** tab of the **Loft** dialog box*

You can apply the following three types of end conditions using the drop-down list that is available when you click on the field on the left of the **Angle** column.

Free Condition

If this option is selected, no end condition is applied to the end sections of the loft feature. In this type of end condition, the **Angle** and **Weight** columns will not be enabled.

Tangent Condition

The **Tangent Condition** option will be available only if the start section or the end section is a planar face of an existing feature. If this option is selected, the resulting loft feature will be tangent to the adjacent faces of the planar face that was selected as one of the end sections. Figure 7-31 shows the preview of the loft feature in which the upper section is a hexagon and the lower section is the cylindrical edge of the top face of a cylinder. In this preview, no end condition is applied by selecting the **Free Condition** option. Figure 7-32 shows the preview using the same conditions. But in this figure, the tangent condition is applied. As evident in Figure 7-32, the loft feature is tangent to the base cylinder at the start section because of the tangent condition.

Figure 7-31 *Loft with no end condition*   *Figure 7-32* *Loft with tangent end condition*

 Tip. *An angle value greater than 90-degree will create an obtuse section in the loft feature. Similarly, an angle value less than 90-degree will create an acute section in the loft feature.*

Direction Condition
The **Direction Condition** button is chosen to define the end conditions using the **Angle** and **Weight** edit boxes. This type of end condition is available only when the section is a 2D profile.

Angle
The **Angle** edit box will be available only when the value in the **Weight** edit box is more than zero (default value). This edit box is used to define the angle at the start section and the end section of the loft. Remember that you cannot define an angle for the intermediate sketches. To specify the value of the angle at the start section, select the first sketch from the **Conditions** area and then set the value in this edit box. Similarly, to specify the value of the angle at the end section, select the last sketch from the **Conditions** area and then set the value in this edit box. Figure 7-33 shows the various angle values at the start and end sections of the loft.

Weight
The **Weight** edit box is used to specify the distance to which the resulting feature will maintain the angle value or tangency at the start or the end sections. Greater the value of weight, more will be the distance to which the angle value or tangency will be maintained. To define the weight value, select the first or the last sketch from the **Conditions** area

and then define the value in this edit box. Figure 7-33 shows the various weight values at the start and end sections of the loft.

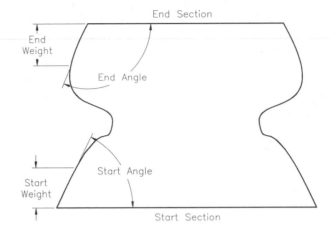

Figure 7-33 Parameters associated with a loft feature

Figure 7-34 shows a loft with weight at the tangent end as 0.75 and weight at the other end as 4. Figure 7-35 shows the same loft with weight at the tangent end as 1.5 and weight at the other end as 8.

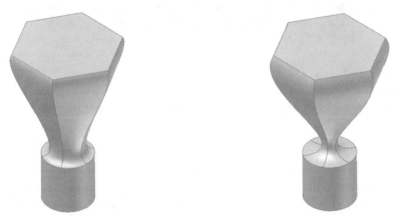

Figure 7-34 Start weight=0.75, end weight=4   *Figure 7-35 Start weight=1.5, end weight=8*

Transition Tab

The options in the **Transition** tab, shown in Figure 7-36, are used to set the mapping options for the segments of the various sections while blending.

Automatic Mapping

This check box is selected by default when you invoke the **Loft** dialog box. As a result, all the segments of the various sections map to each other using the default options and

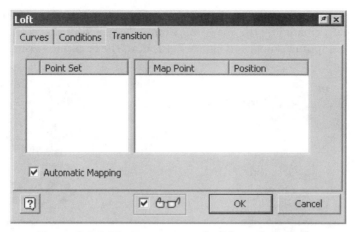

*Figure 7-36 The **Transition** tab of the **Loft** dialog box*

there is minimum or no twisting in the loft feature. If this check box is selected, the remaining areas in the **Transition** tab are not enabled. Figure 7-37 shows the preview of the loft feature between three sections. The lines at the vertices in this figure show how the various segments and points map to each other while blending. Figure 7-38 shows the loft feature created between the three sections using automatic mapping.

Figure 7-37 Preview of the default mapping   *Figure 7-38 Resulting loft feature*

Point Set

The **Point Set** area will be enabled only when the **Automatic Mapping** check box is cleared. This area displays all the sets of points used to map the segments and points of various sections in the loft feature. The number of sets of points in this area is equal to the number of green lines in the preview of the loft feature. The first set of points will be displayed in red in the preview. Similarly, the set of points you click on in this area will be displayed in red in the preview. To introduce twist in the loft feature, delete all the sets of points in this area by clicking on them and then pressing the DELETE key. Next, click on **Click to add**. You will be prompted to select a point. Select one point each on all the sketches. Similarly, to create the second set, click on **Click to add** and then select the set of points on all the sections. Follow this procedure to create the required number of sets. The loft feature will follow the path created by the mapping points. Figure 7-39 shows the path created by selecting the mapping points and Figure 7-40 shows the resulting twisted loft feature.

Figure 7-39 *Defining the mapping points*   *Figure 7-40* *Resulting twisted loft feature*

Map Point Area

The **Map Point** area displays the section points corresponding to the point set selected in the **Point Set** area. For example, **Sketch1** in this area represents the mapping point of the first section corresponding to the point set selected in the **Point Set** area. The number of items in this area depends on the number of sections in the loft.

Position Area

The **Position** area displays the position of the mapping point in terms of the length of the edge on which it lies. The total length of the edge on which the point lies is considered as 1. As a result, if the mapping point lies on the start point of the edge, its position is taken as 0 and so is displayed as 0 in this area. Similarly, if the mapping point lies on the endpoint of the edge, its position is displayed as 1 in this area. You can select any intermediate point on the edge to define the location of the mapping point.

Creating Coil Features

Toolbar:	Part Features > Coil
Panel bar:	Part Features > Coil

 A coil feature is created by sweeping a profile about a helical path. Examples of the coil feature are springs, filaments of light bulbs, and so on. A spring created using the coil feature is shown in Figure 7-41.

To create a coil feature in Autodesk Inventor, you need the profile and an axis that will be used to create the helical path. You can select the standard X, Y, or Z axis to create the coil feature or create a new work axis. The coil features are created using various tabs of the **Coil** dialog box. This dialog box is displayed by choosing the **Coil** button from the **Part Features** panel bar. Depending on the parameters defined in the **Coil** dialog box, an imaginary helical path will be

Figure 7-41 *Spring created using the coil feature*

created and the profile will be swept along that path. Therefore, to create a coil feature, you need only one unconsumed sketch, which will define the profile of the coil section. The options in the **Coil** dialog box are discussed next.

Coil Shape Tab

The options in the **Coil Shape** tab (Figure 7-42) are used to select the profile of the coil feature and the axis about which the imaginary helical path will be created. You can also specify whether the coil will be created in the clockwise direction or the counterclockwise direction using the options in this tab. All the options in this tab are discussed next.

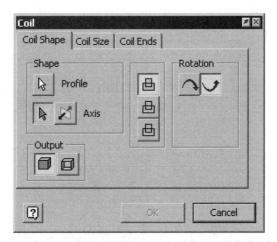

Figure 7-42 *The **Coil Shape** tab of the **Coil** dialog box*

Shape Area

The options in this area are used to select the profile and the axis of the coil.

Profile. The **Profile** button is chosen to select the profile of the coil. If the drawing consists of a single unconsumed sketch, it will be automatically selected as the profile of the coil feature.

Axis. The **Axis** button is chosen to select the axis for creating the coil feature. When you select the axis, an imaginary helical path will be created around the selected axis. The preview of the helical path will be displayed in the graphics window. The entities that can be selected as the axis for creating the coil feature are work axes, linear edges of a model, line segments, and so on. You can reverse the direction of the path by choosing the **Flip** button provided on the right of the **Axis** button.

Join
The **Join** button is the first button in the area between the **Shape** area and the **Rotation** area. This operation is used to create a coil feature by adding material to the model, see Figure 7-43.

Cut
The **Cut** button is provided below the **Join** button. This operation is used to create a coil feature by removing material from the model, see Figure 7-44.

*Figure 7-43 Coil feature created on a cylinder using the **Join** operation*

*Figure 7-44 Coil feature created on a cylinder using the **Cut** operation*

Note
*The **Cut** operation of the **Coil** tool can be used for creating internal or external threads in the model. However, it is recommended that you use the **Thread** tool for directly creating the threads. The use of this tool will be discussed later in this chapter.*

Intersect
The **Intersect** button is provided below the **Cut** button. This operation is used to create a coil feature by retaining material common to the model and the coil. The remaining material will be removed.

Note

*The area with the **Join**, **Cut**, and the **Intersect** button will not be available if the coil is the first feature.*

Shape Area
This area is used to specify whether the resulting coil will be a solid feature or a surface.

Coil Size Tab
The options in this tab are used to define the type of method and the other parameters that will be used for creating the coil, see Figure 7-45.

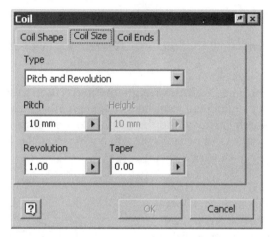

*Figure 7-45 The **Coil Size** tab of the **Coil** dialog box*

Type
The **Type** drop-down list is used to select the method for creating the coil feature. The methods that are available in this drop-down list for creating the coil are discussed next.

Pitch and Revolution. The **Pitch and Revolution** method is used to create the coil by defining the pitch and the number of revolutions in the coil. The pitch value can be specified in the **Pitch** edit box and the number of revolutions can be specified in the **Revolution** edit box. Both these edit boxes will be available when you select the **Pitch and Revolution** option from the **Type** drop-down list. You can also define a taper angle for the coil feature in the **Taper** edit box. A positive taper angle will taper the coil outward and a negative taper angle will taper the coil inward. Figure 7-46 shows a coil created with a positive taper and Figure 7-47 shows a coil created with a negative taper.

Revolution and Height. The **Revolution and Height** method is used to create the coil by defining the number of revolutions in it and its total height. The number of revolutions can be defined in the **Revolution** edit box and the height can be defined in the **Height** edit box. Both these edit boxes will be available when you select the **Revolution and Height** option from the **Type** drop-down list.

Figure 7-46 *Coil feature created with a positive taper angle*

Figure 7-47 *Coil feature created with a negative taper angle*

Pitch and Height. The **Pitch and Height** method is used to create the coil by defining the pitch of the coil and the total height of the coil. The value of the pitch can be defined in the **Pitch** edit box and the height can be defined in the **Height** edit box. Both these edit boxes will be available when you select the **Pitch and Height** option from the **Type** drop-down list.

Spiral. The **Spiral** method is used to create a spiral coil in a single plane. The spiral coil can be created using only the pitch of the coil and the number of revolutions in the coil. Because the spiral coil is created in a single plane, the **Height** edit box will not be available when you use this method. Also, you cannot define the taper angle for a spiral coil and so the **Taper** edit box also will not be available. Figure 7-48 shows a spiral coil.

Figure 7-48 *Spiral coil*

Coil Ends Tab

The options in this tab are used to specify the type of ends of the imaginary helical path that will be used to create the coil, see Figure 7-49. These options are discussed next.

Start Area

The options in the **Start** area are used to specify the end type at the start section of the imaginary helical path. The type of start section can be selected from the drop-down list in this area. These options are discussed next.

Natural. The **Natural** option is the default option that is selected in this drop-down list. If this option is selected, no other option in this area is available.

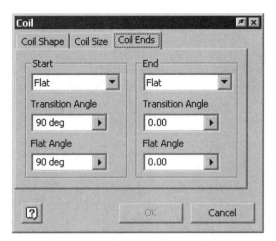

*Figure 7-49 The **Coil Ends** tab of the **Coil** dialog box*

Flat. If the **Flat** option is selected, you can specify a different start section of the helical path. The other options in this area will be available only if this option is selected.

Transition Angle. The **Transition Angle** edit box is used to specify the angle of transition of the coil at the start section of the coil. This option works in association with the number of revolutions in the coil and is generally used in coils with less than one revolution. The value of the transition angle can vary from 0-degree to 360-degree.

Flat Angle. The **Flat Angle** edit box is used to specify the angle through which the coil will extend beyond the transition at the start section of the coil. The value of the transition angle can vary from 0-degree to 360-degree.

End Area
The options in the **End** area are similar to those discussed in the **Start** area. The only difference is that these options are used to specify the end type at the end section of the imaginary helical path.

Creating Threads

Toolbar:	Part Features > Thread
Panel bar:	Part Features > Thread

Autodesk Inventor allows you to directly create internal or external threading in a model. Internal threads are created on the inner surface of a feature. For example, the threads created on the hole inside a cylinder are called internal threads, see Figure 7-50. External threads are created on the outer surface of a feature or a model. For example, the threads created on a bolt, see Figure 7-51.

Figure 7-50 *Internal threads in a cylinder*

Figure 7-51 *External threads on a bolt*

You can create the threads using the **Thread** tool. When you invoke this tool, the **Thread** dialog box is displayed. The options in both tabs of the **Thread** dialog box are discussed next.

Location Tab

The options in the **Location** tab are used to define the location, length, and offset of the threads, see Figure 7-52. These options are discussed next.

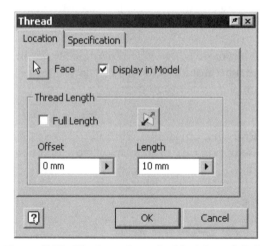

Figure 7-52 *The **Location** tab of the **Thread** dialog box*

Face

The **Face** button is chosen to select the face on which the threads will be created. When you invoke the **Thread** dialog box, this button will be automatically chosen and you will be prompted to select the face on which the threads will be created.

Display in Model

The **Display in Model** check box is selected to display the threads in the model. If this check box is cleared, the threads will be created, but will not be displayed in the model. They will be displayed only in the browser.

Thread Length Area

The options in the **Thread Length** area are used to specify the length of the threads. These options are discussed next.

Full Length. The **Full Length** check box is selected to create the threads through the length of the selected face. By default, this check box is selected. As a result, no other option in the **Thread Length** area will be available. Figure 7-53 shows a bolt with the threads created through its length. If you clear this check box, the remaining options in this area will be activated.

Flip. The **Flip** button is chosen to reverse the direction of thread creation.

Figure 7-53 Full length threads on a bolt

Offset. The **Offset** edit box is used to define the distance by which the threads should be offset from the starting edge of the face selected for creating the threads. By default, the value of the offset distance is zero. If you specify any offset value, the start point of the threads will move away from the start of the face selected for threading. Figure 7-54 shows the threads created at an offset distance of 0 mm from the top face and Figure 7-55 shows the threads created at an offset distance of 20 mm from the top face.

Figure 7-54 Threads at on offset of 0 mm

Figure 7-55 Threads at on offset of 20 mm from the top face

Length. The **Length** edit box is used to specify the length up to which the threads will be created on the selected face.

Note
*You cannot define a negative value for the length of the threads or the offset of the threads. If you want to create the threads in the opposite direction, choose the **Flip** button. The direction will reverse automatically.*

Specification Tab

The options in this tab are used to define the type of threads that will be created and the other parameters related with the type of threads, see Figure 7-56.

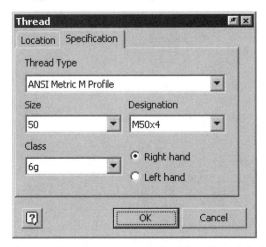

*Figure 7-56   The **Specification** tab of the **Thread** dialog box*

Thread Type

The **Thread Type** drop-down list is used to select the predefined thread types. There are some predefined thread types that are saved in Microsoft Excel spreadsheet. This spreadsheet is stored in the directory *Program Files\Autodesk\Inventor 11\Design Data*. You can also add customized thread types in this spreadsheet and use them in the model.

Size

The **Size** drop-down list is used to select the nominal diameter of the threads. Depending on the type of thread selected from the **Thread Type** drop-down list, the values in this drop-down list will change. You can select the required value of the diameter of the threads from this drop-down list.

Designation

The **Designation** drop-down list is used to select the designation of the required threads. The designation depends on the type and size of threads.

Class

The **Class** drop-down list is used to select the predefined class of threads, which will depend on the face on which the threads will be created.

Right hand/Left hand
These radio buttons are selected to specify whether the resulting threads will be the right hand threads or the left hand threads. The right hand threads are those that allow the screw to get tightened when rotated in the clockwise direction. The left hand threads are those that allow the screw to get tightened when rotated in the counterclockwise direction.

Note
*For some of the thread types, the **Pitch** and the **Class** drop-down lists will not be available.*

Creating Shell Features

Toolbar:	Part Features > Shell
Panel bar:	Part Features > Shell

Shelling is defined as the process of scooping out material from a model and making it hollow from inside. The resulting model will be a structure of walls with a cavity inside. You can also remove some of the faces of the model or apply different wall thicknesses to some of the faces. Figure 7-57 shows a model with constant shelling and with the front face removed.

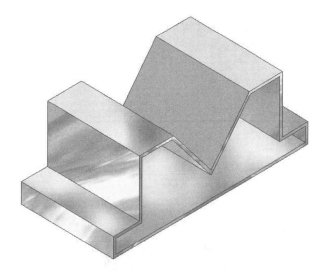

Figure 7-57 Model after creating the shell feature

In Autodesk Inventor, the shell feature is created using the **Shell** tool. When you invoke this tool, the **Shell** dialog box is displayed, see Figure 7-58. The options in the **Shell** tab are discussed next. Note that the options in the **More** tab are similar to those discussed in the **Thicken/Offset** tool. So these options are not discussed here.

Remove Faces

The **Remove Faces** button is used to select the faces of the model that you want to remove. When you invoke this dialog box, this button will be chosen by default and you will be prompted

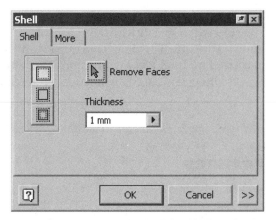

Figure 7-58 The **Shell** tab of the **Shell** dialog box

to select the faces to be removed. The selected faces will be displayed in blue color. Figure 7-59 shows the face selected to be removed and Figure 7-60 shows the resulting hollow model.

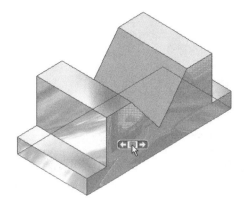

Figure 7-59 *Selecting the face to be removed*

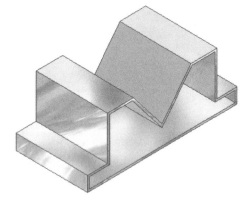

Figure 7-60 *Resulting shelled model*

Tip. *If by mistake you have selected a wrong face to remove, you can remove it from the selection set. This is done by pressing the SHIFT key and selecting the face again. The face will be removed from the current selection set.*

Thickness

The **Thickness** edit box is used to specify the wall thickness of the resulting hollow model. The resulting shell feature will have a wall thickness that you specify in this edit box.

Inside

The **Inside** button is the first button in the area provided on the left side of the **Shell** tab of the **Shell** dialog box. This button is chosen to define the wall thickness inside, with respect to the outer faces of the model. In this case, the outer faces of the model will be considered as the outer walls of the resulting shell feature.

Outside

The **Outside** button is provided below the **Inside** button and is chosen to define the wall thickness outside the model with respect to its outer faces. In this case, the outer faces of the model will be considered as the inner walls of the resulting shell feature.

Both

The **Both** button is provided below the **Outside** button and is chosen to calculate the wall thickness equally in both the directions of the outer faces of the model.

More

The **More** button has two arrows and is provided on the lower right corner of the **Shell** dialog box. When you choose this button, the **Shell** dialog box will expand and display the **Unique face thickness** area, see Figure 7-61. Using the options in this area, you can select the faces and apply different wall thicknesses to them. To select the faces, click on **Click to add**. You will be prompted to select surfaces to apply

Figure 7-61 More options

different wall thicknesses. The thicknesses of these selected surfaces can be specified in the **Thickness** column of the **Unique face thickness** area. Similarly, you can select another set of faces by clicking on **Click to add** and specify different wall thicknesses to them. Figure 7-62 shows a model with different wall thicknesses applied to various faces.

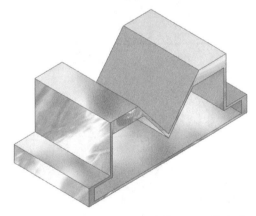

Figure 7-62 Shell feature with different wall thicknesses

Applying Face Drafts

Toolbar:	Part Features > Face Draft
Panel bar:	Part Features > Face Draft

 Face draft is a process of tapering the outer faces of a model for its easy removal from casting during manufacturing. You can add a face draft using the **Face Draft** tool. When you invoke this tool, the **Face Draft** dialog box will be displayed, see Figure 7-63. The options in this dialog box are discussed next.

*Figure 7-63 The **Face Draft** dialog box*

Fixed Edge

This is the first button in the area on the left side of the **Face Draft** dialog box. The **Fixed Edge** button is chosen when you want to draft a face using an edge. Note that all the edges tangent to the edge that you select to create the face draft are automatically selected.

Fixed Plane

The **Fixed Plane** button is available below the **Fixed Edge** button. This button is chosen when you want to create a face draft using a fixed plane. Refer to Figure 7-64. In this figure, the top planar face of the model is selected as the fixed plane to create the face draft.

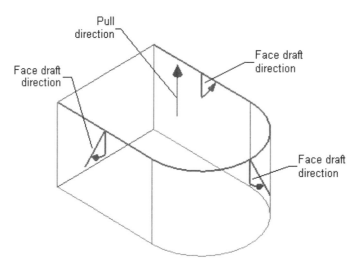

Figure 7-64 Various parameters associated with face draft

Pull Direction/Draft Plane

This is the first button available in the area in the center of the **Face Draft** dialog box. Depending on whether you select the **Fixed Edge** or **Fixed Plane** option, the name of this button will be **Pull Direction** or **Draft Plane**. These buttons are used to define the pull direction in case of a fixed edge and draft plane in case of a fixed plane. The pull direction is the direction defined by a plane that will be used to apply the face draft. The draft angle for the selected faces will be calculated using the plane selected to define the pull direction. Once you have selected the plane or the edge to define the pull direction, an arrow will be displayed. This arrow will define the pull direction for applying the draft angles, see Figure 7-64. You can reverse the pull direction by choosing the **Flip pull direction** button provided on the right of the **Pull Direction** button.

Faces To Draft

The **Faces To Draft** button is chosen to select the faces on which the draft angle will be applied. If the selected face has some tangent faces, they will also be selected for applying the face draft. After you have selected the pull direction, this button will be automatically chosen and you will be prompted to select the faces and the fixed edges to apply the face draft. If you move the cursor close to a face, it will be highlighted and an arrow will be displayed on that face. This arrow will define the direction in which the draft angle will be applied. Depending upon the point that is used to select the face, the nearest edge parallel to the pull direction will be selected. This edge is defined as the fixed edge. The direction of the draft angle will be calculated using this fixed edge. Figure 7-50 shows a model with various parameters associated with the face draft.

Draft Angle

The **Draft Angle** edit box is used to specify a draft angle for the selected faces. Remember that the value of the draft angle should be less than 90-degree.

Figure 7-65 shows a model after applying the face draft using the tangent edge of the top face as the fixed edge and with pull direction upwards. Figure 7-66 shows a model after applying the face draft using the same fixed edge but after reversing the pull direction using the **Flip Direction** button. In both these figures, the value of the draft angle is 15-degree.

Figure 7-65 Face draft with pull direction upward   *Figure 7-66* Face draft with pull direction downward

Creating Split Features

Toolbar:	Part Features > Split
Panel bar:	Part Features > Split

 In Autodesk Inventor, the **Split** tool can be used for splitting the entire part or the faces of the part. The two uses of the **Split** tool are discussed next.

Splitting Faces

The **Split** tool allows you to split all or selected faces of a model. Generally, the faces are split in order to apply different draft angles to both sides of the model. When you invoke the **Split** tool, the **Split** dialog box will be displayed. By default, the **Split Face** button will be chosen from the **Method** area, see Figure 7-67. This button is chosen to split the faces of a model. Because the **Split Face** button is chosen in the **Split** dialog box, the options for splitting faces will be available in this dialog box. These options are discussed next.

*Figure 7-67 The **Face Split** options in the **Split** dialog box*

Split Tool

The **Split Tool** button is chosen to select the tool that will be used to split the faces of the model. The tools that can be used to split the faces are the sketched lines, existing faces of the model, surfaces, or work planes.

 Tip. *If you want to use a sketched line to split the faces of the model, make sure the sketched line intersects the faces to be split in its current form or when it is projected normal to the plane on which it is sketched.*

Faces Area

The options in this area are used to select all faces of the model for splitting or to specify the faces for splitting. These options are discussed next.

All. If the **All** button is chosen, all the faces that the splitting tool intersects in its current form or when projected will be selected for splitting.

Select. The **Select** button is chosen to select the faces for splitting. The faces can be selected by choosing the **Faces to Split** button in the **Faces** area. On choosing the **Faces to Split** button, you will be prompted to select the faces that will be split. Only the faces that you select will be split and the remaining faces will remain unchanged even if they intersect the split tool. Figure 7-68 shows the sketched lines that will be used for splitting the model and Figure 7-69 shows the split faces.

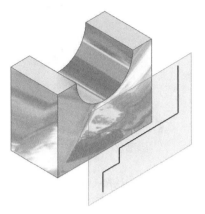

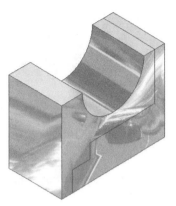

Figure 7-68 *Sketched lines for splitting the faces of the model*

Figure 7-69 *Model after splitting the faces and making the work plane invisible*

Splitting the Model

The same **Split** tool can also be used to split the model. This is done by choosing the **Split Part** button from the **Method** area of the **Split** dialog box. When you choose this button, the options related to splitting the part will be displayed, see Figure 7-70. These options are discussed next.

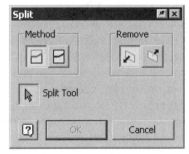

Split Tool

The **Split Tool** button is chosen to select the tool for splitting the model. Similar to splitting the faces, here also you can use the sketched lines, faces, or work planes for splitting the model.

Figure 7-70 *The **Part Split** options in the **Split** dialog box*

Remove Area

The buttons provided in this area are used to select the portion of the model to be removed after splitting. When you select the splitting tool, an arrow will appear on the model. It will point toward the portion of the model that will be removed after splitting. To remove the other portion, choose the other button in the **Remove** area.

Figure 7-71 shows the model before splitting and the surface that will be used to split the model. Figure 7-72 shows the model after splitting and making the surface invisible.

Trimming Surfaces

| Toolbar: | Part Features > Trim Surface |
| Panel bar: | Part Features > Trim Surface |

Trimming surfaces is one of the latest enhancements in Autodesk Inventor. This tool allows you to trim surfaces using another surface, a non-intersecting sketch, a work

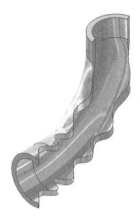

Figure 7-71 *Model before splitting and the surface for splitting the model*

Figure 7-72 *Model after splitting and making the surface invisible*

plane, or a face of an existing model. When you invoke this tool, the **Trim Surface** dialog box will be displayed, as shown in Figure 7-73, and you will be prompted to select surfaces, work planes, or sketches as the cutting tool. As soon as you select the cutting tool, the **Remove** button is chosen and you are prompted to select faces to remove. If you move the cursor on the face to be removed, it will be highlighted in red. Click on the face to select it. You can choose the **Invert Selection** button to select the part of the selected face that lies on the other side of the cutting tool. The **Invert Selection** button is on the right of the **Remove** button and is activated after you select a face to be removed.

Figure 7-73 *The **Trim Surface** dialog box*

Figure 7-74 shows two intersecting surfaces. In this, the horizontal surface is used as the cutting tool. You have the option to trim the lower part of the surface or the upper part, as shown in this figure. Figure 7-75 shows the surfaces after trimming the top part of the vertical surface and the left part of the horizontal surface.

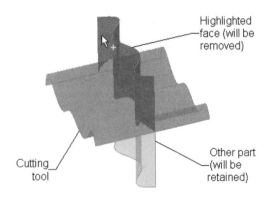

Figure 7-74 *Cutting tool and surface to trim*

Figure 7-75 *Surfaces after trimming*

Figure 7-76 shows a sketch selected as the cutting tool and the part of the surface that will be trimmed. Note that in this figure, the sketch is drawn on a plane that is at some offset from the surface. Figure 7-77 shows the surface after trimming.

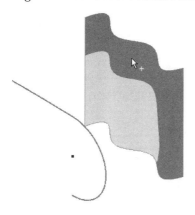

Figure 7-76 Sketch to be used as the cutting tool and the surface that will be trimmed

Figure 7-77 Surfaces after trimming

Extending Surfaces

Toolbar:	Part Features > Extend Surface
Panel bar:	Part Features > Extend Surface

This is also a new tool introduced in this release of Autodesk Inventor. This tool allows you to extend or stretch the edges of the selected surface. When you invoke this tool, the **Extend Surface** dialog box will be displayed, as shown in Figure 7-78. The options available in this dialog box are discussed next.

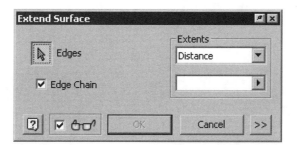

*Figure 7-78 The **Extend Surface** dialog box*

Edges

This button is chosen when you invoke the **Extend Surface** dialog box. As a result, you can select the edges you want to extend or stretch.

Edge Chain

If this check box is selected, all edges that are tangentially connected to the selected edge will also be selected.

Extents

This area provides the options to specify the values of the extended or stretched surfaces. You can select the **Distance** or **To** options from the drop-down list in this area. These options are similar to those discussed in the **Extrude** dialog box.

More

This is the button with two arrow provided on the lower right corner of the dialog box. When you choose this button, the dialog box expands and displays the **Edge Extension** area, as shown in Figure 7-79. These options in this area are discussed next.

Figure 7-79 *More options of the **Extend Surface** dialog box*

Extend

This radio button is selected by default. As a result, the surface is extended along the direction of the edges adjacent to the selected edges. Figure 7-80 shows a surface in which the top edge is being extended using this option. As evident in this figure, the edge is being extended along the direction of the vertical edges that are adjacent to the top edge of the surface.

Stretch

This radio button is selected to extend the surface by stretching it in 3D space. Figure 7-81 shows a surface in which the top edge is being extended using this option. As evident in this figure, the edge is being extended proportionately in the 3D space.

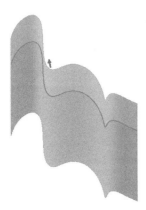

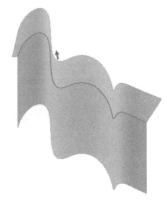

Figure 7-80 *Surface being extended along the direction of the adjacent edges*

Figure 7-81 *Surface being stretched in the 3D space*

Deleting Faces

Toolbar:	Part Features > Delete Face
Panel bar:	Part Features > Delete Face

Autodesk Inventor allows you to delete one or more selected planar faces or nonplanar lumps in a model or in a surface. Depending on the face selected to be deleted, the resulting model is converted into a surface. You can also force the adjacent faces to extend and intersect such that they heal the surface. This tool can also be used to fill the hollow model created using the **Shell** tool without removing any face. When you invoke the **Delete Face** tool, the **Delete** dialog box will be displayed, as shown in Figure 7-82. The options in this dialog box are discussed next.

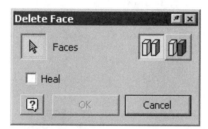

*Figure 7-82 The **Delete** dialog box*

Faces

The **Faces** button is used to select the faces to be deleted. When you invoke this dialog box, this button is chosen automatically and you are prompted to select the faces to be deleted.

Select individual face

The **Select individual face** button is chosen to select individual faces to be deleted. Figure 7-83 shows a model with the top face selected to be removed and Figure 7-84 shows the resulting surface model created by deleting the top face.

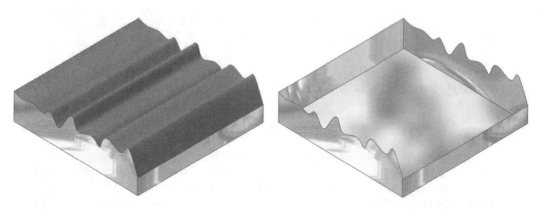

Figure 7-83 Top face selected to be deleted   *Figure 7-84 Resulting surface model*

Select lump or void

The **Select lump or void** button is chosen to select a lump or a void. This button is generally used to select the void created using shelling without removing a face. Because no face of the model is removed, the shelling is not visible until you change the display type to wireframe. To remove such a shelling, choose this button and move the cursor over the model. The cycle tool will be displayed. Cycle through the various entities and then select the void. When you exit this tool, the shelling will be removed.

Heal

The **Heal** check box is selected to force the adjacent faces to extend and meet so that the deleted face is healed. For example, if you delete a filleted or chamfered face and select this check box, the adjacent faces forming the fillet or chamfer are extended to recover the lost face. Note that when you heal the face, the model is not converted into a surface model. Figure 7-85 shows a model with all the fillets and rounds applied. In this model, all the fillets and rounds are applied a different color. Figure 7-86 shows the model after deleting some of the fillets and rounds and healing the faces.

Figure 7-85 *Model with fillets and rounds*   *Figure 7-86* *After deleting and healing some faces*

 Tip. *You can also delete split surfaces using the **Delete Face** tool, refer to Figure 7-61. Note that you can delete only one split surface at a time. To delete another surface, you need to invoke this tool again.*

Replacing Faces with Surfaces

Toolbar:	Part Features > Replace Face
Panel bar:	Part Features > Replace Face

Autodesk Inventor allows you to replace the selected faces of the model with one or more selected surfaces or work planes. Note that the surface must intersect the complete face that you want to replace. Figure 7-87 shows a model and a surface. The top face of the model will be replaced by the surface. The surface in this model is created by sweeping a spline about another spline.

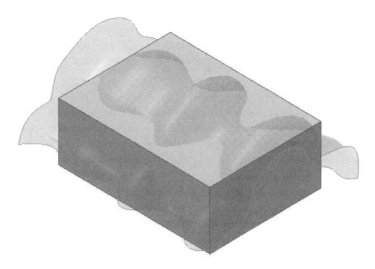

Figure 7-87 Surface and the model before replacing the face

Figure 7-88 shows the model after replacing the top face with the surface and making the surface invisible.

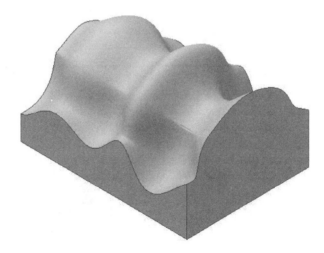

Figure 7-88 Model after replacing the top face with the surface

As evident in Figure 7-88, this tool not only removes the material from the model, but also adds the material to match the profile of the surface. This is the basic difference between splitting a part using the surface and replacing the face. While splitting a part, Autodesk Inventor only removes the material and does not add material to the model.

You can select one or more than one surface to replace the face. To replace the face, invoke the

Replace Face tool. The **Replace Face** dialog box is displayed, as shown in Figure 7-89. The options in this dialog box are discussed next.

*Figure 7-89 The **Replace Face** dialog box*

Existing Faces

The **Existing Faces** button is chosen to select the faces of the model that you want to replace. When you invoke this dialog box, this button is chosen by default.

New Faces

The **New Faces** button is chosen to select the surfaces that will be used to replace the selected faces. Note that the surfaces should completely intersect the selected faces or should extend beyond them. If the surfaces do not intersect the faces, the feature will not be created and an error message will be displayed.

Automatic Face Chain

The **Automatic Face Chain** check box is selected to automatically select all the tangent faces that form a continuous chain with the selected face.

Figure 7-90 shows a model with two surfaces to be used to replace the top face of the model and Figure 7-91 shows the model after replacing the faces and making the surfaces invisible using the browser.

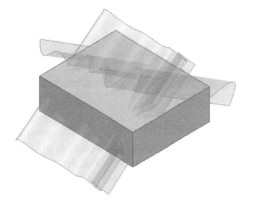

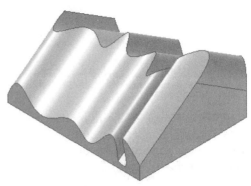

Figure 7-90 Surfaces to replace the top face   *Figure 7-91 Model after replacing the face*

Creating Planar Boundary Patches

Toolbar:	Part Features > Boundary Patch
Panel bar:	Part Features > Boundary Patch

Autodesk Inventor allows you to create planar boundary patches on one ore more closed loops or edges using the **Boundary Patch** tool. When you invoke this tool, the **Boundary Patch** dialog box will be displayed, as shown in Figure 7-92, and you will be prompted to select a profile, which will define the boundary of the planar patch.

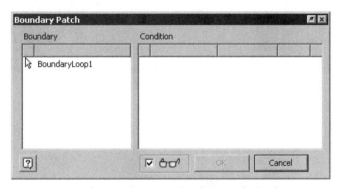

*Figure 7-92 The **Boundary Patch** dialog box*

This dialog box has two areas: **Boundary** and **Condition**. These areas are discussed next.

Boundary Area

The **Boundary** area displays the number of closed loops you select to create the boundary patch. Note that if you select more than one closed loop, the resulting surface will be a blend surface between the two loops.

Condition Area

The **Condition** area displays the entity selected to create the boundary patch. If you select the edges, it will list all the edges that you selected to create the boundary. Similarly, if you select a sketch, it displays the name of the sketch in this area. The third column in this area displays a drop-down list that can be used to specify the edge condition for the boundary patch. You can specify the contact or the tangent condition, depending on the edge selected.

Figure 7-93 shows a surface model without the patch and Figure 7-94 shows the surface model after creating contact boundary patches on the top and bottom faces. Note that both these surfaces are created separately one by one. Figure 7-95 shows the tangent boundary patch created at ends of the faces of the model.

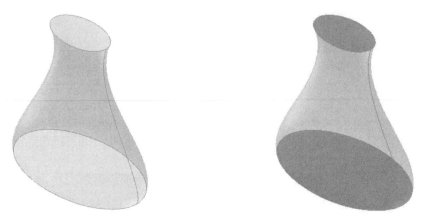

Figure 7-93 *Surfaces before creating the boundary* **Figure 7-94** *Surfaces after creating the contact*
patch   *boundary patch*

Figure 7-95 *Tangent boundary patch on one of the ends*

Stitching Surfaces

Toolbar:	Part Features > Stitch Surface
Panel bar:	Part Features > Stitch Surface

Sometimes while splitting parts, you may need to use more than one surface as the splitting tool. However, the **Split** tool allows you to select only one surface to split parts or faces. In such cases, you can join more than one surface together so that they form a single surface. You can stitch the surface using the **Stitch Surface** tool. When you invoke this tool, the **Stitch Surface** dialog box is displayed as shown in Figure 7-96.

When you invoke this dialog box, the **Surface** button is chosen by default and you are prompted to select the bodies to be stitched. Note that if there is a small gap between the selected surfaces, it will be filled with a new surface. The stitched surface will be displayed as **Stitch Surface** in the browser. Remember that if you want to select stitched surfaces, you will have to select **Stitch Surface** in the browser.

*Figure 7-96 The **Stitch Surface** dialog box*

 Note
*Tutorial 5 in Chapter 13 uses the concept of hybrid surface-solid modeling. You will use the **Stitch Surface** tool in that tutorial to stitch the surfaces.*

Working with the Sculpt Tool

Toolbar:	Part Features > Sculpt
Panel bar:	Part Features > Sculpt

The **Sculpt** tool is one of the latest enhancements in this release of Autodesk Inventor. This tool allows you to add or remove material from an existing model using a surface or a datum plane. The existing model can be a solid model or a surface model. For example, refer to Figure 7-97. This figure shows an existing solid base plate and a revolved surface. Figure 7-98 shows the material added to the base plate using the **Sculpt** tool. As evident from this figure, the shape and size of the material added is defined by the surface.

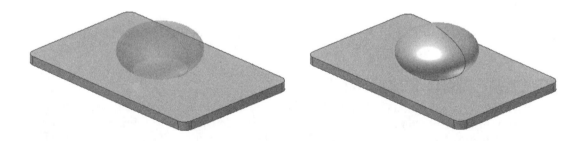

Figure 7-97 The base plate and the surface to create the sculpt feature

*Figure 7-98 The base plate after adding the material using the **Sculpt** tool*

To create the sculpt feature, invoke the **Sculpt** tool; the **Sculpt** dialog box will be displayed, as shown in Figure 7-99. The options in this dialog box are discussed next.

Add
This button is chosen to add material to the existing model. Remember that the shape and size of the material added will be determined by the shape and size of the surface you select.

*Figure 7-99 The **Sculpt** dialog box*

Remove

This button is chosen to remove the material from the existing model.

Surfaces

This button is chosen to select the surface to create the sculpt feature.

Enable/Disable feature preview

This check box is selected to enable or disable the dynamic preview of the sculpt feature in the drawing window.

More

When you choose this button, the **Sculpt** dialog box expands and displays the **Side Selection** area. The surfaces that you select to create the sculpt tool are displayed in this area. The side of the feature creation will be displayed on the right of their names. If you click on the image of the side of feature creation, it is converted into a drop-down list. You can select **Side 1**, **Side 2**, or **Both Sides** option from this drop-down list.

Note
*While removing the material using the **Remove** option of the **Sculpt** tool, the side of the model that turns red will be removed.*

REORDERING FEATURES

Autodesk Inventor allows you to change the order of the feature creation in a model. You can move a feature before or after another feature. However, note that the reordering is possible only between the features that are independent of each other. For example, if the fourth feature of a model is dependent on the third feature, you cannot reorder the fourth feature before the third.

In Autodesk Inventor, the features are reordered using the browser. To reorder the feature, select it in the browser and drag it above or below the other features. If a black circle with a line appears while dragging, you cannot reorder the feature. This is because in some way, the selected feature is dependent on a feature before which you want to drag it. However, if the feature is not dependent, a black line appears while you are dragging the feature. Figure 7-100 shows a model consisting of a base feature, a cut feature on the base feature, rectangular pattern of the cut feature, a shell feature, and finally a split feature.

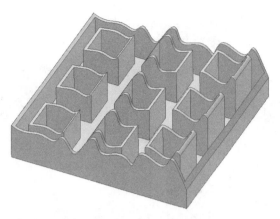

Figure 7-100 *Model with the shell feature created after the cut feature and the pattern of the cut feature*

Note that in this model, the shell feature is created after the rectangular pattern of the cut feature on the base feature. As a result, the same wall thickness is retained around all the instances of the rectangular cut features.

Now, if you reorder the features such that the shell feature is placed before the extruded cut feature and the pattern of the cut feature, all the walls around the rectangular cuts will be removed. Figure 7-101 shows reordering features in the browser.

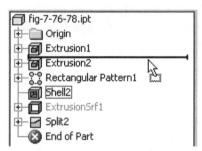

Figure 7-101 *Reordering the shell feature before the extruded cut feature and rectangular pattern of the cut feature*

Figure 7-102 shows the model after reordering the features. Notice that because the shell feature is now created before the rectangular pattern, the resulting model has simple cuts without any walls around them.

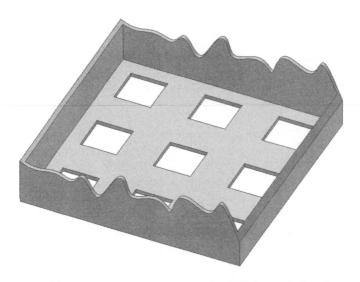

Figure 7-102 *Model after reordering the shell feature before the cut feature and the pattern of the cut feature*

Tip. *Similar to reordering the features, you can also rollback the model using the browser to suppress the features. To rollback the model, select the text **End of Part** that appears at the end of the list of features in the browser. Next, drag and drop this text before the features in the browser. All the features that are placed after this text are automatically suppressed in the model. To resume the features, drag this text to the end of the features in the browser.*

TUTORIALS

Tutorial 1

In this tutorial, you will create the model shown in Figure 7-103a. Its dimensions are given in Figures 7-103b through 7-103d. Save the model with the name given below.

\PersonalProject\c07\Tutorial1.ipt   **(Expected time: 45min)**

Figure 7-103a *Model for Tutorial 1*

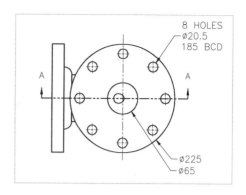

Figure 7-103b *Top view of the model with hidden lines suppressed for clarity*

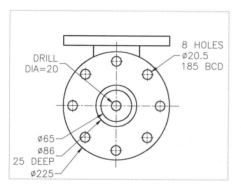

Figure 7-103c *Left-side view of the model with hidden lines suppressed for clarity*

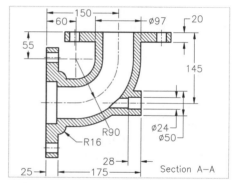

Figure 7-103d *Sectioned front view of the model*

Before you start creating the model, it is recommended that you outline the procedure for creating it. The steps that will be followed to complete this model are listed below.

a. The base feature for the model is a sweep feature. Create the path of the sweep feature on the XZ plane, refer to Figure 7-104. Next, define a work plane normal to the path and positioned at its start point, refer to Figure 7-105. Create the profile of the sweep feature on this work plane, refer to Figure 7-106. Use the **Sweep** tool to create the sweep feature, refer to Figure 7-107.

b. Create the inner cavity using the **Shell** tool, refer to Figure 7-108.

c. Add the remaining join features on both ends of the sweep feature.

d. Create the hole patterns on both ends.

e. Define a work plane at an offset of 200 mm from the front face of the circular feature on the left face of the model. Create the join feature and counterbore hole on this plane.

Creating the Path for the Sweep Feature

As mentioned earlier, the base feature of the model is a sweep feature. To create the sweep feature, you will first create its path on the XZ plane. The path is a combination of two lines and an arc.

1. Start a new metric standard template file and create the path for the sweep feature on the XZ plane. Add the required dimensions. Exit the sketching environment and change the view to the isometric view. The path of the sweep feature is shown in Figure 7-104.

Creating a Work Plane Normal to the Start Section of the Path

After creating the path, you need to create a work plane normal to the start section of the path and positioned at its start point. This work plane is used to draw the profile for the sweep feature. The start section of the path can be either the line of 19 mm length or the line of 35 mm length. In this tutorial, the line with 19 mm length is considered as the start section of the path.

1. Choose **Work Plane** from the **Part Features** panel bar. You are prompted to define a work plane by highlighting and selecting the geometry.

2. Select the line of 19 mm length. You are again prompted to define a work plane by highlighting and selecting the geometry. Select the start point of this line.

When you move the cursor close to the start point of the line, the preview of the work plane is displayed at the start point of the path. As soon as you select the start point of the line, a work plane is created, which is normal to the line and is positioned at its start point. The work plane at the start point of the path is shown in Figure 7-105.

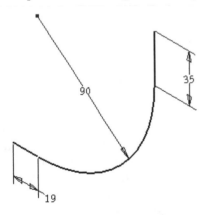
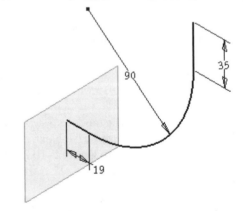

Figure 7-104 Path for the sweep feature   *Figure 7-105* Work plane normal to the path

Drawing the Profile for the Sweep Feature

The profile for the sweep feature is created on the new work plane. Therefore, you need to define a sketch plane on the new work plane.

1. Choose the **Sketch** button from the **Inventor Standard** toolbar and then select the new work plane as the plane for sketching.

   As soon as you select the new work plane as the plane for sketching, the sketching environment is activated. You will notice that the origin of the sketching environment coincides with the start point of the start section of the path. This will help you in positioning the profile of the sweep feature.

2. Draw the sketch for the profile of the sweep feature. This profile will be a circle. Take the origin of the sketching environment as the center of the circle. Exit the sketching environment and change the view to the isometric view. The profile of the sweep feature is shown in Figure 7-106. In this figure, the visibility of the work plane is turned off.

 Tip. *You can avoid the shell feature by creating two circles as the profile for the sweep feature. When you sweep both the circles, the inner circle will be subtracted from the outer one. This way the inner cavity will be created automatically. However, in this tutorial, the* **Shell** *tool will be used to create the inner cavity.*

Sweeping the Profile

1. Choose the **Sweep** button from the **Part Features** panel bar to display the **Sweep** dialog box.

   Since the sweep is the first feature and there are only two unconsumed sketches, the profile is automatically selected and highlighted. The **Path** button is chosen and you will be prompted to select the path.

2. Select the path and then choose **OK** in the **Sweep** dialog box. The sweep feature, after changing the viewing direction, is shown in Figure 7-107.

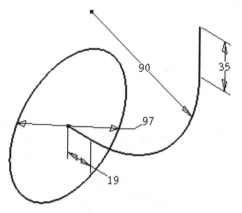

Figure 7-106 Profile for the sweep feature   *Figure 7-107 Sweep feature*

Creating the Shell Feature

The shell feature will scoop out material from the sweep feature and will leave behind a model with some wall thickness. However, you need to remove the front face and the top face of the sweep feature in order to view the cavity inside.

1. Choose the **Shell** button from the **Part Features** toolbar to display the **Shell** dialog box. You are prompted to select the surfaces to be removed.

2. Select the front and the top face of the sweep feature. Both the selected faces are highlighted and displayed in blue.

    The diameter of the inner cavity is 65 mm and the diameter of the sweep feature is 97 mm. As a result, the wall thickness is 32 mm. Since this value is in terms of diameter, the radius value will be 16 mm. Therefore, the resulting wall thickness is 16 mm.

3. Enter 16 mm in the **Thickness** edit box and choose the **OK** button. The model, after creating the shell feature, is shown in Figure 7-108.

Figure 7-108 Base feature after creating the shell feature

Creating the Remaining Features

1. Create the remaining features by defining new sketch planes at the required faces. To create the join feature with a fillet on the left face of the base feature, draw a circle of 129 mm diameter and extrude it to a distance of 16 mm. Then create the fillet of 16 mm on the outer edge of this feature.

    The join feature at the cylindrical tangent surface can be created by defining an offset work plane. The smaller holes can be copied from one of the cylindrical features to the other using the **Paste Features** dialog box. The final model for Tutorial 1 is shown in Figure 7-109.

2. Save the model with the name given below and then close the file.

    \PersonalProject\c07\Tutorial1.ipt

Figure 7-109 Final model for Tutorial 1

Tutorial 2

In this tutorial, you will create a model of the Joint shown in Figure 7-110a. Its dimensions are shown in Figures 7-110b and 7-110c. The threads to be created are **ANSI Metric M Profile** with the size of 14 and M14x2 designation. The class of the threads is 6g. Make sure that the threads are right handed. Save the model with the name *\PersonalProject\c07\Tutorial2.ipt*.

(Expected time: 30 min)

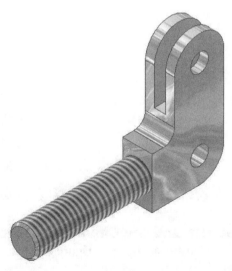

Figure 7-110a Solid model of the Joint

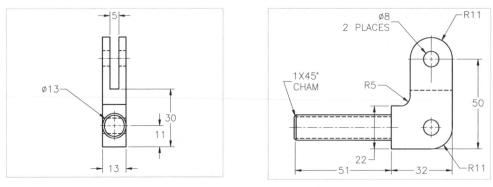

Figure 7-110b *Left-side view of the model*   **Figure 7-110c** *Front view of the model*

As mentioned earlier, you should first outline the procedure for creating the model. The following steps are required to complete the model:

a.   Create the base feature of the model on the YZ plane, refer to Figure 7-111.
b.   Create the cut feature, refer to Figure 7-112.
c.   Create the cylindrical join feature on the left face and then create the chamfer feature.
d.   Finally, create the threads on the cylindrical join feature using the **Thread** tool.

Create the Base Feature
1.   Create the base feature of the model on the YZ plane, as shown in Figure 7-111.

Creating the Cut Feature in the Base Feature
1.   Create the cut feature by defining a sketch plane on the right face of the base feature, as shown in Figure 7-112.

Figure 7-111 *Base feature for the model*   **Figure 7-112** *Model after creating the cut feature*

Creating the Join Feature and the Chamfer Feature
1.   Create the cylindrical join feature, as shown in Figure 7-113.

2.   Create the chamfer feature at the end face of the cylindrical feature, see Figure 7-114.

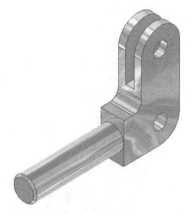

Figure 7-113 *Model after creating the join feature*   **Figure 7-114** *Model after chamfering*

Creating the Threads

1. Choose the **Thread** button from the **Part Features** toolbar to invoke the **Thread** dialog box. Select the cylindrical join feature. The preview of the threads is displayed on the model.

2. Choose the **Specification** tab to display the options related to the specifications of the threads. Select **ANSI Metric M Profile** from the **Thread Type** drop-down list and **14** from the **Size** drop-down list.

3. Select **M14x2** from the **Designation** drop-down list and **6g** from the **Class** drop-down list. Make sure the **Right hand** radio button is selected. Choose **OK** to exit the dialog box and create the threads. The model after creating the threads is shown in Figure 7-115.

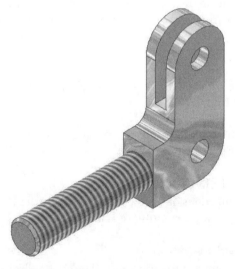

Figure 7-115 *Final model for Tutorial 2*

4. Save the model with the name *PersonalProject\c07\Tutorial2.ipt* and then close the file.

Tutorial 3

In this tutorial, you will create a model of the Nut shown in Figure 7-116a. Its dimensions are shown in Figure 7-116b. The thread to be created are **ANSI Metric M Profile** with size of 10 and M10x1.5 designation. The class of thread is 6H and it is a right-handed thread. Save the model with the name given below.

\PersonalProject\c07\Tutorial3.ipt   **(Expected time: 30 min)**

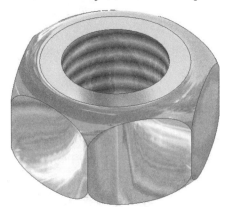

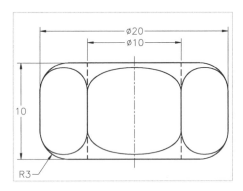

Figure 7-116a *Model of the Nut with threads*   *Figure 7-116b* *Dimensions of the Nut*

The steps that will be followed to create the model are listed below.

a.   Create the base feature, refer to Figure 7-117.
b.   Fillet the top and bottom faces of the cylindrical feature, refer to Figure 7-118.
c.   Define a new sketch plane on the top face of the base feature. Draw a hexagon on this plane and extrude it using the **Intersect** operation, refer to Figure 7-119.
d.   Finally, create the internal threads using the **Thread** tool, refer to Figure 7-120.

Creating the Base Feature
1.   Create the base feature for the Nut as shown in Figure 7-117. The diameter of the outer cylinder is 20 mm and that of hole is 10 mm.

You can draw the smaller circle inside the bigger circle for creating the hole. This will reduce one step of creating the hole feature.

Filleting the Faces of the Base Feature
1.   Fillet the top and bottom edges of the base feature using the **Fillet** tool. The radius of the fillet is 3 mm. The model, after creating the fillet, is shown in Figure 7-118.

Creating the Intersect Feature
The next feature is the intersect feature and will be created by defining a new sketch plane on the top face of the model or on its bottom face. After defining the sketch plane, you will

Figure 7-117 *Base feature for the Nut*   *Figure 7-118* *After filleting the faces*

draw an inscribed hexagon. The diameter of the hexagon should be equal to the diameter of the circle. You can use the **Inventor Precise Input** toolbar for drawing the hexagon.

1. Define a new sketch plane on the top face of the base feature. Draw an inscribed hexagon on the new sketch plane.

   The diameter of the circle in which the hexagon is inscribed should be equal to the diameter of the base feature. You can use the **Inventor Precise Input** toolbar to specify the value of the diameter of the circle in which the hexagon is inscribed.

2. Exit the sketching environment and extrude the sketch using the **Intersect** operation and **All** extents. The model, after creating the intersect feature, is shown in Figure 7-119.

Creating the Threads

1. Choose the **Thread** button from the **Part Features** toolbar to invoke the **Thread** dialog box.

2. Select the inner hole as the face for creating the threads.

3. Choose the **Specification** tab and select **ANSI Metric M Profile** from the **Thread Type** drop-down list.

4. Select **10** from the **Nominal Size** drop-down list and **M10x1.5** from the **Pitch** drop-down list.

5. Select **6H** from the **Class** drop-down list. Make sure the **Right hand** radio button is selected.

6. Choose **OK** to exit the **Thread** dialog box and create the threads. The final model, after creating the threads, is shown in Figure 7-120.

6. Save the model with the name *PersonalProject\c07\Tutorial3.ipt* and then close the file.

Figure 7-119 *After creating the intersect feature*   **Figure 7-120** *Final model of Nut*

Tutorial 4

In this tutorial, you will create the model shown in Figure 7-121a. Its dimensions are shown in Figures 7-121b and 7-121c. After creating the model, apply a face draft on both faces of 58 mm dimension. The angle for the face draft should be 1-degree. After creating the model, save it with the name given below.

\PersonalProject\c07\Tutorial4.ipt   **(Expected time: 45 min)**

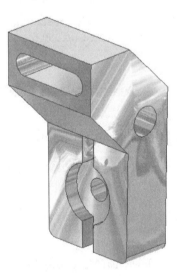

Figure 7-121a *Model for Tutorial 4*

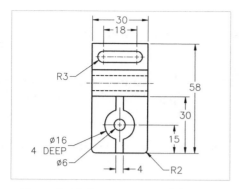

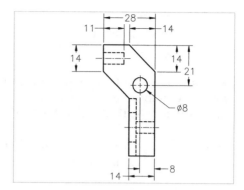

Figure 7-121b Front view of the model   *Figure 7-121c* Right-side view of the model

The following steps are required to complete the model:

a. Create the base feature with a hole on the YZ plane, refer to Figure 7-122.
b. Add two cut features and holes to the base feature, refer to Figure 7-123.
c. Create the face draft by selecting the top face of the model as the pull direction. Make sure it points downward. Select the two faces to apply the face draft. The width of the model at the upper end will remain the same and decrease from the lower end.
d. Finally, create the fillet. Remember that it should be created after the face draft. This is because if you create the fillet first, the two faces will be taken as the faces tangent to the filleted edges. Therefore, the width of the model will remain constant at the bottom and will change from the top.

Creating the Base Feature

1. Create the base feature of the model on the YZ plane, as shown in Figure 7-122.

Adding the Remaining Features

1. Add the remaining cut features to the model, as shown in Figure 7-123.

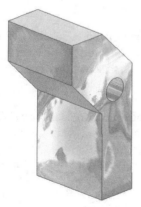

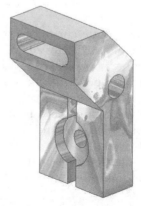

Figure 7-122 Base feature of the model   *Figure 7-123* Model after creating the remaining features

Adding the Face Draft

1. Choose the **Face Draft** button from the **Part Features** toolbar to invoke the **Face Draft** dialog box. Choose the **Fixed Plane** button.

2. Select the top face of the model as the pull direction and make sure that the arrow points downward. If the direction points upward, choose the **Flip pull direction** button provided on the right of the **Draft Plane** button. The direction will be reversed.

    As soon as you specify the pull direction, the **Faces** button will be chosen and you will be prompted to select the face and the fixed edges.

3. Select both the side faces one by one using a point close to the upper horizontal edge of the two faces, see Figure 7-124.

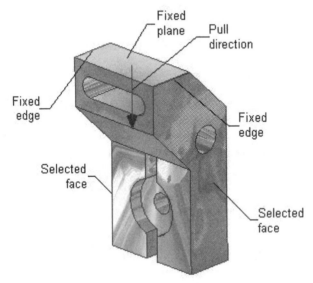

Figure 7-124 Selecting the options for the face draft

When you take the cursor close to the face, it will be highlighted. Also, an edge on the face will be highlighted. This edge will be the fixed edge. In this model, the fixed edge should be the upper horizontal edge of both the faces. Therefore, to select the face, specify a point close to the upper horizontal edge of the faces.

4. Change the value of the draft angle to **1** in the **Draft Angle** edit box. Choose **OK** to exit the **Face Draft** dialog box and apply the face draft on the model.

5. Add fillet to the edges on the bottom face of the model. The final model for Tutorial 4 is shown in Figure 7-125.

6. Save the model with the name given below and then close the file.

\PersonalProject\c07\Tutorial4.ipt

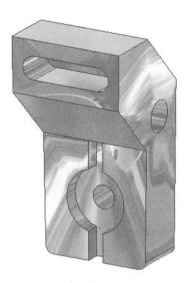

Figure 7-125 *Final model for Tutorial 4*

Tutorial 5

In this tutorial, you will create the solid model of the receiver of a phone shown in Figure 7-126a. The dimensions of Section 1 and Section 2 of this receiver are shown in Figures 7-126b and 7-126c. Section 3 is a mirror image of Section 1, but needs to be created separately as an individual sketch. Save the model with the name given below.

\PersonalProject\c07\Tutorial5.ipt   **(Expected time: 45 min)**

Figure 7-126a *Solid model of the receiver*

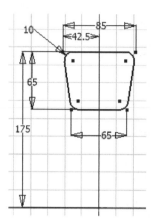

Figure 7-126b *Dimensions of Section 1*

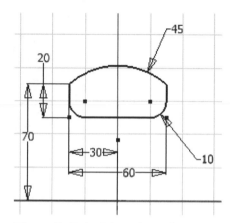

Figure 7-126c *Dimensions of Section 2*

The model consists of three sections blended together using the **Loft** tool. Section 1 is created on the XZ plane. Section 2 is created on the XY plane. Section 3 is again created on the XZ plane. However, this section will be created below the origin. To maintain the accuracy of the sections, you need to dimension them with reference to the origin point. You can place a sketch point at the origin and add the **Fix** constraint to it. Next, dimension the section with respect to this sketched point.

Before you start creating the model, it is recommended that you outline the steps that will be followed to create it. The steps that need to be followed are listed below.

a.   Start a new metric template file and draw the sketch for Section 2 on the XY plane. Because the sketches can be created in any sequence while creating the loft feature, you do not need to create Section 1 first.
b.   Draw the sketch for Section 1 on the XZ plane. Exit the sketching environment.
c.   Again, define the sketch plane on XZ plane and draw the sketch for Section 3.
d.   Exit the sketching environment and invoke the **Loft** tool. Select the three sections to create the loft feature.

Drawing the Sketch for Section 2
1.   Start a new metric template file. Place a sketch point at the origin and add the **Fix** constraint to it.

2.   Draw the sketch for Section 2. Dimension it with respect to the sketched point placed at the origin. Exit the sketching environment.

Drawing the Sketch for Section 1
1.   Define a new sketch plane on the XZ plane. Place a sketch point at the origin and add the **Fix** constraint to it.

2.   Draw the sketch for Section 1 and dimension it with respect to the fixed sketch point. Exit the sketching environment.

Drawing the Sketch for Section 3

The sketch for Section 3 is a mirror image of the sketch of Section 1. You need to first place a sketch point at the origin and add the **Fix** constraint to it.

1. Define a new sketch plane on the XZ plane. Place a sketch point at the origin and add the **Fix** constraint to it.

2. Draw the sketch for Section 3 and dimension it with respect to the sketch point. Exit the sketching environment. The three sketches are shown in Figure 7-127.

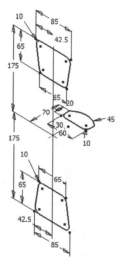

Figure 7-127 *Sketches of the three sections*

Blending the Sections using the Loft Tool

The sections are blended together using the **Loft** tool.

1. Choose the **Loft** button from the **Part Features** panel bar to invoke the **Loft** dialog box.

    The **Curves** tab is active and you are prompted to select a sketch.

2. Select Section 1 as the first sketch. The sketch is highlighted in blue and you are again prompted to select a sketch.

3. Select Section 2 and then Section 3 in the same sequence.

    The preview of the feature appears in the drawing window. However, this is not the kind of feature you require. You need to add some weight at the start and end sections.

4. Choose the **Conditions** tab. An arrow appears on the left of Sketch3 in the **Conditions** area of this tab. This suggests that the settings that you configure will be for this sketch.

5. Choose the **Direction Condition** button in this tab. This button allows you to add direction conditions at the start and end sections.

6. Enter **50** as the value in the **Weight** edit box. This value is for the end section.

7. Next, select Sketch2 from the **Conditions** area and then choose the **Direction Condition** button.

8. Enter **50** as the weight value in the **Weight** edit box. This value is for the start section. Choose **OK** to create the loft feature.

9. Apply **Blue Pastel** color to the model. Change the viewing direction. The model of the phone receiver is shown in Figure 7-128.

Figure 7-128 Solid model of the receiver

10. Save the model with the name given below and then close the file.

    \PersonalProject\c07\Tutorial5.ipt

Self-Evaluation Test

Answer the following questions and then compare your answers with those given at the end of this chapter:

1. To create a solid sweep feature, the profile should be a closed sketch. (T/F)

2. The lofted features are created by blending more than one dissimilar geometries. (T/F)

3. You can also apply different wall thicknesses to the various faces in a shell feature. (T/F)

4. While replacing the selected face with a surface, the material is removed as well as added to the model. (T/F)

5. The _____ method is used to create a spiral coil in a single plane.

6. _____ is defined as the process of scooping out material from the model and making it hollow from inside.

7. The _____ button in the **Shell** dialog box is used to select the faces of the model that should not be displayed in the resulting model.

8. _____ is applied to the faces of a model for its easy removal from casting.

9. You can create the face drafts using a fixed _____ or a fixed _____.

10. If the faces selected to apply the face draft have some _____, they will also be selected for applying the face draft.

Review Questions

Answer the following questions:

1. The _____ operation of the **Coil** tool can also be used for creating internal or external threads in the model.

2. In Autodesk Inventor, the _____ tool can be used to split the faces of the models or the complete model.

3. The _____ dialog box is used to directly create external or internal threads.

4. The _____ tool is used to combine more than one surface into a single surface.

5. The _____ edit box in the **Loft** dialog box is used to specify the distance to which the resulting feature will maintain the angle value at the start or the end sections.

6. Which of the following options allows you to create a coil in a single plane?

    (a) **Revolution and Height**   (b) **Pitch and Revolution**
    (c) **Spiral**   (d) **Pitch and Height**

7. Which check box in the **Delete** dialog box is used to recover the faces by extending the adjacent faces?

    (a) **Heal**   (b) **Delete**
    (c) **Remove**   (d) None

8. Which check box in the **Thread** dialog box is selected to create the threads through the length of the selected face?

    (a) **Length**　　　　　　　　　　(b) **Full Length**
    (c) **Full**　　　　　　　　　　　　(d) None

9. You can clear which one of the following check boxes in the **Thread** dialog box to turn the display of the threads in the solid model?

    (a) **Display in Model**　　　　　(b) **Display**
    (c) **Off**　　　　　　　　　　　　(d) None

10. Using which area in the **Loft** dialog box can you select the points on the sketches that will be used to map the shape of the loft feature?

    (a) **Point Mapping**　　　　　　(b) **Mapping**
    (c) **Mapping Point**　　　　　　(d) None

Exercises

Exercise 1

Create a solid model of the hexagonal headed Cap Screw shown in Figure 7-129a. Its dimensions are shown in Figure 7-129b. The threads to be created are **ANSI Metric M Profile** with size of 10 and M10x1.5 designation. The class of the threads is 6g. Make sure that the threads are right handed. After creating the model, save it with the name given below.

\PersonalProject\c07\Exercise2.ipt　　　　　　　　　　　**(Expected time: 30 min)**

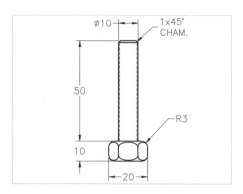

Figure 7-129a   *Solid model of the Cap Screw*   *Figure 7-129b*   *Dimensions of the Cap Screw*

Exercise 2

Create a solid model of the Offset shown in Figure 7-130a. The dimensions to be used are given in Figures 7-130b through 7-130d. Save it with the name given below.

\PersonalProject\c07\Exercise2.ipt   **(Expected time: 45 min)**

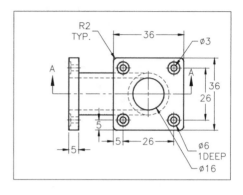

Figure 7-130a Solid model of Offset   *Figure 7-130b Top view of the model*

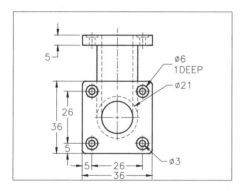

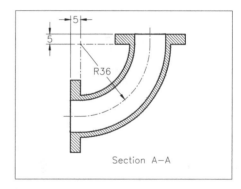

Figure 7-130c Left-side view of the model   *Figure 7-130d Sectioned front view of the model*

Note
*The path for the sweep feature in Exercise 2 consists of two lines of 5 mm length and an arc of radius 36 mm. If you apply the **Tangent** constraint between the two lines and the arc, you will not be required to specify the center of the arc.*

Answers to Self-Evaluation Test

1. F, **2.** T, **3.** T, **4.** T, **5. Spiral**, **6.** Shelling, **7. Remove Faces**, **8.** Face draft, **9.** edge, plane, **10.** tangent faces.

Chapter 8

Assembly Modeling-I

Learning Objectives

After completing this chapter, you will be able to:
- *Understand the concept of the bottom-up and top-down assemblies.*
- *Create components of the top-down assemblies in the assembly file.*
- *Insert components of the bottom-up assemblies in the assembly file.*
- *Understand various assembly constraints and use them to assemble components.*
- *Move and rotate individual components in the assembly file.*

ASSEMBLY MODELING

An assembly is defined as a design consisting of two or more components tied together at their respective working positions. In Autodesk Inventor, the components of the assembly will be bound using the parametric assembly constraints. Because the assembly constraints are parametric in nature, you can modify or delete them whenever you want. In Autodesk Inventor, the assemblies are created in the **Assembly** module. To proceed to the assembly module, invoke the **Open** dialog box and select the **Standard (mm).iam** file, as shown in Figure 8-1.

*Figure 8-1 Opening an assembly file from the **Metric** tab of the **Open** dialog box*

When you select the assembly file, the assembly environment will be activated. The screen display of Autodesk Inventor in the **Assembly** module is shown in Figure 8-2. This figure displays the **Assembly Panel** panel bar and the browser.

Note
*When you enter the **Assembly** module, you will notice that very few tools in the **Assembly Panel** panel bar and toolbar are available. All these tools will be available once you insert or create a component.*

TYPES OF ASSEMBLIES

In Autodesk Inventor, you can create two types of assemblies: top-down assemblies and bottom-up assemblies. Both these assemblies are discussed next.

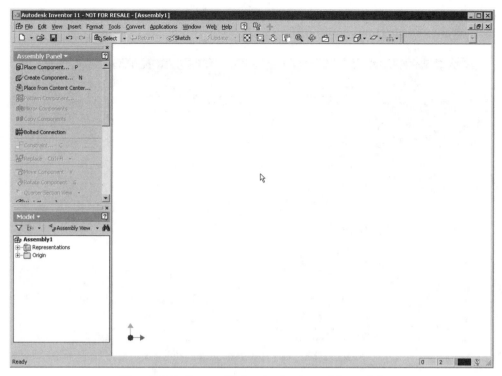

Figure 8-2 *Screen display in the **Assembly** module*

Top-down Assemblies

A top-down assembly is an assembly whose components are created within the assembly file. In this type of assembly, the components are created in the assembly file and then assembled using the assembly constraints. The process of creating the components in the **Assembly** module of Autodesk Inventor is designed in such a way that the components you create in the **Assembly** module are also saved as individual parts or assembly files. This eliminates the risk of losing the individual components, in case there is an error in the assembly file. Also, the assembly file has the information related to only the assembly, which keeps the size of the assembly file to the minimum.

Bottom-up Assemblies

A bottom-up assembly is an assembly whose all components are created as separate part files and are referenced in the assembly file as external components. In this type of assembly, the components are created in the **Part** module as part files *(.ipt)*. Once all components of the assembly are created, you will open an assembly file *(.iam)* and then insert all the component files using the tool in the **Assembly** module. After inserting the components, they are assembled using the assembly constraints. Because the assembly file has information related only to the assembling of components, this file size is not large and so it requires less hard disk space. However, remember that if any of the components referenced in the assembly is moved from its original location, it will not show up when you open the assembly next time. This is because Autodesk Inventor will look for the component only in the folder, in which it was originally stored. Because the component is not found at its original location, the **Resolve**

Link dialog box will be displayed, see Figure 8-3. Using this dialog box, you will have to specify the new location of the component.

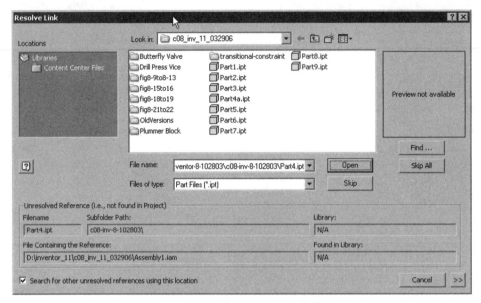

*Figure 8-3 The **Resolve Link** dialog box*

 Note
*An assembly, in which you use a combination of bottom-up and top-down approach, is called the **middle-out assembly**.*

CREATING TOP-DOWN ASSEMBLIES

As mentioned earlier, top-down assemblies are those, in which all components are created within the assembly file. To create the components, you require the environment where you can draw the sketches of the sketched features and also the environment where you can convert the sketches into features. In other words, to create the components in the assembly file, you require the sketching environment and the part modeling environment. Autodesk Inventor provides you the liberty of invoking both these environments in the **Assembly** module also by using the **Create Component** tool. The use of this tool is discussed next.

Creating Components in the Assembly Module

Toolbar:	Assembly Panel > Create Component
Panel bar:	Assembly Panel > Create Component

In Autodesk Inventor, you can create components in the **Assembly** module also. One of the advantages of creating the components in the **Assembly** module is that these components can also be saved as a separate part file (*.ipt*) or an assembly file (*.iam*). Therefore, in case you again require any component created in the **Assembly** module, you can use the individual part or assembly file. The components in the **Assembly** module are created using the **Create Component** tool. When you invoke this tool, the **Create In-Place Component** dialog box will be displayed, see Figure 8-4. The options in this dialog box are discussed next.

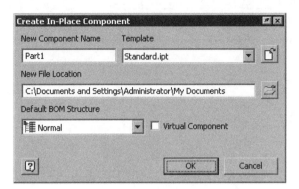

*Figure 8-4 The **Create In-Place Component** dialog box*

New Component Name

The **New Component Name** text box is used to specify the name of the new component that will be created.

Template

The **Template** drop-down list is used to select the template for the new file. There are four default templates in this drop-down list: **Sheet Metal.ipt**, **Standard.iam**, **Standard.ipt**, and **Weldment.iam**. You can also select the template by choosing the **Browse Templates** button. When you choose this button, the **Open Template** dialog box will be displayed, see Figure 8-5. Using this dialog box, you can select the required template for the new file.

Tip. *The assembly template is used to create smaller subassemblies that consist of a few components. These smaller assemblies can be later assembled in a separate assembly file to form the main assembly.*

New File Location

The **New File Location** edit box is used to specify the location for saving the new file. You can either specify the location in this edit box or choose the **Browse to New File Location** button provided on the right of the **File Type** drop-down list to specify the location. When you choose this button, the **New Component** dialog box will be displayed, see Figure 8-6. Using this dialog box, you can select the folder, in which you want to save the new file.

Default BOM Structure

This drop-down list is used to specify the type of Bill of Material (BOM) structure for the new component. You will learn more about BOM structure in the next chapter.

Virtual Component

This check box is used to create a virtual component only for the purpose of adding a row in the BOM.

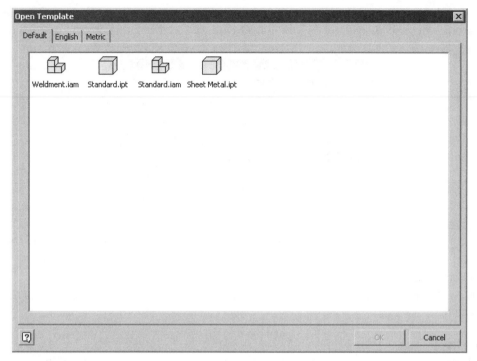

*Figure 8-5 The **Open Template** dialog box*

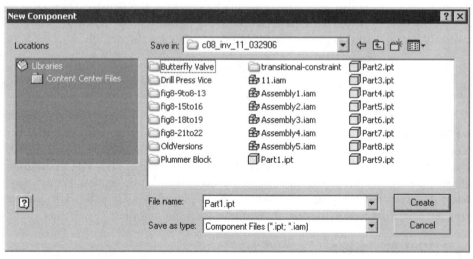

*Figure 8-6 The **New Component** dialog box*

Constrain sketch plane to selected face or plane

The **Constrain sketch plane to selected face or plane** check box is used to constrain the plane on which the base feature of the model will be created to the selected face of an existing model or work plane. If the component that you create is the first component, it will be grounded and this check box will not be available in the **Create In-Place Component** dialog box. A grounded component is the first component of the assembly using which the remaining components will be assembled. All the degrees of freedom of the grounded component will be eliminated so that it is not able to move from its original location. Even if you are placing external components, by default, the first component will be grounded.

Tip. *In the browser, you can easily distinguish between a grounded and an ungrounded component. A grounded component will have a push pin icon on the left of its name in the browser. You can make a grounded component ungrounded by right-clicking on its name in the browser. When you right-click on a grounded component in the browser, you will notice a check mark in front of the* **Grounded** *option in the shortcut menu. To unground the component, choose this option again; the push pin icon will be replaced by the original part icon, suggesting that the component is ungrounded.*

After setting all the options in the **Create In-Place Component** dialog box, choose **OK**; the sketching environment will be activated and you can draw the sketch for the base feature of the model. After creating the sketch, choose the down arrow on the right of the **Return** button and then choose the **Parent** option from the flyout; the part modeling environment will be activated with all the part modeling tools, similar to the **Part** module. Once you have created a part using the sketching environment and the part modeling environment, you can switch back to the **Assembly** module by again choosing the down arrow on the right of the **Return** button and then choosing the **Top** option from the flyout. The **Part Features** panel bar will be replaced by the **Assembly Panel** panel bar and all the tools in the **Assembly Panel** panel bar will be available.

Similarly, you can create as many components as you want in the assembly. Once all the components are created, you can start assembling them using the assembly constraints.

CREATING BOTTOM-UP ASSEMBLIES

As mentioned earlier, bottom-up assemblies are those in which all the components are created as separate part files. All the individual part files are then inserted in an assembly file and are assembled using the assembly constraint. The first component inserted in the assembly will be grounded and its origin will coincide with that of the assembly file. Also, the three default planes of the part file will be placed in the same orientation as that of the default planes of the assembly file. The individual components are inserted in the assembly file using the **Place Component** tool. This tool is discussed next.

Placing Components in the Assembly File

Toolbar:	Assembly Panel > Place Component
Panel bar:	Assembly Panel > Place Component

The **Place Component** tool is used to insert any inventor file in the current assembly file. When you invoke this tool, the **Open** dialog box will be displayed, see Figure 8-7. This dialog box is similar to the simple **Open** dialog box for opening the files. You can also preview the component before inserting it using this dialog box. The type of file you want to insert can be selected from the **Files of type** drop-down list.

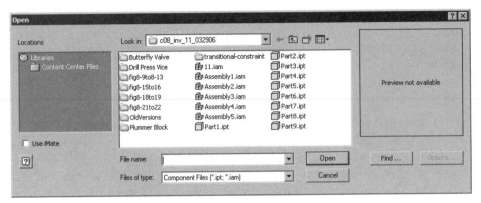

Figure 8-7 *The* **Open** *dialog box*

Select the file to be placed from this dialog box and then choose the **Open** button. If it is the first component in the assembly file, one instance of the selected component will be placed automatically in the current file and you will be prompted to place another instance of the selected component. You can place as many copies of the selected component as you want by specifying the point on the screen. Once you have placed the required number of instances of the component, right-click and choose **Done** from the shortcut menu. As mentioned earlier, the first component will be a grounded component. Therefore, the origin of the first component that will be placed automatically will coincide with the origin of the assembly file.

Similarly, you can place the other components using the **Place Component** tool. However, remember that if one or more components are already placed in the current assembly file, no instance of the selected component will be placed automatically. You will have to manually specify the location of the first instance of the component also.

ASSEMBLING COMPONENTS

Toolbar:	Assembly Panel > Place Constraint
Panel bar:	Assembly Panel > Constraint

In Autodesk Inventor, the components are assembled using four types of assembly constraints, two types of motion constraints, and a transitional constraint. All these constraints are applied using the various tabs of **Place Constraint** dialog box. This dialog box is displayed when you invoke the **Constraint** tool. All the seven types of constraints that can be applied using the **Place Constraint** dialog box are discussed next.

Mate Constraint

The **Mate** constraint is applied using the first button provided in the **Type** area of the **Assembly** tab, see Figure 8-8. This constraint is used to make the selected planar face, axis, or point of a component coincident with that of another component. Depending on the solution selected from the **Solution** area, the components will be assembled with the normal of the faces pointing in the same direction or in the opposite direction. The options in the **Assembly** tab of the **Place Constraint** dialog box when you choose the **Mate** button are discussed next.

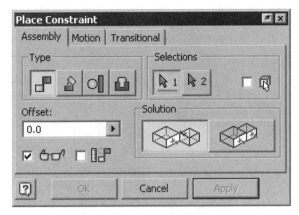

Figure 8-8 *The **Mate** constraint options in the **Assembly** tab of the **Place Constraint** dialog box*

Selections Area

The options in this area are used to select the faces, axes, edges, or points of the selected model for applying the **Mate** constraint. These options are discussed next.

Tip. *You can press and hold the F4 key to rotate the view of the model for the selection purpose. You can also rotate the view of an individual component, which is discussed later in this chapter.*

1 (First Selection)

This button is automatically chosen when you invoke the **Mate** constraint and is used to select a face, axis, edge, or point on the first component to apply the **Mate** constraint. Move the cursor close to the component you want to select. If the cursor is close to a face, it will be highlighted and an arrow will be displayed along with a cross. This arrow will point in the direction of the normal of the selected face. The components are assembled in the direction of the normal of the faces. Similarly, if you move the cursor close to an edge, axis, or a point, it will be highlighted.

2 (Second Selection)

This button is automatically chosen after you select the first component and is used to select a face, axis, edge, or point on the second component to apply the **Mate** constraint. Figure 8-9 shows the **Mate** constraint being applied on the faces of two components. As evident from Figure 8-9, an arrow is displayed on the selected face of both the components. These arrows point in the direction of the normal of the selected face. The selected components will be assembled in the direction of these faces.

Pick part first

The **Pick part first** check box is provided on the right side in the **Selections** area. This check box is used for the assembly that has a large number of components and it is difficult to select the axis, edge, face, or point of one of the components due to the complicacy. If this check box is selected, you will first have to select the component and then select the element in that component to apply the constraint.

Figure 8-9 *Applying the **Mate** constraint on faces*

Note
*You can preview the assembling of the components on the screen after you have selected both the components to apply the constraint. However, remember that until you choose the **Apply** button from the **Place Constraint** dialog box, the constraint will not be actually applied.*

Offset

The **Offset** edit box is used to specify the offset distance between the mating components. If the offset distance is zero, the mating entities will be in contact with each other. However, if there is an offset distance between the mating components, they will be placed at a distance from each other. Figure 8-10 shows the components assembled with an offset distance of 0 mm and Figure 8-11 shows the components assembled with an offset distance of 10 mm between the faces.

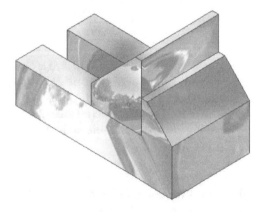

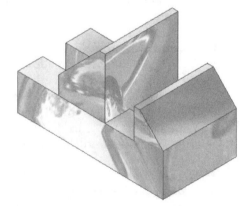

Figure 8-10 *Components assembled with an offset of 0 mm*

Figure 8-11 *Components assembled with an offset of 10 mm*

Tip. *Generally, the components are not assembled with a single constraint. Depending on the components, you require two to three constraints. It can be these many number of the same constraint or a combination of constraints.*

Show Preview

The **Show Preview** check box is selected to display the preview of the assembling components. When you select two components to apply the constraint, a preview of the assembly will be displayed even if you have not chosen the **Apply** button. This is because the **Show Preview** check box is selected. If this check box is cleared, the preview of the assembly will not be displayed.

Predict Offset and Orientation

The **Predict Offset and Orientation** check box is selected to allow Autodesk Inventor to predict the offset and the orientation of the selected components. The predicted offset value is automatically specified in the **Offset** edit box.

Solution Area

The buttons in the **Solution** area are used to specify whether the components being assembled should be placed in a mating position or in a flushing position. A mating position is the one in which the normal of the faces are facing in the opposite direction, see Figure 8-12. A flushing position is one, in which the normal of the faces are facing in the same direction, see Figure 8-13.

Figure 8-12 Mating position   *Figure 8-13 Flushing position*

Angle Constraint

The **Angle** constraint is applied by using the second button in the **Type** area of the **Assembly** tab. This constraint is used to specify the angular position of the selected planar faces or edges of two components. The options that will be displayed when you choose the **Angle** button are displayed in Figure 8-14. Some of the options in this constraint are the same as those in the **Mate** constraint. The remaining options are discussed next.

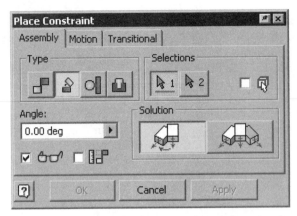

*Figure 8-14 The **Angle** constraint options in the
Assembly tab of the **Place Constraint** dialog box*

Angle

This edit box is used to specify the angle between the selected planar faces or edges of two components. The components will be separated by an angle value specified in this edit box. You can specify a positive or a negative value in this edit box.

Solution Area

This area provides two buttons. The first button is the **Directed Angle** button and is used to apply the **Angle** constraint based on the right hand thumb rule. The second button is the **Undirected Angle** button and is used to apply the constraint based on the default orientation of the components.

Figure 8-15 shows the components selected to apply the **Angle** constraint and Figure 8-16 shows the components after applying the **Angle** constraint of 90-degree.

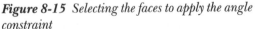

Figure 8-15 Selecting the faces to apply the angle   *Figure 8-16* Components after applying the
constraint   **Angle** constraint of 90-degree

Note

*The remaining options in the **Angle** constraint are the same as those discussed in the **Mate** constraint.*

Tangent Constraint

The **Tangent** constraint is applied by choosing the third button in the **Type** area. This constraint forces the selected circular face of the component to become tangent to the circular face of the other component. The options that are displayed when you choose the **Tangent** button are displayed in Figure 8-17. Some of the options are similar to those discussed earlier. The remaining options are discussed next.

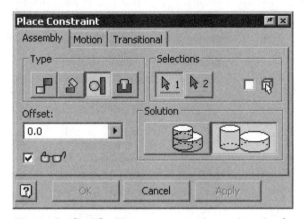

Figure 8-17 The **Tangent** constraint options in the **Assembly** tab of the **Place Constraint** dialog box

Solution Area

The **Solution** area provides the **Inside** and **Outside** buttons for the **Tangent** constraint. Choosing the **Inside** button applies the **Tangent** constraint between the outside of the first selected face and inside of the second selected face. In doing so, the first component is moved inside the second component. Choosing the **Outside** button applies this constraint between the outside of both the selected faces.

Figure 8-18 shows the **Tangent** constraint with the **Inside** solution and Figure 8-19 shows the **Tangent** constraint with the **Outside** solution.

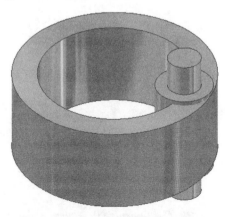 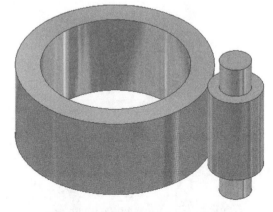

Figure 8-18 The **Inside** solution   *Figure 8-19* The **Outside** solution

Insert Constraint

The **Insert** constraint is applied using the fourth button in the **Type** area of the **Assembly** tab of the **Place Constraint** dialog box. This constraint is used to force two different cylindrical or conical components or features of components to share the same location and orientation of the central axis. This constraint also makes the selected face of the first component coplanar with the selected face of the other component. The options that will be displayed in the **Assembly** tab are shown in Figure 8-20. These options are discussed next.

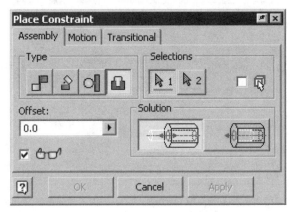

*Figure 8-20 The **Insert** constraint options in the **Assembly** tab of the **Place Constraint** dialog box*

Solution Area

The options provided in the **Solution** area are used to specify whether the normal of the mating faces will point in the same direction or in the opposite direction. If you choose the **Opposed** button, the normal of the mating faces will point in the opposite direction. If you choose the **Aligned** button, the mating faces will point in the same direction. However, the central axes of both the components will share the same orientation. Figure 8-21 shows the components being selected to apply the **Insert** constraint and Figure 8-22 shows the components after applying the **Insert** constraint.

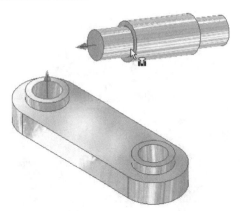

Figure 8-21 Selecting the components   *Figure 8-22 Components after applying the **Insert** constraint*

Note
*The remaining options in the **Tangent** and **Insert** constraints are the same as those discussed in the **Mate** constraint.*

Rotation Constraint

The **Rotation** constraint is applied by choosing the first button in the **Type** area of the **Motion** tab. This constraint is used to rotate one of the components in relation with the other component. The components rotate about the specified central axis. The options that are displayed when you choose the **Rotation** button from the **Type** area of the **Motion** tab of the **Place Constraint** dialog box are shown in Figure 8-23. These options are discussed next.

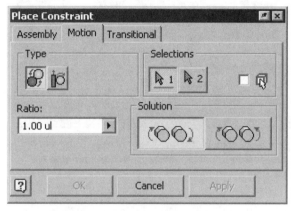

*Figure 8-23 The **Rotation** constraint options in the **Motion** tab of the **Place Constraint** dialog box*

Ratio

The **Ratio** edit box is used to specify the ratio by which the second component will rotate with respect to one complete rotation of the first component. For example, if you enter a value of 2 in this edit box, the second component will rotate two times if the first component is rotated once. Similarly, if you enter a value of 10, the second component will rotate ten times if the first component is rotated once.

Solution

The options in the **Solution** area are used to specify the direction of rotation of the components. Choose the **Forward** button to rotate the components in the forward direction or choose the **Reverse** button to rotate the components in the reverse direction.

Note
*The constraints in the **Motion** tab of the **Place Constraint** dialog box work only with the degree of freedom that is not restricted. These constraints do not interfere with the other assembly constraints.*

*The remaining options in the **Rotation** constraint are the same as those discussed in the **Mate** constraint.*

Rotation-Translation Constraint

The **Rotation-Translation** constraint is applied by choosing the second button in the **Type** area of the **Motion** tab. This constraint is used to rotate the first component in relation with the translation of the second component. The options in the **Motion** tab of the **Place Constraint** dialog box are shown in Figure 8-24. These options are discussed next.

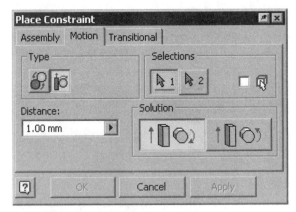

Figure 8-24 The **Rotation-Translation** *constraint options in the* **Motion** *tab of the* **Place Constraint** *dialog box*

Distance

The **Distance** edit box is used to specify the distance by which the second component will move in relation with one complete rotation of the first component. For example, if you enter a value of 2 mm in this edit box, the second component will move a distance of 2 mm for one complete rotation of the first component.

Solution

The buttons in the **Solution** area are used to specify whether the second component will move in the forward direction or the reverse direction for every forward rotation of the first component. Choose the **Forward** button to move the component in the forward direction and the **Reverse** button to move the component in the reverse direction.

Transitional Constraint

The **Transitional Constraint** is applied by choosing its button from the **Type** area of the **Transitional** tab, see Figure 8-25. A transitional constraint ensures that the selected face of the cylindrical component maintains contact with the other selected face when you slide the cylindrical component about the degree of freedom that is not eliminated. The options in this tab are similar to those discussed in the previous constraints.

USING ALT+ DRAG TO APPLY ASSEMBLY CONSTRAINTS

Autodesk Inventor allows you to apply the assembly constraints without actually invoking the **Place Constraint** dialog box. This is done by pressing the ALT key and then dragging the

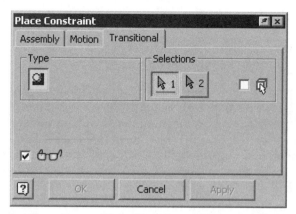

Figure 8-25 *The **Transitional** constraint options in the* ***Transitional*** *tab of the **Place Constraint** dialog box*

component. The following steps explain the procedure to apply assembly constraints using the ALT+Drag method.

1. Press the ATL key and start dragging the component that you want to select as the first component; the symbol of the **Mate** constraint is displayed below the cursor. This is because when you use the ALT+Drag method, by default the **Mate** constraint is applied.

2. Release the ALT key but make sure you do not release the left mouse button. This is because if you release the left mouse button, the constraints will no more be applied. Press the SPACEBAR to change the mate position to the flush position. Drag the selected component to the component that you want to select as the second component and then release the left mouse button. The assembly constraint it applied.

If you do not want to apply the **Mate** constraint, you can use the keyboard keys after releasing the ALT key to apply the other relations. The following table provides the details of the various keys that you can use the apply the assembly constraints:

Key	Description	Function of SPACEBAR
M or 1	Applies the **Mate** constraint	Changes the mate position to the flush position
A or 2	Applies the **Angle** constraint	Reverses the direction of applying the **Angle** constraint
T or 3	Applies the **Tangent** constraint	Reverses to inside or outside face for applying the **Tangent** constraint
I or 4	Applies the **Insert** constraint	Reverses the direction of the insertion
R or 5	Applies the **Rotation** constraint	Reverses the direction of rotation
S or 6	Applies the **Rotation-Translation** constraint	Reverses the direction of translation
X or 8	Applies the **Transitional** constraint	No use of SPACEBAR

MOVING INDIVIDUAL COMPONENTS

Toolbar:	Assembly Panel > Move Component
Panel bar:	Assembly Panel > Move Component

Autodesk Inventor allows you to move the individual unconstrained components in the assembly file without disturbing the position and location of the other components in the assembly file. This is done using the **Move Component** tool. When you invoke this tool, you will be prompted to drag the component to a new location. As you move the cursor close to any component, it will be highlighted. Select the component and then drag it to the desired location. The component will be relocated and the other components in the assembly file will not be disturbed.

ROTATING INDIVIDUAL COMPONENTS IN 3D SPACE

Toolbar:	Assembly Panel > Rotate Component
Panel bar:	Assembly Panel > Rotate Component

You can also rotate individual unconstrained components in the current assembly file without changing the orientation of the other components. This is done using the **Rotate Component** tool. When you invoke this tool, you will be prompted to drag the component to a new location. Select the component that you want to reorient. As soon as you select it, the rim along with the handles will be displayed around the model. Also, the cursor will be changed to rotation mode cursor.

You can use the same tool to rotate other individual components also. After you have finished rotating a component, click on the other component using the rotation mode cursor. You will notice that the rim is now displayed around the component that you selected. Similarly, you can select any individual component to rotate in 3D space.

TUTORIALS

Tutorial 1

In this tutorial, you will create the components of the Butterfly Valve and then assemble them. The Body and the Shaft will be created in the assembly file and the remaining components will be created as individual parts in separate part files. As a result, you will use a combination of top-down and bottom-up assemblies. The dimensions for the components are given in Figures 8-26 through 8-32. Assume the missing dimensions for the components and the parameters for the threads.   **(Expected time: 3 Hrs 30 min)**

Figure 8-26 *Butterfly Valve assembly*

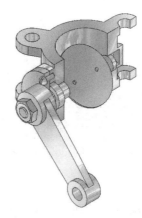

Figure 8-27 *Inside view of the Butterfly Valve*

Figure 8-28a *Solid model of the Body*

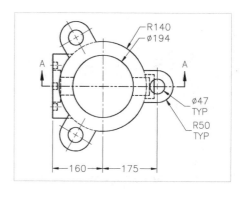

Figure 8-28b *Top view of the Body*

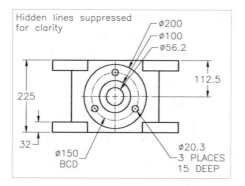

Figure 8-28c *Left-side view of the Body*

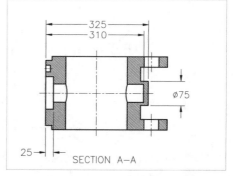

Figure 8-28d *Sectioned front view of the Body*

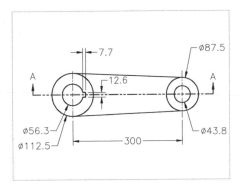

Figure 8-29a *Top view of the Arm*

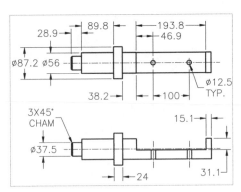

Figure 8-30 *Dimensions of the Shaft*

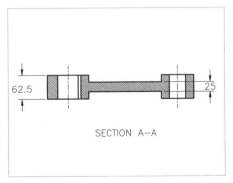

Figure 8-29b *Sectioned front view of the Arm*

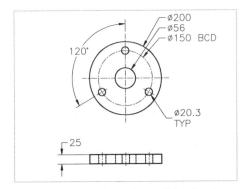

Figure 8-31 *Dimensions of the Retainer*

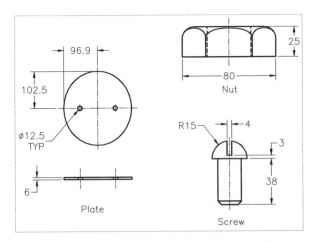

Figure 8-32 *Dimensions of the Plate, Nut, and Screw*

The following steps are required to create the assembly:

a. Create the Body and the Shaft in the assembly file and then assemble these two components using the **Place Constraint** dialog box. Save and close the assembly file.
b. Start new metric standard part files and, one by one, create the other individual components.
c. Open the assembly file and insert the individual components in the assembly file using the **Place Component** tool.
d. Assemble the components using the **Place Constraint** dialog box to complete the Butterfly Valve assembly.

Creating the Body

The Body and the Shaft will be created in the assembly file and therefore, you will use the top-down approach of assembly modeling. To create these two components, you first need to start a new metric assembly file.

1. Choose the **New** button from the **Inventor Standard** toolbar to invoke the **Open** dialog box. Double-click on **Standard (mm).iam** in the **Metric** tab (Figure 8-33) to start a metric assembly file. If you have started a new Autodesk Inventor session, this dialog box is automatically displayed.

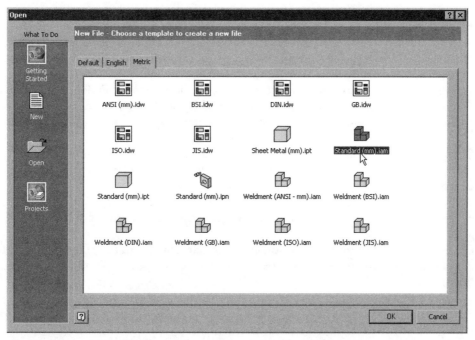

*Figure 8-33 Starting a new metric assembly file using the **Open** dialog box*

The assembly modeling environment is activated with the **Assembly Panel** panel bar on the left of the drawing window, as shown in Figure 8-34.

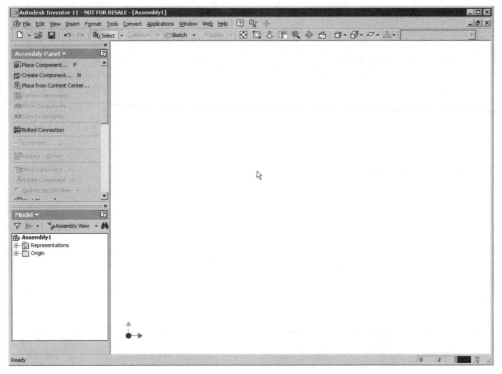

*Figure 8-34 Screen display in the **Assembly** module*

You will notice that very few tools are available in the **Assembly Panel** panel bar. This is because no component is present in the assembly file. Once a component is placed or created, all the other tools will be available for use.

2. Choose the **Create Component** button from the **Assembly Panel** toolbar or choose the **Create Component** button from the **Assembly Panel** panel bar to invoke the **Create In-Place Component** dialog box.

3. Enter the name of the new part file as **Body.ipt** in the **New Component Name** edit box.

4. Choose the **Browse Templates** button and then select **Standard (mm).ipt** from the **Metric** tab of the **Open Template** dialog box. Choose the **OK** button from the **Open Template** dialog box.

5. Specify the location of the new part file in the **New File Location** edit box as *\PersonalProject\c08\Butterfly Valve* and choose the **OK** button from the dialog box.

    The **Autodesk Inventor 11** information box is displayed informing you that the folder you have mentioned does not exist. It will also prompt you if you want to create this folder. Because you did not create any folder for storing the component files before starting the assembly, you need to create it. Therefore, if you choose **OK** in the **Autodesk Inventor 11** information box, it will create the folder for you.

6. Choose **OK** in the **Autodesk Inventor 11** information box.

> **Tip**. *It is recommended that you create separate folders for storing the individual component files of assemblies. The reason for this is that a number of assemblies have components with similar names. For example, the name Body is common to a number of assemblies. Therefore, if you create the Body and store it in the folder of a particular assembly, there will be no confusion in placing the components. Also, when you open the assembly next time, there will be no confusion in referring to the component.*

As soon as you choose **OK** from the **Autodesk Inventor 11** information box, it is closed and you are prompted to select the sketching plane for the base feature. You can now create the Body of the Butterfly Valve assembly.

Note
*Remember that if you save the file when the part modeling environment is active, the part file will be saved and not the assembly file. This means that while creating the Body, if you choose the **Save** button from the **Inventor Standard** toolbar, the Body.ipt file will be saved not the current assembly file. To save the current assembly file, you need to exit the part modeling environment and then choose the **Save** button in the assembly modeling environment. You can also save the assembly file before you start creating the components.*

7. Create the Body of the Butterfly Valve using the given dimensions. The screen display of the assembly file after creating the Body is shown in Figure 8-35.

You will notice that the part modeling environment is still active in the assembly file. To proceed further, you need to save the part file and exit the part modeling environment by choosing the **Return** button from the **Inventor Standard** toolbar.

8. Choose the **Save** button to save the part file and then choose the **Return** button from the **Inventor Standard** toolbar to exit the part modeling environment.

When you choose the **Return** button, you will notice that the assembly modeling environment is activated and the **Part Features** panel bar of the part modeling environment is replaced by the **Assembly Panel** panel bar of the assembly modeling environment.

As mentioned earlier, until you exit the part modeling environment, only the part file will be saved when you choose the **Save** button. The assembly file will be saved only after you exit the part modeling environment.

9. Choose the **Save** button from the **Inventor Standard** toolbar and save the assembly with the name *Butterfly Valve.iam* in the *Butterfly Valve* folder.

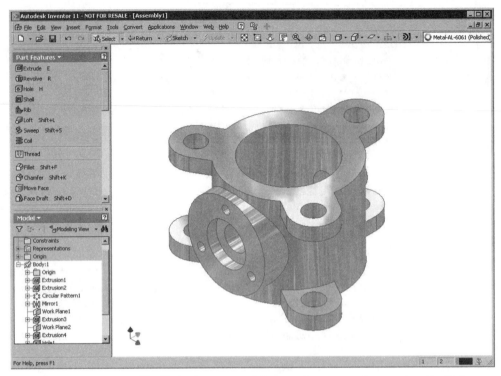

Figure 8-35 *Assembly file in the part modeling environment after creating the Body*

Creating the Shaft

The second component that has to be created in the assembly file is the Shaft. Therefore, you need to again activate the sketching environment and the part modeling environment to create the Shaft. However, because the Body is already present in the assembly file, there are chances that it might restrict with the view of the part that you create next. Considering this, the part modeling environment in the assembly file is designed in such a way that when you start creating the components in the assembly file, all the existing components become transparent so that they do not restrict the view of the new part that you create.

1. Choose the **Create Component** button from the **Assembly Panel** toolbar or choose **Create Component** from the **Assembly Panel** panel bar to invoke the **Create In-Place Component** dialog box.

2. Browse and select a new metric standard part file as the template to create the component. Enter the name of the new part file as **Shaft.ipt** in the **New Component Name** edit box.

3. Specify the location of the new part file in the **New File Location** edit box as *\PersonalProject\c08\Butterfly Valve*.

4. Clear the **Constrain sketch plane to selected face or plane** check box. Choose **OK**.

5. You are prompted to select the plane on which you want to sketch the base feature. Select the XY plane from the browser.

    As soon as you select the XY plane, the sketching environment is activated and the Body becomes transparent. You can now proceed with creating the Shaft.

6. After creating the Shaft, save it before exiting the part modeling environment so that the *Shaft.ipt* file is saved. Exit the part modeling environment by choosing the **Return** button from the **Inventor Standard** toolbar. Save the assembly file by choosing the **Save** button from the **Inventor Standard** toolbar.

    When you exit the part modeling environment, you will notice that the Body is no more transparent. Also, both the components in the assembly file interfere with each other. Therefore, before proceeding with assembling these components, you need to move one of the components such that it does not interfere with the other. You can move the individual component using the **Move Component** tool.

7. Choose **Move Component** from the **Assembly Panel** panel bar. You are prompted to drag the component to a new location. Select the Body and drag it to a new location where it does not interfere with the Shaft. Choose the **Zoom All** button to increase the display area. The screen display of the assembly file with both the components is shown in Figure 8-36.

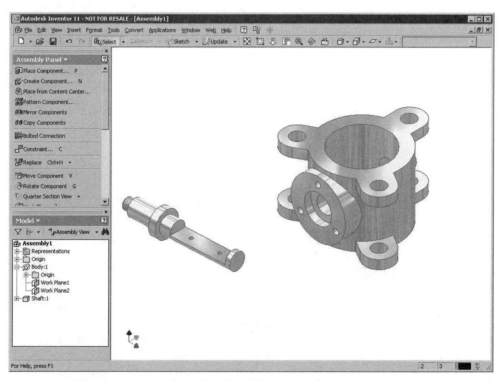

Figure 8-36 *The assembly file after creating the Body and the Shaft*

Note

*If the orientation of the Shaft and the Body is different from the one shown in Figure 8-36, you can reorient them using the **Rotate Component** tool.*

Assembling the Components

The Shaft is a circular part that has to be inserted in the counterbore hole of the Body. Therefore, you can use the **Insert** constraint to assemble these components. As mentioned earlier, the **Insert** constraint forces the selected components or features to share the same location and orientation of the central axis and at the same time makes the selected faces coplanar. Therefore, the Shaft will be assembled with the Body using the **Insert** constraint. Now, the flat part of the Shaft has to be at an angle to the top face of the Body. To assemble it at an angle with the top face, you will have to use the **Angle** constraint. Therefore, the second constraint that will be used is the **Angle** constraint.

1. Choose the **Place Constraint** button from the **Assembly Panel** toolbar or choose **Constraint** from the **Assembly Panel** panel bar to invoke the **Place Constraint** dialog box.

    By default, the **Mate** constraint is selected. For assembling the Shaft with the Body, you require the **Insert** constraint. Therefore, you will have to choose the **Insert** button from the **Type** area of the **Assembly** tab of the **Place Constraint** dialog box.

2. Choose the **Insert** button from the **Type** area. You will notice that the **Insert** constraint symbol is attached to the cursor. This symbol is displayed along with the cursor when you move the cursor in the drawing window.

3. Select the edge of the Shaft, as shown in Figure 8-37.

    You will notice that the selected edge is highlighted and an arrow is displayed along the direction of the central axis of the Shaft. This arrow will also point in the direction in which the Shaft will be assembled. Also, the **2** button in the **Selections** area of the **Place Constraint** dialog box is automatically chosen.

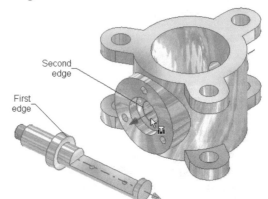

4. Select the inner edge of the counterbore hole, as shown in Figure 8-37. As soon you select the second edge for applying

*Figure 8-37 Selecting the faces to apply the **Insert** constraint*

the constraint, the Shaft will assemble with the Body. This is because by default, the **Show Preview** check box in the **Place Constraint** dialog box is selected.

5. Choose the **Apply** button to assemble the Shaft with the Body.

6. Choose the **Angle** button to apply the **Angle** constraint.

As the assembly is in the isometric view, the flat face of the Shaft is not visible. Therefore, you will have to reorient the assembly using the **Rotate** tool. This tool can be used when you are inside another tool and so when you invoke this tool, you will temporarily switch to the assembly rotating mode. The assembling of components will resume when you exit the **Rotate** tool.

7. Choose the **Rotate** button from the **Inventor Standard** toolbar and rotate the assembly such that the flat face of the Shaft is visible, refer to Figure 8-38. Right-click to display the shortcut menu and choose **Done** to exit this tool.

8. The symbol of the **Angle** constraint will be reattached to the cursor, suggesting that the assembling of components is resumed. Select the flat face of the Shaft as the first face to apply the **Angle** constraint, see Figure 8-38.

9. Select the top face of the Body as the second face to apply the **Angle** constraint, see Figure 8-38.

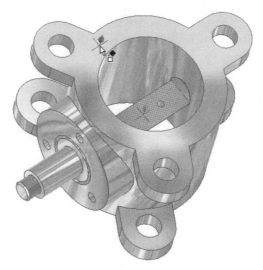

*Figure 8-38 Selecting faces to apply the **Angle** constraint*

10. Enter the value of angle as **45** in the **Angle** edit box. The flat face rotates toward the right side. If the flat face rotates toward the left, enter **-45** in the **Angle** edit box and choose the **Directed Angle** button from the **Solution** area to make sure the face rotates toward the right. Choose **Apply** to apply the constraint. Exit the dialog box by choosing the **Cancel** button. Change the view back to the previous view by pressing the F5 key.

Creating other Components

1. Save the current assembly file and then close it by choosing **File > Close** from the menu bar.

2. Create the other components as individual part files and save them with their names in the *Butterfly Valve* folder.

3.   Exit the part file and then again open the *Butterfly Valve.iam* file.

Assembling the Retainer

The next component that has to be assembled is the Retainer. The Retainer is also a circular part and so can be assembled using the **Insert** constraint. The three holes of the Retainer have to match those on the front planar face of the Body. Also, the central hole of the Retainer has to match with the central hole of the front planar face of the Body. Therefore, you need to apply the **Insert** constraint twice. The first time is to align one of the smaller holes on the Retainer with one of the smaller holes on the left flat face of the Body. The second time it will be used for the central hole. But first, you need to place the Retainer in the assembly using the **Place Component** tool.

1.   Choose **Place Component** from the **Assembly Panel** panel bar to invoke the **Open** dialog box.

By default, the current folder in the **Open** dialog box will be the **Butterfly Valve** folder. All the components that you created are displayed in this folder.

2.   Double-click on the Retainer. You can also select the Retainer and then choose the **Open** button.

The **Open** dialog box is closed and the Retainer is attached to the cursor. Also, you are prompted to place the component.

3.   Place the Retainer at a location where it does not interfere with the existing components.

After you have placed an instance of the Retainer, you are again prompted to place the component. Because you need to place only one instance of the Retainer, you can exit the component placement option.

4.   Right-click in the drawing window to display the shortcut menu and choose **Done** to exit the component placement option.

5.   Choose **Constraint** from the **Assembly Panel** panel bar; the **Place Constraint** dialog box is displayed. If the **Place Constraint** dialog box is restricting the viewing of the components in the drawing window, you can move it by picking it from the blue strip on the top and dragging.

6.   Choose the **Insert** button from the **Type** area. Select the circular edge of one of the smaller holes on the top face of the Retainer as the first edge, see Figure 8-39.

7.   Select the circular edge of one of the smaller holes on the front planar face of the circular feature on the Body to apply the constraint, see Figure 8-39. Choose **Apply**.

As soon as you select the second face, the Retainer moves from its location and is assembled with the Body such that both the selected holes are concentric and the top face of the Retainer is coplanar with the front planar face of the circular feature on the Body. However,

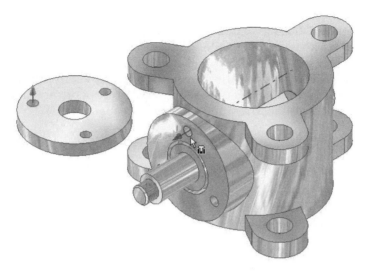

Figure 8-39 *Selecting the faces to apply the **Insert** constraint*

you will notice that the central hole of the Retainer is not concentric with the central hole of the left circular feature of the Body and the Shaft. Therefore, you need to apply the **Insert** constraint once again to align them.

8. Select the inner edge of the Retainer that is coplanar with the Body as the first edge to apply the constraint, see Figure 8-40. You may have to rotate the model to select this edge.

9. Select the outer circular edge on the flat face of the front circular feature on the Body as the second face to apply the constraint, see Figure 8-40. Choose **Apply** to assemble the components and then choose **Cancel** and exit the dialog box.

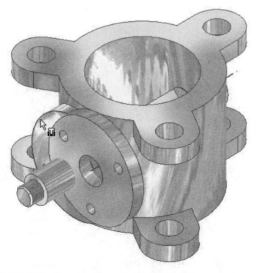

Figure 8-40 *Selecting the faces to apply the **Insert** constraint again*

Assembling the Arm

The next component that has to be assembled is the Arm. Because the Arm is assembled at a certain angle with respect to the Body, you need to use two constraints to assemble it. The first constraint will be the **Insert** constraint, which will insert the already assembled Retainer in the bigger hole of the Arm. The second constraint will be the **Angle** constraint, which will be used to apply an angle between the XZ plane of the Arm and the top face of the Body. You will place the Arm using the **Place Component** tool.

1. Choose the **Place Component** button from the **Assembly Panel** panel bar to invoke the **Open** dialog box.

2. Double-click on the Arm.

3. Place the Arm at a location where it does not interfere with the existing components.

4. Right-click in the drawing window to display the shortcut menu and choose **Done** to exit the component placement option.

5. Choose the **Constraint** button from the **Assembly Panel** panel bar; the **Place Constraint** dialog box is displayed.

6. Choose the **Insert** button and then select the top circular edge of the hole with the keyway in the Arm as the first face, see Figure 8-41.

7. Select the outer circular edge on the front planar face of the Retainer as the second face to apply the **Insert** constraint, see Figure 8-41. Choose the **Apply** button.

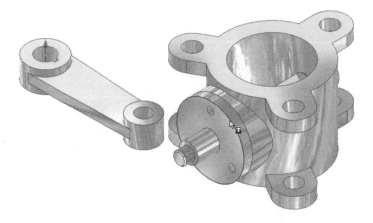

Figure 8-41 *Selecting the faces to apply the **Insert** constraint*

The Arm will be assembled with the Retainer and the Shaft will be inserted in the bigger hole of the Arm. The second constraint will be used to reorient the Arm such that it is assembled at an angle to the top face of the Body. This angle is the same as the angle between the top face of the Body and the flat face of the Shaft.

Note

*In this case, it is presumed that the cylindrical features of the Arm are created on the XY plane. Also, the bigger and smaller cylindrical features are created from left to right respectively along the X axis direction when placed on the XY plane. Therefore, the XZ plane will pass through the center of the two cylindrical features. This XZ plane will be used to apply the **Angle** constraint.*

8. Choose the **Angle** button from the **Type** area. Select the top face of the Body as the first face to apply the constraint.

   The second face that has to be selected to apply the constraint is the XZ plane of the Arm. The XZ plane of the Arm will not be displayed in the browser. You need to click on the + sign located on the left of the Arm in the browser to display the **Origin** folder and then from this folder, select the XZ plane.

9. Click on the + sign located on the left of the Arm in the browser to display the **Origin** folder. Click again on the + sign located on the left of the **Origin** folder to display all the work planes of the Arm. Select the XZ plane.

10. Enter the angle as **-135** in the **Angle** edit box. Choose **Apply** to apply the constraint and then **Cancel** to close the dialog box. Click on the - sign on the left of the Arm to close the folders. The assembly, after assembling the Arm, is shown in Figure 8-42.

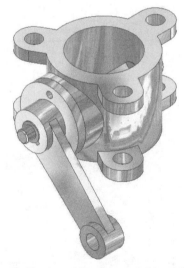

Figure 8-42 Assembly after assembling the Arm

Assembling the Plate

The next component that has to be assembled is the Plate. You need to place it in the assembly file and then assemble it on the flat feature of the Shaft. You need to apply the **Insert** constraint twice to assemble the Plate with the Shaft. The first constraint will align one of the holes on the Plate with one of the holes on the Shaft. The second constraint will align the second hole on the Plate with that on the Shaft.

Because the Shaft is assembled inside the Body, the Body will cause a restriction in viewing the components being assembled. To avoid this, Autodesk Inventor allows you to turn off the display of the components that you do not require for assembling the other components. Therefore, before proceeding with the assembling of the Plate, you can turn off the display of the Body. This is done using the browser.

1. Right-click on the Body in the browser to display the shortcut menu. You will notice that in the shortcut menu, there is a check mark in front of the **Visibility** option, see Figure 8-43. This suggests that the display of this component is turned on. Choose the **Visibility** option again to turn off the display of the Body.

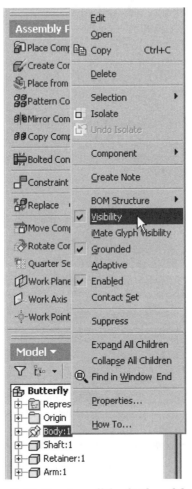

Figure 8-43 *Turning off the display of the Body*

The component whose visibility is turned off will be displayed in gray color in the browser.

2. Choose **Place Component** from the **Assembly Panel** panel bar to invoke the **Open** dialog box.

3. Double-click on the Plate.

4. Place the Plate at a location where it does not interfere with the existing components.

5. Right-click in the drawing window to display the shortcut menu and choose **Done** to exit the component placement option.

6. Choose **Constraint** from the **Assembly Panel** panel bar. The **Place Constraint** dialog box is displayed.

7. Choose the **Insert** button and then select the circular edge of one of the holes on the top face of the Plate as the first face to apply the constraint, see Figure 8-44.

8. Select the circular edge of the right hole on the flat face of the Shaft as the second face to apply the constraint, see Figure 8-44. Choose the **Apply** button to apply the constraint.

Figure 8-44 Selecting the faces to apply the constraint

As soon as you select the second face to apply the constraint, the Plate will move from its location and will be assembled with the Shaft. Now, the second constraint has to be applied on the other hole of the Plate. But the hole has to be selected on the face that is made coplanar with the flat face of the Shaft. Therefore, you need to reorient the model such that the back face of the Plate is visible and you can select the hole on that face to apply the constraint.

9. Reorient the assembly using the **Rotate** tool such that the back face of the Plate is visible.

10. Select the circular edge of the hole on the back face of the Plate as the first face to apply the constraint.

    Because you rotated the model such that the back face of the Plate is visible, the flat face of the Shaft is not visible in the current view. Therefore, you need to switch back to the previous view. Sometimes, when you are inside the **Place Constraint** tool, you cannot use the F5 key to invoke the previous view. You need to invoke the **Rotate** tool again and then right-click to display the shortcut menu and choose **Previous View** from this menu.

11. Press the F5 key or choose the **Rotate** button from the **Inventor Standard** toolbar and right-click in the drawing window to display the shortcut menu. Choose the **Previous View** option to switch back to the previous view. Again, right-click and choose **Done** to exit the **Rotate** tool.

12. Select the other hole on the flat face of the Shaft to apply the constraint. Choose the **Apply** button and then choose the **Cancel** button to exit the dialog box. The assembly, after assembling the Plate, is shown in Figure 8-45.

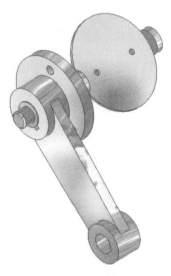

Figure 8-45 *Assembly after assembling the Plate*

Assembling the Screws

There are three instances of the Screw that need to be assembled such that they are inserted in the three holes on the Retainer. But before assembling the Screws, you need to turn off the display of the Arm so that it does not interfere in the display while assembling the other components.

1. Right-click on the Arm in the browser and choose **Visibility** to turn off the display of the Arm in the assembly.

2. Choose **Place Component** from the **Assembly Panel** panel bar to invoke the **Open** dialog box.

3. Double-click on the Screw.

4. Place three instances of the Screw at a location where they do not interfere with the existing components.

5. Choose the **Place Constraint** button from the **Assembly Panel** toolbar or choose **Constraint** from the **Assembly Panel** panel bar. The **Place Constraint** dialog box is displayed.

6. Choose the **Insert** button and then select the circular edge on the flat face of the head of the Screw as the first face to apply the constraint.

7. Select the circular edge of one of the smaller holes on the front face of the Retainer as the second face to apply the constraint. Choose **Apply** to apply the constraint.

8. Similarly, assemble the other two Screws with the other two smaller holes on the Retainer.

Assembling the Nut

The Nut has to be assembled with the Shaft. Since the threaded portion of the Shaft has to be inserted inside the hole of the Nut, you will use the **Insert** constraint to assemble these components.

1. Choose **Place Component** from the **Assembly Panel** panel bar to invoke the **Open** dialog box.

2. Double-click on the Nut.

3. Place the Nut at a location where it does not interfere with the existing components. Rotate the Nut using the **Rotate Component** tool such that the flat face of the Nut is visible in the current view.

4. Choose the **Place Constraint** button from the **Assembly Panel** toolbar or choose **Constraint** from the **Assembly Panel** panel bar. The **Place Constraint** dialog box is displayed.

5. Choose the **Insert** button and then select the hole on the flat face of the Nut as the first face to apply the constraint.

6. Select the end face (not on the side of the chamfered edge) of the threaded feature of the Shaft. Choose **Apply** and then choose **Cancel** to exit the dialog box.

Turning on the Display of the Body and the Arm

1. Right-click on the Body in the browser and choose **Visibility** from the shortcut menu to turn on the display of the Body in the assembly.

2. Similarly, right-click on the Arm in the browser and choose **Visibility**. The display of the Arm will be turned on in the assembly. Choose the **Zoom All** button from the **Inventor Standard** toolbar. The final Butterfly Valve assembly is shown in Figure 8-46.

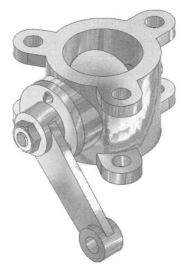

Figure 8-46 Final Butterfly Valve assembly

3. Save the assembly and close the file.

Tutorial 2

In this tutorial, you will create the components of the Plummer Block assembly and then assemble them in the assembly file. All components should be created as separate part files. After creating the components, place them in the assembly file and then assemble them. The dimensions of the components are shown in Figures 8-47 through 8-52. Assume the missing dimensions and the parameters for the threads.   **(Expected time: 3 Hrs)**

Note

The orientation of the Casting you draw should match the orientation of the Casting shown in the assembly in Figure 8-47. This is because when you place the first component in the assembly file, it is placed on the same plane on which it was originally created in the part file. Since the Casting will be the first component you place in the assembly file, the base of it should be created on the XY plane. Therefore, when you place it in the assembly file, it is placed on the XY plane. The orientation of the other components also depends on the first component that you place in the assembly file.

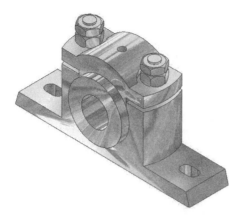

Figure 8-47 Plummer Block assembly

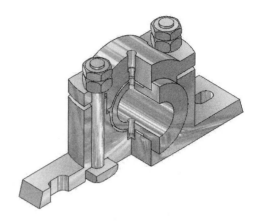

Figure 8-48 Sectioned isometric view of the Plummer Block assembly

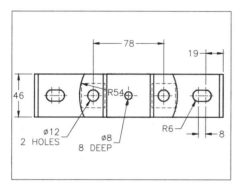

Figure 8-49a Top view of the Casting

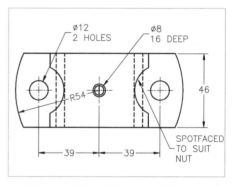

Figure 8-50a Top view of the Cap

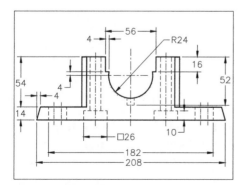

Figure 8-49b Front view of the Casting

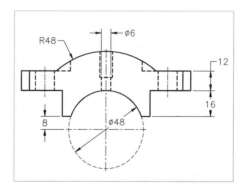

Figure 8-50b Front view of the Cap

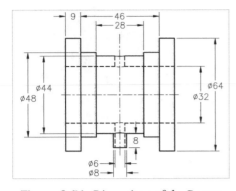

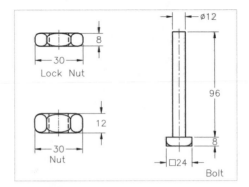

Figure 8-51 *Dimensions of the Brasses*

Figure 8-52 *Dimensions of the Lock Nut, Nut, and Bolt*

The following steps are required to create the assembly:

a. Create all the components of the assembly as separate part files and save them in the \PersonalProject\c08\Plummer Block folder.

b. Start a new metric assembly file and using the **Place Component** tool, place the Casting and the Cap.

c. Assemble the two components using the assembly constraints.

d. Next, turn off the display of the Cap and then place the Brasses in the assembly. Assemble the Brasses with the Casting and then turn off the display of the Brasses too.

e. Place two instances of the Bolt in the assembly file and then assemble them with the Casting.

f. Turn on the display of the Cap and place two instances of the Nut and the Lock Nut. Assemble both the instances of the Nut with the Cap and then the Lock Nut with the Nut.

g. Finally, turn on the display of the Brasses to complete the Plummer Block assembly.

Creating the Components

1. Create all the components of the Plummer Block assembly as separate part files. Specify the names of the files, as shown in Figures 8-49 through 8-52. The files should be saved in the \PersonalProject\c08\Plummer Block folder.

Assembling the Casting and the Cap

The Casting and the Cap will be assembled using two assembly constraints. The first constraint is the **Insert** constraint that will align one of the holes on the top face of the Cap with its corresponding hole on one of the horizontal face of the Casting. You will also apply an offset of 4 mm between the mating faces in this constraint. The other constraint is the **Mate** constraint that will align the front face of the Cap with the front face of the Casting.

1. Start a new assembly file. Save it with the name *Plummer Block.iam* in the \PersonalProject\c08\Plummer Block folder. This is the folder in which all the individual part files are saved.

2. Choose **Place Component** from the **Assembly Panel** panel bar to invoke the **Open** dialog box.

3. Double-click on the Casting.

    Notice that one instance of the Casting is automatically placed in the assembly file. This instance is grounded and has a push pin icon in front of it in the browser. You are again prompted to place the component.

4. Right-click and choose **Done** from the shortcut menu. Similarly, place one instance of the Cap in the current assembly file. The location of the Cap should be such that it does not interfere with the Casting.

5. Choose **Rotate Component** from the **Assembly Panel** panel bar and rotate the Cap such that its bottom face is visible in the current view.

6. Choose **Constraint** from the **Assembly Panel** panel bar; the **Place Constraint** dialog box is displayed.

7. Choose the **Insert** button and then select the circular edge of the right hole on the bottom face of the Cap as the first face to apply the constraint.

8. Select the circular edge of the right hole on the top face of the Casting as the second face to apply the constraint. Enter the value of the offset as **4** in the **Offset** edit box. Choose the **Apply** button.

    The Cap is assembled with the Casting. However, the alignment of the front face of the Cap does not match the alignment of the front face of the Casting. Therefore, you need to apply the **Mate** constraint.

9. Choose the **Mate** button from the **Type** area and then select the front face of the Cap as the first face to apply the constraint.

10. Select the front face of the Casting as the second face to apply the constraint and then choose the **Flush** button from the **Solution** area. Choose **Apply** and then choose **Cancel** to exit the dialog box. The assembly, after assembling the Cap and the Casting, is shown in Figure 8-53.

Assembling the Brasses

The Brasses is a circular part and so can be assembled using the **Insert** constraint. Notice that in the Brasses, there is a circular join feature (snug) created on the cylindrical face. The snug has to match with that of the hole on the circular face of the Casting. To proceed with assembling the Brasses, you first need to turn off the display of the Cap because it is not required in assembling the Brasses.

1. Right-click on the Cap in the browser and choose **Visibility** from the shortcut menu to turn off its display.

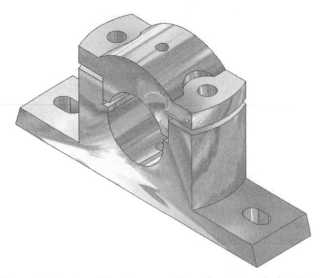

Figure 8-53 *Assembly after assembling the Cap with the Casting*

2. Place the Brasses using the **Place Component** tool. Invoke the **Place Constraint** dialog box using the **Place Constraint** tool. Choose the **Insert** button from the **Type** area and select the semicircular edge of the Casting as the first edge to apply the constraint, see Figure 8-54.

3. Select the circular edge of the Brasses shown in Figure 8-54 as the second edge to apply the constraint. Make sure the arrow points in the backward direction. Choose the **Apply** button.

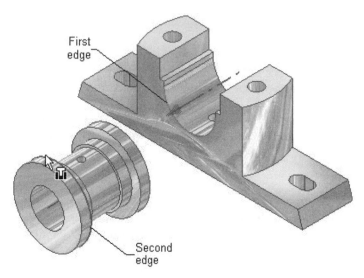

First
edge

Second
edge

Figure 8-54 *Selecting the faces to apply the **Insert** constraint*

The next constraint is used to align the central axis of the snug created on the cylindrical face of the Brasses with that of the hole on the cylindrical face of the Casting. However, because the hole in the casting will not be visible even if you change the orientation of the assembly, you need to change the display mode from shaded to wireframe. In the wireframe display, the inside holes and features will also be displayed.

4. Change the display mode to wireframe by choosing the down arrow on the right of the **Shaded Display** button in the **Inventor Standard** toolbar and choosing **Wireframe Display**. Choose the **Mate** button from the **Type** area and move the cursor close to the snug on the cylindrical face of the Brasses. When you move the cursor close to the snug, the central axis of the snug will be displayed. If not, you can use the **Cycle Through** tool to select the central axis of the circular join feature as the first element to apply the constraint.

5. Select the central axis of the hole in the cylindrical face of the Casting as the second selection set. Choose the **Apply** button and then choose the **Cancel** button to apply the constraint and exit the dialog box.

6. Turn on the visibility of the Cap using the browser and change the display type to **Shaded Display**. The assembly is shown in Figure 8-55.

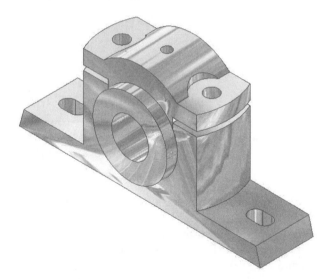

Figure 8-55 *Assembly after assembling the Brasses*

Assembling the Bolts

There are two instances of the Bolts that have to be assembled in the current assembly. But because the Brasses is not required for assembling the Bolts or the Nuts, you can turn off its display. After turning off the display of the Brasses, you will assemble the Bolts.

1. Turn off the display of the Brasses using the browser. Place two instances of the Bolt using the **Place Component** tool.

2. Invoke the **Place Constraint** dialog box and then choose the **Insert** button from the **Type** area. Select the circular edge on the top face of the base square feature of the Bolt as the first face to apply the constraint, see Figure 8-56.

3. Change the display type to wireframe and then select the circular edge on the top face of the square cut on the bottom face of the Casting, see Figure 8-56. Choose **Apply**.

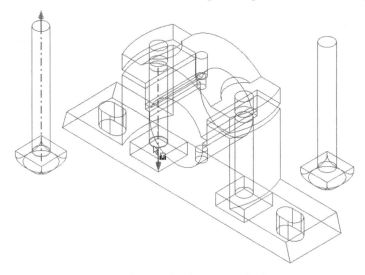

Figure 8-56 Selecting the faces to apply the constraint

4. Similarly, assemble the other Bolt and then change the display type to **Shaded Display**.

Assembling the Nuts and the Lock Nuts

1. Place two instances each of the Nut and the Lock Nut using the **Place Component** tool.

2. Invoke the **Place Constraint** dialog box and choose the **Insert** button. Select the circular edge of the hole on the top face of one of the Nuts as the first face to apply the constraint.

3. Select the circular edge of the left hole on the top face of the Cap as the second face to apply the constraint. The Nut will be assembled with the Cap. Choose the **Apply** button to apply the constraint.

4. Select the circular edge of the hole on the top face of one of the Lock Nuts as the first face to apply the constraint.

5. Select the circular edge of the hole on the top face of the Nut that is assembled with the Cap as the second face to apply the constraint. Choose the **Apply** button to apply the constraint.

6. Similarly, assemble the other Nut and the Lock Nut. Turn on the display of all the invisible components using the browser. The final Plummer Block assembly is shown in Figure 8-57.

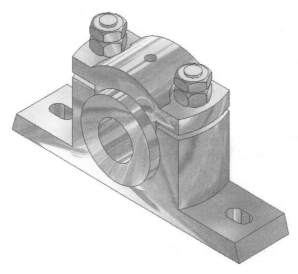

Figure 8-57 *Final Plummer Block assembly*

7.   Save the assembly by choosing the **Save** button from the **Inventor Standard** toolbar.

Self-Evaluation Test

Answer the following questions and then compare your answers with those given at the end of this chapter:

1.   In Autodesk Inventor, you can use the bottom-up approach as well as the top-down approach for creating the assemblies. (T/F)

2.   An assembly in which you use a combination of top-down and bottom-up approach is called a middle-out assembly. (T/F)

3.   You can rotate individual components in the assembly file. (T/F)

4.   You cannot invoke the sketching environment in the assembly file. (T/F)

5.   The _____ tool is used to place the components in the assembly file.

6.   The _____ icon is displayed in front of the grounded component in the browser.

7.   When you invoke the **Place Constraint** tool, the _____ dialog box is displayed.

8. The _____ constraint is used to make the selected planar face, axis, or point of a component coincident with that of another component.

9. By default, the first component placed in the assembly file is _____.

10. The individual components in the assembly file can be moved using the _____ tool.

Review Questions

Answer the following questions:

1. You can change the display type of the components even when you are using a tool to perform a function. (T/F)

2. The components that are not grounded by default can also be grounded when required. (T/F)

3. The display of the components that are not required for assembling the other components can be turned off using the browser. (T/F)

4. If the component files are moved from their original location, they will not show up the next time you open the assembly file. (T/F)

5. The top-down assemblies are those in which all the components are created as individual part files and are placed in the assembly file. (T/F)

6. How many types of assembly constraints are available in Autodesk Inventor?

   (a) 4   (b) 5
   (c) 7   (d) 8

7. How many types of motion constraints are available in Autodesk Inventor?

   (a) 2   (b) 3
   (c) 4   (d) 5

8. Which tool is used to rotate the individual components in the assembly file?

   (a) **Rotate Component**   (b) **Move Component**
   (c) **Rotate**   (d) You cannot rotate the individual components

9. Which constraint is used to rotate one of the components in relation to the other component?

   (a) **Rotation**   (b) **Rotation-Translation**
   (c) **Mate**   (d) **Tangent**

Exercise

Exercise 1

Create the components of the Drill Press Vice assembly and then assemble them, as shown in Figures 8-58 and 8-59. The dimensions for the components are shown in Figures 8-60 through 8-63b. Create a folder with the name *\PersonalProject\c08\Drill Press Vice* and save all the component files and the assembly file in this folder. Assume the missing dimensions. You will use the bottom-up approach for creating this assembly.

(Expected time: 3 Hrs 15 min)

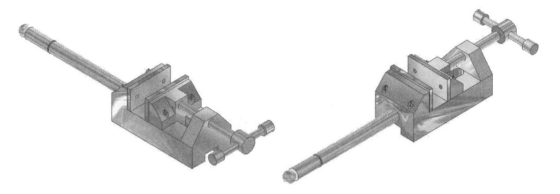

Figure 8-58 Drill Press Vice assembly   *Figure 8-59* Drill Press Vice assembly

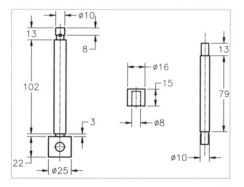

Figure 8-60 Dimensions of the Clamp Screw, Handle Stop, and Clamp Screw Handle

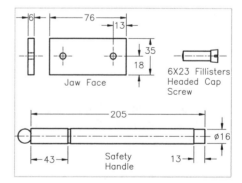

Figure 8-61 Dimensions of the Jaw Face, Cap Screw, and Safety Handle

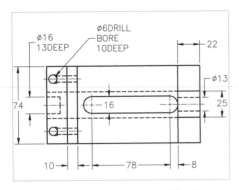

Figure 8-62a Top view of the Base

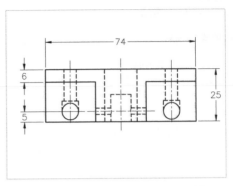

Figure 8-63a Top view of the Movable Jaw

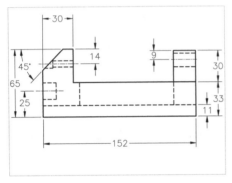

Figure 8-62b Front view of the Base

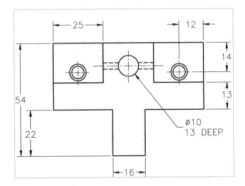

Figure 8-63b Front view of the Movable Jaw

Answers to Self-Evaluation Test
1. T, **2.** T, **3.** T, **4.** F, **5. Place Component, 6.** push pin, **7. Open, 8. Mate, 9.** grounded, **10. Move Component**

Chapter 9

Assembly Modeling-II

Learning Objectives

After completing this chapter, you will be able to:
- *Edit assembly constraints.*
- *Edit components of an assembly.*
- *Check degrees of freedom of a component.*
- *Create a pattern of components in the assembly file.*
- *Replace components in the assembly file with other components.*
- *Mirror components in the assembly.*
- *Use the Content Center window to insert standard components in the assembly file.*
- *Delete components in the assembly file.*
- *Edit the pattern of components.*
- *Delete assembly constraints.*
- *Create the section view of the assemblies in the assembly file.*
- *Analyze assemblies for interference.*
- *Create design views of assemblies.*
- *Drive assembly constraints.*
- *View the Bill of Material of the current assembly.*
- *Understand and create the assembly features.*

EDITING ASSEMBLY CONSTRAINTS

Generally, after creating the assembly or during the process of assembling the components, you have to edit the assembly constraints used to assemble the components. The editing operations that can be performed on the assembly constraints include modifying the type of assembly constraint, the offset or angle values, the type of solution, or changing the component to which the constraint was applied. In Autodesk Inventor, the assembly constraints are edited using the browser. By default, the constraints that are applied on the components will not be displayed in the browser. To display the assembly constraint applied on a component, click on the + sign located on the left of the component in the browser. The **Origin** folder will be displayed along with the list of constraints that are applied to that component. To edit a constraint, right-click on it in the browser and choose **Edit** from the shortcut menu, see Figure 9-1.

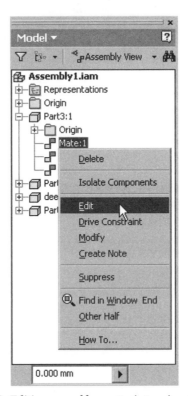

Figure 9-1 *Editing assembly constraints using the browser*

Tip. *If you move the cursor on the assembly constraint in the browser, the components on which that constraint is applied are highlighted in the assembly. The highlighted components will be displayed with a red outline on the graphics screen.*

Note
When you select the assembly constraint in the browser, an edit box is displayed below the browser. This edit box will display the value of the offset or the angle for the selected constraint. You can modify the angle or the offset value using this edit box.

When you choose **Edit** from the shortcut menu, the **Edit Constraint** dialog box will be displayed, see Figure 9-2. This dialog box is similar to the **Place Constraint** dialog box and can be used to edit the assembly constraints. This dialog box can be used to change the constraint type, edit the offset or the angle value, modify the solution, or change the components to which the constraints are applied.

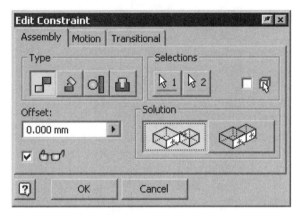

Figure 9-2 *The **Edit Constraint** dialog box for editing the assembly constraints*

 Tip. *Autodesk Inventor allows you to locate the other half of the selected constraint in the browser. This enables you to locate the other component on which the selected constraint has been applied in large assemblies with a huge number of components. To locate the other half of the constraint, choose **Other Half** from the shortcut menu shown in Figure 9-1. The other half of the selected constraint will be highlighted in the browser.*

EDITING COMPONENTS

Sometimes after assembling the components in an assembly, you need to edit the components. In Autodesk Inventor, you can edit the components by two methods. These methods are discussed next.

Editing Components in the Assembly File

The first method of editing components is to invoke the part modeling environment and the sketching environment in the assembly file and edit the component. This method of editing the components is similar to the top-down approach of assembly modeling. To edit the component in the assembly file, right-click on the component in the browser; the shortcut menu will be displayed. In this menu, choose the **Edit** option, see Figure 9-3.

When you choose the **Edit** option, the part modeling environment will be activated in the assembly file. You will notice that the other components in the assembly file have become transparent. Also, they are displayed with a gray background in the browser and the

Figure 9-3 Editing components

component that you selected for editing is displayed with a white background. The component that is displayed in the white background is called the active component. You can edit the active component in the assembly file. Remember that only one component can be active at a time. Once you have edited the component, choose **Return** from the **Inventor Standard** toolbar. You will switch back to the **Assembly** module. You will notice that no component is displayed with a gray background now.

After making the changes in the component in the assembly file, when you save it, the **Save** dialog box will be displayed, see Figure 9-4. If you want to save the changes in the part files, choose **Yes to All** and then choose **OK**. Choosing **OK** will save the changes in all parts. If you do not want to save changes in any part, choose **No to All**.

If you want to save the changes in the selected file, click on **No** in the **Save** column of this dialog box; you will notice that **No** is replaced by **Yes**. As a result, the changes will be saved in the selected file. However, the changes will not be saved in the remaining files that show **No** in the **Save** column.

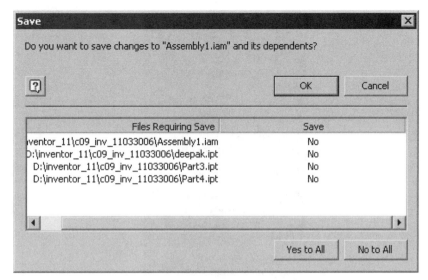

*Figure 9-4 The **Save** dialog box for saving the part files*

Editing Components by Opening their Part Files

The second method of editing the components is by opening their part files and making the necessary changes in them. Once you have made the required changes in the part files, save them and then exit by choosing **Close** from the **File** menu. You will notice that the changes that you made in the part files are already reflected in the assembly file. This is because Autodesk Inventor is bidirectionally associative. This means that the changes made to the components in any of the modules of Autodesk Inventor will be automatically reflected in the other modules.

To open the part file for editing, right-click on the component in the browser. The shortcut menu will be displayed. Choose **Open** in this shortcut menu, as shown in Figure 9-5.

When you choose the **Open** option, the part file of the selected component will be opened. Make the necessary changes in the part file and then save the changes by choosing the **Save** button from the **Standard** toolbar. Now, exit the part file by choosing **Close** from the **File** toolbar. Because the assembly file was already open, it will be displayed now. The changes that you made in the part file will be automatically reflected in that component in the assembly file.

CHECKING DEGREES OF FREEDOM OF A COMPONENT

As mentioned earlier, you can restrict the degrees of freedom of a component by applying assembly constraints to it. You can view the degrees of freedom that are not restricted in a component by choosing **View > Degrees of Freedom** from the menu bar. By default, this option is not selected and therefore, the degrees of freedom of the components are not visible on the screen. However, when you choose this option, the button on the left of this option in the **View** menu will be chosen and the symbol of the degrees of freedom will be displayed on the screen. In Autodesk Inventor, every component has six degrees of freedom. These are

Figure 9-5 Opening the part file for editing

linear movement along X, Y, and Z axes and rotational movement along X, Y, and Z axes. These degrees of freedom are displayed using an icon similar to the 3D Indicator on the lower left corner of the drawing window. For a component whose all degrees of freedom are open, the symbol of degrees of freedom will consist of three linear axes pointing in X, Y, and Z axes direction and circular arrows on all the three axes, see Figure 9-6.

When you apply the assembly constraints, these movements are restricted and therefore, the degrees of freedom are removed. When a particular degree of freedom is removed, it will no more be displayed in the symbol of the degrees of freedom. For example, if you apply the assembly constraint such that the linear movement of the component is restricted along the Z axis, the linear axis along the Z axis will not be displayed in the symbol of degrees of freedom. However, the circular axis along the Z axis will still be displayed, because you have not restricted that movement. Therefore, for a component whose all degrees of freedom are restricted, there will be no symbol of the degrees of freedom.

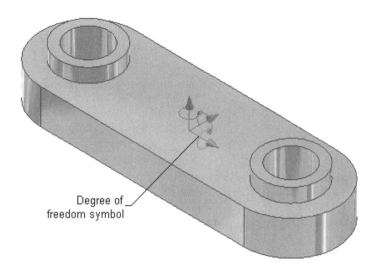

Figure 9-6 *Component with all degrees of freedom open*

Tip. *By default, the first component you place or create in the assembly file is grounded. A grounded component has all its degrees of freedom restricted and therefore, the symbol of the degrees of freedom will not be displayed on it. However, if you unground the grounded component after assembling other components with it, you will notice that the symbol of the degrees of freedom is displayed on it, indicating that all the degrees of freedom of the component are open. You will also notice that a small green color cube is displayed on all the other components that were assembled with the grounded component. This cube suggests that all these components are assembled with an under-constrained component. The component became under-constrained when you ungrounded it. To view the under-constrained component, move the cursor on the green color cube on any one of the assembled components. The green color cube will turn red in color and the under-constrained component will also change to red. It will also be displayed in red in the browser. The component will be changed back to its original color when you move the cursor away from the cube.*

CREATING PATTERN OF THE COMPONENTS IN AN ASSEMBLY

Toolbar:	Assembly Panel > Pattern Component
Panel bar:	Assembly Panel > Pattern Component

While creating the assemblies, you have to sometimes assemble more than one instance of a component about a specified arrangement. For example, in case of a Butterfly Valve assembly, you have to assemble three instances of Screw with the Retainer and the Body (refer to Tutorial 1 of Chapter 8). All these three instances were recalled in the current assembly file and then assembled using the assembly constraint. Also, if you have to increase the number of holes in the Retainer and the Body from three to four, you will have to recall another instance of the Screw and insert it using the assembly constraint. However, this is a very tedious and time-consuming process. Therefore, to reduce the time for assembling the components, Autodesk Inventor has provided a tool for creating the pattern of the components. You can create circular or rectangular patterns. This will reduce the assembling time as well the time taken in recalling the number of instances of the components. Another advantage of creating the pattern is that if you increase the number of instances in the pattern feature on the original part, the number of instances of the components in the pattern will also increase automatically. For example, if you increase the number of holes from three to four in the Retainer of the Butterfly Valve assembly, one more instance of the Screw will be automatically recalled in the assembly file and inserted in the fourth hole of the Retainer.

The pattern of the components in the assembly file is created using the **Pattern Component** tool. When you invoke this tool, the **Pattern Component** dialog box will be displayed. The options in the various tabs of this dialog box are discussed next.

Component

The **Component** button is chosen to select the component in the assembly file that you want to pattern. When you invoke the **Pattern Component** dialog box, this button will be chosen automatically and you will be prompted to select the component to be patterned.

Associative Tab

The **Associative** tab (Figure 9-7) will be active by default when you invoke this tool.

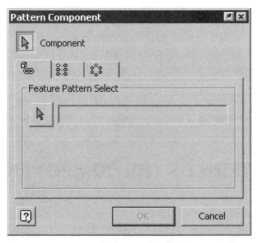

Figure 9-7 *The **Associative** tab of the **Pattern Component** dialog box*

The options in this tab are used to select the pattern of the feature on the base part to which the pattern of components will be associated. This pattern can be selected by choosing the **Associated Feature Pattern** button provided in the **Feature Pattern Select** area of this tab.

When you choose this button, you will be prompted to select the feature pattern to which the pattern of components will be associated. You can select the pattern of the feature on the base part. Depending on whether the pattern selected is rectangular or circular, it will be displayed in the display box provided on the right of the **Associated Feature Pattern** button. Also, the selected component will be assembled with all the instances of the feature pattern. Remember that the number of instances of components assembled using this tool will be modified upon modification in the number of instances in the pattern of feature only if the pattern of the component is created using the **Associative** tab.

Rectangular Tab

The options in this tab are used to create a rectangular pattern of the selected components in the assembly file, see Figure 9-8. The options in this tab are similar to those discussed in the **Rectangular Pattern** dialog box in Chapter 5.

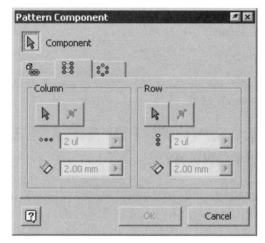

Figure 9-8 *The* ***Rectangular*** *tab of the* ***Pattern*** ***Component*** *dialog box*

Note
Similar to the ***Rectangular Pattern*** *dialog box, the options in the* ***Rectangular*** *tab of the* ***Pattern Component*** *dialog box will be available only after you specify the directions for column placement and row placement.*

Circular Tab

The options in the **Circular** tab of the **Pattern Component** dialog box are used to create a circular pattern of the selected component, see Figure 9-9. The options in this tab are similar to those discussed in the **Circular Pattern** dialog box in Chapter 5.

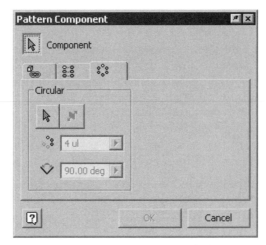

*Figure 9-9 The **Circular** tab of the **Pattern Component** dialog box*

Note
*The **Angle** edit box in the **Circular** tab is used to specify the incremental angle between the individual instances of the pattern.*

REPLACING A COMPONENT IN THE ASSEMBLY FILE WITH ANOTHER COMPONENT

Autodesk Inventor allows you to replace any component in the assembly file with another component that you specify. You can replace the single instance of the component or all the instances of the selected component with another specified component. If the shape of the new component is the same as that of the original component that you replaced, the assembly constraints will be retained. However, if the shape of the new component is not similar to that of the original component, the assembly constraints will be lost and you will have to apply the constraints again. The new component will be placed at the same location as that of the original component. The methods of replacing the components are discussed next.

Replacing a Single Instance of the Selected Component

Toolbar:	Assembly Panel > Replace
Panel bar:	Assembly Panel > Replace

The single instance of the selected component can be replaced by the **Replace Component** tool. When you invoke this tool, you will be prompted to select the component to be replaced. When you select the component to be replaced, the **Open** dialog box will be displayed, as shown in Figure 9-10.

You can use this dialog box to specify the name and location of the new component. You can either double-click on the component or select it and choose the **Open** button. The selected component will be placed at the location of the previous component. Remember that the

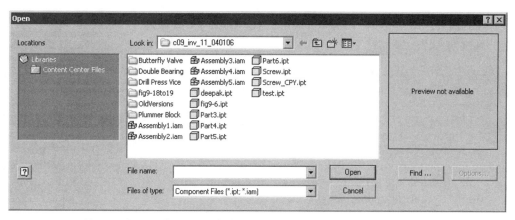

Figure 9-10 *The **Open** dialog box for selecting the new component*

assembly constraints will be retained only if the shape of the new component is the same as that of the original component.

If there are chances that the assembly constraints that you have applied on the component to be replaced are going to be lost, the **Possible Constraint Loss** dialog box will be displayed, as shown in Figure 9-11. This dialog box will inform you that the constraints and notes associated with the component may be lost. Choose the **OK** button to continue with the process of replacement of the component. To abort the process, choose the **Cancel** button.

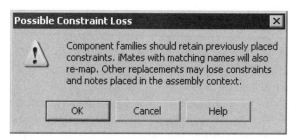

Figure 9-11 *The **Possible Constraint Loss** dialog box*

Replacing All Instances of the Selected Component

Toolbar:	Assembly Panel > Replace > Replace All
Panel bar:	Assembly Panel > Replace > Replace All

You can replace all the instances of the selected component by choosing the down arrow on the right side of the **Replace Component** button and then choosing the **Replace All** button. When you choose this button, you will be prompted to select the component to be replaced. Select it from the screen. On selecting the component to be replaced, the **Open** dialog box will be displayed. You can use this dialog box to select the new component. All the instances of the selected component will be replaced with the component selected in the **Open** dialog box.

MIRRORING SUBASSEMBLIES OR COMPONENTS
OF AN ASSEMBLY

Toolbar:	Assembly Panel > Mirror Components
Panel bar:	Assembly Panel > Mirror Components

One of the enhancements in the latest release of Autodesk Inventor is its ability to allow you to mirror assemblies or assembly components. This can be done using the **Mirror Component** tool. You can use this tool to specify whether the mirrored components or subassemblies will be inserted in the current file or in a new assembly file. When you invoke this tool, the **Mirror Component** dialog box is displayed, as shown in Figure 9-12. The options in this dialog box are discussed next.

*Figure 9-12 The **Mirror Components** dialog box*

Components

The **Components** button is chosen to select the components or subassemblies to be mirrored. You can select them from the drawing window or from the browser. The components or subassemblies that you select are added to the list box in the **Mirror Components** dialog box. Note that the constraints will be copied only if all the components on which the constraints are applied are selected to be mirrored

Mirror Plane

When you invoke the **Mirror Component** dialog box, this button is chosen by default and you are prompted to select the mirror plane. This is the plane about which the assembly or components will be mirrored.

List Box

The list box in the **Mirror Component** dialog box lists the components and subassemblies that you select to mirror. You can also use this area to specify whether the resultant components will be **Mirrored** or **Reused**. By default, the components are mirrored as **Mirror** components. These components have a green circle icon with two arrows facing in opposite directions on the left of their names in the **Mirror Components** dialog box. They are displayed in transparent green in the mirror preview. The components that are mirrored using this option are saved as separate files when you save the assembly file. The name of the files can be specified using the **Mirror Components: File Names** dialog box that will be displayed after you choose **OK** from the **Mirror Components** dialog box.

If you click once on the green circle icon, it changes to a yellow circle with a plus sign in between. This suggests that the selected components are mirrored as reused. The reused components are displayed in transparent yellow in the preview.

If you click again on the yellow circle icon, it changes to gray with an inclined line. This suggests that the components are excluded from the current selection set and will not be mirrored.

More

This is the button with two arrows on the lower right side of the **Mirror Components** dialog box. When you choose this button, the **Mirror Components** dialog box expands and provides the following options.

Reuse Standard Content and Factory Parts

The **Reuse Standard Content and Factory Parts** check box is selected to make sure that the content library components and factory parts are reused and not mirrored.

Preview Components Area

The check boxes in this area are used to specify whether the mirrored, reused, or content library components are shown in the preview or not.

After selecting the components to mirror and setting the parameters in the **Mirror Components** dialog box, when you choose **Next**, the **Mirror Components: File Names** dialog box will be displayed, as shown in Figure 9-13. This dialog box is used to specify whether the resultant components are placed in the same assembly file or copied in a new assembly file. The options in this dialog box are discussed next.

List Box

The list box in this dialog box lists all the subassemblies and components that were selected to be mirrored. This list box has the following four columns.

Name

This column lists the names of the original components or subassemblies selected to be mirrored.

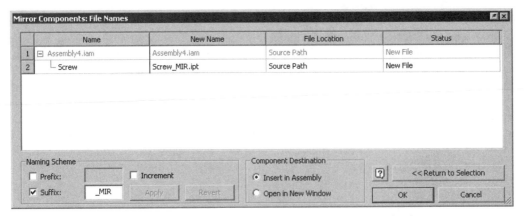

*Figure 9-13 The **Mirror Components: File Names** dialog box*

New Name

This column lists the new name by which the selected components will be saved. You can click on the name field to change the name of the new component. The default naming options also depend on the parameters defined in the **Naming Scheme** area of this dialog box.

File Location

This column lists the location of the part file, in which the new component will be saved. By default, it shows **Source Path**. As a result, the new component file will be saved in the same folder, in which the original file is saved. You can right-click on **Source Path** to change the part to a user defined path or the current workspace.

Status

This column defines the status of the resultant component. By default, it shows **New File**. As a result, the file will be saved as a new part file. If you specify the name of the new component that already exists in the folder in which the part file will be saved, the status changes to **Reuse Existing**. This suggests that a part file with the same name already exists and that you can reuse the existing file.

Naming Scheme Area

This area is used to set the parameters for the default name of the new part files that are listed in the **New Name** column of the list box in this dialog box. By default, the **Suffix** check box is selected and **_MIR** is entered in the text box on the right of the **Suffix** check box. As a result, the name of the new part file is the name of the original part file selected to be mirrored with **_MIR** as suffix. Similarly, you can also add some prefix to the default name by selecting the **Prefix** check box. The prefix that you want to add can be entered in the text box available on the right of the **Prefix** check box. You can select the **Increment** check box to add an incremental number to the name of the new file. Remember that after setting the parameters in this area, you need to choose the **Apply** button. You can restore the original name settings by choosing the **Revert** button.

Component Destination Area

This area is used to specify whether the new components will be placed in the current assembly file or will be inserted in a new assembly file. Select the **Insert in Assembly** radio button to insert the parts in the current assembly file. However, to copy the parts in a new assembly file, select the **Open in New Window** radio button. The selected components will be copied in a new assembly file and that assembly file will be opened on the screen. Note that if you select the **Open in New Window** radio button, you can also modify the name of the new assembly in the **New Name** column of the list box.

Return to Selection

The **Return to Selection** button is chosen to return to the **Mirror Components** dialog box.

After setting the parameters in the **Mirror Copy: File Names** dialog box, choose the **OK** button. The selected components will be mirrored in the current assembly file or will be copied in a new assembly file, depending on the parameters selected.

COPYING SUBASSEMBLIES OR COMPONENTS OF AN ASSEMBLY

Toolbar:	Assembly Panel > Copy Components
Panel bar:	Assembly Panel > Copy Components

Similar to mirroring the components, you can also copy a subassembly or components of an assembly using the **Copy Components** tool. When you invoke this tool, the **Copy Components** dialog box is displayed, as shown in Figure 9-14. This dialog box is similar to the **Mirror Components** dialog box.

*Figure 9-14 The **Copy Components** dialog box*

After selecting the components to copy, when you choose **OK** from this dialog box, the **Copy Components: File Names** dialog box is displayed. The options in this dialog box are similar to the **Mirror Components: File Names** dialog box.

DELETING COMPONENTS

You can delete the unwanted instances or the unwanted components from the assembly using the browser. In the browser, right-click on the unwanted component and choose **Delete** from the shortcut menu; the selected component will be deleted and will not be displayed on the screen.

To delete the components that were assembled using the **Pattern Component** tool, right-click on **Component Pattern** in the browser. Choose **Delete** from the shortcut menu. All instances of the component assembled using the **Pattern Component** tool will be deleted. Note that the original component will not be deleted. You can delete the original instance also by right-clicking on it in the browser and choosing **Delete** from the shortcut menu.

EDITING THE PATTERN OF COMPONENTS

Autodesk Inventor allows you to edit the pattern of the components created using the **Pattern Component** tool. This is done using the browser. To edit the pattern of components, right-click on **Component Pattern** in the browser and choose **Edit** from the shortcut menu. The **Edit Component Pattern** dialog box will be displayed. Note that this dialog box will have only the tab that was used for creating the pattern of the component. For example, if the pattern of the component was created using the **Associative** tab of the **Pattern Component** dialog box, the **Edit Component Pattern** dialog box will have only the **Associative** tab. Similarly, if the pattern of the component was created using the **Circular** tab of the **Pattern Component** dialog box, the **Edit Component Pattern** dialog box will have only the **Circular** tab. Figure 9-15 shows the **Edit Component Pattern** dialog box for editing the pattern created using the **Associative** tab of the **Pattern Component** dialog box.

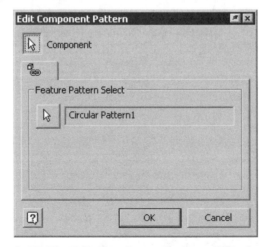

*Figure 9-15 The **Edit Component Pattern** dialog box to edit the pattern of components created using the **Associative** tab of the **Pattern Component** dialog box*

MAKING A PATTERN INSTANCE INDEPENDENT

You can also make a selected instance independent, which will be displayed as a separate component in the browser and will not be deleted when you delete its pattern. To make the selected instance independent, click on the + sign located on the left of **Component Pattern** in the browser. All the instances of the pattern will be displayed as elements in the browser. The first element is the original component and you cannot make this element independent because it is not dependent on the pattern. Right-click on any of the other elements and choose **Independent** from the shortcut menu. You will notice that a red cross is displayed on the left of the independent element in the browser.

You can again make the independent element dependent. Right-click on the independent element in the list of elements in the browser to display the shortcut menu. You will notice that a check mark is displayed on the left of the **Independent** option. Choose this option again. The red cross on the element will no more be displayed, suggesting that it is again made dependent on the pattern. Note that when you make a component dependent again, the instance of the component that was placed in the assembly as a separate component and displayed in the browser will not be removed. You will have to manually delete the component.

Note
*The options in the **Edit Component Pattern** dialog box are similar to those discussed in the **Pattern Component** dialog box.*

DELETING ASSEMBLY CONSTRAINTS

You can delete the unwanted assembly constraints using the browser. To delete the assembly constraint, click on the + sign located on the left of the component in the browser. The **Origin** folder, along with all the constraints that are applied on the component, will be displayed. Right-click on the constraint to be deleted and choose **Delete** from the shortcut menu. The selected component will be deleted.

CREATING THE ASSEMBLY SECTION VIEWS IN THE ASSEMBLY FILE

Sometimes, while assembling components in the assembly, some of the components are hidden behind the other components of the assembly. To visualize such components, Autodesk Inventor allows you to create the section views of the assembly. However, remember that these section views are for reference only and components are not actually chopped when you create the section views. You can create three types of section views: **Quarter section view**, **Half section view**, and **Three quarter section view**.

To create the quarter section view, choose **Quarter Section View** from the **Assembly Panel** toolbar or panel bar. On doing so, you will be prompted to select work planes or planar faces that will be used to section the assembly. Select two planar faces, two work planes, or a planar face and a work plane to section the assembly. The assembly will be sectioned as soon as you select two planes.

You can flip the quarter to be displayed by right-clicking and choosing **Flip Section** from the shortcut menu. Continue choosing this option until the required quarter is displayed. Once the required quarter is displayed, right-click and choose **Done** from the shortcut menu. Using the same shortcut menu, you can create a three quarter section view. You can also create the three quarter section view by choosing the down arrow on the right of the **Quarter Section View** tool and choosing **Three Quarter Section View**. You are prompted to select the work plane or the planar face for creating the section view. When you select the work plane or planar face, you are again prompted to select the work plane or planar face. As soon as you select the second work plane or planar face, the three quarter section view is created.

Similarly, to create the half section view, choose the down arrow on the right of the **Quarter Section View** and choose **Half Section View**. You will be prompted to select the planar face or the work plane for creating the section view. Since for creating a half section, you require only one plane, therefore, as soon as you select the planar face or the work plane, the assembly will be sectioned about it. You can flip the section by right-clicking and choosing **Flip Section** from the shortcut menu. Once the required section is displayed, right-click and choose **Done** from the shortcut menu.

You can exit the section views by choosing the down arrow on the right of the **Quarter Section View** and choosing **End Section View**. The complete assembly will be displayed when you choose this option. Figure 9-16 shows the quarter section view of an assembly and Figure 9-17 shows the three quarter section view of the same assembly.

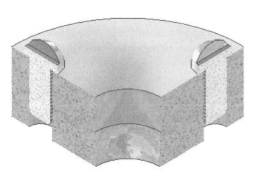   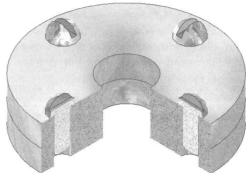

Figure 9-16 *Quarter section view of an assembly*   ***Figure 9-17*** *Three quarter section view of the same assembly*

ANALYZING ASSEMBLIES FOR INTERFERENCE

Menu: Tools > Analyze Interference

Whenever you assemble the components of an assembly, no component should interfere with the other components of the assembly. If there is an interference between the components, this suggests that the dimensions of the components are incorrect or the components are not assembled properly. You will have to eliminate this interference in the assembly to increase the efficiency of the assembly and also eliminate the material loss. In Autodesk Inventor, you can analyze the assemblies for interference using the **Analyze Interference** tool. This tool can be invoked from the **Tools** menu. You need to select two sets of components to analyze interference. When you invoke this tool, the **Interference Analysis** dialog box will be displayed, as shown in Figure 9-18. The options in this dialog box are discussed next.

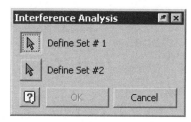

*Figure 9-18 The **Interference Analysis** dialog box*

Define Set # 1

The **Define Set # 1** button is chosen to select the first set of components. When you invoke the **Interference Analysis** dialog box, this button is chosen automatically and you will be prompted to select the component to add to the selection set. The selected components will be highlighted and displayed in a blue outline.

Define Set # 2

The **Define Set # 2** button is chosen to select the second set of components. When you choose this button, the objects selected using the **Define Set # 1** button will be displayed in a green outline. The components that you select now will be displayed in a blue outline.

OK

After selecting the components in the first set and the second set, choose this button to analyze the assembly. If there is no interference between the components, the **Autodesk Inventor** dialog box will be displayed. This dialog box will inform you that there is no interference between the components. However, if there is an interference, the **Interference Detected** dialog box will be displayed and the portion of the interfering components will be displayed in red in the assembly. The **Interference Detected** dialog box will inform you about the number of interferences found and the total volume of interference. This dialog box has a button with two arrows on the lower right corner. If you choose this button, this dialog box will expand and will provide you additional information about the interfering components, see Figure 9-19. You can copy this information on the Clipboard and later paste it in a file or take its printout.

CREATING THE DESIGN VIEW REPRESENTATIONS

Menu: View > Design Views Representations

The design view representations are user-defined views that can be used to view the assemblies or generate presentation views or drawing views of a particular view state of the assembly. You can specify any orientation of the assembly by using a combination of drawing display tools and

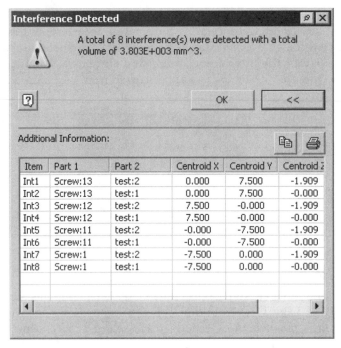

Figure 9-19 *The expanded* **Interference Detected** *dialog box*

then save the assembly view with that orientation. Once the view is saved, you can recall it whenever required. In addition to the assembly file, you can also use design views for generating the views in the presentation file as well as in the drawing file. When you invoke this tool, the **Design View Representations** dialog box will be displayed, see Figure 9-20.

Figure 9-20 *The* **Design View Representations** *dialog box*

The options available in this dialog box are discussed next.

Storage Location Area

Using this area, you can create two types of design view representations: public and private. A public design view representation is the one that is saved with the assembly and can be invoked only in this assembly. A private design view representation is one that is saved as a separate *.idv* file and can be imported in any assembly file. To create a private design view representation, enter the name in the edit box in the **Design View Representation** area and then choose the **New** button. Now, choose the button on the right of the edit box in the **Storage Location** area and specify the location of this design view representation so that it can be imported to another file also. To import a private design view representation, select the **Private File** radio button. Choose the **Browse** button to browse and select the *.idv* file that you want to use in the current assembly. When you import this design view representation in another file, the design view with the name you specified will be displayed in the list box in the **Design View Representation** area. By default, the **Public** radio button is selected. Therefore, a public design view representation is created that can be used only in the current assembly file.

Design View Representation Area

The options in this area are used to create a new design view, delete a design view, or make a design view current. To create a new design view, set the orientation of the assembly using the **Rotate** tool or other drawing display tools. Next, enter the name of the view in the edit box provided in this area and then choose the **New** button. You will notice that the new design view is displayed in the list box above the edit box. You can delete the design view by selecting it from the list box and then choosing the **Delete** button. Note that you can also delete the default design view.

An existing design view can be made the current view by selecting it from the list box and then choosing the **Apply** button. You will notice that the assembly on the graphics screen is reoriented such that it is displayed using the selected design view.

SIMULATING THE MOTION OF COMPONENTS OF AN ASSEMBLY BY DRIVING THE ASSEMBLY CONSTRAINTS

Autodesk Inventor allows you to simulate the motion of the components of an assembly by driving the assembly constraints. Remember that in the **Assembly** module, you can simulate the motion of the component using only one constraint at a time. However, you can create some relation parameters and equations for simulating the motion of the components using more than one constraint at a time. To drive a constraint, right-click on it in the browser and choose **Drive Constraint**, see Figure 9-21.

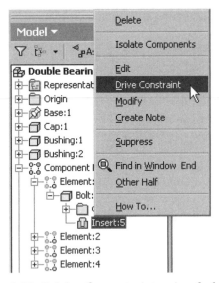

Figure 9-21 *Driving the constraints using the browser*

When you choose **Drive Constraint** from the shortcut menu, the **Drive Constraint** dialog box will be displayed, see Figure 9-22.

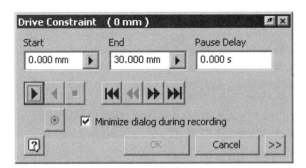

Figure 9-22 *The **Drive Constraint** dialog box*

The options in this dialog box are discussed next.

Start

The **Start** edit box is used to specify the position of the starting point of simulation. The value in this edit box depends on the type of constraint you have selected to drive. For example, if you have selected the **Insert** constraint to drive, the value in this edit box will be entered in mm. If you have selected the **Angle** constraint to drive, the value in this edit box will be entered in degrees. The default value of the angle or offset in this edit box will be the value that you have specified for the constraint. For example, if you have applied an angle value of 90-degree between two components, the default value in the **Start** edit box will be 90.

Note

*The value of the **Start** edit box will also be displayed on the right of the name of the **Drive Constraint** dialog box. Therefore, if the value of start point of the constraint simulation is -90-degree, the name of the dialog box will be **Drive Constraint (-90 deg)**.*

End

The **End** edit box is used to specify the position for ending the simulation. Similar to the **Start** edit box, the values in this edit box will be dependent on the type of constraint selected for simulation. The default value in this edit box will be the default value in the **Start** edit box plus 10.

Pause Delay

The **Pause Delay** edit box is used to specify some delay in the simulation of the components. The value in this edit box is entered in terms of seconds. By default, the value in this edit box is zero. Therefore, there will be no delay in the simulation of the components. If you enter a value of 2 in this edit box, there will be a delay of 2 seconds between the steps of the simulation.

Forward

The **Forward** button is used to start the simulation of the component in the forward direction.

Reverse

The **Reverse** button is used to start the simulation of the component in the reverse direction.

Pause

The **Pause** button is used to temporarily stop the simulation of the component. The simulation can be resumed by choosing the **Forward** button or the **Reverse** button again.

Minimum

The **Minimum** button is chosen to reset the simulation such that the component is positioned at the start point of the simulation.

Reverse Step

The **Reverse Step** button is chosen to position the component one step behind the current step in the simulation. This button will not be available if the component is positioned at the start point of the simulation.

Forward Step

The **Forward Step** button is chosen to position the component one step ahead of the current step in the simulation. This button will not be available if the component is positioned at the endpoint of the simulation.

Maximum

The **Maximum** button is chosen to reset the simulation such that the component is positioned at the endpoint of the simulation.

Record

The **Record** button is chosen to record the simulation of the component in the form of a *.avi* file. When you choose this button, the **Save As** dialog box will be displayed. Using this dialog box, you can specify the name of the avi file, in which you want to record the simulation. After specifying the name and location of the avi file, choose the **Save** button; the **Video Compression** dialog box will be displayed. This dialog box is used to specify the compressor and the compression quality of the *.avi* files. After specifying the compression options, choose the **Forward** or the **Reverse** button to record the simulation. You can also choose both the buttons one by one to record the complete cycle of simulation. After recording the simulation, choose this button again to exit recording.

Note

While recording the simulation, whatever is displayed inside the graphics window will be recorded. Remember that if you activate another application while the simulation is being recorded, the work done in that application will also be recorded in the avi file.

More

The **More** button is the one with two arrows on the lower right corner of the **Drive Constraint** dialog box. When you choose this button, the dialog box expands and displays more options to simulate the components, see Figure 9-23. These options are discussed next.

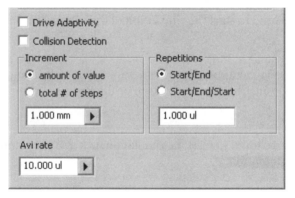

*Figure 9-23 More options in the **Drive Constraint** dialog box*

Drive Adaptivity

If the **Drive Adaptivity** check box is selected, the adaptive components will adapt during the process of simulation. If you select this check box, the **Collision Detection** check box will not be available.

Collision Detection

If the **Collision Detection** check box is selected, the simulation will stop at the point where the collision is detected. The collision will be displayed in red and the **Autodesk Inventor** information box will also be displayed. This dialog box will inform you that a collision has been detected. If you select this check box, the **Drive Adaptivity** check box will not be available.

Increment Area

The options in the **Increment** area are used to specify the method for defining the increment during the simulation of the component. These options are discussed next.

Amount of value

The **amount of value** radio button is selected to specify the increment of simulation in terms of value of the steps. The value of the steps can be entered in the edit box available in the **Increment** area.

Total # of steps

The **total # of steps** radio button is selected to specify the increment of simulation in terms of the total number of steps in the simulation. The number of steps can be entered in the edit box in the **Increment** area.

Repetitions Area

The options in the **Repetitions** area are used to specify the method for defining the number of repetitions of the cycles in the simulation. These options are discussed next.

Start/End

The **Start/End** radio button is selected to simulate the component such that the simulation is between the start position and the end position. If the number of repetitions is more than one, the component will be repositioned at the start position after the first cycle is over and before the second cycle starts. Since the component is repositioned at the start position after the first cycle is completed, the second cycle will start from the start position.

Start/End/Start

The **Start/End/Start** radio button is selected to simulate the component such that the simulation is between the start position and the end position and then again from the end position to the start position. If the number of repetitions is more than one, the second cycle will be between the end position and the start position. The third cycle will be between the start position and the end position. Similarly, the fourth cycle will be between the end position and the start position. So if you want to simulate the assembly from the start position to the end position and then again from the end to start, you need to enter a value of 2.

In addition to these radio buttons, there is an edit box in the **Repetitions** area. This edit box is used to specify the number of cycles in the simulation.

Avi rate

The **Avi rate** edit box is used to specify the number of steps that will be removed before a step of simulation is recorded in the *.avi* file.

Note

*After driving the constraints, when you choose **Apply** from the **Drive Constraint** dialog box, the **Autodesk Inventor 11** dialog box will be displayed that will inform you that value of the constraint must be overridden in the current positional representation to preserve the value. Choose **Yes** from this dialog box.*

CREATING POSITIONAL REPRESENTATIONS

Positional representations are the views of the assembly that represent assemblies in different component positions. For example, you can create a positional representation of an assembly in which the components are driven to a certain distance from their original assembly position. By default, every assembly has a main default positional representation. This positional representation represents the components at their default assembly position. You can create additional positional representations in which you can move the components from their default location by driving their constraints. To create positional representations, click on the + sign located on the left of **Representations** in the browser; the tree view expands. Right-click on **Position** and choose **New** from the shortcut menu, as shown in Figure 9-24; the name **Position** is changed to **Position : Position1** in the browser and the + sign is added to its left. Click on the + sign; the tree view expands and shows **Master** and **Position1** in the browser. Also, a check mark is displayed on the left of **Position1**, suggesting that this representational view is current by default. Now, drive the constraints of the assembled components to create a positional representation of the assembly.

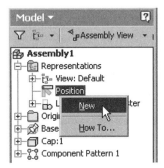

Figure 9-24 Creating a new positional representation

Before saving and exiting the assembly document, you need to restore the master positional representation. To do so, double-click on **Master** in **Position: Position 1** in the browser.

Note
*Whenever you try to save an assembly in a positional representation, an error message will be displayed and you will be informed that an assembly cannot be saved in a positional representation. Further, you will be prompted to specify whether you want save the master assembly. If you choose **Yes** from this dialog box, the master representation will be invoked and the assembly will be saved.*

To restore a user-defined positional representation, double-click on it in **Position** in the browser.

VIEWING THE BILL OF MATERIAL OF THE CURRENT ASSEMBLY

Autodesk Inventor allows you to view the Bill Of Material of the current assembly in the assembly document itself. To do so, choose **Tools > Bill of Materials** from the menu bar; the **Bill of**

Materials dialog box that lists that components of the current assembly in a tabular form will be displayed, as shown in Figure 9-25.

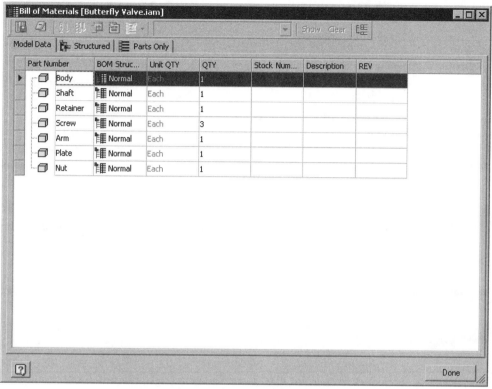

*Figure 9-25 The **Bill of Materials** dialog box*

By default, the **Model Data** tab is active. As a result, if there is any subassembly in the current assembly file, it will be displayed as a single component with a + sign on its left in the **Item** column. You can click on this + sign to view the components of the assembly. You can also invoke the **Parts Only** BOM view that shows all components of the subassembly also as separate components. To do so, choose the **Parts Only** tab and then choose the down arrow on the right of the **View Options** button that is in the toolbar provided above the two tabs in the **Bill of Materials** dialog box. On doing so, a flyout is displayed. Choose the **Enable BOM View** button from the flyout; all components of the assembly and the subassembly will be displayed as separate components in the BOM. You can also select the option from the drop-down list in this dialog box to view the BOM structure, with all components or the **Model** structure, with the subassembly as a single component.

WORKING WITH ASSEMBLY FEATURES

Autodesk Inventor allows you to perform some metal cutting operations such as extruded, revolved, and swept cuts, chamfer, and holes in an assembly file. Note that these operations are restricted only to the assembly file and are not performed on individual components. For example, if you create an extruded cut feature on a component in the assembly environment, the cut feature created in the assembly is not created on the original component. This is the reason this cut feature will be displayed only in the assembly environment and not if you open the original component file. Note that these operations are not restricted to a particular component, but extends to all the components of the assembly. For example, if you create a through all cut feature, the material will be removed from all the components that the sketch comes across and not only from the component on which the sketch is created.

To create assembly cut features such as extruded, revolved, and swept cuts, you first need to select a sketching plane on which the sketches will be drawn. To select the sketching plane, choose the **Sketch** button from the **Inventor Standard** toolbar and then select a planar face of any component or a work plane. The sketching environment will be activated and all the sketching tools will be available in the **2D Sketch Panel** panel bar. This panel bar replaces the **Assembly Panel** panel bar when you invoke the sketching environment.

Note

The basic difference between editing the components in the assembly file and working with the assembly features is that the assembly features are not created on the original component. On the other hand, the editing operations performed on a component while editing them are actually made on the original component.

TUTORIALS

Tutorial 1

In this tutorial, you will open the Butterfly Valve assembly created in Tutorial 1 of Chapter 8 and then analyze the assembly for interference. Next, you will delete the last two instances of the Screw and assemble the remaining instances by creating a pattern of the first instance.

(Expected time: 30 min)

Before you start working on the tutorial, it is important to understand the procedure of completing the tutorial. The following steps are required to complete this tutorial:

a. Copy the *Butterfly Valve* folder from the *c08* folder to the *c09* folder.
b. Open the *Butterfly Valve.iam* file and analyze it for interference using the **Analyze Interference** tool.
c. Delete two instances of the Screw assembled with the Retainer and then create the two instances using the **Pattern Component** tool.

Saving the Butterfly Valve Assembly

In this tutorial, you will open the Butterfly Valve assembly created in Chapter 8. However, it is recommended that before opening the assembly file, you should copy the entire folder of the Butterfly Valve in the *c09* folder. This way when you make the modifications in the Butterfly Valve Assembly, the assembly of Chapter 8 is not affected. Therefore, you will first copy the *Butterfly Valve* folder in the *c09* folder and then open the *Butterfly Valve.iam* file from this folder.

1. Start a new session of Autodesk Inventor. Choose **Open** in the **Open** dialog box and then open the folder *PersonalProject\c08*.

    You will notice that there is a folder with the name *Butterfly Valve* in *c08* folder. This is the folder, in which you stored all the part files and the assembly file of Butterfly Valve.

2. Right-click on the *Butterfly Valve* folder and choose **Copy** from the shortcut menu.

3. Now, open the folder *PersonalProject\c09*.

    If this folder does not exist, you can create it using the **Create New Folder** button in the **Open** dialog box.

4. Right-click in the folder and paste the *Butterfly Valve* folder in *c09* folder. Open the *Butterfly Valve* folder and from this folder, open the *Butterfly Valve.iam* file.

    The Butterfly Valve assembly will be opened on the screen.

Analyzing the Assembly for Interference

When the assembly file is displayed on the screen, you will invoke the **Analyze Interference** tool and analyze the assembly for interference. There should be no interference in the assembly. The **Analyze Interference** tool can be invoked from the **Tools** menu.

1. Choose **Tools > Analyze Interference** from the menu bar to display the **Interference Analysis** dialog box.

    The **Define Set # 1** button is chosen and you are prompted to select the components to add to the selection set.

2. Select Body from the graphics screen and then choose the **Define Set # 2** button from the dialog box. You are again prompted to select the components to add to the selection set. Select the remaining components using the browser.

3. Choose the **OK** button. The **Analyzing Interference** dialog box will be displayed and you will notice that the system is analyzing the assembly for interference. After the analysis is complete, the **Autodesk Inventor** dialog box is displayed, which informs you that no interference is detected. Choose **OK** in this dialog box to exit it.

Creating the Pattern of the Screw

While creating the Butterfly Valve assembly in Chapter 8, you assembled three instances of the Screw with the Retainer. You will retain the first instance of the Screw and delete the other two instances from the assembly. The other two instances will be assembled using the **Pattern Component** tool.

1. Select **Screw:2** from the browser and then press the SHIFT key and select **Screw:3** from the browser. You will notice that both the selected components are displayed in blue in the browser and with a blue outline in the graphics screen.

2. Press the DELETE key to delete the two instances of the Screw.

    Since the holes on the Retainer are not visible in the current view, you will have to turn off the visibility of the Arm.

3. Turn off the visibility of the Arm using the browser.

4. Choose the **Pattern Component** button from the **Assembly Panel** toolbar or choose **Pattern Component** from the **Assembly Panel** panel bar to invoke the **Pattern Component** dialog box.

    The **Pattern Component** dialog box is displayed. The **Component** button is chosen and you are prompted to select the component to be patterned.

5. Select the Screw as the component to be patterned. Choose the **Associated Feature Pattern** button from the **Feature Pattern Select** area of the **Associative** tab. You are prompted to select the feature pattern to associate to.

6. Select the hole on the lower right side of the Retainer. You will notice that the two instances of the Screw are assembled with the two holes on the Retainer. Also, the display box on the right of the **Associate Feature Pattern** button will display **Circular Pattern1**. This is the name of the pattern of holes on the Retainer.

    Note
    *If you have created the holes on the Retainer as circles while creating its basic sketch, you cannot use them to create associative component patterns. The reason is that you can associate the pattern to only the feature pattern and not the sketch pattern. In this case, you can create a non-associative pattern using the **Circular** tab of the **Pattern Component** dialog box. However, as mentioned earlier, the pattern created using a tab other than the **Associative** tab will not be modified if the number of instances of the feature in the feature pattern is increased.*

7. Choose **OK** to create the pattern of the component and exit the **Pattern Component** dialog box.

    You will notice that the Screw is no more displayed in the browser. Instead, **Component Pattern 1** will be displayed. If you click on the + sign on the left of this, there will be three instances of the Screw with the name **Element:1**, **Element:2**, and **Element:3**.

8. Turn on the display of the Arm using the browser. Choose the **Save** button from the **Inventor Standard** toolbar to save the changes in the assembly. The display of the browser, after making all the modifications in the assembly, is shown in Figure 9-26.

9. Save the changes in the assembly and close the file.

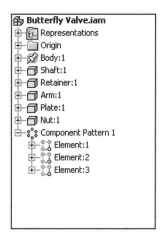

Figure 9-26 *Display of the browser for Tutorial 1*

Tutorial 2

In this tutorial, you will open the Drill Press Vice assembly created in Exercise 1 of Chapter 8 and then check the interference between the Base and the remaining components of the assembly. After checking the interference, you will drive the **Insert** constraint applied between the Clamp Screw and the Movable Jaw. **(Expected time: 30 min)**

The following steps are required to completing this tutorial:

a. Copy the Drill Press Vice assembly from *c08* folder to *c09* folder.
b. Open the *Drill Press Vice.iam* file and analyze it for interference.
c. Drive the **Insert** constraint applied between the Clamp Screw and the Movable Jaw.

Saving the Drill Press Vice Assembly

Since you do not want to modify the assembly created in Chapter 8, you need to copy the entire folder of Drill Press Vice assembly to *c09* folder. After copying the files, you will open the assembly file and check the components for interference. There should be no interference between the components.

1. Invoke the **Open** dialog box by choosing the **Open** button. Open the folder *\PersonalProject\c08*.

   You will notice that there is a folder with the name *Drill Press Vice* in *c08* folder.

2. Right-click on the *Drill Press Vice* folder and choose **Copy** from the shortcut menu.

3. Open the folder *\PersonalProject\c09*. Right-click and choose **Paste** to paste the *Drill Press Vice* folder in *c09* folder.

4. Open the *Drill Press Vice.iam* file from this *Drill Press Vice* folder.

Checking the Assembly for Interference

1. Choose **Tools > Analyze Interference** from the menu bar to invoke the **Interference Analysis** dialog box.

    The **Define Set # 1** button is chosen by default and you are prompted to select the components to add to the selection set.

2. Select Base from the graphics screen. Choose the **Define Set # 2** button from the dialog box and then select the remaining components from the browser. Choose **OK**.

    The **Analyzing Interference** dialog box is displayed, informing you that the interference is being analyzed.

3. After the analysis is complete, the **Autodesk Inventor** dialog box will be displayed and it will inform you that no interference was found in the assembly.

Driving the Constraint to Simulate the Motion of Assembly

The Clamp Screw Handle and the two instances of the Handle Stop were assembled with the Clamp Screw using the assembly constraints. Therefore, when you simulate the Clamp Screw by driving its constraint, you will notice that the Clamp Screw Handle and both the instances of the Handle Stop will also move along with the Clamp Screw.

1. Click on the + sign located on the left of the Clamp Screw in the browser. It will expand and the **Origin** folder, along with the various constraints applied to it, is displayed.

2. Move the cursor over the **Insert** constraint. The Clamp Screw and the Movable Jaw are highlighted on the graphics screen. This is to make sure that the constraint you select is the correct one. Right-click on the **Insert** constraint and choose **Drive Constraint** from the shortcut menu. The **Drive Constraint** dialog box is displayed.

3. Enter 30 in the **End** edit box as the end value of the simulation.

4. Choose the **More** button to expand the dialog box. Select the **Start/End/Start** radio button from the **Repetitions** area and then enter 2 in the edit box provided in the same area.

    The value of 2 is entered in the edit box to have two cycles of simulation. The first cycle will be from the start position to the end position and the second cycle will be from the end position to the start position.

5. Choose the **Forward** button. You will notice the simulation of the Clamp Screw along its central axis. Also, the other components assembled to it are moved along with it. Because there are two repetitions, the components will first move to a distance of 30 mm away from the Movable Jaw and then move back to the start position.

6. Exit the **Drive Constraint** dialog box by choosing the **Cancel** button. Save the changes to the assembly.

Tutorial 3

In this tutorial, you will create the components of the Double Bearing assembly and then assemble them, as shown in Figure 9-27. Figure 9-28 shows the exploded view of the assembly. Use the **Pattern Component** tool while assembling the Bolts. The dimensions of various components are given in Figures 9-29 through 9-31. After assembling the components, drive the **Insert** constraint of the first Bolt such that the remaining three instances are also simulated. Create a positional representation with the Bolts at the new location.   **(Expected time: 2 Hrs)**

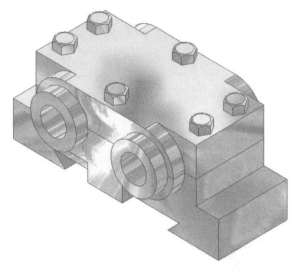

Figure 9-27 *Double Bearing assembly*

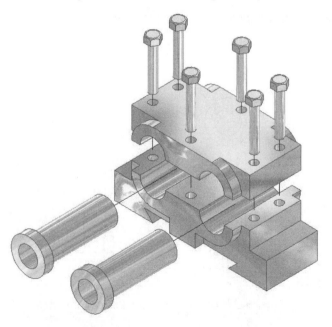

Figure 9-28 *Exploded view of the Double Bearing assembly*

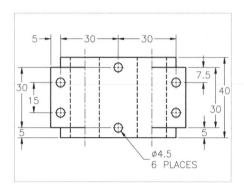

Figure 9-29a Top view of the Cap

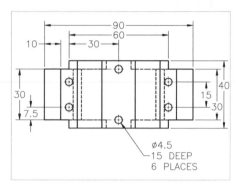

Figure 9-30a Top view of the Base

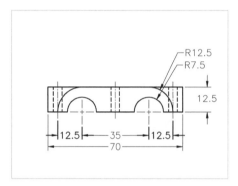

Figure 9-29b Front view of the Cap

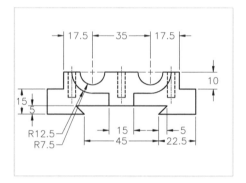

Figure 9-30b Front view of the Base

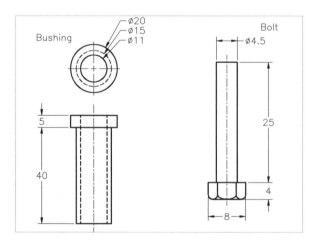

Figure 9-31 Dimensions of the Bushing and Bolt

The following steps outline the procedure of completing the tutorial:

a.   Create a folder with the name *Double Bearing* inside the *c09* folder. Create all the components of the Double Bearing assembly and store them in this folder.
b.   Open a new assembly file and assemble the components of the Double Bearing assembly. Only two instances of Bolt should be assembled and the rest should be created by patterning.
c.   Create a new positional representation in the assembly document.
d.   Drive the **Insert** constraint applied between one of the Bolts and the Cap so that the Bolts are moved to a new location in the current positional representation.

Creating the Components

1.   Create a folder with the name *Double Bearing* in the *\PersonalProject\c09* folder and then create all the components in the individual part files and save them in this folder.

2.   Open a new assembly file and save it with the name *Double Bearing.iam* in the folder *\PersonalProject\c09\Double Bearing*.

Assembling the Components

The first component that has to be recalled is the Base. After this component, you will recall the Cap and assemble these two components using the assembly constraints. Next, you will assemble two instances of the Bushing and then two instances of the Bolt. The remaining instances of the Bolt will be assembled using the **Pattern Component** tool.

1.   Place one instance each of the Base and the Cap in the assembly file using the **Place Component** tool.

2.   Assemble these components using the **Place Constraint** tool. The assembly, after assembling the Base and the Cap, is shown in Figure 9-32.

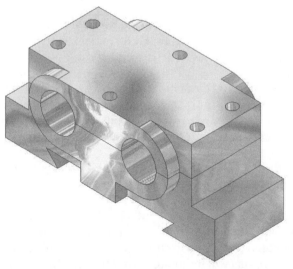

Figure 9-32 Assembly of the Base and the Cap

3.   Place two instances of the Bushing and assemble them using the **Place Constraint** tool.

4.   Similarly, place two instances of the Bolt and assemble them, as shown in Figure 9-33.

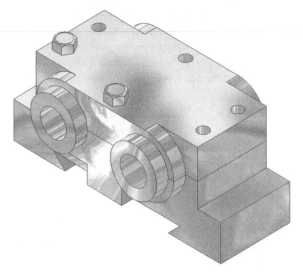

Figure 9-33 *After assembling two instances each of the Bolt and Bushing*

It is presumed that one of the four holes at the corners of the Cap was created and the other three were patterned. Similarly, one of the holes in the middle of the Cap was created and the other was patterned. Since all the six holes were not created using the single pattern, you will have to use the **Pattern Component** tool twice. The first time it will assemble the Bolt on the remaining three holes at the corners and the second time it will assemble the Bolt in the remaining hole in the middle of the Cap.

5.   Choose the **Pattern Component** button from the **Assembly Panel** toolbar or choose **Pattern Component** from the **Assembly Panel** panel bar to invoke the **Pattern Component** dialog box. You are prompted to select the component to be patterned.

6.   Select the Bolt at the lower left corner of the Cap.

7.   Choose the **Associate Feature Pattern** button from the **Feature Pattern Select** area. You are prompted to select the feature pattern to associate to.

8.   Select one of the three holes at the corners of the Cap. Three instances of the Bolt are assembled at the three holes.

Because the **Pattern Component** tool is still active, you are again prompted to select the component to be patterned. Note that to complete the assembling of the Bolts using the **Pattern Component** tool, you need to choose **OK** and exit this dialog box. If you select the Bolt again, the pattern that will be created is not the one that is required.

9. Choose **OK** to exit this dialog box and assemble the remaining three instances of the Bolt.

10. Invoke the **Pattern Component** dialog box again and select the Bolt assembled with the hole in the middle of the Cap.

11. Choose the **Associate Feature Pattern** button from the **Feature Pattern Select** area. You are prompted to select the feature pattern to associate to.

12. Select the other hole at the middle of the Cap. Choose **OK**. The final Double Bearing assembly is shown in Figure 9-34.

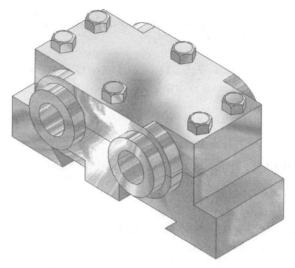

Figure 9-34 *Double Bearing assembly*

13. Choose the **Save** button from the **Inventor Standard** toolbar to save the assembly.

Creating Positional Representation

As mentioned in the tutorial description, you need to create the positional representation of the assembly with the Bolts moved to an offset position of 30 mm. You first need to create a positional representation and then drive the constraints of Bolts such that the Bolts are moved to a new location in the current positional representation. The positional representations are created using the browser.

1. Click on the + sign located on the left of **Presentations** in the browser to expand the tree view.

2. Right-click on **Position** in the browser and choose **New** from the shortcut menu; a + sign is added to the left of **Position** in the browser.

3. Click on the + sign located on the left of **Position : PositionalRep1** in the browser; the tree view expands. You will notice that a check mark is displayed on the left of **PositionalRep1**, suggesting that this representation is current.

Driving the Constraint of the Bolt

When you drive the constraint of the first Bolt at the lower left corner of the Cap, you will notice that the remaining three instances at the corners of the Cap also simulate along with the first Bolt. This is because the remaining three instances were assembled using the **Pattern Component** tool. This tool will force the three instances to behave similar to the original Bolt.

1. Click on the + sign located on the left of **Component Pattern 1**. You will notice that four instances of the Bolts are displayed with the name **Element:1**, **Element:2**, **Element:3**, and **Element:4**.

2. Click on the + sign on the left of **Element:1**; **Bolt:1** is displayed. Click on the left of **Bolt:1** to display the **Origin** folder and the **Insert** constraint.

3. Right-click on the **Insert** constraint and choose **Drive Constraint** from the shortcut menu. The **Drive Constraint** dialog box is displayed.

4. Enter 30 as the value in the **End** edit box. Choose the **More** button to expand the dialog box.

5. Select **Start/End/Start** radio button from the **Repetitions** area and then enter 2 in the edit box available in this area.

6. Choose the **Forward** button; all four bolts at the corners will be simulated and moved to a distance of 30 mm in the upward direction. All bolts are then moved back to their original position without any pause between the cycles.

    Because you need to create a positional representation of the assembly with the bolts at an offset of 30 from the original location, you need to stop the movement of the Bolts at the top most position. To do this, you need to modify the value in the edit box in the **Repetitions** area of the **Drive Constraint** dialog box.

7. Enter **1** as the value in the edit box in the **Repetitions** area and then choose the **Forward** button; the Bolts move up to a distance of 30 in the upward direction. Figure 9-35 displays the assembly with the four bolts at the new position.

8. Choose the **Apply** button. Choose **Yes** if the **Autodesk Inventor 11** dialog box is displayed and you are informed that the value of the constraint must be overridden in the current positional representation to preserve the value.

9. Exit the **Drive Constraint** dialog box by choosing the **Cancel** button. A positional representation is created with the Bolts moved to an offset of 30 mm from their original location.

10. Choose the **Save** button from the **Inventor Standard** toolbar; the **Autodesk Inventor 11** dialog box will be displayed and you will be informed that you cannot save the assembly when the assembly is in a positional representation.

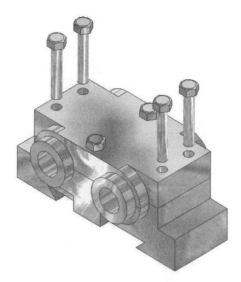

Figure 9-35 *Simulating the motion of the Bolts*

11. Choose **Yes** from this dialog box to restore the master position and save the assembly document.

12. Close the assembly document.

Self-Evaluation Test

Answer the following questions and then compare your answers with those given at the end of this chapter:

1. The components assembled using the **Pattern Component** tool can be replaced by other components. (T/F)

2. You can edit the components in the assembly file. (T/F)

3. The degrees of freedom symbol for a grounded component will not be displayed. (T/F)

4. The pattern of the component created using the **Circular** tab of the **Pattern Component** dialog box will be automatically modified, if the pattern of the feature is modified. (T/F)

5. Autodesk Inventor allows you to open the part file of the component for editing it. This is done by right-clicking on the component in the browser and choosing _____ from the shortcut menu.

6. If a component is assembled using an under-constrained component, a green color _____ is displayed on the component.

7. The assembly constraints applied on a component can be edited by right-clicking on the constraint in the browser and choosing _____ from the shortcut menu.

8. The three types of assembly section views that can be created in the assembly file are _____, _____, and _____.

9. To analyze the assembly for interference, choose _____ from the _____ menu.

10. The motion of assembly components can be simulated using the _____ dialog box.

Review Questions

Answer the following questions:

1. You can replace all instances of a component in the assembly file. (T/F)

2. Any instance of a component assembled using the **Pattern Component** tool can be made independent. (T/F)

3. You can flip the section of the section view in the assembly. (T/F)

4. The information of interference between the components can be printed. (T/F)

5. The simulation of the components of assembly can be saved to an avi file. (T/F)

6. You can use which one of the following tools to replace only one instance of a component in the assembly?

    (a) **Replace**   (b) **Replace All**
    (c) **Replace Component**   (d) None

7. You can store the information related to the simulation of the components in the avi file by using which one of the following buttons in the **Drive Constraint** dialog box?

    (a) **Record**   (b) **Forward**
    (c) **Reverse**   (d) None

8. By default, the design view files are saved in which of the following formats?

    (a) avi   (b) idv
    (c) ipt   (d) iam

9. Which one of the following buttons should be chosen to exit the section views in the assembly file?

    (a) **Full Section View**   (b) **No Section View**
    (c) **Half Section View**   (d) **End Section View**

10. If the pattern of a component is created using the **Circular** tab of the **Pattern Component** dialog box, which one of the following tabs will be available in the **Edit Component Pattern** dialog box?

    (a) **Associative**   (b) **Rectangular**
    (c) **Circular**   (d) None

Exercise

Exercise 1

Open the Plummer Block assembly created in Tutorial 2 of Chapter 8 (Figure 9-36) and then create a design view representation with the name **Plummer Block**. After creating the design view, analyze the assembly for interference and then simulate the motion of the two Bolts. The bolts should move in the downward direction.   **(Expected time: 30 min)**

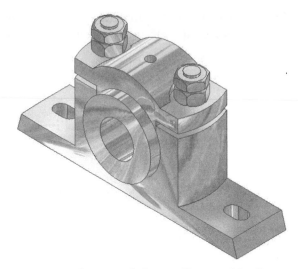

Figure 9-36 *Plummer Block assembly created in Chapter 8*

Answers to Self-Evaluation Test

1. T, **2.** T, **3.** T, **4.** F, **5. Open**, **6.** cube, **7. Edit**, **8.** quarter section view, half section view, three quarter section view, **9. Analyze Interference**, **Tools**, **10. Drive Constraint**

Chapter 10

Working with Drawing Views-I

Learning Objectives

After completing this chapter, you will be able to:
* *Understand the use of drawing views.*
* *Understand various types of drawing views in Autodesk Inventor.*
* *Create drawing views.*
* *Edit drawing views.*
* *Delete drawing views.*
* *Move drawing views.*
* *Copy drawing views.*
* *Rotate drawing views.*
* *Assign different hatch patterns to different components in assembly section views.*
* *Suppress components in assembly section views.*

THE DRAWING MODULE

After creating a solid model or an assembly, you will need to generate their drawing views. Drawing views are two-dimensional (2D) representations of a solid model or an assembly. Autodesk Inventor provides you with a specialized environment for generating drawing views. This specialized environment is called the **Drawing** module and has only those tools that are related to the drawing views. As mentioned earlier, all the modules of Autodesk Inventor are bidirectionally associative. This property ensures that any modifications made in a part or an assembly are reflected in the drawing views. Also, changes in the dimensions of a component or an assembly in the **Drawing** module are reflected in the part or assembly file. You can invoke the **Drawing** module for generating the drawing views by selecting any *.idw* format file from the **Metric** tab of the **Open** dialog box, see Figure 10-1. Autodesk Inventor has provided various *.idw* files with predefined drafting standards such as the ISO standard, BIN standard, DIN standard, and so on. You can use the required standard file and proceed to the **Drawing** module for generating the drawing views. The selected sheet will follow its standard in generating and dimensioning the drawing views. However, you can change the standards that will be followed by modifying the standards in the sheet.

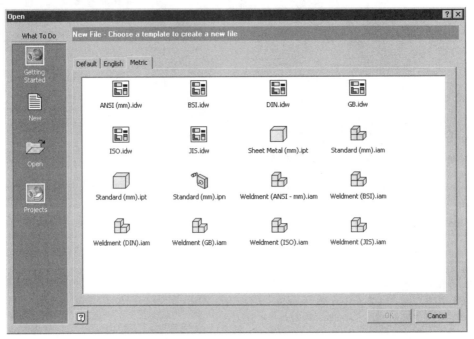

Figure 10-1 *Various .idw format files for starting a new file in the **Drawing** module*

The default screen appearance of a sheet in the **Drawing** module is shown in Figure 10-2. Note that a default sheet with a title block is available when you start this module. This drawing sheet is similar to that on which the drawing views are drawn using the manual methods. This sheet is your working environment and you can generate as many views as you want on it. You can also change the sheet style, title block style, or add more sheets for generating the drawing views.

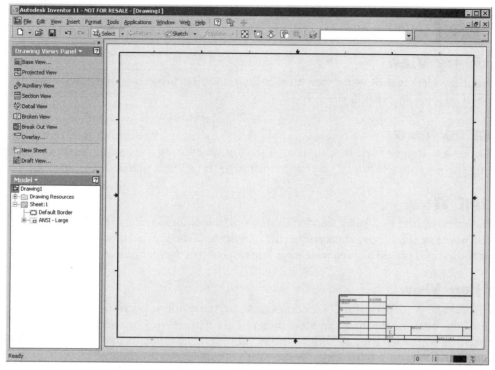

Figure 10-2 *Screen display in the **Drawing** module*

TYPE OF VIEWS

In Autodesk Inventor, you can generate eight type of views from a model, assembly, or presentation. Additionally, you can also draft a view using the sketcher entities. The technique of generating drawing views from models, assemblies, and presentations is called generative drafting. This is because you generate the drawing views. The technique of drafting a drawing view using the sketcher entities is called interactive drafting. The types of drawing views that you can generate are discussed next.

Base View

The base view is the first view generated in the drawing sheet. This view is generated using the original model, assembly, or presentation. The base view is an independent view and is not affected by changes in any other view in the drawing sheet. Most of the other views in the sheet will be generated taking this view as the parent view.

Projected View

The projected view is generated taking any of the existing views as the parent view. This view is generated by projecting the lines normal to the parent view or at an angle to the parent view to generate a 3D view. If the lines are projected normal to the parent view, the resulting view will be an orthographic view such as top view, front view, side view, and so on. If the lines are projected at an angle, the resulting view will be a 3D view such as an isometric view. In this view, you can visualize the X, Y, and Z axes of the model. These views are 2D representations of a three-dimensional (3D) model.

Auxiliary View

An auxiliary view is a drawing view that is generated by projecting the lines normal to a specified edge of an existing view.

Section View

A section view is generated by chopping a part of an existing view using a plane and then viewing the parent view from a direction normal to the section plane.

Detail View

A detail view is used to display the details of a portion of an existing view. You can select the portion whose detailing has to be shown in the parent view. The portion that you have selected will be magnified and placed as a separate view. You can control the magnification of the detail view.

Broken View

A broken view is used to display a component by removing a portion of it from between, keeping the ends of the drawing view intact. This type of view is used for displaying the components whose length and width ratio is very high. This means that either the length is very large as compared to the width or the width is very large as compared to the length. The broken view will break the view along the horizontal or vertical direction such that the drawing view fits the area you require. Note that in these views, the dimension of the edge that is broken will still be displayed as the actual value. However, that dimension will have a broken symbol suggesting that this dimension value is for the edge that is broken in the view.

Break Out View

A break out view is used to remove a part of the existing view and display the area of the model or the assembly behind the removed portion. This type of view is generated using a closed sketch that is associated with the parent view.

Overlay View

An overlay view is used to display an alternate position of the components in an assembly. It uses positional representations created in the assembly environment for generating the drawing view.

Note
*To create sketches that are associated with the drawing view, select the drawing view from the drawing sheet and then choose the **Sketch** button from the **Inventor Standard** toolbar. The sketching environment will be activated. The sketch that you will draw in this environment will be associated with the drawing view.*

GENERATING DRAWING VIEWS

The method of generating all eight types of views is discussed next.

Generating the Base View

Toolbar:	Drawing Views Panel > Base View
Panel bar:	Drawing Views Panel > Base View

As mentioned earlier, the first view that will be generated in the drawing sheet is the base view. This view is generated using the **Base View** tool. You can also invoke this tool by right-clicking on the sheet in the drawing window or in the browser and choosing **Base View**. When you invoke this tool, the **Drawing View** dialog box will be displayed. The options in this dialog box are discussed next.

Component Tab

The options in the **Component** tab (Figure 10-3) are used to select the component or the assembly whose drawing view you want to generate, the scale, the orientation, and the display style of the drawing view. These options are discussed next.

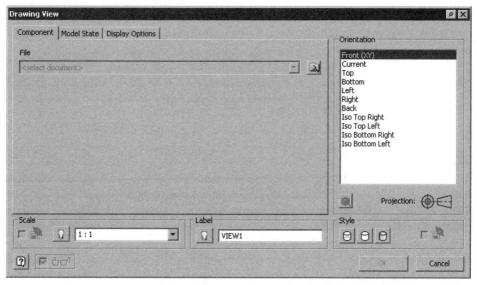

Figure 10-3 The Component tab of the Drawing View dialog box

File

The **File** drop-down list displays the files that are selected for creating the drawing views. By default, this drop-down list is grayed out. This is because no file is selected. To select a file for generating the drawing views, choose the **Explore Directories** button located on the right of the **File** drop-down list; the **Open** dialog box will be displayed. Using this dialog box, you can select a part, sheet metal, assembly, or presentation file to generate the drawing views. After you have selected the file, you will notice that its name and location is displayed in the **File** drop-down list. Similarly, if you select any other file, its information will also be displayed in the **File** drop-down list.

Representation Area

This area will be displayed if the selected file is an assembly file. The options in this area are discussed next.

Design View List Box. If the selected assembly file has some design views associated to it, they will be displayed in the **Design View** list box. If the design view files of the selected file are not saved in the current folder, choose the **Explore directories** button on the right of this drop-down list to select the folder, in which the design view files are saved.

Associative. This check box is selected to make the design view associative to the view that you generate. As a result, if the design view changes, the drawing view also changes automatically.

Positional Representation. This drop-down list is used to select the positional representation of an assembly using which the drawing views will be generated.

Level of Detail. This drop-down list is used to select the level of detail that is required for a drawing view.

Presentation View

This area will be displayed if the selected file is a presentation file. The presentation views created in the presentation file will be displayed in the list box. You can make the drawing view associated to the presentation view by selecting the **Associative** check box.

Scale Area

The **Scale** area is used to specify the scale for the drawing view. You can enter the scale in the edit box or select the predefined standard scales by choosing the down arrow on the right of the edit box. The **Toggle Scale Visibility** button on the left of the edit box is used to specify whether or not the scale of the drawing view will appear on the drawing view.

Label Area

The **Label** area allows you to specify a label for the view. You can specify the label in the text box available in this area. Note that the label will appear on the drawing sheet only if the **Toggle Label Visibility** button is chosen.

Orientation Area

The options in this area are used to specify the orientation of the drawing view. You can select any predefined view such as top, front, right, left, isometric top-right, isometric top-left, and so on. The resulting view will be based on the option selected from this list box. You can also create a drawing view with a user-defined orientation by choosing the **Change view orientation** button provided below the list box. When you choose this button, the **Custom View** window will be displayed, as shown in Figure 10-4.

The default view of the model will be displayed in this window. The **Inventor Standard** toolbar in this window has only the drawing display tools that can be used to modify the view orientation. Once you have achieved the required view orientation, choose the **Exit**

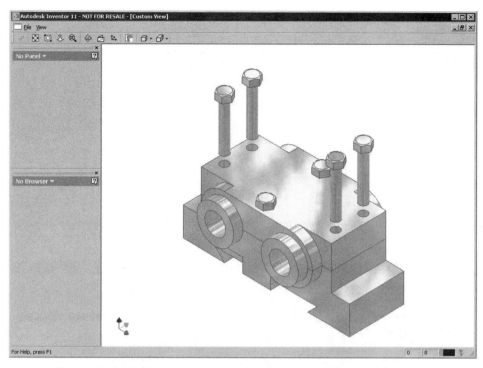

*Figure 10-4 The **Custom View** window for creating the user-defined view*

Custom View button, which is the first button in the **Inventor Standard** tool bar; the **Custom View** window will be closed and you will return to the original Autodesk Inventor window. The preview of the view created using the **Custom View** window will be attached to the cursor and you will be prompted to click on a location to place the view.

Style Area
The buttons in the **Style** area are used to specify the display type for the drawing views. You can generate the view with hidden lines, without hidden lines, or with shaded display by choosing their respective buttons from this area. Figure 10-5 shows the drawing view with hidden lines and Figure 10-6 shows the drawing view without hidden lines.

Model State Tab
The options in the **Model State** tab (Figure 10-7) are discussed next.

Weldment Area
The **Weldment** area will be displayed only when you select the weldment file to generate the drawing views. You can specify the weldment state to be displayed in the drawing view by selecting its respective radio button from this area.

Member
This list box is available only for assemblies with positional representations and is used to select the member that should be selected from an iAssembly file to be displayed in the drawing views.

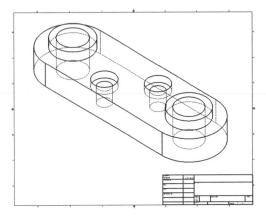

Figure 10-5 *Drawing view with hidden lines*

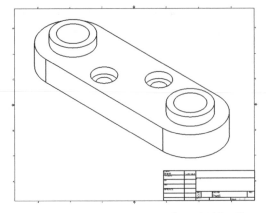

Figure 10-6 *Drawing view without hidden lines*

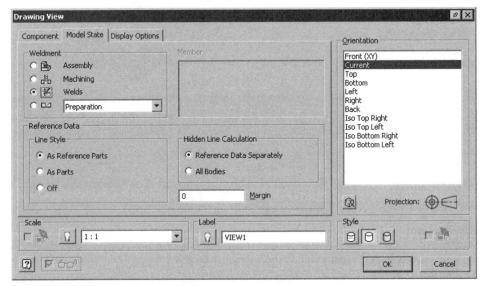

Figure 10-7 *The **Model State** tab of the **Drawing View** dialog box*

Reference Data Area

The options in the **Reference Data** area are used to set the line style for the reference data. You can select the desired line style from the **Line Style** area. The **Hidden Line Calculation** area is used to set the option for the calculation of hidden lines. You can set the option to calculate hidden lines separately for reference data. The **Margin** edit box is used to specify the value by which the view boundaries will be extended on all sides to display additional reference data in the drawing view.

Display Options Tab

The options in the **Display Options** tab (Figure 10-8) are used to select the parameters that you want to display in the drawing views. For example, if you select the **All Model Dimensions** check box, the parametric dimensions that were used to create the model in the **Part** module are

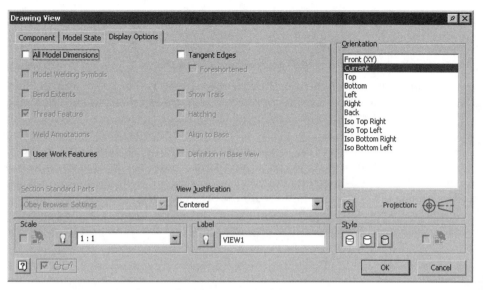

*Figure 10-8 The **Display Options** tab of the **Drawing View** dialog box*

displayed. Similarly, you can also specify whether or not the thread features or tangent edges should be displayed in the drawing view.

The **Section Standard Parts** drop-down list is used to select the option to specify whether or not the standard parts inserted using the Content Library will be sectioned in the assembly section view. By default, the **Obey Browser Settings** option is selected. As a result, the settings that you configure in the browser will be used. Selecting **Always** will always section the standard parts in the assembly section view and selecting **Never** will never section the standard parts.

The **View Justification** drop-down list is used to specify the justification for the drawing view. By default, the justification is **Centered**. You can also select the **Fixed** justification from this drop-down list.

Note
*In the **Display Options** tab, only the options that are applicable to the selected view will be enabled. Some of these options also depend on whether you select a part file or an assembly file to generate the drawing view. For example, the option to display model dimensions will not be available while generating the drawing views of an assembly.*

Tip. *By default, the model dimensions are displayed in the drawing view using the default dimensioning standards and dimension style. If the default dimension standard uses dimensions in inches, the dimensions in the drawing views will be displayed in inches even if the dimensions were specified in millimeters in the model. However, you can modify the dimension standards as well as the dimension style. This will be discussed in later chapters.*

Generating Projected Views

Toolbar:	Drawing Views Panel > Projected View
Panel bar:	Drawing Views Panel > Projected View

 As mentioned earlier, the projected views are generated by projecting the lines from an existing view. To generate a projected view, invoke this tool and then select the parent view that you want to use to generate the projected view. After selecting the parent view, you will be prompted to specify a location for the projected view. Left-click on the drawing sheet to specify the location. If you move the cursor in the horizontal or the vertical direction, an orthographic view will be generated. If you move the cursor at an angle from the parent view, a 3D view will be generated. You can preview the resulting view on the drawing sheet. Once you have specified the location for the projected view, a rectangle will be displayed at that location and you will again be prompted to specify the location of the projected view. To generate the view, right-click on the drawing sheet and choose **Create** from the shortcut menu.

Note

The display type of the projected views will be the same as that of the parent view. However, you can later modify the display type of the projected view.

Figure 10-9 shows the drawing sheet with the base view and projected views. The base view is the top view placed on the top of the drawing sheet. The top and isometric views are generated as projected views using the front view as the parent view.

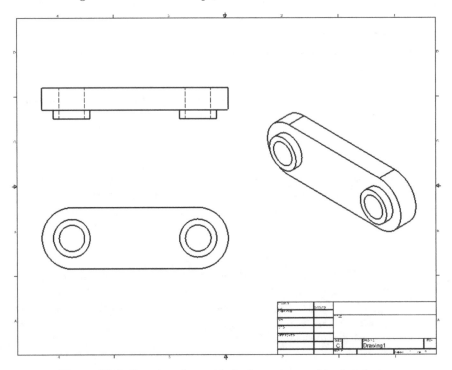

Figure 10-9 *Drawing sheet with the base view and projected views*

Tip. *If while generating the projected view, you move the cursor in the horizontal or the vertical direction from the parent view, a center line will be displayed from the center of the parent view to the center of the projected view. This center line will suggest that the view is being projected normal to the parent view. Therefore, the resulting view will be an orthographic view.*

Generating Auxiliary Views

Toolbar:	Drawing Views Panel > Auxiliary View
Panel bar:	Drawing Views Panel > Auxiliary View

As mentioned earlier, auxiliary views are generated by projecting lines normal to a specified edge in the parent view. To generate an auxiliary view, invoke the **Auxiliary View** tool and then select the parent view. When you select the parent view, the **Auxiliary View** dialog box will be displayed, as shown in Figure 10-10. The options in this dialog box are discussed next.

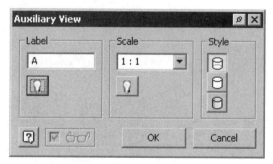

Figure 10-10 *The* **Auxiliary View** *dialog box*

Label Area

The text box in the **Label** area is used to enter the label for the auxiliary view. By default, this label will not be displayed on the drawing view. If you choose the **Toggle Label Visibility** button, the label of the view will be displayed on the drawing sheet.

Scale Area

The edit box in the **Scale** area is used to specify the scale factor for the auxiliary view. By default, the scale of the auxiliary view will be the same as that of the parent view. However, you can create an auxiliary view with a different scale by specifying the scale factor in this edit box. You can also select the predefined scale factors by choosing the down arrow on the right of this edit box and selecting the scale factor from the list that is displayed. The **Toggle Label Visibility** button can be chosen to display the scale factor on the drawing view. This check box is cleared by default.

Style Area

The buttons in the **Style** area are used to specify the display type for the drawing view. By default, it will be the same as that of the parent view. However, you can specify the required display type by choosing its button from this area.

After you select the parent view, you will notice that an inclined line is attached to the cursor to remind you to select an edge in the parent view that will be used for generating the auxiliary view. When you select the edge, the preview of the auxiliary view that will be generated is displayed on the sheet. You will notice that the view that is being generated is parallel to the selected edge. Also, a center line will be displayed that will be normal to the edge as well as the auxiliary view, see Figure 10-11. This center line and the **Auxiliary View** dialog box will be automatically removed once you place the view.

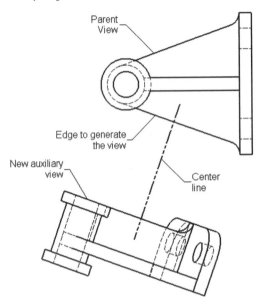

Figure 10-11   *Generating the auxiliary view*

Generating Section Views

Toolbar:	Drawing Views Panel > Section View
Panel bar:	Drawing Views Panel > Section View

As mentioned earlier, section views are generated by chopping a portion of an existing view using a cutting plane (defined by sketched lines) and then viewing the parent view from the direction normal to the cutting plane. To create a section view, invoke the **Section View** tool and then select the parent view. A red rectangle will appear around the parent view and the cursor, which was originally an arrow, will be replaced by a + cursor that is used to define the cutting plane. In Autodesk Inventor, the cutting plane will be defined by sketching one or more than one lines. You can use the temporary tracking option for drawing the lines that will define the section plane. After you have drawn the lines, right-click on the drawing sheet and choose **Continue** from the shortcut menu. The **Section View** dialog box will be displayed, as shown in Figure 10-12, and you will be prompted to enter the location for the section view. You will notice that the line that you had drawn is converted into a section plane now and the preview of the section view is displayed on the drawing sheet. This preview will move as you move the cursor on the drawing sheet. However, it will always remain parallel to the section plane.

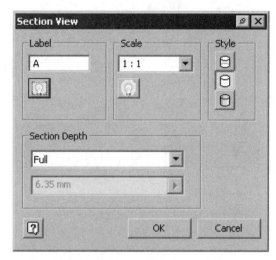

Figure 10-12 The Section View dialog box

You can use the options in the **Section Depth** area to specify the offset distance of another section plane behind the original section plane. By default, the **Full** option is selected. To define the depth of sectioning, select the **Distance** option and then set the distance value in the edit box in the **Section Depth** area. Another section plane will be defined parallel to the original section plane at the distance you define and will chop the model. To see the use of this option, generate the isometric view of the section view.

When you specify the location of the section view, the **Section View** dialog box will be closed and the section view will be generated. The part of original view that is sectioned will be displayed with hatching lines in the section view. Figure 10-13 shows the section view generated from the parent view.

You can also use the **Section View** tool to generate the aligned section view. This type of view is used to create a section view of the features that are at a certain angle. In an aligned section view, the section portion revolves about an axis normal to the viewing plane such that it is straightened. For example, see Figure 10-14. This figure shows an aligned section view of a model. Notice that the inclined feature that is sectioned in this view is straightened. As a result, the section view is longer than the parent view.

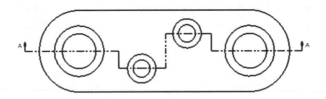

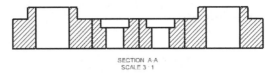

SECTION A-A
SCALE 3 : 1

Figure 10-13 *Base view and section view*

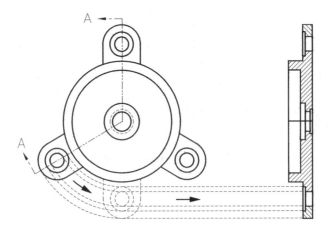

Figure 10-14 *Base view and the aligned section view*

Tip. *You can also create a sketch associated with a drawing view and then use it to generate the section views. To create an associated sketch, select the drawing view and then choose Sketch from the Inventor Standard toolbar. The sketching environment will be activated. Draw the sketch to be used to generate the section view and exit the sketching environment. Now, right-click on the sketch that you created; the shortcut menu will be displayed. Choose Create Section View from it to generate the section view using the associated sketch.*

Generating Detail Views

Toolbar:	Drawing Views Panel > Detail View
Panel bar:	Drawing Views Panel > Detail View

 Detail views are used to display the details of a portion of an existing view by magnifying that portion and displaying it as a separate view. To create a detail view, invoke the **Detail View** tool and then select a view. This view will be the parent view for the detailed view. When you select the parent view, the **Detail View** dialog box will be displayed, as shown in Figure 10-15. The options in this dialog box are similar to those discussed in the **Auxiliary View** dialog box.

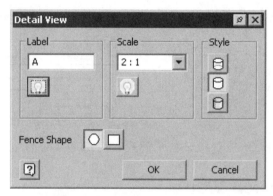

*Figure 10-15 The **Detail View** dialog box*

In addition to the **Detail View** dialog box that is displayed when you select the parent view, a circle will be attached to the cursor and you will be prompted to specify the start point of the fence. The fence is actually the boundary that encloses the portion of the parent view to be magnified and displayed as the detail view. You can select the option to draw a rectangular or a circular boundary by choosing its respective button from the **Fence Shape** area. Next, select a point on the parent view. This point should lie on the area that you want to magnify. The specified point will be taken as the center of the circular or rectangular boundary and you will be prompted to specify the endpoint of the fence. Move the cursor to specify the endpoint. The portion that is enclosed in the boundary will be magnified by the value defined in the **Detail View** dialog box and the view will be attached to the cursor. Also, you will be prompted to specify the location for the view. Specify the placement point for the drawing view; the detail view will be placed at the point that you specify. Figure 10-16 shows the drawing sheet with a base view, two projected views, and a detail view.

Note

In Figure 10-16, the isometric view is generated using the front view as the base view.

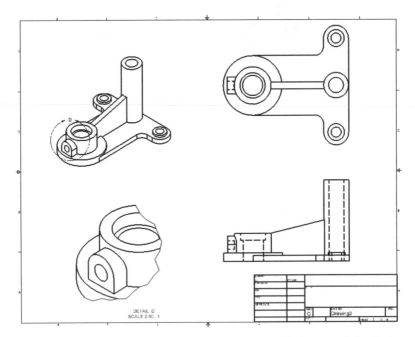

Figure 10-16 *Drawing sheet with base view, projected views, and detail view*

Generating Broken Views

Toolbar:	Drawing Views Panel > Broken View
Panel bar:	Drawing Views Panel > Broken View

The broken view is used to display a component by removing a portion of it from between, keeping the ends of the drawing view intact. These views are generally used to display the models that have a high length to width ratio. Note that this tool will not create a separate view. It will break an existing view such that a specified portion of the view is removed and the remaining portion is displayed along with the ends of the views. The views will be broken with the help of two planes defined by lines. You do not have to draw the lines for defining the cutting planes. You just have to specify the location of the first and the second cutting plane. The portion of the view that lies inside the two cutting planes will be removed and the remaining view will be displayed. To break the view, invoke this tool and then select the view to be broken; the **Broken View** dialog box will be displayed, as shown in Figure 10-17, and you will be prompted to select the start point of the material to be removed. The options in this dialog box are discussed next and the method to define the break lines is discussed after the dialog box explanation.

Style Area
The buttons in the **Style** area are used to specify the style for displaying the break symbol. The style options provided in this area are discussed next.

Rectangular Style
The **Rectangular Style** button is used to break the views of a noncylindrical component.

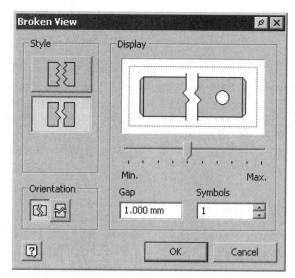

*Figure 10-17 The **Broken View** dialog box*

Structural Style

The **Structural Style** button is used to break the views of a cylindrical component.

Orientation Area

The buttons in the **Orientation** area are used to specify the break in the horizontal or the vertical direction. Depending on whether the view is vertical or horizontal, the option from this area will be selected.

Display Area

The options in the **Display** area are used to control the display of break lines in the broken view. The preview window in this area will display the break lines that will be displayed on the broken view. As you modify the options in the **Display** area, the preview in the preview window will also change. The scale of break lines can be modified using the slider bar in this area. The preview of the change in scale will be displayed in the preview window and on the drawing sheet when you move the cursor on the drawing sheet.

Gap

The **Gap** edit box is used to specify the value of the break gap in the broken view.

Symbols

The **Symbols** spinner is used to specify the number of break spinners in the break line when the **Structural Style** button is selected from the **Style** area. The maximum number of symbols that are allowed is three. This spinner will not be available, if you choose the **Rectangular Style** button from the **Style** area.

You will notice that when you select the view to be broken, two lines with a break symbol will be attached to the cursor and you will be prompted to specify the start point for the material to be removed. This will be the point where the first cutting plane will be placed. After you specify the first point, you will notice that two break lines are placed at that point. These break lines will be based on the style that you have selected from the **Style** area. You will now be prompted to specify the endpoint for the material to be removed. This point will define the position of the second cutting plane. After you specify the location of the second cutting plane, you will notice that the view will shrink as the material between the two cutting planes is removed. Also, the break lines of the selected style will be displayed on the view. Figure 10-18 shows a broken view created using the rectangular style and Figure 10-19 shows a broken view created using the structural style with three symbols.

Figure 10-18 *Broken view created using the rectangular style*

Figure 10-19 *Broken view created using the structural style*

Tip. *If you break a projected orthographic view or a section view using the **Broken View** tool, the parent view will also be converted into a broken view. The scale and style of the broken parent view will be similar to that of the projected or section view. Similarly, if you break a view that is used as a parent view for generating other views, the dependent views will also be converted into broken views. Note that the isometric view generated by projecting the lines from an existing view is not dependent on the parent view, and so will not be converted into a broken view.*

Generating Break Out Views

Toolbar:	Drawing Views Panel > Break Out View
Panel bar:	Drawing Views Panel > Break Out View

As mentioned earlier, the break out views are generated to remove a portion of the drawing view and display the area that lies behind the removed portion. These views are generated using the closed sketches that are associated with the view. As a result, you first need to create a closed sketch associated with this view by selecting the view and choosing the **Sketch** button from the **Inventor Standard** toolbar. Next, invoke the **Break Out View** tool; you will be prompted to select a view. Select a view that has a closed sketch associated with it. If you select a view that has no sketch associated with it, a message box will be displayed and you will be informed that the selected view has no sketch associated with it.

The options in the **Break Out View** dialog box (Figure 10-20) are discussed next.

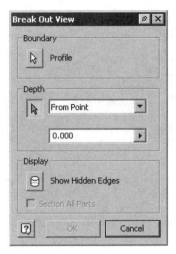

*Figure 10-20 The **Break Out View** dialog box*

Boundary Area

This area has the **Profile** button that is chosen to select the closed sketch associated with the view to create the break out view. When you invoke this dialog box, the **Profile** button is chosen automatically. This is the reason you will be prompted to select the profile when you invoke this dialog box.

Depth Area

The options in the **Depth** area are used to select the method for specifying the depth of the break out view. You can select the method for specifying the depth from the drop-down list in this area. The options in this drop-down list are discussed next.

From Point

The **From Point** option is used to select a point from which you will define the depth of the break out view. The depth is defined in the edit box available below this drop-down list. Figure 10-21 shows the point from which the depth will be defined. Figure 10-22 shows the resulting break out view. The depth from the point in this view is 20 mm.

 Tip. *You can open the part file for editing the component whose drawing views you are generating. To open the part file, right-click on the drawing view and choose **Open** from the shortcut menu.*

To Sketch

This option is selected to use a sketch to define the depth of the break out view. Note that to get a better view, it is recommended that the sketch should be associated with a different view. Figure 10-23 shows the drawing views with the sketch used to specify the depth and the resulting break out view. Note that in this figure, the sketch used to define the depth is the one on the front view and the sketch to define the break out is the same as that in Figure 10-21.

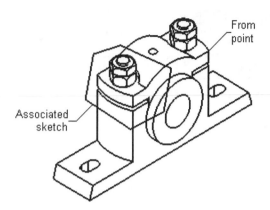

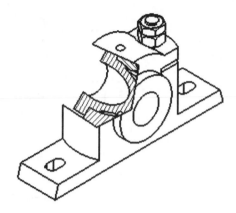

Figure 10-21 *Sketch and the point to define the break out view*

Figure 10-22 *Resulting break out view*

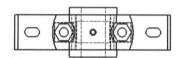

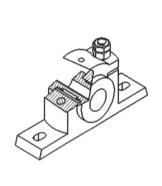

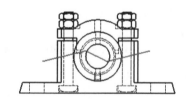

Figure 10-23 *Sketch to define the depth and the resulting break out view*

To Hole

This option is selected to use the hole on the selected view define the depth of the break out view. Figure 10-24 shows a break out view created using the central hole of the Brasses as the hole to define the depth of the break out view.

Through Part

This option is selected to use the depth of a selected part to define the depth of the break out view. When you select this option, you will be prompted to select a part to define the depth.

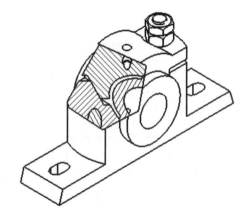

Figure 10-24 *Break out view generated up to the central hole of the Brasses*

The **Depth** area also has the **Show Hidden Edges** check box that is selected to show the hidden edges in the selected view. The hidden edges help you define the depth of the break out view. Note that the display type of the view will change to the original one after the view is created.

Generating Overlay Views

| **Toolbar:** | Drawing Views Panel > Overlay View |
| **Panel bar:** | Drawing Views Panel > Overlay |

 As mentioned earlier, the overlay views are used to show the alternate position of components in an assembly. This view can be generated only if you have created positional representations for the assembly in the assembly modeling environment. The alternate position of the components is shown by dashed lines in an existing view.

To create an overlay view, choose the **Overlay** button from the **Drawing Views Panel** panel bar; you will be prompted to select a view. Select a drawing view of an assembly for which the positional representations were created; the **Overlay View** dialog box will be displayed, as shown in Figure 10-25. Most of the options in this dialog box are similar to those discussed while generating earlier drawing views. The two remaining options are discussed next.

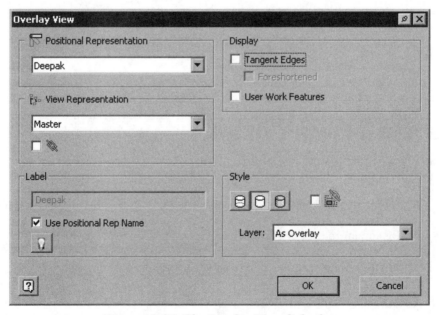

*Figure 10-25 The **Overlay View** dialog box*

Positional Representation Area

The drop-down list in this area lists all the available positional representations for the selected assembly. You can select the desired positional representation to generate the overlay view from this drop-down list.

View Representation Area

The drop-down list in this area lists all the available design views for the selected assembly. The overlay view will use the design view you select from this drop-down list.

After specifying the parameters in the **Overlay View** dialog box, choose **OK**; the overlay view will be generated in the selected view and the alternate position of the components will be displayed using dashed lines. Figure 10-26 shows the overlay view generated on an isometric view. As evident in this view, the alternate position of the components is shown using dashed lines.

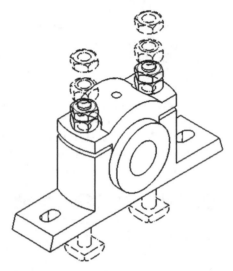

Figure 10-26 Overlay view generated on an isometric view

DRAFTING DRAWING VIEWS

Toolbar:	Drawing Views Panel > Draft View
Panel bar:	Drawing Views Panel > Draft View

In addition to generating all the above-mentioned views, Autodesk Inventor also allows you to draft a drawing view using the sketching tools. After sketching, these views will behave similar to the generated views. The drawing views can be sketched using the **Draft View** tool. When you invoke this tool, the **Draft View** dialog box will be displayed, as shown in Figure 10-27. The options in this dialog box are discussed next.

Label Area
The edit box in the **Label** area is used to specify the label of the view. You can select the **Toggle Label Visibility** check box to display the label in the drawing sheet.

Scale Area
The edit box in the **Scale** area is used to specify the scale of the view. Selecting the **Toggle Scale Visibility** check box will display the scale of the drawing view on the drawing sheet.

After specifying the label and the scale, choose the **OK** button; the sketching environment will be invoked. All the sketching tools in this environment can be used to sketch the drawing view.

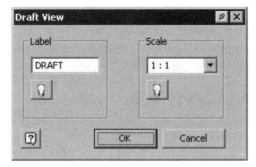

Figure 10-27 The **Draft View** dialog box

EDITING DRAWING VIEWS

In Autodesk Inventor, you can edit a drawing view by using the shortcut menu displayed upon right-clicking on the drawing view in the browser or on the sheet. If you move the cursor over a drawing view in the sheet, you will notice that a red box is drawn around the view using dotted lines. This box is the bounding box of the view. To edit a view, double-click when the bounding box is displayed. Alternatively, you can right-click on the view when the bounding box is displayed and then choose **Edit View** from the shortcut menu. The **Drawing View** dialog box will be displayed. You can also display this dialog box by double-clicking on the required view in the browser. Figure 10-28 shows the **Component** tab of the **Drawing View** dialog box invoked to edit a drawing view.

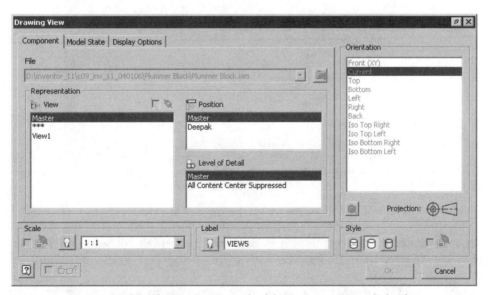

Figure 10-28 The **Component** tab of the **Drawing View** dialog box

Note
*The options in the **Component** tab and the **Options** tab of this dialog box will be available based on the type of view selected for editing. All these options are similar to those discussed in the **Create View** dialog box used for generating the drawing views.*

DELETING DRAWING VIEWS

The unwanted drawing views can be deleted from the sheet using the browser or directly from the sheet. To delete the drawing view, move the cursor over the drawing view in the browser or on the drawing sheet; a dotted rectangle, which is actually the bounding box of the drawing view, will be displayed. Select the drawing view when the bounding box is displayed and then press the DELETE key. You can also right-click and choose **Delete** from the shortcut menu.

If the selected drawing views have some dependent drawing views, the **Delete View** dialog box will be displayed. It will confirm whether you want to delete the selected view and its dependent views. Choose **OK** to delete the views. To view the views that are dependent on the selected view, choose the **More** button on the bottom right corner of this dialog box. The dialog box will expand and provide the list of the dependent views, see Figure 10-29.

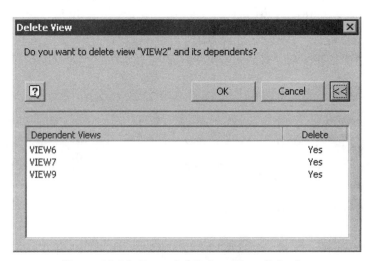

Figure 10-29 *Expanded **Delete View** dialog box*

By default, this dialog box will show **Yes** for all the views in the **Delete** column of the expanded area. This suggests that all the dependent views will be deleted if you delete the parent view. If you do not want to delete a dependent view, click on **Yes** once; **Yes** will be replaced by **No**. This suggests that the selected dependent view will not be deleted if you delete the parent view.

Tip. *On selecting a view to delete, you will notice that red rectangles are drawn around all the dependent views. If you change **Yes** to **No** for a view in the **Delete View** dialog box, the red box will no more be displayed. This suggests that the drawing view will not be deleted.*

MOVING DRAWING VIEWS

You can relocate the existing drawing view by moving it from its current location to a new location. However, remember that if the selected view has some dependent views, they will also move along with the parent view. To move the view, move the cursor over the view; the bounding box of the view is displayed. Move the cursor over one of the edges of the bounding box. Now, press and hold the left mouse button down and drag the view to a new location in the sheet. Note that the section views, auxiliary views, and the projected orthographic views can be moved only along the axis, in which they were projected. The isometric views and detail views can be moved to any location in the drawing sheet.

Tip. *You can suppress the option to move the dependent views along with the parent view if you do not want to move them with the parent view. This is done by clearing the **Align to Base** option from the **Display Options** tab of the **Create View** dialog box, which is displayed on double-clicking on the dependent views.*

COPYING DRAWING VIEWS

Autodesk Inventor allows you to copy an existing view at a new location in a new sheet. You can also copy the existing view in a new drawing file. To copy the view, move the cursor over the view and right-click when the bounding box of the view is displayed. Choose **Copy** from the shortcut menu that is displayed on right-clicking. You can also right-click on the drawing view in the browser and choose **Copy** from the shortcut menu. You can paste this drawing view at a new location in a new sheet or in a new drawing file. Note that if the selected drawing view has some dependent views, they will not be copied along with the parent view.

Note
The process of adding more sheets will be discussed in the next chapter.

ROTATING DRAWING VIEWS

Autodesk Inventor allows you to rotate the selected drawing view about its center point. If you rotate a drawing view that has some dependent views, they will also be affected. However, if you rotate the dependent view, the parent view is not affected. You can rotate an existing drawing view by right-clicking on it in the browser or on the sheet and choosing **Rotate** from the shortcut menu. When you choose this option, the **Rotate View** dialog box will be displayed, as shown in Figure 10-30. The options in this dialog box are discussed next.

By Area

The drop-down list in the **By** area is used to select the method of rotating the selected drawing view. There are two methods for rotating the drawing views. These methods are discussed next.

Edge

The **Edge** method is used to force the orientation of the selected view such that the selected edge becomes horizontal or vertical. The orientation will depend on whether you select the **Horizontal** or the **Vertical** radio button, which will be displayed in the **By** area when you select **Edge** from

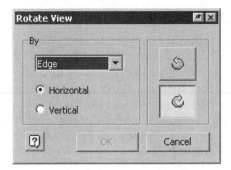

*Figure 10-30 The **Rotate View** dialog box*

the drop-down list. To rotate the view using this method, select the **Horizontal** or the **Vertical** radio button and then select the edge in the selected view.

Angle

The **Angle** method is used to rotate the selected view by specifying the rotation angle of the view. The angle can be specified in the edit box that is displayed in the **By** area when you select the **Angle** option from the drop-down list.

Counter clockwise

The **Counter clockwise** button is the first button in the area that is on the right of the **By** area. This button is chosen to rotate the selected view in the counterclockwise direction.

Clockwise

The **Clockwise** button is available below the **Counter clockwise** button and is chosen to rotate the selected view in the clockwise direction.

ASSIGNING DIFFERENT HATCH PATTERNS TO THE COMPONENTS IN THE ASSEMBLY SECTION VIEWS

Whenever you generate section views of an assembly, by default, all of them are assigned similar hatch patterns. Although the angle of hatching lines between the adjacent components is different, but this creates confusion, if the assembly has a number of components. For example, Figure 10-31 shows the drawing views of the Plummer Block assembly. In this figure, the components in the section view are assigned similar hatch patterns.

This confusion can be avoided by assigning different hatch patterns to the components of the assembly. To modify the hatch pattern, move the cursor over the hatching lines in the component in the section view. The hatch pattern will turn red. Once the hatch pattern turns red, right-click to display the shortcut menu. In this shortcut menu, choose the **Modify Hatch** option. When you

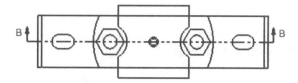

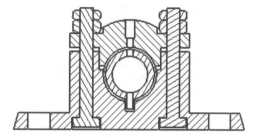

Figure 10-31 Similar hatch patterns of components in the section view

choose this option, the **Modify Hatch Pattern** dialog box will be displayed, see Figure 10-32. The options in this dialog box are discussed next.

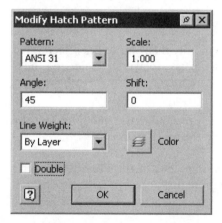

*Figure 10-32 The **Modify Hatch Pattern** dialog box*

Pattern

The **Pattern** drop-down list is used to select the hatch pattern for the selected hatching. You can select the required hatch pattern from the list of patterns in this drop-down list. The preview of the selected pattern can be displayed on the sheet. The selected hatch pattern will be assigned to the selected component. However, note that this hatch pattern will not be assigned to the other instances of the selected component. The other instances of the selected component will still be hatched using the default hatch pattern.

Angle

The **Angle** edit box is used to specify the angle of the hatching lines. You can specify the required angle value by entering it in this edit box.

Line Weight

The **Line Weight** drop-down list is used to specify the line weight of the hatching lines. You can specify the required line weight by selecting it from the predefined line weights available in this drop-down list.

Scale

The **Scale** edit box is used to specify the scale factor of the hatching lines. You can specify the required scale factor by entering its value in this edit box. You can also select the predefined scale factors by selecting them from the list displayed upon choosing the down arrow on the right of this dialog box.

Shift

The **Shift** edit box is used to offset the hatch pattern from its location through the specified distance. The hatch pattern is shifted to avoid confusion with the hatch pattern of the adjacent component. Generally, the shift value should lie between 1 and 5. You can view the effect of shifting the hatch pattern on the sheet when you enter a value in this edit box.

Color

The **Color** button is used to modify the color of the selected hatch pattern. When you choose this button, the **Color** dialog box is displayed for selecting the required color.

Double

The **Double** check box is used to double the hatching lines by drawing another set of lines normal to the original lines in the hatch pattern.

Figure 10-33 shows the drawing views of the Plummer Block assembly with different hatch patterns assigned to the components.

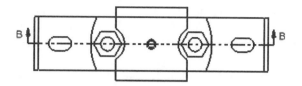

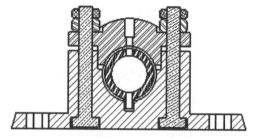

Figure 10-33 *Different hatch patterns of components in the section view*

SUPPRESSING COMPONENTS IN THE ASSEMBLY SECTION VIEWS

When you generate the section views of an assembly, all the components that are intersected by the cutting plane are sectioned, as shown in Figure 10-34.

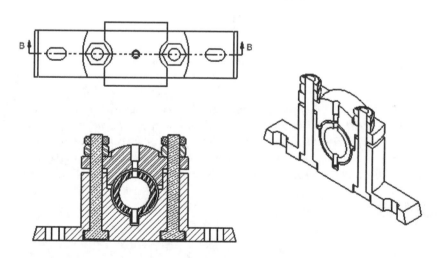

Figure 10-34 *All components sectioned by the cutting plane*

However, according to the drawing standards, the components such as nuts, bolts, lock nuts, and so on should not be sectioned while generating the section view. Therefore, you will have to suppress these components before or after generating the assembly section view.

To prevent the components from sectioning, click on the + sign located on the left of the section view; the name of the assembly will be displayed. Click on the + sign located on the left of the assembly name to display all the components of the assembly in the browser. Now, hold the CTRL key down and using the left mouse button, select all the components that you want to exclude from sectioning. Once all the components are selected, they will be displayed with a blue background in the browser. Right-click on any of the selected components to display the shortcut menu. You will notice that there will be a check mark on the left of the **Section** option in the shortcut menu. Choose this option again to clear this option. All the selected components will be excluded from sectioning and will not be displayed in the section, see Figure 10-35.

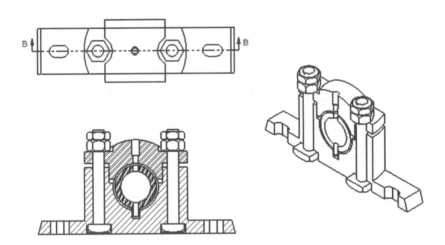

Figure 10-35 Drawing views with components suppressed from sectioning

Note
*If the file that you selected for generating the drawing views is not in the current folder, the **Autodesk Inventor 11** information box will be displayed. This box will inform you that the location of the selected file is not in the current project folder. It will also inform you that to make sure that the file is found the next time you open the assembly in which that file is referenced, add the location of the file in the project or move the file in the current project folder.*

TUTORIALS

Tutorial 1

In this tutorial, you will generate the top view, full sectioned front view, and isometric view of the sectioned front view of the model created in Tutorial 2 of Chapter 6. Use the JIS standard template file for generating the views. After generating the drawing views, save the sheet with the name *PersonalProject\c10\Tutorial1.idw*.   **(Expected time: 30 min)**

The following steps are required for generating the drawing views:

a. Copy the model whose drawing views you want to generate in the current folder.
b. Open a JIS template file and generate the base view using the **Base View** tool.
c. Generate the section view by sketching the section plane.
d. Use the **Projected View** tool to project the lines at an angle from the section view to generate the isometric view.

Copying the Model in the Current Folder

Before generating the drawing views of the model, it is important to copy the model whose drawing views are to be generated in the current folder. The reason is that when you open the drawing file the next time, the component will be searched in the current *c10* folder. Because the component is not available in the current folder, the **Resolve Link** dialog box will be displayed. This dialog box will prompt you to specify the location and path of the component file. Therefore, all the components or assemblies should be copied in the current folder or the drawing file should be saved in the folder in which the component and assembly file is located.

1. Create a folder with the name *c10* in the *PersonalProject* folder and copy the *Tutorial2.ipt* file from the *\PersonalProject\c06* folder to this folder.

Starting a New Drawing File

As mentioned in the tutorial description, you need to use the JIS standard template for generating the drawing views. Therefore, you will use the *JIS.idw* file for generating the drawing views.

1. Start Autodesk Inventor and then choose **New** from the **What To Do** area to display the **Default**, **English**, and **Metric** tabs.

2. Choose the **Metric** tab to display the metric templates. Select the **JIS.idw** option and then choose the **OK** button, see Figure 10-36.

The standard template file that follows the JIS standards for drafting will be opened on the screen, as shown in Figure 10-37.

Note
The color of the sheet is changed to white for the purpose of clarity. The sheet that will be displayed on your screen will be of a shade of yellow.

Generating the Base View

As mentioned earlier, the base view is the first view in the drawing sheet. Once you have generated the base view, you can use it as the parent view for generating the other views. The base view is generated using the **Create View** tool.

1. Choose the **Base View** button from the **Drawing Views Panel** panel bar; the **Drawing View** dialog box is displayed.

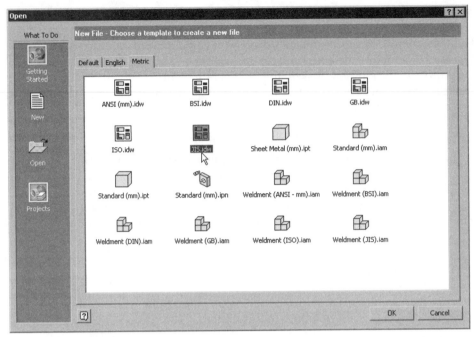

Figure 10-36 Opening the JIS standard drawing template from the **Open** dialog box

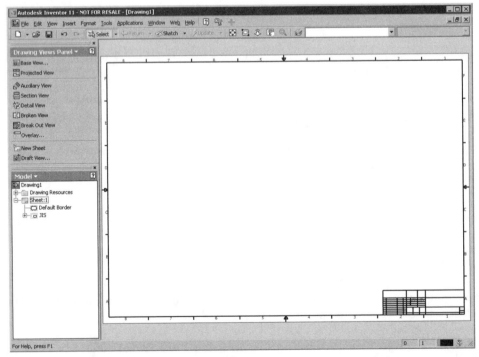

Figure 10-37 Screen display of the JIS standard drawing file

The preview of the drawing view is not displayed on the sheet because you have not selected any part file whose drawing view you want to generate. Therefore, you need to first select the part file whose drawing view will be generated.

2. Choose the **Explore Directories** button on the right of the **File** drop-down list in the **Component** tab; the **Open** dialog box is displayed.

3. Select the file *\PersonalProject\c10\Tutorial2.ipt* and then choose the **Open** button.

    You will notice that the preview of the drawing view using the default orientation is now attached to the cursor. The view moves as you move the cursor and will be generated at the point that you specify in the drawing window. In the default orientation, the cylindrical feature of the model is along the -Y axis of the sheet. You need to first reorient the model such that the cylindrical feature is along the -X axis.

4. Choose the **Change view orientation** button that is provided below the list box in the **Orientation** area.

    As soon as you choose this button, the **Custom View** window will be displayed. This window is used to reorient the model. Also, as mentioned earlier, the orientation that is achieved in this window will be selected as the orientation of the drawing view.

5. Choose the **Rotate at Angle** button from the **Inventor Standard** toolbar of the new window to display the **Incremental View Rotate** dialog box.

6. Enter **90** as the value of rotation of the view in the **Increment** edit box and then choose the **Clockwise** button. You will notice that as soon as you choose the **Clockwise** button, the view in the **Custom View** window will be rotated through an angle of 90-degree in the clockwise direction.

7. Choose **OK** to exit the **Incremental View Rotate** dialog box.

8. As the new orientation of the view is what you require, you can now exit the **Custom View** window. Choose the **Exit Custom View** button provided on the extreme left of the **Inventor Standard** toolbar.

    When you exit the **Custom View** window, the drawing sheet will be redisplayed. Also, the cylindrical feature of the model is shown along the -X axis in the preview of the drawing view.

9. Modify the value of the scale to **1.5** in the **Scale** edit box. Specify the placement point of the view close to the top right corner of the sheet, see Figure 10-38.

Note
*If the **Drawing View** dialog box restricts you from specifying the point on the sheet, you can move it on the left side by holding it from the blue area on top of it.*

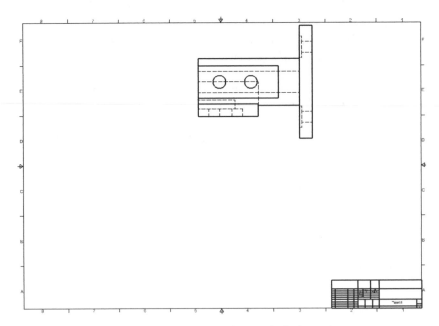

Figure 10-38 *Drawing sheet with the base view*

Generating the Section View

The section view can be generated using the **Section View** tool. However, if you generate the view using this tool, you will first need to select the drawing view that has to be sectioned and then define the section plane. But if you use the shortcut menu displayed upon right-clicking on the base view in the browser or in the drawing sheet, you do not need to select the drawing view since it is already selected. Therefore, you will generate the section view using the shortcut menu.

1. Move the cursor over the base view on the sheet to display the red dotted box, which is the bounding box of the view. When the bounding box is displayed, right-click and choose **Create View > Section** from the shortcut menu.

    The cursor changes to the sketch cursor and you are prompted to enter the endpoints of the section line.

2. Move the cursor close to the midpoint of the extreme left vertical edge of the base view. The cursor snaps to the midpoint and turns green in color.

3. After the cursor snaps to the midpoint of the edge, move the mouse to a small distance horizontally toward the left of the view. You will notice that an imaginary horizontal line is being drawn from the midpoint of the left vertical edge. This is due to the temporary tracking option.

4. Specify a point after moving the cursor to a small distance horizontally toward the left of the view. The specified point is selected as the first point of the section plane.

When you move the cursor toward the right, the symbol of the perpendicular constraint will be attached to the cursor. You can reconfirm that the line defining the section view is horizontal if this symbol is displayed. This symbol suggests that the line is normal to the extreme left vertical edge of the base view. This perpendicular constraint will be applied because you snapped to the midpoint of the left vertical edge of the base view.

5. Move the cursor horizontally toward the right of the view. You will notice that a horizontal line is being drawn. Move the cursor to a small distance on the right of the extreme right vertical edge of the base view. Make sure that the cursor does not snap to the midpoint of the right vertical edge and the line that is being drawn is horizontal.

6. Specify a point on the right of the right vertical edge of the base view. This point will be selected as the second point of the section plane.

7. Right-click and choose **Continue** from the shortcut menu. The **Section View** dialog box is displayed and the preview of the section view appears on the sheet. You are prompted to specify the location of the section view. Note that hatching lines will not be displayed in the preview of the section view.

8. Specify the location of the section view below the base view, see Figure 10-39. The **Section View** dialog box is automatically closed when you specify the location of the section view.

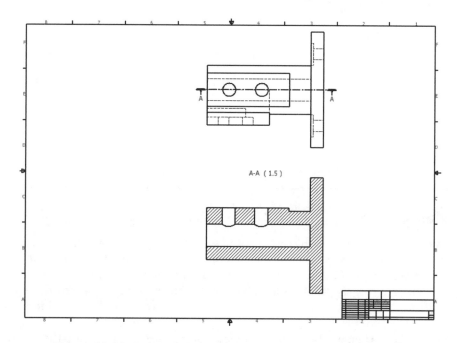

Figure 10-39 *Drawing sheet with the base view and the section view*

Generating the Isometric View of the Section View

The isometric view of the section view can also be generated using the shortcut menu.

1. Move the cursor over the section view and when the dotted rectangle is displayed, right-click to display the shortcut menu.

2. Choose **Create View > Projected** from the shortcut menu.

3. Move the cursor toward the left of the section view and then move it upwards until the preview of the isometric view appears. Now, specify the location of the view. Right-click and choose **Create** to create the drawing view. The sheet, after generating all the views, is shown in Figure 10-40.

4. Save the drawing file with the name *PersonalProject\c10\Tutorial1.idw* and close the file.

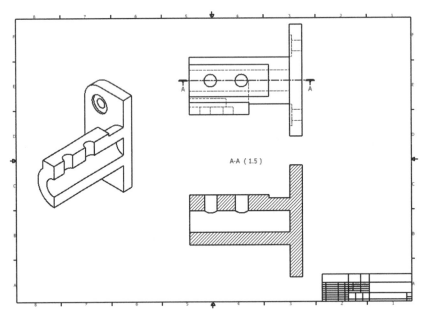

Figure 10-40 *Drawing sheet after generating all the views*

Tutorial 2

In this tutorial, you will generate the top view, full sectioned front view, and isometric view of the section view of Plummer Block assembly created in Tutorial 2 of Chapter 8. The Nuts and Bolts should not be sectioned in the section view. Also, all the sectioned components should have different hatch patterns. Use the JIS standard drawing file for generating the drawing views of assembly. **(Expected time: 45 min)**

As mentioned earlier, it is better to outline the procedure of completing the tutorial. The following steps outline the procedure for generating the drawing views:

a. Copy the *Plummer Block* folder from the *c08* folder to the *c10* folder.

b.   Generate the top view of the assembly.

c.   Show the contents of the base view and then suppress the Bolts, Nuts, and Lock Nuts so that they are not sectioned.

d.   Take the top view as the parent view to generate the full section front view.

e.   Modify the hatch of Casting and Cap.

f.   Generate the projected isometric view of the sectioned front view.

Copying the Plummer Block Folder

As mentioned earlier, you will have to copy the file that will be used to generate the drawing views in the current folder. Since in this tutorial the drawing views of an assembly will be generated, you will have to copy the folder in which the files of the assembly are stored. Also, note that the drawing file will be saved in the folder of the assembly and not in the *c10* folder.

1.   Copy the Plummer Block folder from *\PersonalProject\c08* folder to *\PersonalProject\c10* folder.

Starting a New Drawing File

1.   Choose the **New** button from the **Inventor Standard** toolbar to invoke the **Open** dialog box. Choose the **Metric** tab and then double-click on the **JIS.idw** option to open a JIS standard drawing file.

Generating the Top View of the Assembly

1.   Choose the **Base View** button from the **Drawing Views Panel** panel bar; the **Drawing View** dialog box is displayed.

2.   Choose the **Explore Directories** button on the right of the **File** drop-down list in the **Component** tab to display the **Open** dialog box.

3.   Browse to the *\PersonalProject\c10\Plummer Block* folder and then select the *Plummer Block.iam* file. Choose the **Open** button to select the assembly for generating the drawing views.

     You will return to the drawing sheet and the preview of the top view of the assembly appears on the sheet. You are also prompted to specify the location of the view.

4.   Modify the scale to **1.25** in the **Scale** edit box. Now, specify the location of the drawing view close to the upper right corner of the sheet, see Figure 10-41.

Suppressing the Components from Sectioning

As mentioned in the tutorial description, the Nuts, Bolts, and Lock Nuts should not be sectioned by the cutting plane. Therefore, you will have to suppress these components such that they are not sectioned in the section view.

1.   Click on the + sign located on the left of the view in the browser to display **Plummer Block.iam**. The assembly name will also have a + sign located on the left in the browser.

2.   Click on the + sign located on the left of **Plummer Block.iam** to display all components of

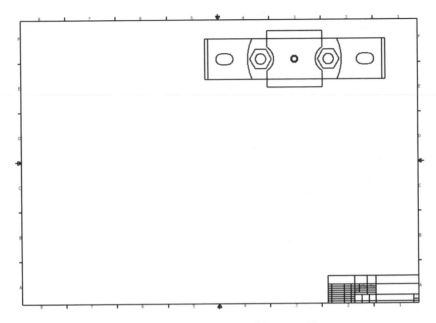

Figure 10-41 *Top view of the assembly*

the assembly. Press and hold the CTRL key down and select both the instances of Nut, Bolt, and Lock Nut using the left mouse button. The selected components will be displayed in blue background in the browser.

3. Right-click on any selected component in the browser to display the shortcut menu. In the shortcut menu, the **Section** option will be chosen and will have a check mark on the left of it.

4. Choose the **Section** option again to exclude the selected components from sectioning. After doing so, if you right-click on any selected component again, you will notice that the check mark on the left of the **Section** option is not displayed. This suggests that the selected components will not be sectioned.

5. Pick a point on the sheet to clear the selection of components.

Generating the Section View

Because you turned off the option of sectioning some of the components, they will not be sectioned when you generate the section view.

1. Move the cursor over the top view and right-click when the bounding box is displayed. Choose **Create View > Section** from the shortcut menu.

    The cursor turns into a + cursor and you are prompted to enter the endpoints of the section line.

2. Move the cursor close to the midpoint of the extreme left vertical edge of the top view. The cursor will snap to the midpoint and will turn green in color.

3. When the cursor snaps to the midpoint, move it horizontally toward the left to a small distance and specify a point there as the start point of the section plane.

4. Now, move the cursor horizontally toward the right.

5. Specify a point on the right of the extreme right vertical edge of the top view as the second point of the section plane. Note that the line should be horizontal and not inclined.

6. Right-click and choose **Continue** to display the **Section View** dialog box. The preview of section view is displayed and you are prompted to specify the location of the section view. Specify the location below the top view, as shown in Figure 10-42.

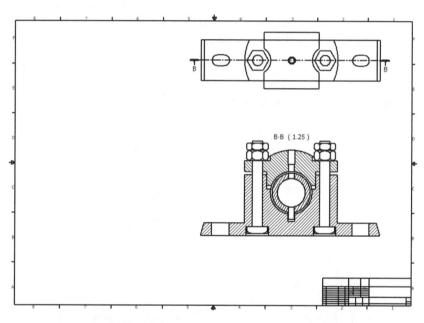

Figure 10-42 *Sheet with the top view and the sectioned front view*

Modifying the Hatch Patterns

The section view displays three components in section. These are Casting, Cap, and Brasses. One of these three components can retain the current hatching style and the style in the remaining two needs to be modified. In this tutorial, Brasses will retain the current style and you will modify the hatching in Casting and Cap.

1. Move the cursor over the hatching in Casting; the hatching lines turn red. Next, right-click to display the shortcut menu. Choose **Modify Hatch** from the shortcut menu to display the **Modify Hatch Pattern** dialog box.

2. Select **ISO02W100** from the **Pattern** drop-down list and then select the **Double** check box. Choose **OK** to exit this dialog box.

3. Move the cursor over the hatching in Cap and right-click when the hatching turns red in color. Choose **Modify Hatch** from the shortcut menu to display the **Modify Hatch Pattern** dialog box.

4. Select the **Double** check box and then choose **OK** to exit this dialog box. All three components that are sectioned will have different hatch patterns now.

Generating the Isometric View of the Section View

The third view that you need to generate is the isometric view of the section view. This view is also generated using the shortcut menu.

1. Move the cursor on the section view to display the bounding box. Note that the cursor should not be over any hatch pattern. When the bounding box is displayed, right-click to display the shortcut menu. Choose **Create View > Projected** from the shortcut menu.

2. Move the cursor toward the left of the section view in the horizontal direction and then move the cursor upward until the preview of the isometric view is displayed. When the isometric view is displayed, specify the point to define the location of this view.

3. Right-click and choose **Create** from the shortcut menu; the isometric view of the section view will be generated. The drawing sheet, with all the drawing views, is shown in Figure 10-43.

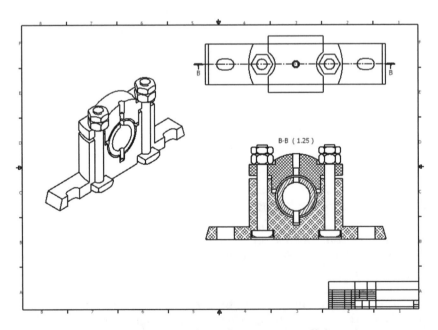

Figure 10-43 Drawing sheet after generating all three views

4. Save the drawing sheet with the name given below and then close the file.

\PersonalProject\c10\Plummer Block\Tutorial2.idw

The file is saved in the *Plummer Block* folder because the Plummer Block assembly file that is used to generate the drawing views is stored in it.

Self-Evaluation Test

Answer the following questions and then compare your answers with those given at the end of this chapter:

1. You cannot generate the drawing views of an assembly file. (T/F)

2. The **Drawing** module of Autodesk Inventor is not bidirectional in nature. (T/F)

3. You can add more sheets for generating the drawing views.

4. The display type of the view once set can be modified. (T/F)

5. While generating the base view, you can display the model dimensions by selecting the _____ check box in the **Display Options** tab of the **Drawing View** dialog box.

6. By default, the display type of the projected views will be the same as that of the _____.

7. The _____ views are generated by projecting the lines normal to a specified edge in the parent view.

8. In Autodesk Inventor, the cutting plane will be defined by _____ one or more than one line.

9. The part of the original view that is sectioned will be displayed with _____ in the section view.

10. When you delete any view, by default its _____ views are also deleted.

Review Questions

Answer the following questions:

1. You cannot prevent the dependent views from getting deleted if the parent view is deleted. (T/F)

2. The hatch pattern of a component in the section view can be modified. (T/F)

3. You can prevent some components from getting sectioned in the section view. (T/F)

4. You can suppress the option to move the dependent views along with the parent view, if you do not want to move them with the parent view. (T/F)

5. You can copy the selected drawing view in a new drawing file. (T/F)

6. Which one of the following tools is used to sketch a drawing view?

   (a) **Draft View**   (b) **Base View**
   (c) **New View**   (d) You cannot sketch a drawing view

7. Which one of the following windows is displayed using the **Drawing View** dialog box for modifying the orientation of the base view?

   (a) **Rotate View**   (b) **Orient View**
   (c) **Custom View**   (d) None

8. Which one of the following tools is used to generate a drawing view by removing a portion of it from between, keeping the ends of the component intact?

   (a) **Draft View**   (b) **Base View**
   (c) **Broken View**   (d) You cannot remove a portion of a drawing view

9. Which one of the following tools is used to display the details of a portion of an existing view by magnifying that portion and displaying it as a separate view?

   (a) **Detail View**   (b) **Base View**
   (c) **New View**   (d) None

10. Autodesk Inventor allows you to generate the isometric views using which one of the following tools?

   (a) **Draft View**   (b) **Base View**
   (c) **Projected View**   (d) None

Exercise

Exercise 1

Generate the top view, right half sectioned front view, isometric view, and overlay view on the isometric view of the section view of the Double Bearing assembly with a scale of 2.5:1. The overlay view should be created using the positional reference. This assembly was created in Tutorial 3 of Chapter 9. The Nut that is intersected by the cutting plane should not be sectioned and the components should have different hatch patterns, as shown in Figure 10-44. Use the JIS standards for generating the views. **(Expected time: 45 min)**

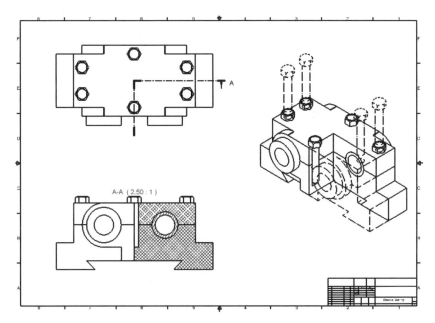

Figure 10-44 *Drawing views to be generated for Exercise 1*

Answers to Self-Evaluation Test

1. F, **2.** F, **3.** T, **4.** T, **5. Get Model Dimensions**, **6.** parent view, **7.** auxiliary, **8.** sketching, **9.** hatching lines, **10.** dependent.

Chapter 11

Working with Drawing Views-II

Learning Objectives

After completing this chapter, you will be able to:
- *Modify drawing standards.*
- *Insert additional sheets in the current drawing.*
- *Activate a drawing sheet.*
- *Add parametric and reference dimensions to the drawing views.*
- *Modify the current sheet style.*
- *Create dimension styles.*
- *Modify the dimension appearance using the shortcut menu.*
- *Create and edit the parts list for the assembly drawing views.*
- *Set the standard of the parts list.*
- *Add balloons to the assembly drawing views.*

MODIFYING DRAWING STANDARDS

As mentioned in Chapter 10, by default, the selected sheet will follow its standards in generating and dimensioning the drawing views. However, you can modify the standards of the current sheet. For example, you can open a JIS standard drawing file and assign the ANSI standards to it such that when you generate the drawing views and dimension them, the ANSI drafting standards are followed. You can modify the standards of the current sheet by choosing **Format > Styles Editor** from the menu bar. When you do so, the **Style and Standards Editor [Library - Read Only]** dialog box will be displayed. Select **All Style** from the **Filter Styles** drop-down list on the top right corner of this dialog box. All available standards will be displayed under the **Standard** heading in the left pane of this dialog box and the current sheet standard will be displayed in bold face, as shown in Figure 11-1.

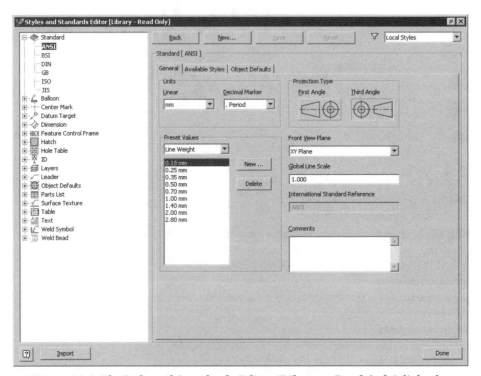

*Figure 11-1 The **Style and Standards Editor [Library - Read Only]** dialog box*

To assign a different standard to the current sheet, select the standard from the **Standard** heading. Right-click and choose the **Active** option from the shortcut menu. The selected standard will be assigned to the current sheet.

Using the options in the **Standard** area on the right pane of this dialog box, you can change the projection type from first angle to third angle, and vice-versa.

You can also select other headings from the left pane and expand them to display the standards for that heading. By selecting a standard, you can modify the options in it.

INSERTING ADDITIONAL SHEETS

Panel Bar:	Drawing Views Panel > New Sheet
Toolbar:	Drawing Views Panel > New Sheet

When you open a new drawing file, only one sheet is available. However, you can insert more drawing sheets for generating the drawing views using the **New Sheet** tool. You can also insert a new drawing sheet by right-clicking in the browser or on the drawing sheet and choosing **New Sheet** from the shortcut menu. When you invoke this tool, a new sheet is automatically added. Note that the new sheet added will be the active sheet. An active sheet is the one on which you can generate the drawing views. The active sheet will be displayed with a white background in the browser. The other drawing sheets will be displayed with a gray background in the browser.

ACTIVATING A DRAWING SHEET

You can activate any drawing sheet by right-clicking on it in the browser and choosing **Activate** from the shortcut menu, as shown in Figure 11-2. Note that if any sheet is already activated, this option will not be available when you right-click on a sheet in the browser. You can also make a sheet active by simply double-clicking on it in the browser.

Figure 11-2 *Activating a drawing sheet using the browser*

DISPLAYING DIMENSIONS IN THE DRAWING VIEWS

As mentioned in Chapter 10, you can display the model dimensions on the drawing views while generating them. Model dimensions are also called parametric dimensions and are the dimensions that were used to create the model in the part file. These are the dimensions that were applied on the sketches or in various dialog boxes while defining features. To display model dimensions while generating a drawing view, select the **All Model Dimensions** check box in the **Display** area of the **Options** tab of the **Drawing View** dialog box. Note that this option will not be available when you generate the drawing views of an assembly.

You can retrieve the model dimensions after placing the drawing views and select the dimension that you need to retain. In addition to the model dimensions, Autodesk Inventor also allows you to add reference dimensions to the drawing views. The reference dimensions are those that were not applied to the model in the **Part** module. These dimensions are used only for reference and not during the manufacturing of a part. The methods of retrieving the model dimensions and placing the reference dimensions are discussed next.

Retrieving Parametric Dimensions in the Drawing Views

Panel Bar: Drawing Annotation Panel > Retrieve Dimensions
Toolbar: Drawing Annotation Panel > Retrieve Dimensions

The **Retrieve Dimensions** tool is used to retrieve the model dimensions after placing the drawing view. When you invoke this tool, the **Retrieve Dimensions** dialog box will be displayed and you will be prompted to select a view, draft view, or a drawing sheet sketch. When you select a view, the options in this dialog box will be enabled, as shown in Figure 11-3. You can also select a drawing view and then right-click on it to display the shortcut menu. From the shortcut menu, choose **Retrieve Dimensions**.

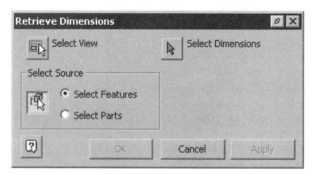

*Figure 11-3 The **Retrieve Dimensions** dialog box*

You can use this dialog box to select the parts or the features whose dimensions you want to retrieve. The options in this dialog box are discussed next.

Tip. *Before retrieving the dimensions, it is recommended that you first set the dimension style parameters by expanding the **Dimension** option in the left pane of the **Style and Standards Editor [Library - Read Only]** dialog box and then modifying the required dimension style. You may have to select the **All Styles** option from the **Filter Style** drop-down list on the top right corner of the dialog box to display all the styles. Before you exit this dialog box, choose the **Save** button to save the changes in the current style. Now, after invoking the **Retrieve Dimensions** dialog box, make the dimension style current by selecting it from the second drop-down list in the **Inventor Standard** toolbar.*

Select View

This button is chosen to select the view, in which you want to retrieve the dimensions. Note that when you invoke the **Retrieve Dimensions** tool using the panel bar or using the toolbar, the **Select View** button is chosen by default and you are prompted to select the view, in which you want to retrieve the dimensions. Also, after retrieving the required dimensions in the selected view, you can choose this button again to select another view to retrieve the dimensions.

Select Source Area

The options in the **Select Source** area are used to specify whether you want to retrieve the dimensions of a selected feature or of the entire part. Depending on the source using which you want to retrieve the dimensions, select the radio button. Next, select the part or the feature in the view; the dimensions of the selected part or feature will be retrieved in that view.

Select Dimensions

You will notice that even after retrieving the dimensions of a selected feature or part, the **OK** button in the **Retrieve Dimensions** dialog box is not available. This is because this command is not complete until you choose the **Select Dimensions** button and also select the dimensions that you want to retain. You can select the dimensions to be retained using a crossing or a window, or by holding the CTRL key down and selecting the dimensions.

After retrieving and selecting the dimensions, choose the **Apply** button to select another view to retrieve the dimensions. In this case, the retrieved dimensions will turn gray in color and the **Select View** button will be chosen to let you select another view for retrieving the dimensions. You can choose the **OK** button, if you do not want to select any other view to retrieve the dimensions.

Adding Reference Dimensions

Panel Bar:	Drawing Annotation Panel > General Dimension
Toolbar:	Drawing Annotation Panel > General Dimension

 Autodesk Inventor allows you to add reference dimensions to the drawing view using the **General Dimension** tool. This tool is similar to the **General Dimension** tool in the **Part** module. The method of adding dimensions is also similar in both the tools.

MODIFYING THE MODEL DIMENSIONS

Autodesk Inventor allows you to modify the model dimensions displayed in the drawing view. However, as mentioned earlier, all modules of Autodesk Inventor are bidirectionally associative. This nature of Autodesk Inventor will ensure that if you modify any dimension value in the **Drawing** module, the changes will be reflected in the model in the **Part** module. Therefore, you will have to be very careful while modifying the model dimensions. To modify the model dimension, right-click on it and choose **Edit Model Dimension** from the shortcut menu, see Figure 11-4. Based on the dimension selected to be edited, the dialog box or the **Edit Dimension** toolbar will be displayed with the current dimension value. You can modify the dimension value in the dialog box or the toolbar and then exit the dialog box or toolbar. You will notice that the dimension is modified and it is reflected in the feature in the drawing views.

Figure 11-4 Editing model dimensions

EDITING DRAWING SHEETS

Autodesk Inventor allows you to edit the selected drawing sheet. You can modify the size of the sheet, relocate the title block, modify the orientation of the drawing sheet, and so on. To edit the drawing sheet, right-click on its name in the browser and choose **Edit Sheet** from the shortcut menu. When you choose this option, the **Edit Sheet** dialog box is displayed, as shown in Figure 11-5. The options in this dialog box are discussed next.

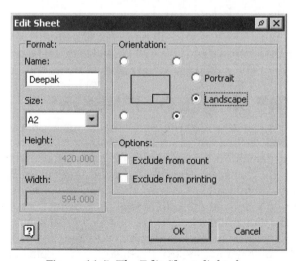

Figure 11-5 The **Edit Sheet** dialog box

Format Area

The options in the **Format** area are used to define the name and size of the drawing sheet. These options are discussed next.

Name

The **Name** edit box is used to enter the name of the drawing sheet. The name you enter in this edit box will be displayed in the browser.

Size

The **Size** drop-down list is used to define the size of the drawing sheet. You can select predefined drawing sheet sizes from this drop-down list. To specify a user-defined size, select **Custom Size (inches)** or **Custom Size (mm)** from this drop-down list. Using these options, you can specify a user-defined size in inches or in millimeter. The height and width of the user-defined size will be defined in the **Height** and **Width** edit boxes. These edit boxes will be available below the **Size** drop-down list when you select the option to specify the user-defined size.

Orientation Area

The options in the **Orientation** area are used to specify the orientation of the sheet and the location of the title block. This area displays a sheet and has four radio buttons close to the four corners of the sheet. These radio buttons define the location of the title block in the sheet. By default, the radio button provided close to the lower right corner of the sheet is selected. This forces the title block to be placed on the lower right corner of the sheet. You can place the title block on any of the four corners by selecting their respective radio buttons. You can also define whether the orientation of the drawing sheet should be portrait or landscape by selecting the **Portrait** or **Landscape** radio button.

Options Area

The options in the **Options** area are discussed next.

Exclude from count

By default, when you open a drawing file, one sheet is available. This sheet is assigned number 1. If you add more sheets, they will be numbered 2, 3, and so on. The **Exclude from count** check box is selected, if you do not want the current sheet to be included in this count. If you select this check box, the current sheet will not be assigned any number and the sheet numbers of the other sheets will be adjusted accordingly.

Exclude from printing

The **Exclude from printing** check box is selected to exclude the current sheet from printing. If this check box is selected, the current sheet will not be considered while printing.

CREATING DIMENSION STYLES

Dimension styles are used to control the appearance and positioning of the parameters related to the dimensions. Autodesk Inventor provides a number of dimension styles that you can use for displaying the dimensions. However, if the predefined dimension style does not meet your requirements, you can define a new dimension style and set its options as per your requirement. To create a new dimension style, choose **Format > Styles Editor** from the menu bar; the **Style and Standards Editor [Library - Read Only]** dialog box will be displayed. Expand the **Dimension** option from the left pane and then select the dimension style you want to use. The options related to the selected dimension style are displayed in the right pane of the dialog box, as shown in Figure 11-6.

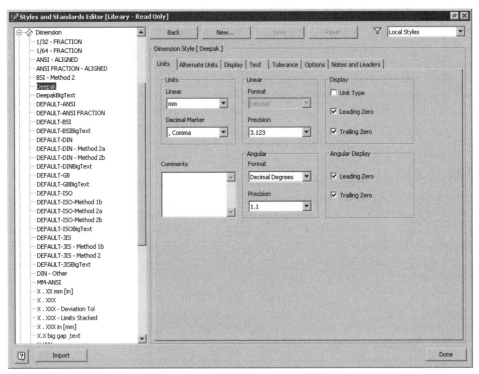

*Figure 11-6 The **Style and Standards Editor [Library - Read Only]** dialog box*

As evident in the figure, the right pane of the dialog box provides various tabs for setting the options related to the dimension style. You can also create a new dimension style using this dialog box. To create a new dimension style, choose the **New** button and then enter the name of the dimension style in the **New Style Name** dialog box. Now make the necessary changes in the parameters related to the dimensions in the tabs of the **Style and Standards Editor [Library - Read Only]** dialog box. After making all the necessary changes, choose the **Save** button. The new drawing views will be dimensioned using this dimension style.

APPLYING DIMENSION STYLES

To apply a dimension style, invoke the **Retrieve Dimension** dialog box and then select the required dimension style from the second drop-down list in the **Inventor Standard** toolbar. The dimensions that you place will use the selected dimension style. If any existing drawing view is already dimensioned, the dimensions in that drawing view will not be modified based on the new dimension style. To modify the dimension style of the existing dimensions, select them and change the dimension style from the second drop-down list in the **Inventor Standard** toolbar.

MODIFYING THE DIMENSION APPEARANCE USING THE SHORTCUT MENU

You can also modify the dimension appearance using the shortcut menu that is displayed when you right-click on the dimension. Depending on the type of dimension selected, the options in this shortcut menu are displayed. For example, Figure 11-7 shows a shortcut menu that will be displayed when you right-click on a linear dimension.

You can use this menu to control the display of extension lines, dimension text, leaders, arrowheads, and so on. You can also hide the dimension value using this shortcut menu. Note that if you choose the option to hide the dimension value, it will not be displayed in the drawing view. Instead, **<TEXT>** will appear in place of the dimension value. You can show the dimension value again using the shortcut menu that is displayed when you right-click on the dimension. You can also choose an option to edit the existing dimension style used to generate dimensions or create a new dimension style.

Figure 11-7 *Shortcut menu to modify the dimension appearance*

ADDING THE PARTS LIST

| Panel Bar: | Drawing Annotation Panel > Parts List |
| Toolbar: | Drawing Annotation Panel > Parts List |

The parts list is a table that provides the information related to the number of components in an assembly, their names, their quantity, and other related information. It is extremely useful in providing the information related to the components of an assembly in the drawing views. When you invoke this tool, the **Parts List** dialog box will be displayed, as shown in Figure 11-8. The options in this dialog box are discussed next.

Source Area

This area provides the options for selecting the source for generating the parts list. These options are discussed next.

Select View

This button is chosen by default in the **Parts List** dialog box and is used to select an existing drawing view as the source for generating the parts list.

Browse for file

This button is chosen to select a file that will be used as a source to generate the parts list. When you choose this button, the **Open** dialog box that you can use to select the file for generating the parts list will be displayed. The name and location of the selected file is displayed in the drop-down list on the left of this button.

*Figure 11-8 The **Parts List** dialog box*

BOM Settings and Properties Area

The options in the area are used to specify the Bill of Material related settings and properties. These options are discussed next.

BOM View

This drop-down list is used to specify the Bill of Material view to be used for generating the parts list. You can select the **Structured** or the **Parts Only** option. If the **Structured** option is selected, the subassemblies in the main assembly will be displayed as a single item in the parts list and the individual components of the subassemblies will not be listed. However, if you select the **Parts Only** option, the components of the subassemblies will also be displayed.

Note
*If the **Parts Only** option is not turned on in the assembly document, an error message will be displayed stating that this option is not enabled. You can enable this option in the assembly document using this error message dialog box.*

Level/Numbering

The **Level** drop-down list is available when you select the **Structured** option from the **BOM View** drop-down list. This drop-down list is used to specify whether only the first level components will be displayed or all level components will be displayed in the BOM. The **Numbering** drop-down list is available when you select the **Parts Only** option from the **BOM View** drop-down list. You can specify whether the numbering for the components will be numeric or alpha.

Min. Digits

This drop-down list is used to set the minimum digits for numbering the components in the BOM. The range varies from 1 to 6.

Table Wrapping Area

The options in the **Table Wrapping** area are used to specify the format of the parts list. These options are generally used for the assemblies that have a large number of components. The parts list of such an assembly get very lengthy. You can split it into two or three sections to reduce its length. However, in such parts lists, the width increases as the columns are increased by two or three times. The options in this area are discussed next.

Direction to Wrap Table

The **Left** and **Right** radio buttons in this area are used to specify the side of the parts list to which the additional section will be added if the number of sections are more than 1.

Enable Automatic Wrap

This check box is used to set the option for enabling automatic wrapping. When you select this check box, the **Maximum Rows** or the **Number of Sections** radio buttons are enabled. The **Maximum Rows** radio button is selected to specify the maximum number of rows after which the parts list will be wrapped to the specified side. You can specify the number of rows in the edit box on the right of this radio button. The **Number of Sections** edit box is used to specify the number of sections, in which the parts list will be split.

After setting the options in the **Part List** dialog box, choose the **OK** button; the dialog box will be closed and you will return to the drawing sheet. You will notice that the parts list is attached to the cursor. Place the parts list at the desired point. Figure 11-9 shows the drawing views of the Double Bearing assembly with the parts list.

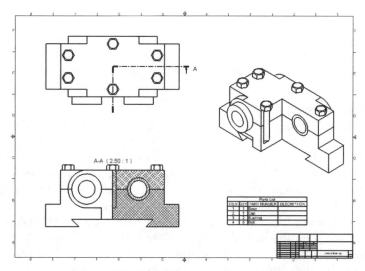

Figure 11-9 *Drawing views of an assembly with the parts list*

EDITING THE PARTS LIST

The default parts list that is placed has only the selected columns. To add more columns to the parts list or delete some of the columns, you will have to edit it. You can edit the parts list by double-clicking or by right-clicking on it and choosing **Edit Parts List** from the shortcut menu. The **Edit Parts List** dialog box will be displayed, as shown in Figure 11-10.

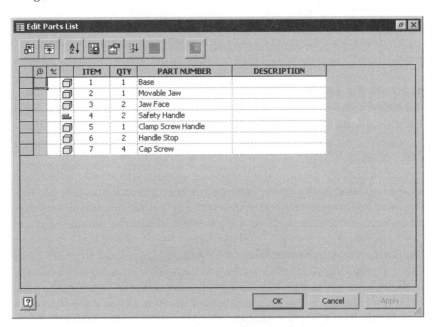

Figure 11-10 The Edit Parts List dialog box

The default columns and their values are displayed in this dialog box. You will notice that some of the values are displayed in red color and some in black color. To modify the value of any field, click on it and enter the new value. However, note that the fields displayed in red color cannot be modified. The other options in this dialog box are discussed next.

Column Chooser

The **Column Chooser** button is used to select the columns that will be displayed in the parts list. By default, it displays some preselected columns. To display more columns in the parts list, choose this button. The **Parts List Column Chooser** dialog box will be displayed, as shown in Figure 11-11. This dialog box has two main areas: **Available Properties** and **Selected Properties**. The **Selected Properties** area displays all the columns that are selected and displayed in the parts list. The **Available Properties** area displays all the columns that can be selected. Select the column you want to display in the parts list from the **Available Properties** area and then choose the **Add** button. The selected column will be displayed in the **Selected Properties** area. Similarly, if you want to remove any column from the **Selected Properties** area, select the column and choose the **Remove** button.

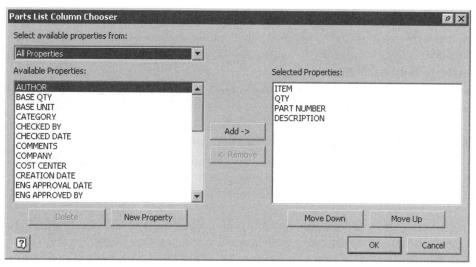

*Figure 11-11 The **Parts List Column Chooser** dialog box*

Group Settings

 The **Group Settings** button is chosen to invoke the **Group Settings** dialog box. You can use this dialog box to group similar items in the parts list.

Sort

 The **Sort** button is chosen to sort the items in the parts list. When you choose this button, the **Sort Parts List** dialog box is displayed. Using this dialog box, you can sort the items in the parts list.

Export

 The **Export** button is chosen to export the parts list to an external file. When you choose this button, the **Export Parts List** dialog box is displayed. You can use this dialog box to specify the file type of the new file and its location.

Table Layout

 The **Table Layout** button is chosen to define the heading of the parts list and its location in the table. When you choose this button, the **Parts List Table Layout** dialog box will be displayed. The name of the parts list can be specified in the **Parts List Title** edit box and the location can be specified using the **Heading Placement** drop-down list. If you select the **No Heading** option, the heading of the parts list will not be displayed. This dialog box is also used to define the line spacing of the parts list.

Renumber Items

The **Renumber Items** button is chosen to renumber the items in the parts list. If the parts list has some items that are improperly numbered, they will be numbered according to their original numbering.

Save Item Overrides to BOM

This button is chosen to save the changes that you make in the parts list to the assembly BOM.

Member Selection

This button is chosen to display the **Member Selection** dialog box that allows you to select the members to be included in the parts list.

Adding/Removing Custom Parts

To add a custom part row, move the cursor over the gray color button on the extreme left. The cursor will be replaced by a small arrow pointing in the direction of the row. Now, right-click and choose **Insert Custom Part** from the shortcut menu; a new custom part row will be added.

To delete a custom part row, move the cursor over the gray color button on the extreme left of the custom row. The cursor will be replaced by a small arrow pointing in the direction of the row. Now, press the left mouse button. The custom row will be selected and highlighted in black color. Right-click on the selected row and choose **Remove Custom Part**. The custom part row will be removed.

Shortcut Menu Options

In addition to the buttons in the **Edit Parts List** dialog box, you can also use the shortcut menu that is displayed when you right-click on a column heading to modify the parts list. This shortcut menu is shown in Figure 11-12. Most of the options in this shortcut menu are similar to those in the **Edit Parts List** dialog box. The remaining options are discussed next.

Figure 11-12 Shortcut menu displayed upon right-clicking on a column heading

Format Column

This option is used to modify the format of the columns in the parts list. When you choose this option, the **Format Column** dialog box will be displayed. You can use the **Column Format** tab of this dialog box to modify the justification and heading of the selected column. You can also modify the units formatting using this tab. You can use the **Substitution** tab of the **Format Column** dialog box to substitute the value of a selected field with that of the other selected field.

Column Width

This option is used to modify the width of the column. When you choose this option, the **Column Width** dialog box will be displayed. This dialog box will be used to modify the width of the columns in the parts list.

SETTING THE STANDARD FOR THE PARTS LIST

You can set the standard for the parts list using the **Style and Standards Editor [Library - Read Only]** dialog box. This dialog box is displayed when you choose **Format > Styles Editor** from the menu bar. After invoking this dialog box, expand the **Parts List** option and then select the required parts list standard. If you have an existing parts list in the drawing sheet, you can right-click on it and choose **Edit Parts List Style** from the shortcut menu to invoke this dialog box. The options related to the selected parts list standard will be displayed in the right pane, as shown in Figure 11-13. Using these options, you can set the parameters related to the parts list. After you have made the necessary modifications in the parts list standards, choose the **Save** button. You will notice that the changes are reflected in the parts list on the sheet.

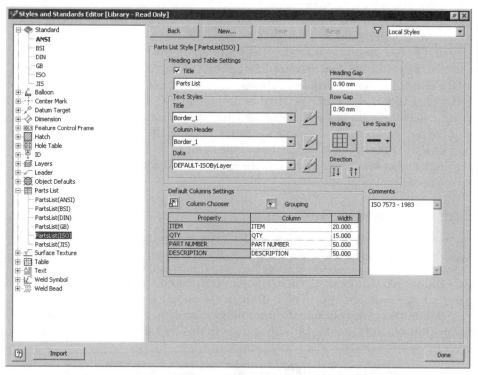

*Figure 11-13 The **Style and Standards Editor [Library - Read Only]** dialog box with parts list options*

ADDING BALLOONS TO THE ASSEMBLY DRAWING VIEWS

Whenever you add the parts list to assembly drawing views, all components in the assembly are listed in the parts list in a tabular form. You will notice that each component in the parts list is assigned a unique number. As a result, if an assembly has ten components, all of them will be listed in the parts list with a different serial number assigned to them. However, in the drawing views, there is no reference about these components. Therefore, if you are not familiar with the names of the components, it is difficult to recognize them in the drawing view. To avoid this confusion, Autodesk Inventor allows you to add a callout, called balloons, to the components in the drawing view. These callouts are based on the serial number of the components in the parts list. If the component is assigned serial number 1 in the parts list, the callout will also show number 1. Balloons make it convenient to relate the components in the parts list to those in the drawing view. You can manually add balloons to the selected components or automatically add them to all components. The methods of adding balloons are discussed next.

Adding Balloons to the Selected Components

Panel Bar:	Drawing Annotation Panel > Balloon
Toolbar:	Drawing Annotation Panel > Balloon

You can add balloons to the selected components in the drawing view using the **Balloon** tool. After invoking this tool, move the cursor over one of the edges of the component to which you want to add the balloon; the component will be highlighted in red. Also, a symbol of the coincident constraint will be displayed on the right of the cursor. This symbol suggests that the coincident constraint will be applied to the start point of the balloon and the edge of the selected component. Select the edge and move the cursor away from the component; one end of the balloon will be attached to the component and the other end will be attached to the cursor. Specify the point for placing the balloon and right-click to display the shortcut menu. From the shortcut menu, choose **Continue** to place the balloon. You will notice that a callout is added to the selected component and the name of the callout is the same as that in the parts list. Remember that you can add as many number of balloons as you want by selecting the edges of components.

Adding Automatic Balloons

Panel Bar:	Drawing Annotation Panel > Balloon > Auto Balloon
Toolbar:	Drawing Annotation Panel > Balloon > Auto Balloon

You can also automatically add balloons to all the components in the selected drawing view in a single attempt. This is done by choosing the down arrow on the right of the **Balloon** tool and choosing the **Auto Balloon** tool; the **Auto Balloon** dialog box will be displayed, as shown in Figure 11-14. The options in this dialog box are discussed next.

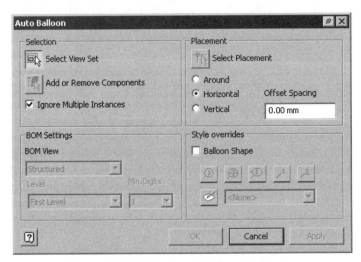

Figure 11-14 The **Auto Balloon** dialog box

Selection Area

This area provides the options to select the view and the components to which the balloons will be added. When you invoke the **Auto Balloon** dialog box, the **Select View Set** button in this area will be chosen automatically and you will be prompted to select the view to add balloons. As soon as you select the view, the **Add / Remove Components** button will be chosen and you will be prompted to select the components for ballooning. You can use window or crossing selection methods to select multiple components. The **Ignore Multiple Instances** check box is selected by default because of which the multiple instances of the same component are not ballooned.

Placement Area

The options in the **Placement** area are automatically enabled as soon as you select the components to be ballooned. Using the options in this area, you can specify whether the balloons should be placed along a horizontal or vertical line, or around the view. The distance between the balloons can be set using the **Offset Spacing** spinner in this area. After selecting the option to place the balloon, choose the **Select Placement** button in this area; the preview of the balloons will be displayed and you will be prompted to select the balloon placement. If you are not satisfied with the orientations of the balloons after placing them, you can select any other option from the **Auto Balloon** dialog box. You can also choose the **Select Placement** button and place the balloons again.

BOM Settings Area

The options in this area are similar to those mentioned in the **Parts List** dialog box.

Style overrides Area

The options in this area are used to override the default balloon styles. To override the style, select the **Balloon Shape** check box and then select the required balloon shape. If the current drawing document has some sketch symbols, you can override them also by choosing the **User-Defined Symbol** button. When you choose this button, the drop-down list in this area is available and you can select the required sketch symbol.

After placing the balloons, choose **OK** from the **Auto Balloon** dialog box. Figure 11-15 shows a drawing sheet with the parts list and balloons added to the components in the drawing view.

Tip. *You can modify the styles of balloons using the **Style and Standards Editor [Library - Read Only]** dialog box. Invoke this dialog box and then expand the **Balloon** options. Now, select the desired balloon style and modify its parameter from the **Balloon Style** area in the right pane of the dialog box. Save the style before you exit.*

*The balloons use the leader styles for arrowheads and note text style for the text. Therefore, to modify these parameters, you need to modify the respective substyles from the **Sub-styles** area in the right pane of the **Style and Standards Editor [Library - Read Only]** dialog box when the balloon options are displayed. After setting the substyles, you can choose the **Back** button to restore the balloon options.*

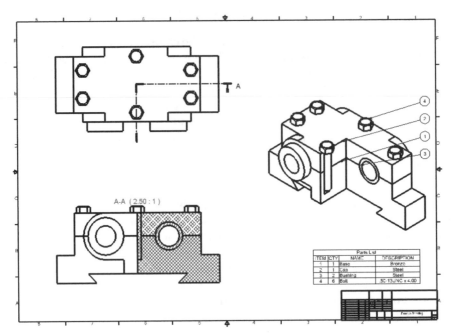

Figure 11-15 *Drawing sheet with parts list and balloons*

ADDING TEXT TO THE DRAWING SHEET

Autodesk Inventor allows you to add user-defined text to the drawing sheet. Depending upon your requirement, you can add multiline text with or without a leader. The methods of adding both types of text are discussed next.

Adding Multiline Text without Leader

Panel Bar:	Drawing Annotation Panel > Text
Toolbar:	Drawing Annotation Panel > Text

You can add multiline text without a leader using the **Text** tool. On invoking this tool, you will be prompted to specify the location of the text or define a rectangle by dragging the mouse to define the bounding box of the text. After you specify the location of the text or the bounding box of the text, the **Format Text** dialog box will be displayed, as shown in Figure 11-16. You can enter the text in the text box of this dialog box. You can also modify the format, style, and alignment of the text using this dialog box.

After writing the text in the text box, choose the **OK** button. The text will be placed at the specified location. Note that after placing the text, you will again be prompted to define the location of the text or define a box using two points. This means that you can define the text at as many locations as you want in a single attempt. You can exit this tool by pressing the ESC key.

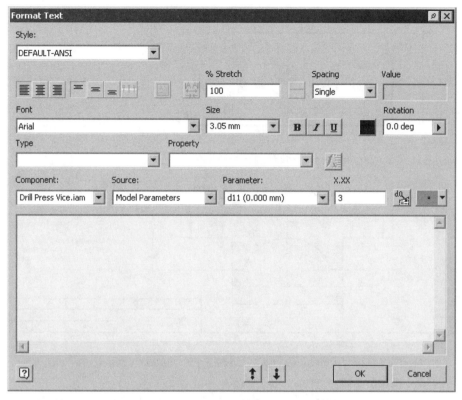

*Figure 11-16 The **Format Text** dialog box*

Adding Multiline Text with Leader

Panel Bar:	Drawing Annotation Panel > Leader Text
Toolbar:	Drawing Annotation Panel > Leader Text

The text with a leader is generally added to the entities to which you want to point and add some information. You can add the text with a leader using the **Leader Text** tool. After invoking this tool, select the entity to which you want to add the leader text. As you move the cursor close to an entity, it will be highlighted in red. Also, the symbol of the coincident constraint will be attached to the cursor. This symbol suggests that the coincident constraint will be added to the selected entity and the arrowhead of the leader. After selecting the entity, move the cursor away and define the second vertex of the leader. You can define as many vertices as you want in the leader line. Once you have defined the leader line, right-click to display the shortcut menu and choose **Continue**; the **Format Text** dialog box will be displayed. This dialog box is similar to the one that is displayed when you invoke the **Text** tool. You can enter the text in this dialog box and then choose **OK**. The leader text will be added to the drawing sheet. Figure 11-17 shows a drawing sheet after adding text with and without a leader.

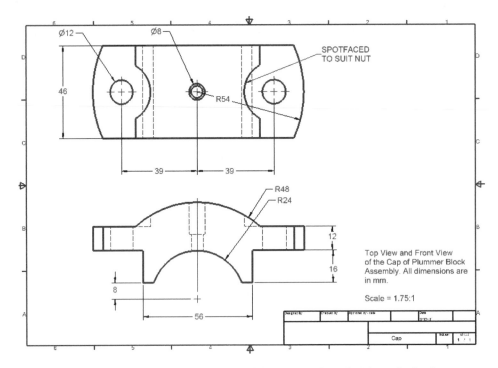

Figure 11-17 Drawing sheet after adding text with and without the leader

 Tip. *You can edit the text by double-clicking on it. When you double-click on a text, the **Format Text** dialog box is displayed with the current text.*

*To add a center mark to a circle, choose the **Center Mark** tool from the **Drawing Annotation** toolbar or panel bar and select the circle.*

TUTORIALS

Tutorial 1

In this tutorial, you will generate the top view, front view, right-side view, and isometric view of the model created in Exercise 1 of Chapter 4. You will use the ANSI mm standard drawing sheet of A2 size. The drawing views should be dimensioned, as shown in Figure 11-18. Create a new dimension style with the name **Custom** for dimensioning the drawing view. The dimension style should have the following specifications:

Dimension Units: mm
Linear Precision: 0
Text Size: 5 mm
Terminator Length: 5 mm
Terminator Width: 2 mm   **(Expected time: 30 min)**

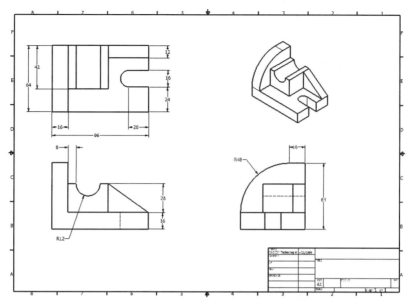

Figure 11-18 *Dimensioned drawing views to be generated for Tutorial 1*

Before you start generating the drawing views, it is recommended that you outline the steps for completing this tutorial. The following steps will be followed to complete this tutorial:

a. Copy the model of Exercise 1 of Chapter 4 in the current folder and then start a new ANSI mm standard drawing file.
b. Create a new dimension style with the name **Custom** and modify the parameters as mentioned in the tutorial description.
c. Generate the required drawing views.
d. Retrieve the model dimensions in the drawing views. Drag the dimensions so that they are displayed as desired.

Copying the Model in the Current Folder

As mentioned in the previous chapter, you should copy the model whose drawing views you are generating in the current folder.

1. Create a folder with the name *c11* inside the folder *PersonalProject*.

2. Copy the file *Exercise1.ipt* from the folder *PersonalProject\c04* to the current folder.

Starting a New Drawing File

As mentioned in the tutorial description, you need to start a new ANSI mm standard drawing sheet for generating the drawing views.

1. Choose the **New** button to invoke the **Open** dialog box. Choose the **Metric** tab and double-click on the **ANSI (mm).idw** option; the default ANSI mm standard drawing sheet is displayed on the screen.

2. Right-click on **Sheet:1** in the browser and choose **Edit Sheet** from the shortcut menu to invoke the **Edit Sheet** dialog box.

3. Select **A2** from the **Size** drop-down list and then close the **Edit Sheet** dialog box.

Creating the Dimension Style

As mentioned in the tutorial description, you need to create a new dimension style with the defined settings. The new dimension style will be created taking the ANSI mm dimension style as the base style.

1. Choose **Format > Styles Editor** from the menu bar to invoke the **Style and Standards Editor [Library - Read Only]** dialog box.

2. Select **Local Styles** from the **Filter Styles** drop-down list on the upper right corner of the dialog box, if it is not already selected.

3. Click on the plus sign (+) located on the left of **Dimension** in the left pane of the dialog box to display the available local dimension styles.

4. Select **Default - mm (ANSI)** from the list and then choose the **New** button. Enter the name of the new dimension style as **Custom** in the **New Style Name** dialog box. Choose **OK** to exit this dialog box

    A new dimension style is created with the name **Custom** and is selected. The parameters related to this dimension style are displayed in various tabs in the **Dimension Style [Custom]** area in the right pane of this dialog box.

5. Select **0** from the **Precision** drop-down list in the **Linear** area of the **Units** tab. The precision for a linear dimension will be forced to 0. This means that no digit will be displayed after decimal in the dimensions.

6. Choose the **Text** tab to display the text options. Choose the **Vertical Dimensions** flyout in the **Orientation** area and choose the first button in this flyout. This will force the text of the vertical dimension to be placed horizontally.

7. Similarly, choose the **Aligned Dimensions** flyout and then choose the first button. The text of the aligned dimensions will also be placed horizontally.

8. Choose the **Save** button to save these changes in the dimension style.

9. Now, choose the **Edit Text Style** button provided on the right of the **Primary Text Style** drop-down list to display the text parameters.

10. Enter **5** as the value in the **Text Height** edit box in the **Character Formatting** area.

11. Choose the **Save** button and then the **Back** button to redisplay the dimension style parameters.

12. Choose the **Display** tab. In the **Terminator** area, enter **5** as the size in the **Size (X)** edit box and enter **2** as the value in the **Height (Y)** edit box. Choose **Save** to save the changes in the dimension style and then choose **Done** to exit the dialog box.

Generating the Drawing Views

In this tutorial, you need to generate four drawing views. The base view is the top view and the remaining views are projected views. The front view is generated by using the top view as the parent view, and the right-side view and the isometric view are generated by using the front view as the parent view. Note that while generating the drawing views, the dimensions will not be displayed. They will be displayed after generating the drawing views.

1. Using the **Base View** tool, generate the top view of the model in Exercise 1 of Chapter 4. The scale of the view is 1.5. Place the view close to the top left corner of the drawing sheet. This will place the top view of the model.

2. Taking the top view as the parent view, generate the front view. Place the view below the top view. Similarly, taking the front view as the parent view, generate the right-side view and the isometric view. Modify the scale of the isometric view to 1, see Figure 11-19.

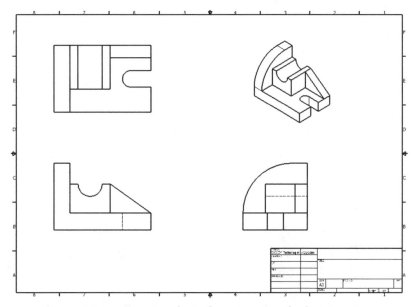

Figure 11-19 *Drawing sheet after generating the drawing views*

Retrieving the Model Dimensions

As mentioned earlier, the model dimensions are those that were used while creating the model.

1. Move the cursor over the top view and right-click when the dotted rectangle is displayed; the shortcut menu will be displayed.

2. Choose **Retrieve Dimensions**; the **Retrieve Dimensions** dialog box is displayed.

3. Select the **Custom** option from the second drop-down list in the **Inventor Standard** toolbar to apply it to the dimensions that will be retrieved.

4. Select the **Select Parts** radio button from the **Select Source** area and then select the part in the top view; the dimensions are displayed.

5. Choose the **Select Dimensions** button and then drag a crossing around the dimensions for selecting them to be retained. Next, choose the **Apply** button. The selected dimensions in the top will be retrieved and the **Select View** button will be automatically chosen in the **Retrieve Dimensions** dialog box.

6. Select the front view, and then select the part in the front view. The dimensions in the front view are retrieved. Choose the **Select Dimensions** button and then drag a crossing around the dimensions to be retained.

7. Similarly, retrieve the dimensions in the right-side view. Exit the **Retrieve Dimensions** dialog box.

8. Use the **General Dimensions** tool to add the missing dimensions.

    You will notice that the dimensions that are displayed on these drawing views are staggered and are not aligned. You will have to align these dimensions by dragging them.

9. One by one select the dimensions and drag them to place them neatly in the drawing views. The sheet, after aligning the dimensions, is shown in Figure 11-20.

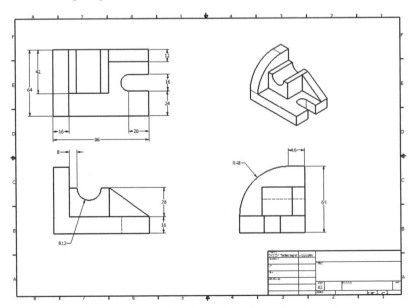

Figure 11-20 Drawing sheet after adding the dimensions

10. Save the file with the name *\PersonalProject\c11\Tutorial1.idw* and then close the file.

Tutorial 2

In this tutorial, you will open the drawing views of the Double Bearing assembly generated in Exercise 1 of Chapter 10. After opening the drawing views, you will add the parts list and balloons to the components. The balloons should be added in the isometric view of the sectioned front view. The parts list should appear, as shown in Figure 11-21.   **(Expected time: 45 min)**

Parts List			
ITEM	QTY	NAME	DESCRIPTION
1	1	Base	Bronze
2	1	Cap	Steel
3	2	Bushing	Steel
4	6	Bolt	.50-13UNC X 4.00

Figure 11-21 Parts list for Tutorial 2

The following steps are required to complete this tutorial:

a.   Copy the *Double Bearing* folder from the *\PersonalProject\c10* folder to the current folder.
b.   Open the *Exercise1.idw* file from this folder.
c.   Place the default parts list by using the **Parts List** tool. Use the isometric view of the sectioned front view for placing the parts list.
d.   Modify the parts list such that it resembles the one shown in Figure 11-21.
e.   Use the **Balloon** tool to add balloons to the components in the isometric view.

Copying the Double Bearing Folder in the Current Folder

1.   Copy the *Double Bearing* folder from the *\PersonalProject\c10* folder to the current folder.

2.   Open the file *\PersonalProject\c11\Double Bearing\Exercise1.idw*.

The drawing file is opened with the top view, sectioned front view, and isometric view that were generated in Exercise 1 of Chapter 10.

Placing the Parts List

As mentioned earlier, the parts list is placed using the **Parts List** tool. However, when you place the parts list, the data will be listed in it using the default parameters. For example, the fields under the **DESCRIPTION** column will not display any data. You need to modify the parts list after placing so that it appears similar to the one that is given in Figure 11-21.

1.   Choose the **Parts List** button from the **Drawing Annotation Panel** panel bar; the **Parts List** dialog box is displayed.

As mentioned earlier, the parts list can be placed taking the reference of a drawing view. It is recommended that the drawing view you use as a reference for placing the parts list should have all the components so that all of them are listed in the parts list.

2. Select the isometric view as the reference view for placing the parts list.

3. Accept the other default options in this dialog box and choose the **OK** button to exit this dialog box.

   Notice that a rectangle is displayed on the screen and is attached to the cursor. This rectangle is the parts list that will be placed at the point that you specify.

4. Specify the location of the parts list close to the bottom right corner of the sheet above the title block. The sheet with the default parts list is shown in Figure 11-22.

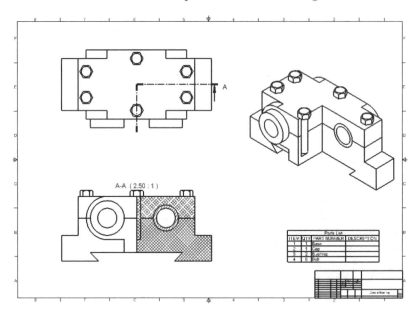

Figure 11-22 Drawing sheet with the default parts list

Modifying the Parts List

Whenever you place a parts list in the drawing views, it will be displayed in the drawing sheet and in the browser. You can modify the parts list by double-clicking on it in the browser or in the drawing sheet. You need to modify the heading **PART NUMBER** to **NAME**, enter the data in the fields below the **DESCRIPTION** column, and center align the data in this column.

1. Double-click on the parts list in the drawing sheet; the **Edit Parts List** dialog box is displayed.

2. Click on the first field below the **DESCRIPTION** column and type Bronze.

3. Similarly, click on the remaining fields in the **DESCRIPTION** column and enter the description about the remaining components. Refer to Figure 11-20 for more information about the data to be entered.

By default, the data in the **DESCRIPTION** column is left aligned. You need to modify the alignment such that the text is center aligned.

4. Move the cursor over the heading **DESCRIPTION**. You will notice that the cursor is replaced by an arrow that points in the downward direction.

5. Right-click when the arrow is displayed and choose **Format Column** from the shortcut menu to display the **Format Column : DESCRIPTION** dialog box.

6. Choose the **Center** button in front of **Value** in the **Justification** area to center align the data in the fields below the **DESCRIPTION** heading. Choose **OK** to exit this dialog box.

You will notice that the data in the selected field are center aligned now.

7. Again, right-click on the **DESCRIPTION** heading and choose the **Column Width** option from the shortcut menu. Enter **60** as the value in the **Column Width** edit box. This will increase the width of the fields below the **DESCRIPTION** heading.

By default, the heading of the column that displays the name of the components is **PART NUMBER**. You need to modify this heading to **NAME**.

8. Move the cursor over the heading **PART NUMBER** and right-click when the cursor is replaced by an arrow. Choose **Format Column** from the shortcut menu to display the **Format Column : PART NUMBER** dialog box.

9. Enter **NAME** in the **Heading** edit box and exit this dialog box.

10. Choose the **OK** button to exit the **Edit Parts List** dialog box. The sheet after editing the parts list is shown in Figure 11-23.

Adding Balloons to the Components

As mentioned earlier, the balloons are the callouts attached to the components in the drawing view so that they can be referred to in the parts list. These are based on the item numbers in the parts list. You can add balloons using the **Balloon** tool or the **Auto Balloon** tool. In this tutorial, the balloons are added using the **Balloon** tool.

Before you add the balloons, you need to set the parameters related to them.

1. Invoke the **Style and Standards Editor [Library - Read Only]** dialog box and expand the **Balloon** option in the left pane.

2. Select the **Balloon(JIS)** option; the parameters related to this balloon standard are displayed on the right pane of the dialog box.

3. Choose the **Edit Leader Style** button on the right of the **Leader Style** drop-down list.

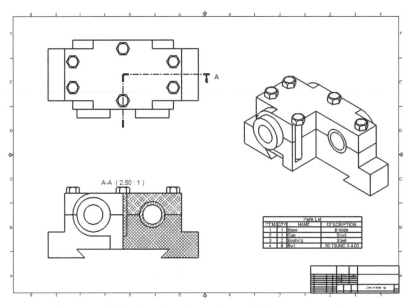

Figure 11-23 *Drawing sheet after modifying the parts list*

4. Select the **Filled** option from the **Arrowhead** drop-down list in the **Terminator** area.

5. Enter **6** as the value in the **Size (X)** edit box and **2** as the value in the **Height (Y)** edit box in the **Terminator** area. Save the changes and then exit the dialog box.

6. Choose the **Balloon** button from the **Drawing Annotation Panel** toolbar. Move the cursor over one of the edges of the Bolt on the upper left corner of the assembly in the isometric view; the component is highlighted and it turns red in color. The symbol of coincident constraint is displayed on the left of the cursor.

7. Select the component; you will notice that the start point of the balloon is attached to the selected edge and the other end of the balloon is attached to the cursor.

 Tip. *If you selected a wrong component to add the balloon, you can clear it from the current selected set before choosing **Continue** from the shortcut menu. To do this, right-click and choose **Back** from the shortcut menu.*

8. Specify the location of the other end of the balloon above the view, refer to Figure 11-24.

9. Now, right-click and choose **Continue** from the shortcut menu. The balloon is created and it displays number 4 inside the circle. Number 4 corresponds to the Bolt in the parts list.

10. Next, move the cursor over the circular edge of the Bushing that is not sectioned in the isometric view. Select when the component is highlighted; one end of the balloon is attached to the edge.

11. Specify the location of the other end on the left of the view, refer to Figure 11-24. Right-click to display the shortcut menu and choose **Continue** to place the balloon.

12. Similarly, add balloons to the Base and the Cap, refer to Figure 11-24.

13. After placing the balloons, right-click to display the shortcut menu. Choose **Done** from it to exit this tool. The drawing sheet, after adding the parts list and the balloons, is shown in Figure 11-24.

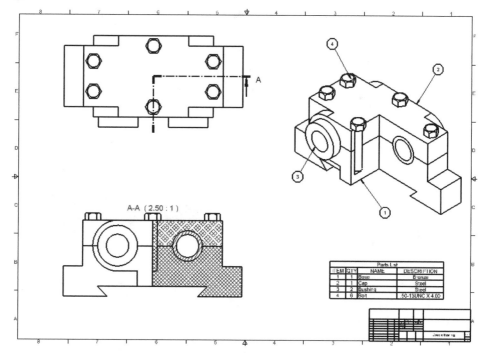

Figure 11-24 *Drawing sheet after adding balloons*

Tip. *If you double-click on the parts list after adding the balloons to the components, you will notice that the symbol of the balloon is displayed in front of all the components that are ballooned. This suggests that the balloons corresponding to the components are added to the drawing sheet.*

*To change the arrowhead of the balloon, right-click on it and choose **Edit Arrowhead**; the **Change Arrowhead** toolbar will be displayed with a drop-down list. You can select the required arrowhead style from this drop-down list.*

14. Save the file with the name *Tutotial2.idw* in *\PersonalProject\c11\Double Bearing* folder and then close the file.

Note

If the drawing file consists of more than one sheet, irrespective of which sheet was active at the time of closing the file, the first sheet will be active when you open the drawing file next time.

Tutorial 3

In this tutorial, you will generate the drawing views of the Drill Press Vice assembly created in Exercise 1 of Chapter 8. The drawing views that need to be generated are shown in Figure 11-25. After generating the drawing views, add parts list and balloons to the components. The parts list should resemble the one shown in Figure 11-26. You will use the ANSI mm standard sheet. Use the A3 size sheet for generating the drawing views.   **(Expected time: 45 min)**

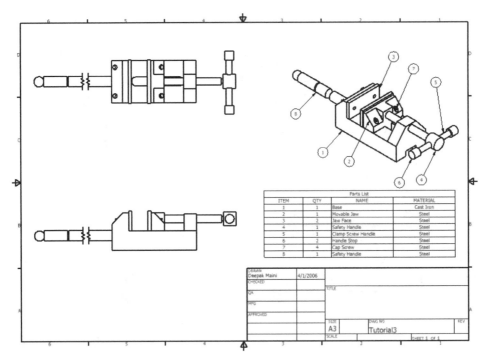

Figure 11-25 *Drawing sheet for Tutorial 3*

Parts List			
ITEM	QTY	NAME	MATERIAL
1	1	Base	Cast Iron
2	1	Movable Jaw	Steel
3	2	Jaw Face	Steel
4	1	Clamp Screw	Steel
5	1	Clamp Screw Handle	Steel
6	2	Handle Stop	Steel
7	4	Cap Screw	Steel
8	1	Safety Handle	Steel

Figure 11-26 *Parts list to be added*

The following steps are required to complete this tutorial:

a.   Copy the *Drill Press Vice* folder from *c08* folder to *c11* folder. Start a new ANSI mm standard drawing file using the **Metric** tab of the **Open** dialog box.
b.   Modify the sheet to A3 size sheet.
c.   Modify the drafting standards and generate the required drawing views.
d.   Add the parts list and modify it such that it resembles the one shown in Figure 11-25.
e.   Finally, add the balloons to the components.

Copying the Drill Press Vice Assembly
1.   Copy the *Drill Press Vice* folder from the *\PersonalProject\c08* folder to the current folder.

Starting a New ANSI mm Standard File
1.   Start a new metric file with ANSI mm standards.

     The default ANSI mm standard drawing sheet will be displayed. The size of default sheet is C. You need to change this size to A3.

2.   Right-click on **Sheet:1** in the browser and choose **Edit Sheet** from the shortcut menu; the **Edit Sheet** dialog box is displayed.

3.   Select **A3** from the **Size** drop-down list in the **Format** area. Choose **OK** to exit the dialog box; the sheet size changes to A3.

Generating the Drawing Views
1.   Generate the top view of the Drill Press Vice assembly with a scale of 0.5. Break the view such that the length of the Safety Handle is reduced.

2.   Generate the front view and the isometric view, as shown in Figure 11-27.

Placing the Parts List
1.   Choose the **Parts List** button from the **Drawing Annotation Panel** panel bar; the **Parts List** dialog box is displayed.

2.   Select the isometric view as the reference view for placing the parts list.

3.   Accept the default options in this dialog box and choose **OK**. A rectangle, which is actually the parts list, is attached to the cursor and you are prompted to specify the location of the parts list.

4.   Place the parts list above the title block.

Modifying the Parts List
1.   Double-click on the parts list to display the **Edit Parts List** dialog box.

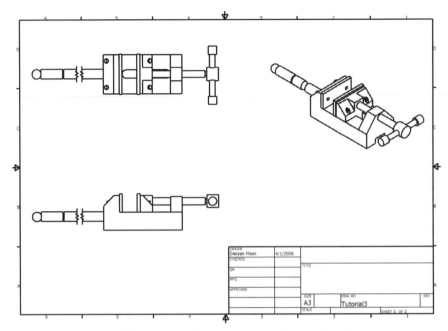

Figure 11-27 *Drawing sheet after generating the drawing views*

2. Right-click on the **DESCRIPTION** heading and choose the **Format Column** option to display the **Format Column : DESCRIPTION** dialog box. Enter the heading of this column as **MATERIAL** in the **Heading** edit box.

3. Choose the **Center** button on right of **Value** in the **Justification** area to center align the data in the **MATERIAL** column. Exit this dialog box.

4. Similarly, right-click on the **PART NUMBER** column and modify its heading to **NAME** in the **Heading** edit box of the **Format Column : PART NUMBER** dialog box.

5. Enter the data in the **MATERIAL** field based on the parts list shown in Figure 11-26.

Adding Balloons to the Components

The final step in this tutorial is to add the balloons to the components in the isometric view. In this assembly, you will add the balloons using the **Balloon** tool. You also need to drag the balloons such that they are placed at a proper location in the drawing sheet. But before generating the drawing views, you need to modify the standards of the current sheet based on the tutorial description.

1. Invoke the **Style and Standards Editor [Library - Read Only]** dialog box and expand the **Balloon** option in the left pane.

2. Select the **Balloon(ANSI)** option; the parameters related to this balloon standard are displayed on the right pane of the dialog box.

3. Choose the **Edit Leader Style** button on the right of the **Leader Style** drop-down list to display the leader parameters.

4. Enter **4** in the **Size (X)** edit box and **1.5** in the **Height (Y)** edit box. Choose **Save** and then choose **Done** to exit this dialog box. This is done to increase the size of arrowheads in the balloons.

5. Choose the **Balloon** button from the **Drawing Annotation Panel** panel bar.

6. Move the cursor over one of the edges of the Base in the isometric view for adding the balloon. Move the cursor away from the Base and place it below the component, refer to Figure 11-28. Right-click and choose **Continue** from the shortcut menu.

7. Similarly, add balloons to the remaining components, refer to Figure 11-28.

8. Drag the balloons to a proper location in the drawing sheet. The final drawing sheet, after adding the parts list and the balloons, is shown in Figure 11-28.

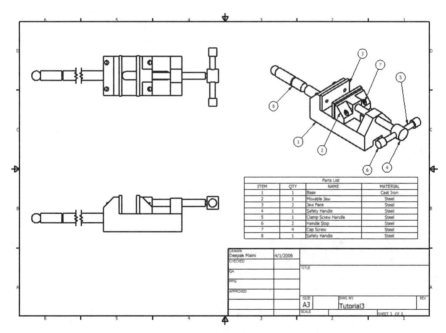

Figure 11-28 *Final drawing sheet for Tutorial 3*

9. Save this file with the name given below and then close the file.

\PersonalProject\c11\Drill Press Vice\Tutorial3.idw

Self-Evaluation Test

Answer the following questions and then compare your answers with those given at the end of this chapter:

1. The drafting standards of a drawing sheet can be modified using the **Style and Standards Editor [Library - Read Only]** dialog box. (T/F)

2. You can add parametric dimensions and reference dimensions to the drawing views. (T/F)

3. When you create a new dimension style, all existing dimensions will be modified based on the new style. (T/F)

4. The default parts list cannot be modified. (T/F)

5. You can add parts list to the assembly drawing views using the _____ tool.

6. You can add a multiline text without a leader using the _____ tool.

7. When you open a new drawing file, only _____ sheet is available by default.

8. The _____ make it convenient to relate the components in the parts list to the components in the drawing views.

9. If you assemble some of the components in a separate assembly file and insert the subassembly in the current assembly file, the components of the subassembly will be called _____ components.

10. You can modify the size of the drawing sheet by using the _____ dialog box.

Review Questions

Answer the following questions:

1. You cannot control the line weight of lines in the drawing views. (T/F)

2. Whenever you open an old drawing file that has more than one sheet, the sheet that was active last time will be displayed as the active sheet. (T/F)

3. You can modify the size of arrowheads of the balloons using the **Style and Standards Editor [Library - Read Only]** dialog box. (T/F)

4. Autodesk Inventor allows you to add a user-defined text to the drawing sheet. (T/F)

5. You can edit the text by double-clicking on it. (T/F)

6. Which one of the following tools can be used to add text with a leader?

(a) **Text**   (b) **Leader**
(c) **Leader Text**   (d) None

7. Which one of the following tools can be used to add center marks to the circles in the drawing views?

(a) **Center Mark**   (b) **Center Line**
(c) **Center**   (d) None

8. Which one of the following options of **Style and Standards Editor [Library - Read Only]** dialog box can be used to create a new dimension style?

(a) **Dimension**   (b) **Terminator**
(c) **Common**   (d) **Sheet**

9. Which one of the following dialog boxes can be used to create a new dimension style?

(a) **Dimension Style**   (b) **Dimension Text**
(c) **Drafting Standards**   (d) **Style and Standards Editor [Library - Read Only]**

10. Which one of the following dialog boxes is displayed when you double-click on the parts list to edit it?

(a) **Parts List**   (b) **Edit Parts List**
(c) **Edit**   (d) You cannot edit parts list

Exercise

Exercise 1

Add the parts list and the balloons to the drawing views of the Plummer Block assembly created in Tutorial 2 of Chapter 10, as shown in Figure 11-29. The parts list to be added is shown in Figure 11-30. **(Expected time: 45 min)**

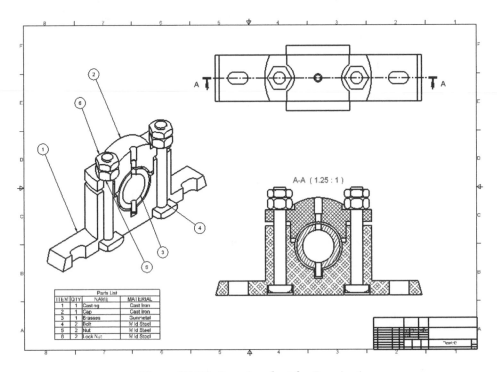

Figure 11-29 *Drawing sheet for Exercise 1*

Parts List			
ITEM	QTY	NAME	MATERIAL
1	1	Casting	Cast Iron
2	1	Cap	Cast Iron
3	1	Brasses	Gunmetal
4	2	Bolt	Mild Steel
5	2	Nut	Mild Steel
6	2	Lock Nut	Mild Steel

Figure 11-30 *Parts list for Exercise 1*

Answers to Self-Evaluation Test

1. F, **2.** T, **3.** F, **4.** F, **5. Parts List**, **6. Text**, **7.** one, **8.** balloons, **9.** second-level, **10. Edit Sheet**

Chapter 12

Presentation Module

Learning Objectives

After completing this chapter, you will be able to:
- *Create or restore the assembly view for creating the presentation.*
- *Tweak the components and add trails to them.*
- *Rotate views using the Precise View Rotation tool.*
- *Animate the tweaked view.*

THE PRESENTATION MODULE

As mentioned earlier, Autodesk Inventor allows you to animate the assemblies created in the **Assembly** module. You can view some of the assemblies in motion by animating them. The animation of assemblies can be created in the **Presentation** module. You can also use the **Presentation** module for creating the exploded views of an assembly. An exploded view is one in which the assembled components are moved to a defined distance from their original location. To invoke the **Presentation** module, double-click on the **Standard (mm).ipn** file in the **Metric** tab of the **Open** dialog box, see Figure 12-1.

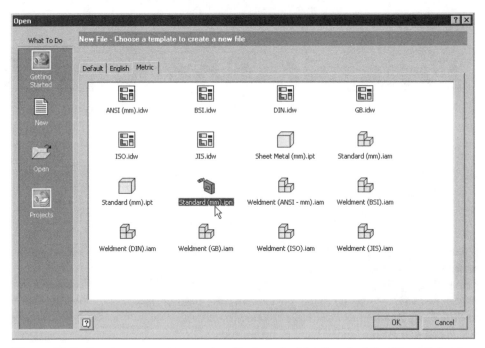

*Figure 12-1 Opening a new presentation file from the **Metric** tab of the **Open** dialog box*

The default screen appearance of the **Presentation** module is shown in Figure 12-2.

Note
*You will notice that when you open a new presentation file, only the **Create View** tool will be available in the **Presentation Panel** panel bar. This is because you need to first create the presentation view of the assembly. Once the presentation view is created, other tools will become available in this module.*

*As mentioned earlier, all the modules of Autodesk Inventor are bidirectionally associative. Therefore, if you make any modification in the assembly or components of the assembly, the changes will be automatically reflected in the **Presentation** module.*

*You cannot modify the assembly or its components in the **Presentation** module.*

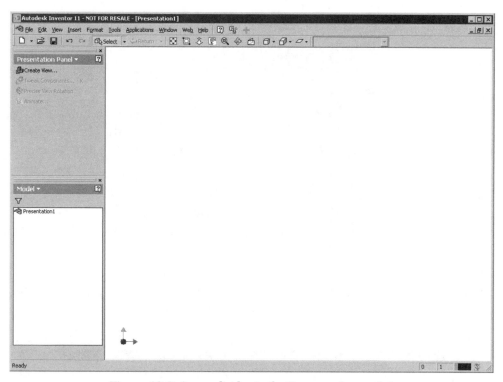

Figure 12-2 *Screen display in the* **Presentation** *module*

CREATING THE PRESENTATION VIEW

Toolbar:	Presentation Panel > Create View
Panel Bar:	Presentation Panel > Create View

After proceeding to the **Presentation** module, the first step is to create the presentation view. The presentation view can be used to animate the assembly or to create its exploded state. The presentation views can be created by using the **Create View** tool. You can also invoke this tool by right-clicking in the drawing window and choosing **Create View** from the shortcut menu. When you invoke this tool, the **Select Assembly** dialog box will be displayed, as shown in Figure 12-3. The options in this dialog box are discussed next.

Assembly Area

The options in the **Assembly** area are used to select the assembly for creating the presentation view. These options are discussed next.

File

The **File** drop-down list displays the assembly file selected for creating the presentation view. By default, this drop-down list displays **<select assembly document>**. This is because no assembly file is selected. To select an assembly file, choose the **Explore Directories** button on the right of

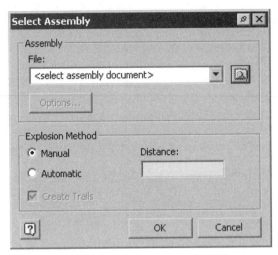

*Figure 12-3 The **Select Assembly** dialog box*

this drop-down list. When you choose this button, the **Open** dialog box will be displayed, see Figure 12-4. You can use this dialog box for selecting the assembly file that will be used for creating the presentation.

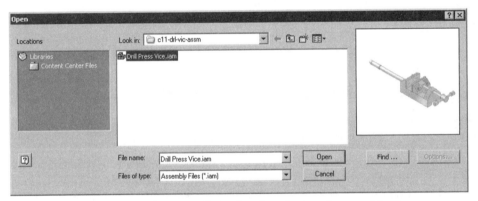

*Figure 12-4 The **Open** dialog box for selecting the assembly file*

The selected assembly file and its location is displayed in the **File** drop-down list.

Tip. *In the **Open** dialog box, the **Files of type** drop-down list displays only the **Assembly Files (.iam)** option. This is because you can create the presentation views of only the assembly files.*

Options

You can choose the **Options** button to display the **File Open Options** dialog box. Using this dialog box, you can select the design view representation or positional representation that you want to use to generate the presentation view.

Explosion Method Area

As mentioned earlier, an exploded view is one in which the components of an assembly are moved to a specified distance from their original location in the assembly. The options in the **Explosion Method** area are used to select the method for exploding the selected assembly. These options are discussed next.

Manual

If the **Manual** radio button is selected, the assembly in the presentation view will not be exploded. This option is selected when you want to explode the assembly manually using other tools. Note that because the assembly will not be exploded, no other option in the **Explosion Method** area will be available if the **Manual** radio button is selected.

Automatic

The **Automatic** radio button is selected to automatically explode the assembly when the presentation view is created. The components of the assembly will move in the direction of the constraint that is used to assemble them. The distance to which the components will move is specified in the **Distance** edit box. This edit box will be available when you select the **Automatic** radio button.

Create Trails

Trails are defined as the parametric lines that display the path and direction of the assembled components. These lines can be used as a reference for determining the path and the direction in which the components are assembled. The **Create Trails** check box is selected to create the trails when the assembly is exploded. This check box will be available only when the **Automatic** radio button is selected.

Figure 12-5 shows the Drill Press Vice assembly exploded using the **Automatic** option. The distance of explosion is 25 mm. This figure also shows the trails that define the path and direction of the assembled components.

Tip. *If the explosion distance is large, the result of exploding the assemblies using the **Automatic** method may not be what is desired. This is because with the large explosion distance, the components of the assembly will move to a large distance and start interfering with the other components, refer to Figure 12-5. Therefore, it is recommended that if the components need to be moved to a large distance, you should explode the assemblies using the manual method.*

*To increase the value of the automatic explosion after creating the presentation view, click on the + sign located on the left of **Explosion1** in the browser to display the name of the assembly. Right-click on the name and choose **Auto Explode** from the shortcut menu to display the **Auto Explode** dialog box. Enter the value of distance in the **Distance** edit box. The new value of the distance is added to the previous distance value. Remember that you cannot enter a negative distance value.*

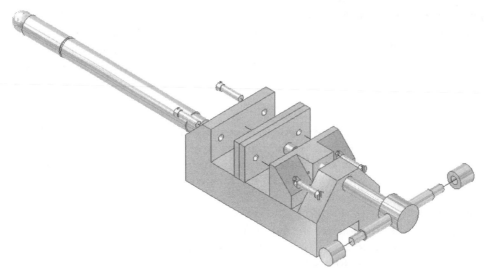

Figure 12-5 *Exploded assembly with trails*

DEFINING UNITS FOR THE PRESENTATION FILES

Autodesk Inventor allows you to define the units in the presentation (*.ipn*) file. By defining the units in the presentation file, you can control the distance and angle while specifying the tweak. To define the units in the presentation file, choose **Tools > Document Settings** from the menu bar; the **Document Settings** dialog box will be displayed. Invoke the **Units** tab and specify the length and angular units.

TWEAKING COMPONENTS IN A PRESENTATION VIEW

Toolbar:	Presentation Panel > Tweak Components
Panel Bar:	Presentation Panel > Tweak Components

As mentioned earlier, if the distance by which the components should move in the exploded view is large, the components in the automatically created exploded view start interfering with the other components. For example, refer to Figure 12-6. This figures shows an automatic exploded view, in which the components are moved to a distance of 42 mm. Notice the interference between the Movable Jaw and the Base, between the two Jaw Faces, and between the Clamp Screw and the Base. To avoid such situations, it is recommended that if the components need to be exploded to a large distance, you should create the exploded view manually by tweaking the components. Tweaking is defined as the process of adjusting the position of the assembled components with respect to the other components of the assembly by transforming them in the specified direction. The components can be tweaked by using the **Tweak Components** tool. The tweaked components can also be animated, thus creating the animation of the assemblies.

When you invoke this tool, the **Tweak Component** dialog box will be displayed, as shown in Figure 12-7. The options in this dialog box are discussed next.

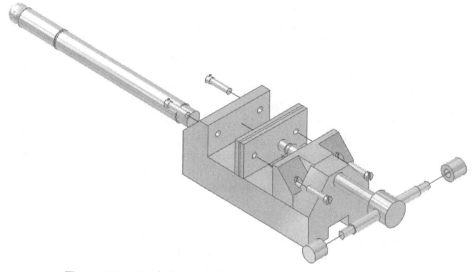

Figure 12-6 *Exploded assembly displaying interfering components*

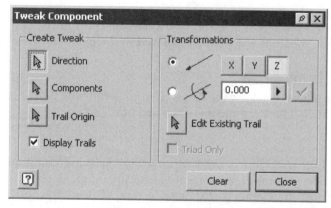

Figure 12-7 *The* **Tweak Component** *dialog box*

Create Tweak Area

The options in the **Create Tweak** area are used to select the component to be tweaked, the direction of tweaking, and options related to the trails. These options are discussed next.

Direction

The **Direction** button is the first button in the **Create Tweak** area and is used to select the direction of moving or rotating the components. This button is chosen by default when you invoke the **Tweak Component** dialog box. When this button is chosen, you will notice that the direction symbol is attached to the cursor. This symbol will be visible when you move the cursor in the drawing window. You can define the direction of rotation or movement by using any linear edge, face, or feature of the components in the assembly. If you select a cylindrical component, you can use its central axis as the direction of tweaking. When you move the cursor close to any component for selecting the direction, you will notice that a triad is displayed. It displays the X, Y, and Z directions. Once you select the direction of tweaking, the triad will be fixed at the selected component. Also, the **Components** button will be chosen in the **Create Tweak** area. You can change the direction of tweaking by choosing the **Direction** button again and redefining the direction.

Components

The **Components** button is chosen to select the components that will be tweaked. This button will be automatically chosen when you define the direction of tweaking. When this button is chosen, you will notice that a symbol of a 3D model and an arrow is attached to the cursor. This symbol suggests that you need to select the components to be tweaked. You will also be prompted to select the components to be tweaked.

Trail Origin

As mentioned earlier, trails are parametric lines defining the direction and path of the assembled components. By default, when you tweak the components, the trails are created at the center of the components. You can use the **Trail Origin** button to redefine the origin of trail using two points.

Display Trails

The **Display Trails** check box is selected to display the trails in the exploded view. If this check box is cleared, the trails will not be displayed in the exploded view of the assembly.

Transformations Area

The options in the **Transformations** area are used to specify the type of transformation, its direction, and distance. These options are discussed next.

Linear

 The **Linear** option is used to tweak the selected components in the linear direction. Whenever you select the direction of tweaking by using the **Direction** button in the **Create Tweak** area, a triad is displayed with three axes. If the **Linear** option is selected, the selected components will be tweaked in the linear direction along one of these three axes. By default, the components will be tweaked in the Z direction. This axis is displayed in blue in the triad. The remaining two axes will be displayed in green. This is because the **Z** button is chosen in the **Transformations** area. If you want to tweak the components in the X or Y direction, choose the respective button from the **Transformations** area. The selected axis will be displayed in blue and the remaining two axes will be displayed in green. The distance of tweaking will be entered in the edit box provided in this area. After entering the value in the edit box, choose the **Apply** button on the right of the edit box. Until you choose the **Apply** button, the components will not be tweaked.

Rotational

 The **Rotational** option is used to rotate the selected components around a specified axis of the triad. The triad is displayed when you select the direction by using the **Direction** button from the **Create Tweak** area. You can select the required axis by choosing its button from the **Transformations** area. The angle of rotation will be entered in the edit box provided on the right of the **Rotational** radio button. After entering the angle of rotation in the edit box, choose the **Apply** button to tweak the components.

Edit Existing Trail

The **Edit Existing Trail** button is chosen to edit an existing trail. When you choose this button, the remaining options in the **Tweak Component** dialog box will not be enabled. Choose this button and then select the trail from the graphics screen. The **Direction** button in the **Create Tweak** area and the edit box in the **Transformations** area will be available. You can modify the direction and distance/angle of the existing trail.

Triad Only

The **Triad Only** check box is selected to rotate only the triad around the axis selected in the triad. Remember that you cannot move the triad without moving the components. However, you can rotate it without rotating the components. The angle of rotation will be specified in the edit box provided on the right of the **Rotational** option. This check box is generally selected when you want to rotate the triad through a certain angle and then use the directions of the rotated triad to add tweaks to the components. After rotating the triad, you can add a linear or rotation tweak to the components.

Figure 12-8 shows the exploded view of the Drill Press Vice assembly.

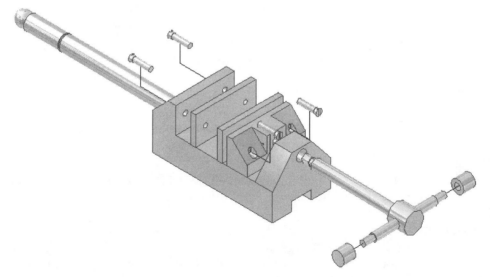

Figure 12-8 Exploded view of the Drill Press Vice assembly

Clear

The **Clear** button is chosen to clear the current settings in the **Tweak Component** dialog box. When you choose this button, all the current settings are reset to the default values and you can proceed with tweaking the other components.

Tip. *To modify the individual tweak values of the components, click on the + sign located on the left of the name of the assembly in the browser; all components in the assembly will be displayed. Click on the + sign located on the left of any component to display the tweak value. Select the tweak and an edit box will appear below the browser. Modify the value of the tweak in this edit box.*

ANIMATING ASSEMBLIES

Toolbar:	Presentation Panel > Animate
Panel Bar:	Presentation Panel > Animate

 The tweaked or exploded assemblies can be animated by using the **Animate** tool. When you invoke this tool, the **Animation** dialog box will be displayed, as shown in Figure 12-9. The options in this dialog box are discussed next.

*Figure 12-9 The **Animation** dialog box*

Parameters Area

The options in the **Parameter** area are used to set the interval of a tweak in the animation and the number of repetitions in the animation. These options are discussed next.

Interval

The **Interval** spinner is used to specify the interval between the tweaks in an animation. You can use the spinner to specify the value or enter the value directly.

Repetitions

The **Repetitions** edit box is used to enter the number of repetitions in an animation. You can specify the number of repetitions by setting the value of the **Repetitions** spinner directly or entering a value in this edit box.

Motion Area

The options in the **Motion** area are used to set the motion of components or record the animation. These options are discussed next.

Forward By Tweak

The **Forward By Tweak** button is chosen to force the tweaked components to be moved to the end value of the tweak distance. If you have tweaked the selected components to a linear distance of 25 mm in the Z direction, then choosing this button will move all the tweaked components forward by the complete tweak distance, that is 25 mm in this case.

Forward By Interval

Whenever you create an animation, the total tweak distance or tweak angle is automatically divided into small intervals that are used as the animation sequence. The **Forward By Interval** button is chosen to force the tweaked components to move forward by one interval in the animation.

Reverse By Interval

The **Reverse By Interval** button is chosen to force the tweaked components to move backward by one interval in the animation.

Reverse By Tweak

The **Reverse By Tweak** button is chosen to force the tweaked components to be moved to the start value of the tweak distance. This button will work only if one cycle of the animation is completed or the components are moved to the end position by using the **Forward By Tweak** button.

Play Forward

The **Play Forward** button is chosen to play the animation of the assembly in the forward direction. The number of cycles in the animation will be based on the value of **Repetitions** spinner in the **Parameter** area. If the number of repetitions is more than one, the components will be repositioned at the start point of the forward cycle after the first repetition is completed and the second repetition will again begin from the start point of animation.

Auto Reverse

If the **Auto Reverse** button is chosen, the animation of the assembly will be first played in the forward direction and then played automatically in the reverse direction. The number of forward and reverse cycles will depend upon the value of the **Repetitions** spinner. Note that in this case the forward and reverse movement of components is considered as one cycle.

Tip. *If the components are already moved to the end value of the tweak distance, that is, at the start position of the animation in the reverse direction, choosing the Auto Reverse button will animate the components in only the reverse direction if the number of repetitions is one.*

Play Reverse

The **Play Reverse** button is chosen to play the animation of assembly in the backward direction. The number of cycles in the animation will be based on the value of **Repetitions** spinner in the **Parameter** area. If the number of repetitions is more than one, the components will be repositioned at the start point of the reverse cycle after the first repetition is completed and the second repetition will again begin from the end point of the animation.

Pause

The **Pause** button is chosen to temporarily stop the animation of the assembly.

Record

The **Record** button is chosen to store the animation of an assembly. You can record the animation in the *.wmv* or *.avi* format. When you choose this button, the **Save As** dialog box will be displayed to specify the name and location of the animation file, see Figure 12-10.

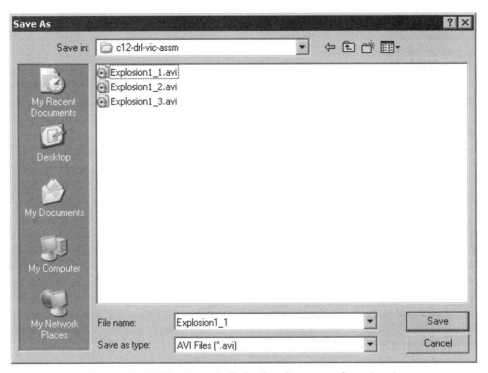

*Figure 12-10 The **Save As** dialog box for saving the animation*

After you specify the name of the avi file for saving the animation, the **Video Compression** dialog box will be displayed, see Figure 12-11. Set the values in this dialog box and then choose **OK**.

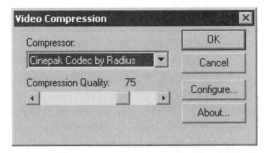

*Figure 12-11 The **Video Compression** dialog box*

Once the video compression parameters are set, you are ready for creating the avi file. Now, choose the **Play Forward**, **Play Reverse**, or the **Auto Reverse** button to create the avi file of the animation. After the animation is recorded, choose this button again to exit recording.

Minimize dialog during recording

The **Minimize dialog during recording** check box is selected to minimize the **Animation** dialog box while the animation is being recorded. This is done because when the animation is being recorded, whatever appears on the graphics screen will also be recorded in the avi file. If the dialog box is not minimized, it will also be recorded and will appear in the avi file.

Apply

The **Apply** button is chosen to apply the changes made to the parameters in this dialog box.

Reset

The **Reset** button is chosen to reset the parameters in the **Animation** dialog box to the default values.

More

This is the button with two arrows provided on the lower right corner of the **Animation** dialog box. When you choose this button, the **Animation** dialog box expands to display the **Animation Sequence** area, see Figure 12-12. All the tweaked components, along with their tweak values, are displayed in the list box in this area. Note that all the components that were selected together while tweaking are displayed as a single sequence. The buttons in this area are discussed next.

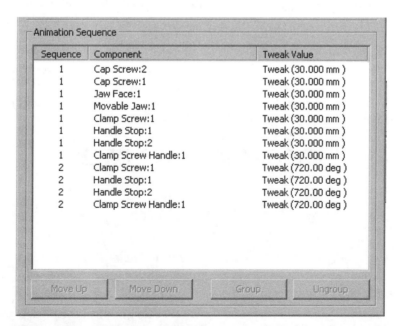

Figure 12-12 *The **Animation Sequence** area displayed on choosing the* **More** *button*

Move Up

The **Move Up** button is chosen to move the selected sequence up in the order in the list box. Remember that the sequence that is displayed on top in the list box will be played first in the animation.

Move Down

The **Move Down** button is chosen to move the selected sequence down in the order in the list box.

Group

The **Group** button is chosen to group various sequences in the animation. All the grouped sequences will show the same sequence number after grouping.

Tip. *The **Group** button is chosen when you want to club different tweak sequences together. Grouping a rotational and a linear tweak will provide the effect of linear and rotational movement together.*

Ungroup

The **Ungroup** button is chosen to ungroup the grouped sequences in the animation.

Note

*After grouping or ungrouping the sequences, choose the **Apply** button. If you do not choose the **Apply** button, the buttons to start the animation in the **Motion** area will not be available.*

ROTATING THE PRESENTATION VIEW PRECISELY

Toolbar:	Presentation Panel > Precise View Rotation
Panel Bar:	Presentation Panel > Precise View Rotation

Autodesk Inventor allows you to precisely rotate the presentation view in the **Presentation** module. This is done by using the **Precise View Rotation** tool. When you invoke this tool, the **Incremental View Rotate** dialog box is displayed, see Figure 12-13. The options provided in this dialog box are discussed next.

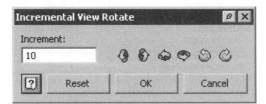

*Figure 12-13 The **Incremental View Rotate** dialog box*

Increment

The **Increment** edit box is used to specify the value through which the presentation view will be rotated.

Rotate Down

The **Rotate Down** button is chosen to rotate the presentation view in the downward direction. The angle through which the view will be rotated is specified in the **Increment** edit box. Enter the increment value and then choose this button to rotate the view.

Rotate Up

The **Rotate Up** button is chosen to rotate the presentation view in the upward direction. The angle through which the view will be rotated is specified in the **Increment** edit box. Enter the increment value and then choose this button to rotate the view.

Rotate Left

The **Rotate Left** button is chosen to rotate the presentation view toward the left. The angle through which the view will be rotated is specified in the **Increment** edit box. Enter the increment value and then choose this button to rotate the view.

Rotate Right

The **Rotate Right** button is chosen to rotate the presentation view toward the right. The angle through which the view will be rotated is specified in the **Increment** edit box. Enter the increment value and then choose this button to rotate the view.

Roll Counter Clockwise

The **Roll Counter Clockwise** button is chosen to rotate the presentation view in the counterclockwise direction. The angle through which the view will be rotated is specified in the **Increment** edit box. Enter the increment value and then choose this button to rotate the view.

Roll Clockwise

The **Roll Clockwise** button is chosen to rotate the presentation view in the clockwise direction. The angle through which the view will be rotated is specified in the **Increment** edit box. Enter the increment value and then choose this button to rotate the view.

Reset

The **Reset** button is chosen to reset the current view to the isometric view. Irrespective of the current orientation of the view, if you choose this button, the isometric view will be restored.

TUTORIALS

Tutorial 1

In this tutorial, you will explode the Plummer Block assembly and then create an animation of disassembling (exploding) and assembling (unexploding) of the assembly. The exploded state of the Plummer Block assembly is shown in Figure 12-14.   **(Expected time: 45 min)**

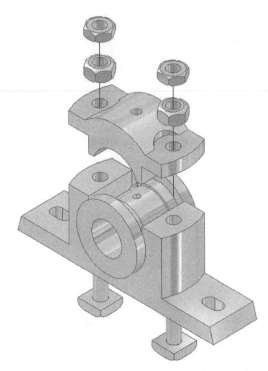

Figure 12-14 Exploded view of the Plummer Block Assembly

It is recommended that before starting with the tutorial, you should outline the procedure for completing it. The following steps are required to complete this tutorial:

a. Copy the *Plummer Block* folder from the *c11* folder to the *c12* folder.
b. Open a new metric presentation file and create a new presentation view by using the **Create View** tool, refer to Figure 12-16. Do not explode the assembly automatically.
c. Manually explode the assembly in four sequences. The first sequence will tweak the two Bolts. The second sequence will tweak the Cap, the Lock Nuts, and the Nuts. The third sequence will tweak the Lock Nuts. The final sequence will tweak the Nuts, refer to Figure 12-19.
d. Invoke the **Animate** tool and then combine all the four sequences.
e. Finally, animate the sequences by using the **Auto Reverse** button in the **Animation** dialog box.

Copying the Folder

The presentation view is generated by using the Plummer Block assembly. Therefore, you need to copy the *Plummer Block* folder from the *c11* folder to the *c12* folder.

1. Create a folder with the name *c12* inside the *\PersonalProject* folder.

2. Copy the *Plummer Block* folder from the *c11* folder to the *c12* folder.

Starting a New Presentation File

1. Invoke the **New** dialog box and then choose the **Metric** tab.

2. Double-click on the **Standard (mm).ipn** option, see Figure 12-15; a new presentation file is started.

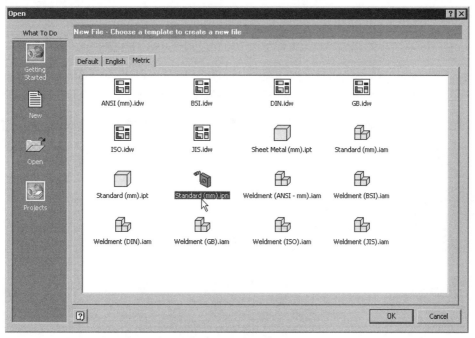

Figure 12-15 *Starting a new presentation file from the **Metric** tab of the **Open** dialog box*

Creating the Presentation View

When you open a new presentation file, only the **Create View** tool is available in the **Presentation Panel** panel bar. This is because you first need to create the presentation view.

1. Choose the **Create View** button from the **Presentation Panel** panel bar to invoke the **Select Assembly** dialog box.

2. Choose the **Explore Directories** button on the right of the **File** drop-down list in the **Assembly** area to invoke the **Open** dialog box.

3. Open the folder *\PersonalProject\c12\Plummer Block*.

   You will notice that only the *Plummer Block.iam* file is available in this folder. This is because you can select only the assembly file for creating the presentation view.

4. Double-click on the *Plummer Block.iam* file to select this assembly for creating the presentation view.

The **Open** dialog box is closed and the **File** drop-down list in the **Assembly** area of the **Select Assembly** dialog box displays the name and path of the selected assembly.

By default, the **Manual** radio button is selected in the **Explosion Method** area. This radio button is selected when you do not want to automatically add tweaks to the components. Because in this tutorial, you need to manually explode the assembly, you can accept the default options in the **Explosion Method** area.

5. Accept the default options in the **Explosion Method** area and choose the **OK** button.

The presentation view is created and the current view is changed automatically to the isometric view. The file, after creating the presentation view, is shown in Figure 12-16.

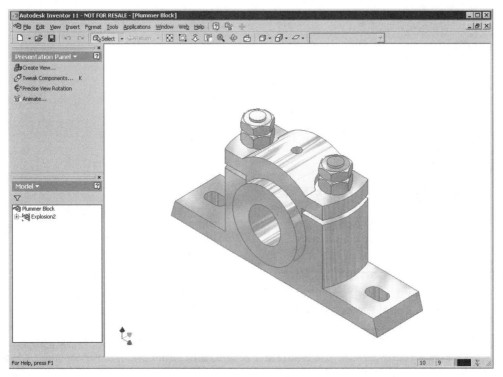

Figure 12-16 *Presentation file after creating the presentation view*

Tweaking the Components

As mentioned earlier, you can explode the assembly or add tweaks to the components of the assembly using the **Tweak Components** tool.

1. Choose the **Tweak Components** button from the **Presentation Panel** panel bar to invoke the **Tweak Component** dialog box.

When you invoke the **Tweak Component** dialog box, the **Direction** button in the **Create Tweak** area is chosen by default and you are prompted to select the direction for the tweak.

2. Select the vertical edge on the front face of the Casting as the direction for the tweak, see Figure 12-17.

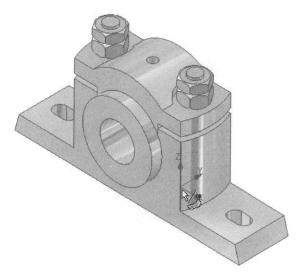

Figure 12-17 Selecting the direction for the tweak

As soon as you select the direction of the tweak, a triad is displayed on the selected edge. The X, Y, and Z axes of the triad are along the X, Y, and Z axes of the current coordinate symbol displayed on the lower left corner of the graphics screen. Also, the Z axis of the triad is displayed in blue. This suggests that the current tweak direction is along the Z axis.

Notice that after you define the direction of tweak, the **Components** button in the **Create Tweak** area is automatically chosen and you are prompted to select the components to be tweaked.

3. One by one select both Bolts to tweak from the portion where they extend out of the Lock Nuts.

The top faces of the Bolts are displayed with a blue outline. This suggests that the components are selected and can be tweaked.

4. Make sure the **Display Trail** check box in the **Create Tweak** area is selected.

You need to add the **Linear** tweak to the components and by default, the **Linear** radio button is selected in the **Transformations** area. Therefore, you just need to enter the value of the linear tweak. Note that the Z axis of the triad points in the upward direction. But you need to tweak the components in the downward direction. Therefore, you need to enter a negative value of tweak.

5. Enter **-50** as the value in the edit box on the right of the **Rotational** radio button. Then choose the **Apply** button on the right of the edit box.

The two Bolts move in the downward direction, see Figure 12-18. This is the first sequence of tweak.

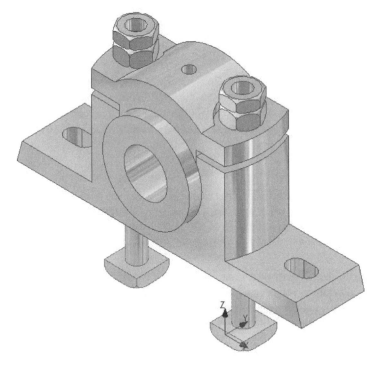

Figure 12-18 *Assembly after tweaking the two Bolts*

Because the **Tweak Components** tool is still active, you are again prompted to select the components to be tweaked. Also, notice that the two Bolts are still displayed with a blue outline. This suggests that these components are still selected and if you enter a tweak value in the edit box, these components will be tweaked by that distance. Therefore, you first need to remove these components from the selected set.

6. Press and hold the SHIFT key down and then one by one click on both Bolts. You will notice that the Bolts are no more displayed with a blue outline.

7. Select the Cap, two Nuts, and two Lock Nuts; all the selected components are displayed with a blue outline.

8. Enter **50** as the value in the edit box on the right of the **Rotational** radio button in the **Transformations** area. Then, choose the **Apply** button on the right of the edit box.

    The selected components move in the upward direction by a distance of 50 mm. This is the second tweak sequence.

9. Next, press and hold the SHIFT key down and then one by one click on the Cap and both the Nuts to remove them from the current selection set. You will notice that only the two Lock Nuts are displayed with a blue outline now.

10. Choose the **Apply** button on the right of the edit box in the **Transformations** area to move the two Lock Nuts further up by a distance of 50 mm.

    This is the third tweak sequence. You will notice that the blue trails are also created as you tweak the components. This is because the **Display Trails** check box in the **Create Tweak** area is selected.

11. Choose the **Zoom All** button from the **Inventor Standard** toolbar to increase the drawing display area. The complete exploded assembly is displayed on the graphics screen.

12. Press and hold the SHIFT key down and one by one click on the two Lock Nuts to remove them from the selection set. Release the SHIFT key and then select the two Nuts.

    You will notice that the two Nuts are displayed with a blue outline.

13. Enter **25** as the value in the edit box on the right of the **Rotational** radio button in the **Transformations** area. Then, choose the **Apply** button on the right of the edit box.

    The two Nuts move in the upward direction by a distance of 25 mm and are now placed between the Cap and the two Lock Nuts. This is the fourth and the final tweak sequence.

14. Choose the **Close** button to exit the **Tweak Component** dialog box.

    You will notice that the triad that was displayed in the assembly is removed from the drawing window. The assembly, after creating the four tweak sequences, is shown in Figure 12-19.

Animating the Assembly

The next step, after tweaking the assembly, is to animate it. The animation will carry out the simulation of exploding and unexploding the assembly. Note that when you tweak the components, the assembly is exploded and the components move to the tweaked position. Therefore, the first cycle in the animation will be to unexplode the assembly by moving the components back to their original assembled position and the second cycle will be to explode the assembly by moving the components to the tweaked position.

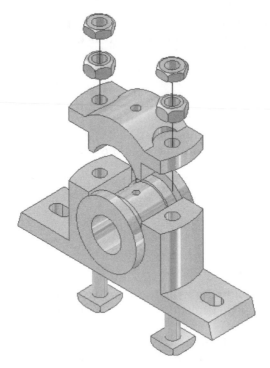

Figure 12-19 *The exploded assembly*

1. Choose the **Animate** button from the **Presentation Panel** panel bar to display the **Animation** dialog box.

2. Choose the **More** button provided on the lower right corner of the dialog box to expand it.

   You will notice that there are four sequences in the **Animation Sequence** area. If you animate the assembly now, you will notice that the assembly will animate in four steps. These four steps are actually the four sequences displayed in the **Animation Sequence** area. Remember that the next step will start only after the previous step is completed. In order to animate the assembly such that all the sequences animate together, you need to select and group all of them together.

3. Press and hold the SHIFT key down and select all sequences displayed in the **Animation Sequence** area.

   All the sequences are displayed with a blue background. Also, only the **Group** button is available in the **Animation Sequence** area.

4. Choose the **Group** button from the **Animation Sequence** area to group all the sequences together.

   All the tweaks are now grouped together under sequence 1.

5. Choose the **Apply** button to apply the changes to the assembly.

6. Hold the **Animation** dialog box from the blue portion and drag it to the left of the drawing window such that it does not overlap with the assembly.

7. Choose the **Auto Reverse** button from the **Motion** area.

You will notice that all the tweaked components in the animation move together to their original assembled position and then move back to the tweaked position.

8. Choose the **Cancel** button in the **Animation** dialog box to exit it. Save the assembly with the name given below and then close the file.

\PersonalProject\c12\Plummer Block\Tutorial1.ipn

Tutorial 2

In this tutorial, you will animate the Drill Press Vice assembly. The animation should consist of a rotational tweak and a linear tweak. Save the animation in an avi file with the name *Drill Press Vice.avi*.   **(Expected time: 1 Hr)**

The following steps are required to complete this tutorial:

a. Copy the *Drill Press Vice* folder from the *c11* folder to the *c12* folder.
b. Start a new metric presentation file and create the presentation view of the Drill Press Vice assembly by using the **Create View** tool.
c. Tweak the components by using the **Tweak Components** tool.
d. Invoke the **Animation** dialog box and group the sequences.
e. Create the avi file and store the animation in the avi file.

Copying the Drill Press Vice Assembly
1. Copy the *Drill Press Vice* folder from the *c11* folder to the *c12* folder.

Starting a New Presentation File
1. Choose the **New** button from the **Standard** toolbar to invoke the **Open** dialog box.

2. Choose the **Metric** tab and double-click on the **Standard (mm).ipn** option to start a new metric presentation file.

Creating the Presentation View
1. Choose the **Create View** button from the **Presentation Panel** panel bar to invoke the **Select Assembly** dialog box.

2. Choose the **Explore Directories** button on the right of the **File** drop-down list in the **Assembly** area to invoke the **Open** dialog box.

3. Open the folder *\PersonalProject\c12\Drill Press Vice*. The *Drill Press Vice.iam* file will be displayed in this folder.

4. Double-click on the *Drill Press Vice.iam* file.

    The assembly will be selected and will be displayed along with its path in the **File** drop-down list in the **Assembly** area.

5. Accept the remaining default options and choose the **OK** button.

    The presentation view is created and the current view is changed to the isometric view, see Figure 12-20.

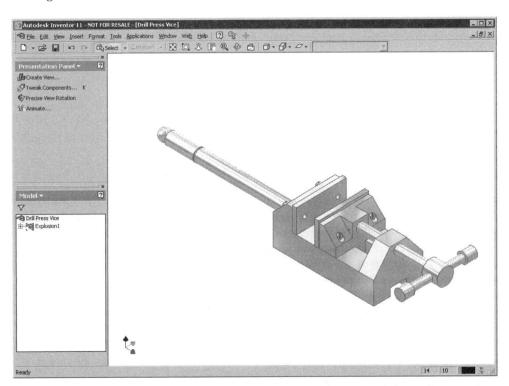

Figure 12-20 *Presentation file after creating the presentation view of the Drill Press Vice assembly*

Tweaking the Components

In this assembly, you need to apply the rotational tweak to the Clamp Screw, Clamp Screw Handle, and the two Handle Stops. After that you need to apply the linear tweak to the above-mentioned components and also to the Movable Jaw, the Jaw Face assembled with the Movable Jaw, and the two Cap Screws that are used to assemble the Jaw Face and the Movable Jaw.

1. Choose the **Tweak Components** button from the **Presentation Panel** panel bar to invoke the **Tweak Component** dialog box.

    As mentioned earlier, when you invoke the **Tweak Component** dialog box, the **Direction** button in the **Create Tweak** area is chosen by default and you are prompted to select the direction for the tweak.

2. Move the cursor close to the cylindrical face of the head of the Clamp Screw, see Figure 12-21.

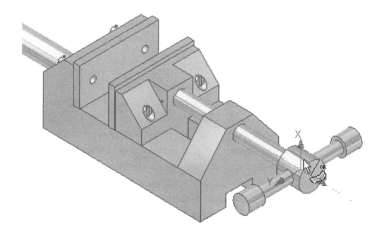

Figure 12-21 *Defining the tweak direction on the head of the Clamp Screw*

You will notice that the head of the Clamp Screw is displayed with a red outline and a triad is displayed on the component. Also, as shown in Figure 12-21, the Z axis of the triad coincides with the central axis of the Clamp Screw. This is displayed with a red dotted line.

3. Select the Clamp Screw when the triad is displayed and the Z axis of the triad coincides with the central axis of the Clamp Screw.

    Remember that if the Z axis of the triad is not coinciding with the central axis of the Clamp Screw, the resultant animation will not be what is actually required. In case you have selected a wrong direction of tweaking, choose the **Direction** button in the **Create Tweak** area again. You will be prompted to select the direction for the tweak.

    Now, you are prompted to select the components to be tweaked.

4. Select the Clamp Screw, the Clamp Screw Handle, and the two Handle Stops. The selected components are displayed with a blue outline.

5. Clear the **Display Trail** check box in the **Create Tweak** area.

This will ensure that the trails are not created when you tweak the components.

6. Select the **Rotational** radio button from the **Transformations** area.

    Elliptical arrows indicating a positive direction of rotation will be displayed on all the three axes of the triad. The Z axis of the triad and the elliptical arrow on it will be displayed in blue color.

7. Enter **720** as the value in the edit box on the right of the **Rotational** radio button. Choose the **Apply** button on the right of the edit box.

    The rotational tweak will be applied to the selected components. This is the first sequence of the tweak. Note that the effect of the rotational tweak will not be evident on the screen at this time.

    Next, you need to apply the linear tweak to the components. Some of the components are already selected and you need to select the remaining components to apply the linear tweak.

8. Select the Movable Jaw, the Jaw Face assembled with the Movable Jaw, and the two Cap Screws that are used to fasten the Jaw Face with the Movable Jaw.

    All the selected components are displayed with a blue outline. However, the rotational tweak is still active and you need to change it to the linear tweak.

9. Select the **Linear** radio button from the **Transformations** area.

    The elliptical arrows are no more displayed on the triad, but the Z axis of the triad is still displayed in blue. This suggests that the selected components will move along the Z axis of the triad.

10. Enter **25** as the value in the edit box in the **Transformations** area and then choose the **Apply** button on the right of the edit box.

    The selected components are moved to a distance of 25 mm along the Z axis of the triad. This is the second sequence of the tweak.

11. Choose the **Close** button to exit the **Tweak Component** dialog box. Now, choose the **Zoom All** button to increase the drawing display area and fit the assembly in the current view. The assembly, after tweaking, is shown in Figure 12-22.

Animating the Assembly
1. Choose the **Animate** button from the **Presentations Panel** panel bar to display the **Animation** dialog box.

2. Choose the **More** button provided on the lower right corner of the dialog box to expand it.

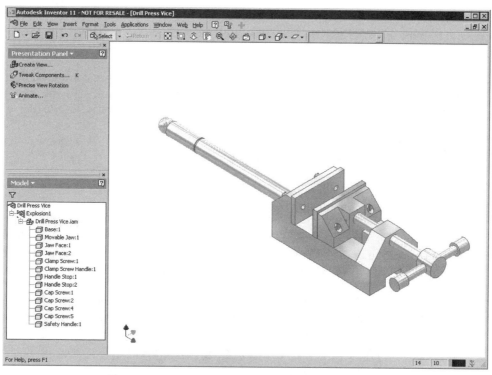

Figure 12-22 *Assembly after tweaking the components*

You will notice that two sets of sequences are displayed in the **Animation Sequence** area. You need to group these sequences to rotate and move the components at the same time.

3. Press and hold the SHIFT key down and then select all the sequences from the **Animation Sequence** area. All the sequences are displayed with a blue background.

4. Choose the **Group** button to group all the sequences in a single sequence.

5. Choose the **Apply** button so that the changes are applied to all the tweaked components.

    It is recommended that before you store the animation in the avi file, you should play it once to make sure the animation is correct.

6. Move the dialog box to the left of the screen such that it does not overlap with the assembly. Now, choose the **Auto Reverse** button to play the animation in the forward and the reverse direction.

    You will notice that all the tweaked components move in the forward direction and at the same time the Clamp Screw, Clamp Screw Handle, and the two Handle Stops rotate in the clockwise direction around the central axis of the Clamp Screw. This is because you applied the rotational tweak to the Clamp Screw, Clamp Screw Handle, and the two Handle Stops. After the forward cycle is completed, all the components will move in the reverse direction and the components to which the rotational tweak is applied will rotate in the counterclockwise direction. This gives the effect of working of the Drill Press Vice assembly.

Now, you can store the animation of the assembly in a *.avi* file. However, before you proceed with storing the animation in the avi file, it is recommended that you increase the interval of the sequence. This is because higher the interval value, the smoother is the *.avi* file.

7. Choose the **Cancel** button from the **Animation** dialog box to close it. Now, choose the **Browser Filters** button on the top left corner of the browser to display the flyout.

8. Choose the **Sequence View** option from the flyout.

   You will notice that **Task1** and the **Drill Press Vice.iam** options are displayed below the **Explosion1** heading in the browser. If these options are not displayed, click on the + sign located on left of **Explosion1**. These options will be displayed.

9. Right-click on **Task1** and then choose **Edit** from the shortcut menu to display the **Edit Task & Sequences** dialog box, see Figure 12-23.

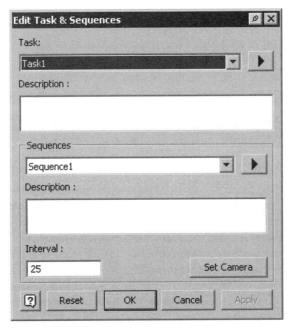

*Figure 12-23 The **Edit Task & Sequences** dialog box*

Tip. *Notice that there is only one sequence with the name* **Sequence1** *in the drop-down list in the* **Sequences** *area. This is because you grouped the two sequences together in a single sequence. If you invoke this dialog box before grouping the sequences, all the sequences you created will be displayed in the drop-down list.*

10. Enter **75** as the value in the **Interval** edit box and then choose the **Apply** button. Choose **OK** to close this dialog box.

11. Invoke the **Animation** dialog box again and then choose the **Record** button. When you choose this button, the **Save As** dialog box will be displayed for defining the name and location of the avi file.

The **Drill Press Vice** folder is open by default. If not, open this folder.

12. Select **AVI Files (*.avi)** from the **Save as type** drop-down list. Enter the name of the animation file as **Drill Press Vice** in the **File name** edit box and then choose the **Save** button.

The animation file will be saved with the name *Drill Press Vice.avi* in the folder *\PersonalProject \c12\Drill Press Vice*.

13. As soon as you choose the **Save** button in the **Save As** dialog box, the **Video Compression** dialog box is displayed. Accept the default options from this dialog box and choose **OK** to close this dialog box.

14. Make sure the **Minimize dialog during recording** check box in the **Motion** area is selected. Now, choose the **Auto Reverse** button.

The assembly will start animating and the dialog box will be minimized. After the animation is completed and the avi file is created, the dialog box will be restored on the screen.

15. Choose the **Record** button to exit the recording and then close the **Animation** dialog box.

The animation file is created and you now can view it by using the Windows Media Player.

16. Save the presentation file with the name give below and then close the file.

\PersonalProject\c12\Drill Press Vice\Tutorial2.ipn

Self-Evaluation Test

Answer the following questions and then compare your answers with those given at the end of this chapter:

1. Autodesk Inventor allows you to explode the assemblies in a special environment called the **Presentation** module. (T/F)

2. Different presentation templates are provided in the **Metric** tab of the **Open** dialog box for creating different presentations. (T/F)

3. If the explosion distance in the automatic explosion is large, the components start interfering with each other. (T/F)

4. When you open a new presentation file, only the **Create View** tool is available. (T/F)

5. The **Open** dialog box that is displayed while creating the design view can be used to select only the _____ files.

6. The animation of the assemblies can be stored in the _____ or _____ format.

7. There are two types of tweaks. They are _____ and _____.

8. You can animate the assemblies in the forward direction as well as in the reverse direction by choosing the _____ button in the **Motion** area of the **Animation** dialog box.

9. After you specify the name of the avi file in the **Save As** dialog box, the _____ dialog box is displayed.

10. The _____ button in the **Animation** dialog box is chosen when you want to club different tweak sequences together in a single sequence.

Review Questions

Answer the following questions:

1. You can modify the individual tweak values of the components. (T/F)

2. You can modify the interval value of an animation. (T/F)

3. You cannot ungroup the sequences grouped together. (T/F)

4. After grouping an animation, you need to choose the **Apply** button. (T/F)

5. The avi files can be viewed in the Windows Media Player. (T/F)

6. You cannot move the triad without moving the components but you can rotate it without rotating the components. (T/F)

7. Autodesk Inventor allows you to precisely rotate the presentation view in the **Presentation** module with the help of which one of the following tools?

    (a) **Rotate View**   (b) **Precise View**
    (c) **Precise View Rotation** (d) None

8. Which tweak will be used to rotate the selected components about a specified rotational axis?

    (a) Linear   (b) Circular
    (c) Rotational (d) None

9. The assemblies can be exploded with the help of which one of the following dialog boxes?

    (a) **Tweak Component**   (b) **Explode Component**
    (c) **Tweak Assemblies** (d) None

10. Which one of the following check boxes in the **Animation** dialog box is used to display the trails in the exploded view?

    (a) **Trail**   (b) **Trail On**
    (c) **Display Trail** (d) None

Exercise

Exercise 1

Create the animation of exploding and unexploding the Butterfly Valve assembly. The exploded view of the Butterfly Valve is shown in Figure 12-24. Save the animation with the name given below.

\PersonalProject\c12\Butterfly Valve\Butterfly Valve.avi   (**Expected time: 1 Hr**)

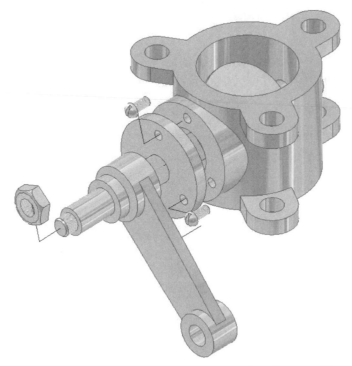

Figure 12-24 *Exploded view of the Butterfly Valve assembly*

Answers to Self-Evaluation Test
1. T, 2. F, 3. T, 4. T, 5. assembly, 6. *.wmv, .avi*, 7. linear, rotational, 8. **Auto Reverse**,
9. **Video Compression**, 10. **Group**

Chapter 13

Working with Special Design Tools

Learning Objectives

After completing this chapter, you will be able to:
- *Understand the concept of adaptivity and create adaptive parts.*
- *Define parameters for creating parts.*
- *Create standard and custom iPart factories.*
- *Place the iParts using the custom and standard iPart factories.*
- *Create 3D Sketches.*
- *Work with hybrid surface-solid models.*

ADAPTIVE PARTS

Adaptive parts are the ones that automatically change their dimensions based on the dimensions and functions of the other parts with which they are assembled. While creating adaptive parts or adaptive features, they should not be fully constrained. Instead, they should be under-dimensioned. The missing dimension will then be modified based on the sizes of other components. You can remove the adaptivity of components any time and add the missing dimensions so that the parts do not change their size. To convert a feature or sketch into an adaptive feature or sketch, right-click on it in the browser and choose **Adaptive** from the shortcut menu. Similarly, to convert a part into an adaptive part in the **Assembly** module, right-click on the part in the browser and choose **Adaptive** from the shortcut menu. Two arrows pointing in the counterclockwise direction will be displayed on the left of the adaptive part, feature, or sketch in the browser. Remember that components originally created in the other solid modeling tools and imported in the Inventor file cannot be converted into an adaptive part.

DEFINING PARAMETERS

Menu:	Tools > Parameters
Toolbar:	2D Sketch Panel > Parameters
	Part Features > Parameters

As mentioned earlier, every dimension in Autodesk Inventor is assigned a unique name, termed as parameter. When you specify the value for the dimension, the dimension parameter is equated in an expression with the value that you specified. Autodesk Inventor allows you to use parameters or expressions instead of entering the value while dimensioning a sketch. These parameters or expressions can also be entered in the edit boxes of a dialog box while creating a feature. You can create a new parameter by defining it in terms of the other parameter in an expression. The new parameters can be created before or after creating the sketch. You can use the **Parameters** tool to create new parameters. When you invoke this tool, the **Parameters** dialog box will be displayed, see Figure 13-1. This dialog box has two types of parameters. These are discussed next.

Model Parameters

Model parameters are those that are automatically created when you apply the dimensions to the entities or create a feature. The model parameters are displayed in a tabular form, as shown in Figure 13-1. The options in this table are discussed next.

Parameter Name

The **Parameter Name** column displays the names of parameters. To modify the name of a parameter, click on its field in the **Parameter Name** column. The field will change to an edit box and you can enter the new name in it. Note that you cannot duplicate the name of parameters. This means you cannot have two parameters with the same name.

Unit

The **Unit** column displays the unit of measuring the parameters. Note that you cannot modify the unit of a parameter.

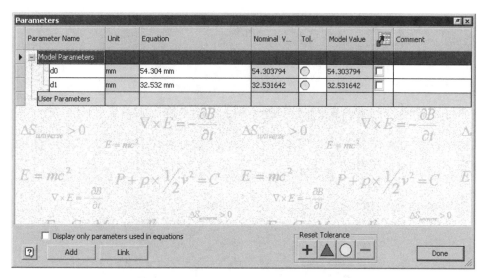

*Figure 13-1 The **Parameters** dialog box*

Equation

Equations are mathematical expressions, in which the parameters are equated with the algebraic or the trigonometric functions. Autodesk Inventor allows you to define the parameters using existing parameters and equations. For example, to define a parameter d2, you can use the equation such as d2=(d0/2+d1)*1.25, where d0 and d1 are existing parameters. However, in the d2 field of the **Equation** column, you will not enter "d2=". All you need to enter is (d0/2+d1)*1.25 as the equation. Since it is entered in the d2 field of the **Equation** column, Autodesk Inventor will automatically equate it with the d2 parameter.

You can also add tolerance to the parameter using the **Equation** column. To add tolerance, right-click on the **Equation** field of the selected parameter. A shortcut menu will be displayed. Choose **Tolerance** from this shortcut menu. The **Tolerance** dialog box will be displayed, as shown in Figure 13-2. You can set the tolerance parameters using the options in this dialog box.

Nominal Value

The **Nominal Value** column displays the ideal value that a particular parameter should have.

Tolerance

The **Tolerance** column is used to select the nominal, upper, or the lower tolerance size for the dimension. You can select the required tolerance size from this drop-down list.

Model Value

Generally, it is not possible for a component to be manufactured using the nominal values. As a result, you assign some tolerance to the dimension. The **Model Value** column shows the actual value after assigning the tolerance. The value in this column depends on the tolerance assigned to the dimension.

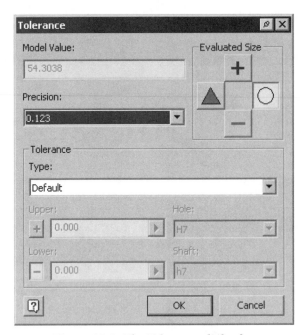

*Figure 13-2 The **Tolerance** dialog box*

Export Parameter

The **Export Parameter** column displays the check boxes for each parameter. If you select the check box of a parameter, that parameter will be added to the custom properties and can be displayed in the parts list.

Comment

The **Comment** column is used to enter some information about the selected parameter. To enter a value, click on this field. The field is changed into a text box and you can enter the desired comment in it.

User Parameters

User parameters are those that are defined by the user for specifying the dimensions of entities and features. To create a user-defined parameter, choose the **Add** button; a new row will be displayed in the **User Parameters** table. You can specify the new settings of the user-defined parameters in the table. Note that you can modify the units of the user-defined parameter. To modify the units, click on the field below the **Unit** column; the **Unit Type** dialog box will be displayed, as shown in Figure 13-3, and you can select the desired units from this dialog box.

Note

*The options in the **User Parameters** table are similar to those in the **Model Parameters** table.*

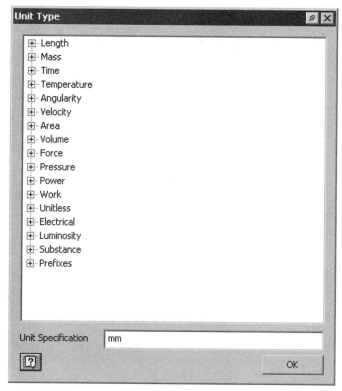

*Figure 13-3 The **Unit Type** dialog box*

Display only parameters used in equations

If the **Display only parameters used in equations** check box is selected, only those parameters will be displayed that are used in equations for defining other parameters.

Link Parameters

In addition to the model parameters and the user-defined parameters, Autodesk Inventor also allows you to create link parameters. The link parameters are created in a separate Microsoft Excel spreadsheet. Note that the model parameters and the user-defined parameters can be used only in the current file, whereas the link parameters can be used in as many number of files as you require. This is because the link parameters are external parameters that can be imported to any file. To import a link parameter, choose the **Link** button. When you choose this button, the **Open** dialog box is displayed, as shown in Figure 13-4. You can specify the name and the location of the Microsoft Excel spreadsheet by using the **Open** dialog box.

When you select the spreadsheet, its location and name will be displayed in the dialog box and a new table will be displayed. This table will show the parameters imported from the selected spreadsheet.

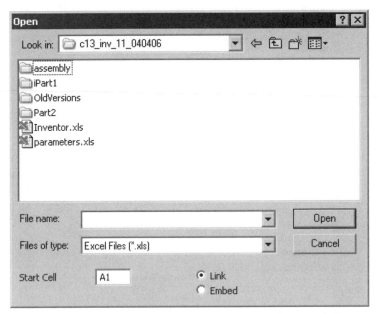

Figure 13-4 *The **Open** dialog box for selecting the spread sheet*

The following table gives a sample of the spreadsheet that can be created in order to be used as link parameters.

LEN	60
LEN1	30
WID	20
HT	15

WORKING WITH iPARTS

Autodesk Inventor allows you to use a special technique to create parts at the places where "**collaborative engineering**" is brought into use. This special technique is called iPart factories. The iPart factories can be shared by the members in the collaborative engineering environment to create iParts. The properties and dimensions of an iPart factories are saved in a table and you can use these dimensions to create an iPart in an assembly modeling environment.

Types of iPart Factories

In Autodesk Inventor, you can create two types of iPart factories. These are the Standard iPart factories and the Custom iPart factories. Both these types of iPart factories are discussed next.

Standard iPart Factories

The Standard iPart factories create iParts whose dimensions cannot be changed. This type of iPart factory is used to create standard parts. You can store these parts in the location of standard parts so that other members can also use them.

Custom iPart Factories

The Custom iPart factories create iParts with different dimensions. You can specify the dimension of the iPart while inserting it in the assembly modeling environment.

Creating iParts Factories

Menu bar:	Tools > Create iPart

The iPart factories are created using standard parts. However, it is recommended that the dimensions of the standard parts should be defined in terms of the model or user-defined parameters using the **Parameters** dialog box. To create the iPart factories, create a standard part using parameters and then choose the **Tools > Create iPart** from the menu bar. The **iPart Author** dialog box is displayed. The options in this dialog box are discussed next.

Parameters Tab

The options in the **Parameters** tab (Figure 13-5) are used to select the parameters and dimensions to be included in the iPart factory. When you invoke this tool, the **Parameters** tab is active. This tab of the **iPart Author** dialog box is divided into three areas. These areas are discussed next.

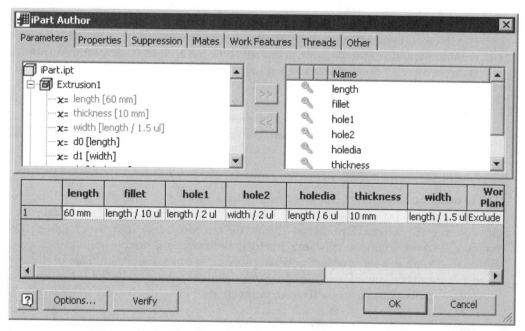

Figure 13-5 *The **Parameters** tab of the **iPart Author** dialog box*

Part Parameters Pane

The **Part Parameters** pane is on the left side in the **Parameters** tab. This pane lists all the parameters and dimensions in the current part.

Selected Parameters Pane

The **Selected Parameters** pane is on the right side in the **Parameters** tab. This pane lists all the parameters that are included in the iPart factory. All the user-defined parameters in the current file appear in this pane automatically when you invoke the **iPart Author** dialog box. You can remove a parameter from this pane by selecting it and choosing the **Remove** button (**<<**) on the left of this pane. The selected parameter is removed from the iPart factory and you cannot modify the value related to this parameter when you create an iPart using this iPart factory. Similarly, to add a parameter, select it from the **Part Parameters** pane and then choose the **Add** button (**>>**) button.

Assigning Keys. When you assign a key to a parameter, you can select its value from the available set of values of that parameter while creating an iPart from the custom iPart factory. To assign a key to a parameter, click on its corresponding key in the **Key** column; a key of numeric value 1 is assigned to the parameter and the key of that parameter turns blue. The keys of the remaining parameters are gray. To modify the numeric value of the key, click on the value; a flyout is displayed. Select the required key value from the flyout.

Making a Parameter Column Custom. Making a parameter column custom allows you to change its value while creating the iPart. To create a standard iPart factory, do not make any parameter column custom. However, to create a custom iPart factory, you need to make at least one parameter custom. To make a parameter column custom, first make sure no key is assigned to it. Next, right-click on it to display the shortcut menu. Choose **Custom Parameter Column** from the shortcut menu that is displayed; the selected parameter is made custom and the current iPart factory is made the custom iPart factory. Whenever you create an iPart using this factory, you can change the value of the custom parameter. The custom parameter column is displayed in blue in the **iPart Table** below the two list boxes in the **iPart Author** dialog box.

iPart Table

The **iPart Table** is available below the two list boxes. By default, this table has only one row with the default values of the parameters. The number of columns depend on the number of parameters in the **Selected Parameters** list box. You can add rows to this table by right-clicking on any cell of the table and choosing **Insert Row** from the shortcut menu. A new row is added to the table. Each row in the **iPart Table** represents a separate iPart in the iPart factory. You can edit the value of the iPart parameter by clicking on its field. The new iPart created using this iPart factory will use the value that you specify.

Note
*You can also make a particular cell of the **iPart Table** custom by right-clicking on it and choosing **Custom Parameter Cell** from the shortcut menu.*

Properties Tab

The options in the **Properties** tab (Figure 13-6) are used to select the summary of the component, the project properties, and the physical properties.

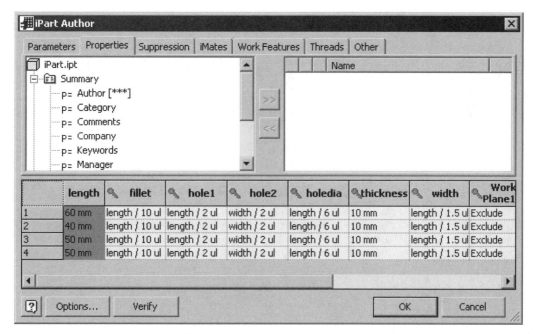

Figure 13-6 *The **Properties** tab of the **iPart Author** dialog box*

You can select a property from the **File Properties** pane on the right and add it to the **Selected Properties** pane on the right.

Suppression Tab

The options in the **Suppression** tab (Figure 13-7) are used to specify whether the selected features will be computed or suppressed while creating a part using the iPart factory.

If you want that a feature should be suppressed when you create a part using the iPart factory, select it from the **Model Features** pane and add it to the **Selected Features** pane. Next, right-click on it and choose **Custom Parameter Column** from the shortcut menu. The selected feature will be made custom and you can now specify whether the feature will be computed or suppressed while creating a part using the iPart factory. At that time if you select to suppress the feature, it will not appear in the model.

iMates Tab

The options in the **iMates** tab (Figure 13-8) are used to select the iMates applied to the part to be included in the iPart factory. To include the iMates in the iPart factory, select them from the **Model iMates** pane and add to the **Selected iMates** pane. The selected iMates will be added to the iPart factory.

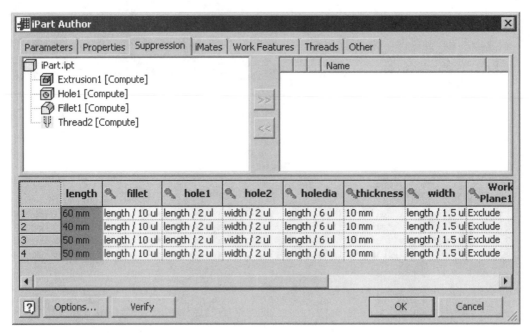

Figure 13-7 The **Suppression** tab of the **iPart Author** dialog box

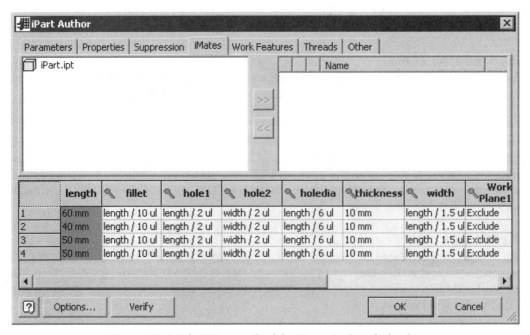

Figure 13-8 The **iMates** tab of the **iPart Author** dialog box

Work Features Tab

The options in the **Threads** tab (Figure 13-9) are used to add the parameters related to the threads to the iPart factory. You can select the threads parameters from the **Thread definition tree** and add it to the **Selected thread variable** pane.

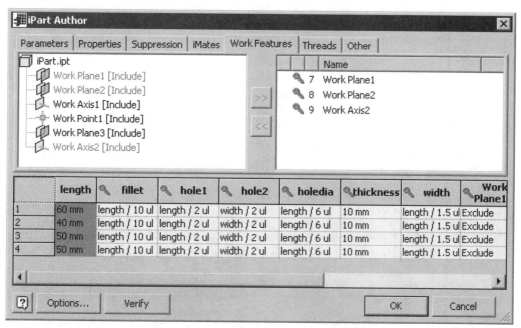

*Figure 13-9 The **Work Features** tab of the **iPart Author** dialog box*

Threads Tab

The options in the **Threads** tab (Figure 13-10) are used to add the parameters related to the threads to the iPart factory. You can select the threads parameters from the **Thread definition tree** and add it to the **Selected thread variable** pane.

Other Tab

The options in the **Other** tab (Figure 13-11) are used to add other parameters to the iPart factories. Note that these parameters cannot control the size of the part created using the iPart factory.

To add the other parameter, click on **Click here to add value** and then enter the value of the other parameter in the text box that appears in the **Other Parameters** pane. You will notice that the parameter that you add in the **Other Parameters** pane is also added to the **iPart Table**. You can modify the value of the individual cells by selecting each field of the new parameter in the **iPart Table**.

After setting the options in the various tabs of the **iPart Author** dialog box, save the file. The saved file will act as the iPart factory to place the parts in the assembly files.

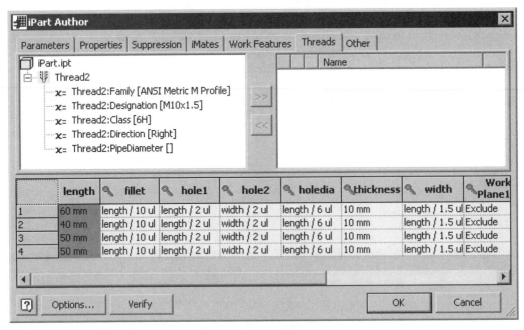

Figure 13-10 The **Threads** tab of the **iPart Author** dialog box

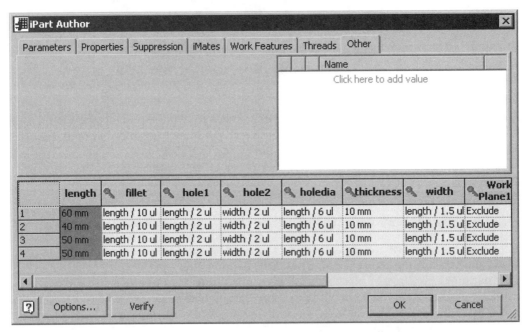

Figure 13-11 The **Other** tab of the **iPart Author** dialog box

Note

*When you create an iPart factory, an item **Table** is added to the browser above the **Origin** folder. If you click on the + sign located on the left of the **Table** in the browser, the tree view will expand and the parameters in the iPart factory will be displayed.*

Placing an iPart in an Assembly

You can insert an iPart in an assembly file using the **Place Component** tool. Depending on whether you select a standard iPart factory or the custom iPart factory, the dialog box for placing the part will differ. The procedure for placing both these types of iPart factories is discussed next.

Placing Standard iParts in an Assembly

To place a part using the standard iPart factory, invoke the **Place Component** tool. Select the standard iPart. The **Place Standard iPart** dialog box will be displayed. The options in the three tabs of this dialog box are discussed next.

Keys Tab

The **Keys** tab (Figure 13-12) consists of the **Predefined values** pane that displays the name and the value of the parameters that were assigned keys in the **Selected Parameters** pane of the **iPart Author** dialog box. Note that because it is a standard iPart, you cannot modify the value of any of the parameters in this dialog box. However, if more than one columns were created in the **iPart Table**, you can select the standard values from the list of available values.

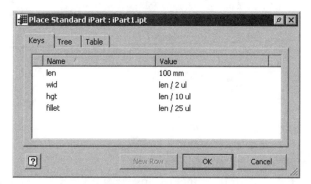

*Figure 13-12 The **Keys** tab of the **Place Standard iPart** dialog box*

Tree Tab

The **Tree** tab (Figure 13-13) displays the name and values, in the form of a tree view, of the parameters that were assigned keys in the **iPart Author** dialog box. You can click on the + sign on the left of each parameter to expand the tree view.

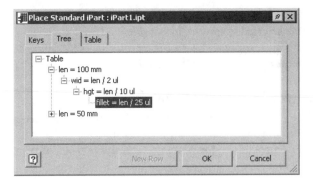

*Figure 13-13 The **Tree** tab of the **Place Standard iPart** dialog box*

Table Tab

The **Table** tab (Figure 13-14) displays the iPart table created in the **iPart Author** dialog box. As mentioned earlier, each row in this table represents a part. Also, different fields in the rows can be set different values in the **iPart Author** dialog box, As a result, you can select any row from this tab to insert the iPart. Depending on the value of the parameters defined for the selected row in the **iPart Author** dialog box, the part will be placed.

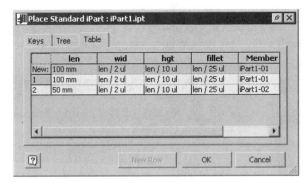

*Figure 13-14 The **Table** tab of the **Place Standard iPart** dialog box*

Placing Custom iParts in an Assembly

To place a part using the custom iPart factory, invoke the **Place Component** tool. Select the custom iPart. The **Place Custom iPart** dialog box will be displayed. The options in the three tabs of this dialog box are discussed next.

Keys Tab

The **Keys** tab of the **Place Custom iPart** dialog box (Figure 13-15) has two panes. The pane on the left is the **Predefined values** pane and displays all the parameters that were not made custom in the **iPart Author** dialog box. Note that you cannot modify the values of the parameters available in this pane. The pane on the right is called the **Custom values** pane. It displays all the parameters that were made custom using the **iPart Author** dialog box. To modify the value of the parameter, click on the **Value** field of that parameter. The field changes to an edit box. Enter the new value in it. The part that will be placed using this iPart factory will have the specified value of the parameter.

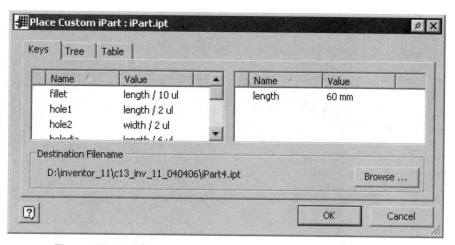

*Figure 13-15 The **Keys** tab of the **Place Custom iPart** dialog box*

Tree Tab

The **Tree** tab (Figure 13-16) also has two panes. The left pane displays the name and values, in the form of a tree view, of the parameters that were assigned keys in the **iPart Author** dialog box. The right pane displays all the parameters that were made custom using the **iPart Author** dialog box.

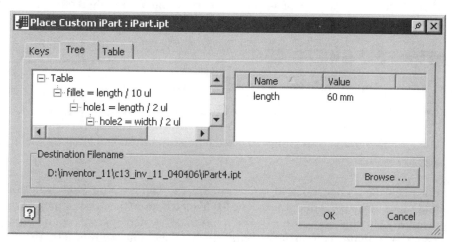

*Figure 13-16 The **Tree** tab of the **Place Custom iPart** dialog box*

Table Tab

The **Table** tab of the **Place Custom iPart** dialog box (Figure 13-17) is similar to that of the **Place Standard iPart** dialog box. It displays the iPart table that was created in the **iPart Author** dialog box. You can select the table to place the part based on the values in that table.

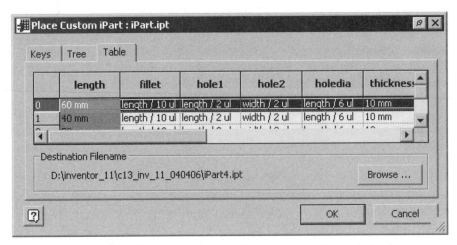

*Figure 13-17 The **Table** tab of the **Place Custom iPart** dialog box*

Changing the iParts in the Assembly File

If the iPart factory used to place the iPart in the assembly file has more than one row in the iPart
table, you can replace the iPart with the other iPart defined in the rows. To change the iPart,
right-click on **Table** under **iPart** in the browser; a shortcut menu will be displayed. Choose
Change Component from the shortcut menu. The **Place Standard iPart** dialog box or the **Place
Custom iPart** dialog box will be displayed. Choose the **Table** tab and then select the row of the
required iPart; the previous iPart will be replaced by the other iPart whose row you select.

CREATING 3D SKETCHES

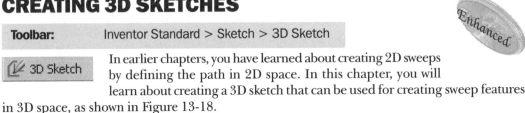

Toolbar: Inventor Standard > Sketch > 3D Sketch

In earlier chapters, you have learned about creating 2D sweeps
by defining the path in 2D space. In this chapter, you will
learn about creating a 3D sketch that can be used for creating sweep features
in 3D space, as shown in Figure 13-18.

To create a 3D sketch, choose the down arrow on the right of the **Sketch** button in the
Inventor Standard toolbar and then choose the **3D Sketch** button; the 3D sketching environment
will be activated. Note that because a 3D sketch has to be created, you will not be prompted to
select the sketching plane. As soon as you enter the 3D sketching environment, the **3D Sketch**
panel bar will be displayed above the browser. Notice that there are only a few tools for creating
a 3D sketch. Out of these tools, some were discussed in the previous chapters. The functions of
the remaining tools are discussed next.

Line

The **Line** tool is used to create a line in the 3D space. Note that similar to drawing the
line in a 2D sketch, you can create a line by specifying the points on the graphics
screen. The 3D line can also be created by using work points, vertices of an existing

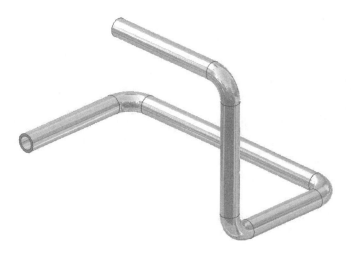

Figure 13-18 *Pipe created by sweeping a profile about a 3D path*

model, or center points of a cylindrical feature or hole. You can also turn on the option of creating bends at the corners of a 3D line. By default, this option is turned off. To turn on this option, invoke the **Line** tool in the 3D sketching environment and then right-click in the drawing window to display the shortcut menu. Choose the **Auto-Bend** option. Now, when you draw a 3D line, it will be automatically bent at the corners and the bend radius will be displayed. The bend radius will be displayed as the value at the first instance. At the remaining instances, the value will be displayed as the function of the first value. As a result, when you modify the first value, the remaining values will be modified automatically. If you want to modify any other value, double-click on it and modify it using the **Edit Dimension** toolbar. However, in this case, the modified value will no more be the function of the first value. Figure 13-19 shows a 3D line created by using the vertices of an existing model and the center points of the holes.

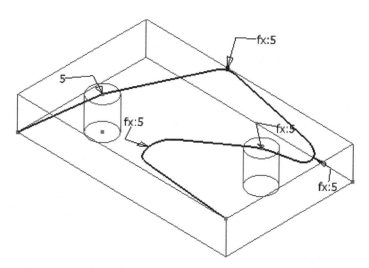

Figure 13-19 *3D line created using work points and vertices of a model*

Spline

The **Spline** tool is used to create splines in the 3D sketching environment. This tool works similar to the **Line** tool. This is the reason the 3D spline can only be created using work points, vertices of an existing feature, or center points of holes or cylindrical features.

> **Tip**. *Unlike sweeping the profile about the 2D paths, the profile that will be swept about a 3D path need not be normal to the start point of the path. You can draw the profile at an angle to the 3D path.*

Bend

The **Bend** tool is used to manually create the bends at the corners of the 3D line. When you invoke this tool, the **3D Sketch Bend** toolbar is displayed, as shown in Figure 13-20. You can specify the radius of the bend in this toolbar and then select the two lines that comprise the corner where the bend will be created. Note that at the corners at which the bend cannot be created, a cross will be displayed when you move the cursor over the line to select it. This cross suggests that you cannot select this line for creating a bend.

Figure 13-20 The 3D Sketch Bend toolbar

Include Geometry

The **Include Geometry** tool is used to include an existing 2D geometry in the 3D sketch. You can also select an edge of an existing model to be included in the 3D sketch. This is similar to projecting geometries or cutting edges. The only difference is that in this case, the selected entities are projected in a 3D sketching environment.

3D Intersection

The **3D Intersection** tool is used to create a 3D curve using the intersection of two surfaces, work planes, or existing components. When you invoke this tool, the **3D Intersection Curve** dialog box will be displayed, as shown in Figure 13-21.

When you invoke this dialog box, the **Select intersecting geometry** button is chosen by default. Select the first intersecting geometry. The **Select geometry to be intersected** button will be chosen automatically. Now, select the other intersecting geometry. When you select the second curve, a 3D curve will be created using the intersection of the two selected geometries.

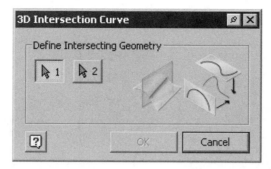

*Figure 13-21 The **3D Intersection Curve** dialog box*

Figure 13-22 shows two intersecting surfaces and Figure 13-23 shows the resultant 3D curve created using the intersecting surfaces.

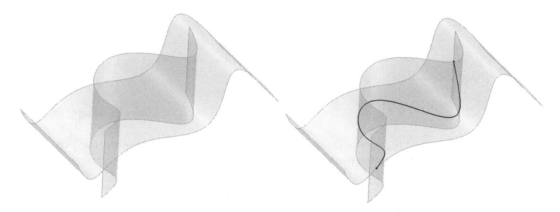

Figure 13-22 Intersecting surfaces   *Figure 13-23 3D curve created using the surfaces*

Note
You cannot save a file in the 3D sketching environment. You need to exit the 3D sketching environment to save the part file.

The other options in this environment are similar to those discussed in the 2D sketching environment and part modeling environment.

TUTORIALS

Tutorial 1

In this tutorial, you will create new parameters and then use them in sketching and extruding the model shown in Figure 13-24. The dimensioned sketch is shown in Figure 13-25. The sketch should be extruded to a distance of EXT. The dimensions in the sketch should be displayed as equations, as shown in Figure 13-25.

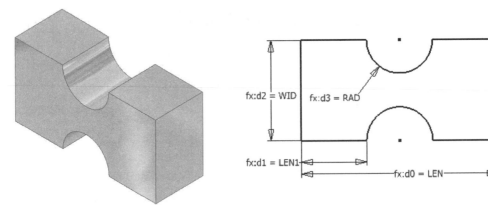

Figure 13-24 Model for Tutorial 1   **Figure 13-25** Sketch for the model

The numeric values of the parameters are given below.

LEN = 60
LEN1 = LEN/3
WID = LEN/2
RAD = LEN/6
EXT = LEN1   **(Expected time: 30 min)**

Before you start working on the tutorial, it is recommended that you outline the procedure for completing it. The following steps are required to complete this tutorial:

a. Start Autodesk Inventor and then start a new metric standard part file.
b. Create the sketch and add the required constraints, refer to Figure 13-26.
c. Invoke the **Parameters** tool and create the required parameters, refer to Figure 13-27.
d. Invoke the **Document Settings** dialog box and select the option to display the dimensions as equations.
e. Invoke the **General Dimension** tool and dimension the sketch by entering parameters instead of values in the **Edit Dimension** toolbar, refer to Figure 13-28.
f. Exit the sketching environment and extrude the sketch. Enter the parameter instead of value in the extrusion distance edit box.

Starting a New Part File

1. Start Autodesk Inventor and then choose **New** from the **Open** dialog box.

2. Choose the **Metric** tab and start a new metric part file. Exit the sketching environment and define a new sketch plane on the XZ plane.

Drawing the Sketch

1. Draw the sketch for the model by using the sketching tools. Add the required constraints. The sketch is shown in Figure 13-26.

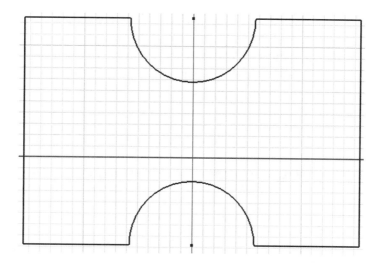

Figure 13-26 Sketch after adding the required constraints

Creating the Parameters

As mentioned earlier, the parameters are created by using the **Parameters** dialog box. You can invoke this dialog box by choosing the **Parameters** button from the **2D Sketch Panel** panel bar.

1. Choose the **Parameters** button from the **2D Sketch Panel** panel bar to invoke the **Parameters** dialog box.

2. Choose the **Add** button to enter a new row in the **User Parameters** table. Enter the name of the parameter as **LEN** in the **Parameter Name** field. Now, press ENTER.

    You will notice that a new row with the name LEN is created. The unit of the parameter is mm and the equation and value is 1. You now need to modify the value of the parameter.

 Note
*Remember that the parameter names are case sensitive. As a result, if you enter the name in all capital letters, you need to enter the same letters while defining the values in the **Edit Dimension** toolbar or any dialog box.*

3. Click on the **Equation** field of the LEN row. It will change into an edit box. Enter **60** as the value of this parameter in this edit box and then press ENTER.

    You will notice that the value of the **Nominal Value** field and the **Model Value** field is automatically changed to **60.000000**.

4. Again, choose the **Add** button to add another row in the **User Parameters** table.

5. Enter **LEN1** as the name of the parameter in the **Parameter Name** field.

6. Click on the **Equation** field and enter **LEN/3** in this field and then press ENTER.

   You will notice that the value in the **Value** field is automatically changed to **20.000000**. This is because the value of the LEN parameter is 60 and LEN1 = LEN/3 = 60/3 = 20. Also, notice that **ul** is automatically added on the right of the equation. You do not have to enter this while defining the equation as it is added by Autodesk Inventor.

7. Similarly, create the remaining parameters. The **Parameters** dialog box, after creating all the parameters, is shown in Figure 13-27. Choose **Done** to exit the **Parameters** dialog box.

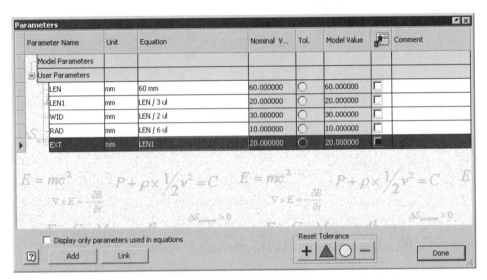

Figure 13-27 The **Parameters** dialog box after adding the user-defined parameters

Note
*As you have not dimensioned the sketch until now, no row will be displayed in the **Model Parameters** table. Once you add dimensions to the sketch, the parameters will be added in the Model Parameters table.*

Displaying the Dimensions as Equations

It is mentioned in the tutorial description that you need to display the dimensions as equations. Therefore, you need to select this option from the **Document Settings** dialog box.

1. Choose **Tools > Document Settings** from the menu bar to invoke the **Document Settings** dialog box.

2. Invoke the **Units** tab and select the **Display as expression** radio button from the **Modeling Dimension Display** area. Choose **Apply** and then choose **OK** to exit the dialog box.

Dimensioning the Sketch

Now, you can dimension the sketch using the parameters. As mentioned earlier, the parameters are case sensitive. This means that if you have specified the name of the parameter in capital letters, you need to enter the name in the **Edit Dimension** toolbar in capital letters. If you do not enter the name of the parameter as you specified it in the **Parameters** dialog box, the **Autodesk Inventor** dialog box will be displayed and you will be informed that this expression cannot be evaluated.

1. Invoke the **General Dimension** tool and then one by one select the vertical lines at the two ends of the sketch. Place the dimension below the sketch; the **Edit Dimension** toolbar is displayed.

2. Enter **LEN** as the value in the **Edit Dimension** toolbar and then press ENTER.

    You will notice that the dimension is automatically modified and is displayed as an equation on the graphics screen. This is because you selected the option of displaying the dimensions as equations.

3. Select the left vertical line and then place the dimension on the left of the sketch. Enter **WID** as the value in the **Edit Dimension** toolbar and then press ENTER.

4. Select the upper arc and then place the dimension on the left of the arc. Enter **RAD** as the value in the **Edit Dimension** toolbar and then press ENTER.

5. Select the lower left horizontal line and then place the dimension above the previous dimension. Enter **LEN1** as the value in the **Edit Dimension** toolbar and press ENTER.

    This completes the dimensioning of the sketch. The sketch, after adding the dimensions, is shown in Figure 13-28. In this figure, the grid lines and the axes are not displayed for the clarity of the sketch.

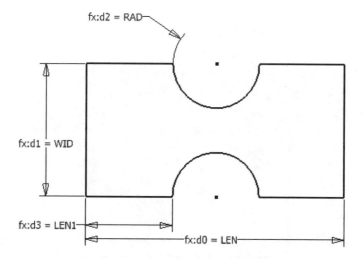

Figure 13-28 Sketch displaying the dimensions as equations

Note

If you do not dimension the sketch in the same sequence as mentioned above, the names of the model parameters with which the user parameters are equated will be different from those shown in Figure 13-27.

Extruding the Sketch

1. Exit the sketching environment and then change the current view to the isometric view.

2. Invoke the **Extrude** dialog box and then enter **EXT** as the value in the edit box provided in the **Extents** area. Accept the remaining default options and then choose the **OK** button.

    The sketch will be extruded through a distance defined by the EXT parameter.

3. Save the model with the name given below and then close the file.

\PersonalProject\c13\Tutorial1.ipt

Tutorial 2

In this tutorial, you will create the assembly of the Outer Plate and the Inner Plate shown in Figure 13-29. The dimensions of the Outer Plate are shown in Figure 13-30. Create the Inner Plate as an adaptive part that should automatically adjust its size to fit inside the Outer Plate. Apply the **Mate** constraints with an offset of 10 mm to all the outer faces of the Inner Plate and the inner faces of the groove in the Outer Plate. After assembling the components, edit the inner cavity of the Outer Plate such that the Inner Plate again adjusts its dimensions automatically.   **(Expected time: 1 Hr)**

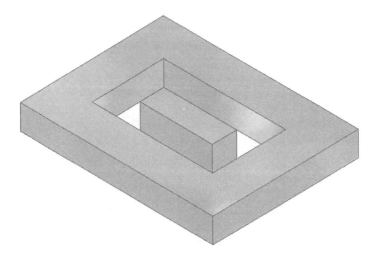

Figure 13-29 *Assembly for Tutorial 2*

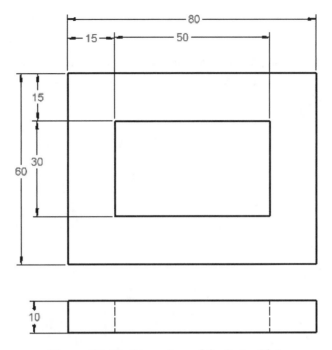

Figure 13-30 *Dimensions of the Outer Plate*

Note
Because the Inner Plate has to be an adaptive part, its dimensions are not required.

The following steps are required to complete this tutorial:

a.   Start a new metric assembly file and then create the Outer Plate, refer to Figure 13-31.
b.   Invoke the **Create Component** tool and then select the top face of the Outer Plate as the
     sketching plane for the Inner Plate.
c.   Make the sketch of the Inner Plate adaptive and then set the parameters in the **Assembly**
     tab of the **Options** dialog box.
d.   Sketch the Inner Plate and then extrude it up to the bottom face of the Outer Plate.
e.   Save the model and then exit the part modeling environment, refer to Figure 13-32.
f.   Add the **Mate** constraint to all the inner faces of the groove in the Outer Plate and outer
     faces of the Inner Plate. The size of the Inner Plate will automatically change in order to
     adjust inside the Outer Plate, refer to Figure 13-33.
g.   Modify the dimensions of the inner cavity of the Outer Plate. The size of the Inner Plate
     will again change automatically in order to retain the design intent, refer to Figure 13-35.

Creating the Outer Plate
You can directly create the Outer Plate and the Inner Plate in the assembly file.

1. Start a new metric standard assembly file and then create the Outer Plate on the XY plane. The assembly file, after creating the Outer Plate, is shown in Figure 13-31.

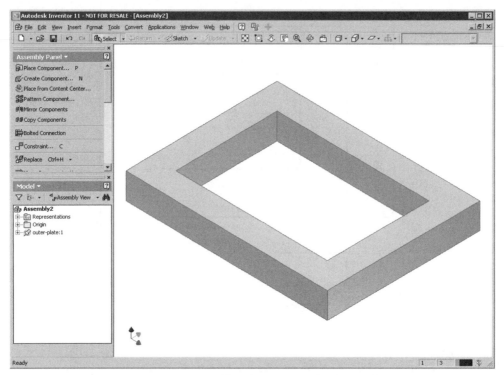

Figure 13-31 *Assembly after creating the Outer Plate*

Creating the Inner Plate

The Inner Plate will be sketched by taking the top face of the Outer Plate as the sketching plane. Remember that the sketch plane should be constrained to the selected face.

1. Invoke the **Create Component** tool. Make sure that the **Constrain sketch plane to selected face or plane** check box is selected in the **Create In-Place Component** dialog box. The name of the component should be Inner Plate. Choose **OK** in the dialog box and then select the top face of the Outer Plate as the sketching plane

2. Right-click on **Sketch1** in the browser and choose **Adaptive** from the shortcut menu. This will make the Inner Plate adaptive and this component will now adjust its size automatically based on the surrounding environment.

3. Choose **Tools > Application Options** from the menu bar to display the **Options** dialog box. Choose the **Assembly** tab to display the options in this tab.

4. Select all the check boxes in the **In-Place Features** area.

The check boxes are selected so that the model you create is adaptive. Also, because you will extrude the model up to the bottom face of the Inner Plate, selecting these options will automatically modify the new part when the parent part is modified.

5. Choose **Apply** and then choose **OK**. Draw the sketch for the Inner Plate and then extrude it up to the bottom face of the Outer Plate. Save the part file and then exit the part modeling environment.

    You will not add dimensions to the Inner Plate since it is an adaptive part. The assembly, after creating the Inner Plate, is shown in Figure 13-32.

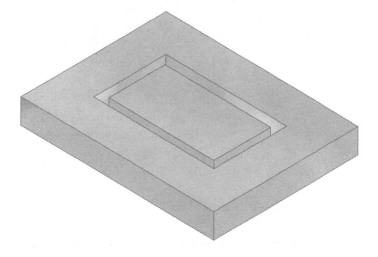

Figure 13-32 *Assembly after creating the Inner Plate*

6. Now, apply the **Mate** constraint with an offset of 10 mm on the inner left vertical face of the Outer Plate and the outer left vertical face of the Inner Plate. The Inner Plate will shift toward the right.

7. Change the display type to wireframe and then apply the **Mate** constraint with an offset of 10 mm on the inner lower horizontal face of the Outer Plate and the outer lower horizontal face of the Inner Plate. The Inner Plate will shift upwards.

8. Now, apply the **Mate** constraint with an offset of 10 mm on the inner right vertical face of the Outer Plate and the outer right vertical face of the Inner Plate.

    Notice that the size of the Inner Plate is reduced in order to fit inside the cavity of the Outer Plate. This is because of the adaptive property of the Inner Plate.

9. Similarly, apply the **Mate** constraint with an offset of 10 mm on the inner upper horizontal face of the Outer Plate and the outer upper horizontal face of the Inner Plate.

Notice that the size of the Inner Plate is further reduced, in order to fit inside the cavity of the Outer Plate.

10. Close the **Place Constraint** dialog box and then change the display type back to shaded. The assembly, after applying the constraint, is shown in Figure 13-33. Notice the change in the size of the Inner Plate.

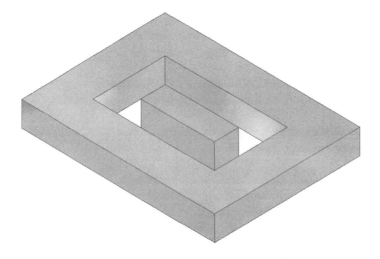

Figure 13-33 Assembly after applying the constraint

Modifying the Dimensions of the Cavity of the Outer Plate

You can edit the dimensions of the cavity of the Outer Plate in the assembly file itself. Since the Inner Plate is an adaptive part, it will automatically change its dimensions when the dimensions of the cavity are modified.

1. Double-click on **Outer Plate:1** in the browser to activate this component.

2. Modify the dimensions of the cavity, as shown in Figure 13-34.

3. Now, choose **Return** from the **Inventor Standard** toolbar to exit the sketching environment.

4. Again, choose **Return** from the **Inventor Standard** toolbar to exit the part modeling environment. Change the current view to the isometric view.

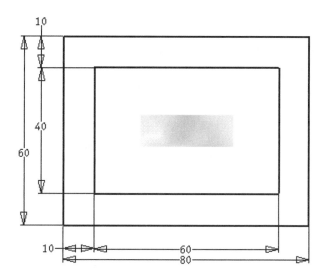

Figure 13-34 *Modifying the dimensions of the cavity*

You will notice that the dimensions of the Inner Plate are again modified in order to retain the design intent of the assembly. The assembly after modifying the dimensions of the cavity is shown in Figure 13-35. Notice the change in the dimensions of the Inner Plate.

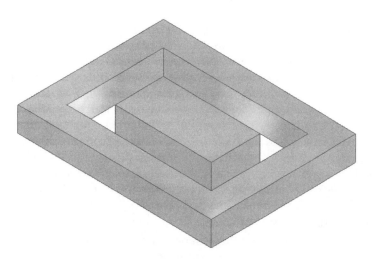

Figure 13-35 *Modified assembly*

5. Save the assembly with the name *\PersonalProject\c13\Tutorial2.iam*. You will be prompted to save the individual part files. Save the changes in the part files also.

Tutorial 3

In this tutorial, you will create the pipe in 3D space, as shown in Figure 13-36. Assume the dimensions of the pipe.   **(Expected time: 30 min)**

Figure 13-36 *Pipe for Tutorial 3*

The following steps are required to complete this tutorial:

a.   Create the first 2D sketch consisting of three lines on the XY plane and then exit the sketching environment, refer to Figure 13-37.
b.   Define a new work plane normal to the existing sketch and then create the second 2D sketch on this new work plane, refer to Figure 13-38. The start point of the first line in the second sketch should be the endpoint of the right vertical line in the first sketch.
c.   Exit the sketching environment and then invoke the 3D sketching environment.
d.   Using the **Include Geometry** tool, select all the lines to be included in the 3D sketch.
e.   Add bends on all corners and then exit the 3D sketching environment, refer to Figure 13-39.
f.   Define a new work plane at the start point of the path and then sketch the profile of the pipe. Take the reference of the start point of the first line for drawing the sketch.
g.   Exit the sketching environment and sweep the sketch about the 3D path.

Drawing the First 2D Sketch

1.   Invoke the **Open** dialog box and then choose the **Metric** tab.

2.   Start a new metric part file and then draw the first sketch on the XY plane, as shown in Figure 13-37.

Drawing the Second 2D Sketch

The second 2D sketch will be created on a work plane that is defined normal to the third line of the first 2D sketch. Therefore, first you need to define a new work plane normal to the third line of the sketch.

1. Define a new work plane normal to the right vertical line in the sketch and then select it as the sketching plane for drawing the next 2D sketch.

2. Draw the next sketch starting from the origin of the sketch plane. The origin of the sketch plane is the endpoint of the right vertical line of the first sketch.

   To make sure that the start point of the line is at the origin even after dimensioning, you need to project the third line of the sketch. The line will be projected as a point, which will be placed at the origin. Now, apply the **Coincident** constraint between the endpoint of the line and the projected point.

3. Exit the sketching environment and turn off the display of the work plane. The first and the second 2D sketches are shown in Figure 13-38.

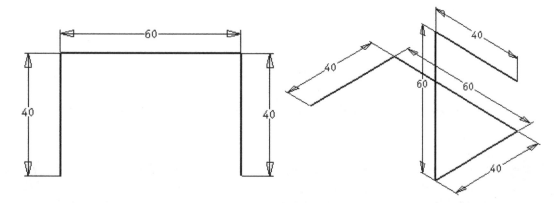

Figure 13-37 First 2D sketch   *Figure 13-38* After drawing the second 2D sketch

Creating the 3D Sketch

1. Choose the down arrow on the right of **Sketch** in the **Inventor Standard** toolbar and choose **3D Sketch** to invoke the 3D sketching environment.

2. Choose the **Include Geometry** button from the **3D Sketch** toolbar or choose **Include Geometry** from the **3D Sketch** panel bar.

3. One by one, select all lines in the first 2D sketch and the second 2D sketch.

4. Choose the **Bend** button to display the **3D Sketch Bend** toolbar. Enter **10** as the value in this toolbar and then select all the lines that form the corners of the 3D sketch.

   You will notice that a fillet kind of bend is created on all the corners and the dimension is displayed on all the bends.

5. Exit the 3D sketching environment.

6. Now, turn off the visibility of the two 2D sketches using the browser.

    The 3D sketch, after turning off the visibility of the 2D sketches, is shown in Figure 13-39.

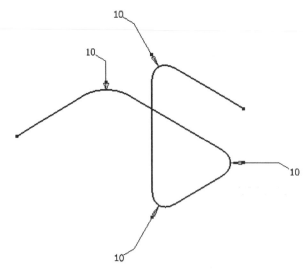

Figure 13-39 *3D sketch after turning off the visibility of the 2D sketches*

 Note
If you are not able to fillet the vertex at the intersection of the first and the second 2D sketch, this implies that the endpoint of the first 2D sketch is not coincident with that of the second 2D sketch. In other terms, the start point of the first line of the second 2D sketch is not at the origin. As a result, you need to edit the second 2D sketch and move it to the origin.

Creating the Profile for the Sweep Feature

To create the profile, you need to first define a new work plane at the start point of the first 2D sketch. Next, select this work plane as the new sketching plan and draw the sketch of the profile.

1. Define a new work plane at the start point of the 3D path, which is from where the first 2D sketch started. Select the work plane as the new sketching plane.

2. Draw the sketch of the profile of the sweep feature. The sketch of the profile consists of two concentric circles. The center of the circles should be at the start point of the first line of the 3D path. Specify 6 mm as the diameter of the outer circle and 4 mm as the diameter of the inner circle. Note that the center point of the circles should lie at the origin.

3. Exit the sketching environment.

Sweeping the Profile about the 3D Path

1. Invoke the **Sweep** dialog box and select the area between the two circles as the profile of the sweep feature. The area between the two circles turn blue.

2. Choose the **Path** button in the **Shape** tab of the **Sweep** dialog box and then select the 3D path as the path of the sweep feature. The complete 3D path turns blue.

3. Choose **OK** to close the **Sweep** dialog box. The final pipe for Tutorial 3 is shown in Figure 13-40.

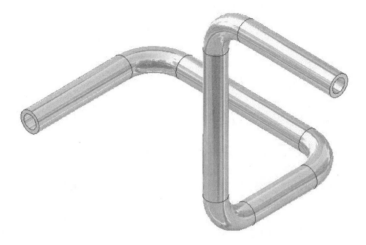

Figure 13-40 *Pipe for Tutorial 3*

4. Save this model with the name *\PersonalProject\c13\Tutorial3.ipt*.

Tutorial 4

In this tutorial, you will open the model saved in Tutorial 1 and add another parameter to it with the name FILLET, where FILLET = LEN/10. You will fillet the model using this parameter, as shown in Figure 13-41. You will then change this model into a custom iPart factory. Make the LEN and FILLET variables custom and suppress the FILLET variable. Finally, place two iParts in an assembly file using the custom iPart factory that you created. The details of the two iParts that you need to place are given below.

iPart 1
Value of LEN = 60
Suppress the fillet in the model

iPart 2
Value of LEN = 100   **(Expected time: 30 min)**

Figure 13-41 *Model after filleting the edges using the FILLET parameter*

The following steps are required to complete this tutorial:

a. Open the *Tutorial1.ipt* file and save it with the name *Tutorial4.ipt*.
b. Open the *Tutorial4.ipt* file and create a new user-defined parameter FILLET. The value of this parameter is LEN/10.
c. Fillet the model using the FILLET parameter.
d. Invoke the **iPart Author** dialog box and make the LEN parameter custom.
e. Add one more row in the iPart table. Change the value of the LEN parameter to 100.
f. Invoke the **Suppression** tab and suppress the FILLET variable.
g. Make the FILLET variable custom.
h. Save the file and then open a new assembly file.
i. Place iParts in an assembly file using the custom iPart factory created earlier. The details of the iParts to be placed are given in the tutorial description.

Opening the Tutorial 1 File

1. Open the *Tutorial1.ipt* file and save it with the name *Tutorial4.ipt*.

2. Close the current file and then open the *Tutorial4.ipt* file.

Adding a User-Defined Parameter

You need to add a user-defined parameter in the current file that will be used to fillet the model. Because the **Parameters** dialog box can also be invoked from the **Part Features** panel bar, you do not need to invoke the sketching environment.

1. Choose the **Parameters** button from the **Part Features** panel bar to invoke the **Parameters** dialog box.

2. Choose the **Add** button to enter a new row in the **User Parameters** table. Enter the name of the parameter as FILLET in the **Parameter Name** field. Now, press ENTER.

    A new row of the user-defined parameter is added. The value of this parameter at this stage is 1.00 mm in the **Equation** column. You need to equate this parameter in terms of the LEN parameter.

3. Click on the **Equation** field in the FILLET row. The field changes to an edit box.

4. Enter LEN/10 in the edit box and then press ENTER. You will notice that the value of this parameter automatically changes to **6.000000** in the **Nominal Value** and **Model Value** edit boxes.

5. Exit the **Parameters** dialog box.

Adding a Fillet to the Model Using the FILLET Parameter

1. Choose **Fillet** from the **Part Features** panel bar to invoke the **Fillet** dialog box.

2. Select the four edges to be filleted from the model.

3. Enter FILLET as the value in the **Radius** field of the **Constant** tab of the **Fillet** dialog box.

    Remember that when you enter the values in terms of parameters, you need to delete **mm** also from the edit boxes.

4. Choose **OK**. The fillet is added to the model and looks similar to the one shown in Figure 13-42.

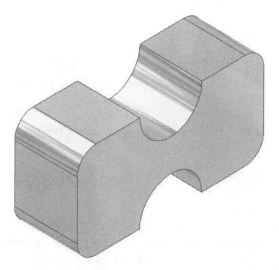

Figure 13-42 *Filleted model viewed from a different direction*

Creating Custom iPart Factory

Next, you need to create the custom iPart factory. The iPart factory will be made custom by making the LEN parameter custom and also suppressing the fillet feature.

1. Choose **Tools > Create iParts** from the menu bar; the **iPart Author** dialog box is displayed and the **Parameters** tab is active.

    All the user-defined parameters are added to the **Selected Parameters** pane. You will also notice that only one row is available in the iPart table. This row has the default values of the variables.

2. Right-click on the LEN variable in the iPart table to display the shortcut menu. Choose **Custom Parameter Column** from it.

    The **LEN** column in the iPart table turns blue and the key on the left of this parameter in the **Selected Parameters** pane is removed.

3. Click on the key corresponding to the LEN1 parameter. A key with numeric value 1 will be assigned to the LEN1 parameter.

4. Choose the **Suppression** tab and then select **Fillet1** from the **Model Features** tab. Choose the **Add** button (**> >**) to add this feature to the **Selected Features** pane.

5. Next, right-click on **Fillet1** in the iPart table and choose **Custom Parameter Column** from the shortcut menu. This feature is made custom. As a result, you can suppress or compute it while inserting the iParts using this iPart factory.

    This completes the iPart factory. You can now save it and use it to place the iParts.

6. Choose the **Save** button from the **Inventor Standard** toolbar and then close this file.

Placing iParts Using the Custom iPart Factory

The iParts are placed in the assembly files. This is the reason you need to start a new assembly file.

1. Start a new assembly file and then invoke the **Place Component** tool; the **Open** dialog box is displayed.

2. Select the *Tutorial4.ipt* file to place the iParts; the **Place Custom iPart** dialog box is displayed.

    The **Predefined values** pane shows only the LEN1 parameter. This is because only this variable was assigned the key. On the other hand, the **Custom values** pane shows the LEN parameter and the **Fillet1** feature. As a result, you can modify the value of the LEN parameter and suppress or compute the Fillet1 feature.

3. Click on the **Value** field of the **Fillet1** feature in the **Custom values** pane; the field is changed into a drop-down list.

4. Select **Suppress** from this drop-down list. Next, click anywhere on the screen to place the component.

5. Choose **OK** and then choose **Dismiss** to close the dialog box.

    Notice that an iPart is placed in the assembly file and the fillet in this part is suppressed.

> **Tip**. *If you want to unsuppress the fillet in the iPart placed in the current assembly file, click on the + sign located on the left of the part in the browser; the tree view expands and **Table** and **Origin** appear in the browser. Right-click on the **Table** and choose **Change Component** from the shortcut menu; the **Place Custom iPart** dialog box is displayed. Change **Suppress** to **Compute** in the **Value** field of **Fillet1**. Choose **OK** to exit the dialog box; the fillet is computed and is now shown in the model.*

6. Next, you need to place another iPart with a different value. Invoke the **Place Component** tool and select the *Tutorial4.ipt* file to place the iPart.

7. The **Place Custom iPart** dialog box is displayed. Click on the **Value** field of the **LEN** parameter; the field changes into an edit box.

8. Enter **100** as the value in this edit box and then click anywhere on the graphics screen. Right-click and choose **Done** from the shortcut menu; the component is placed and the dialog box is closed.

    You can now use these components to create an assembly.

Tutorial 5

In this tutorial, you will use the hybrid surface-solid modeling to create the model shown in Figures 13-43 and 13-44. The dimensions of this model are provided in the tutorial steps.

(Expected time: 45 min)

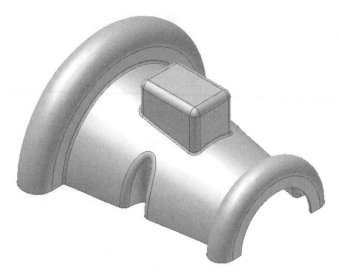

Figure 13-43 *Model for Tutorial 5*

Figure 13-44 *Alternate view of the model for Tutorial 5*

The following steps are required to complete this tutorial:

a.   Open a new part file and then create the sketch shown in Figure 13-45 on the default XY plane.

b.   Revolve this sketch through an angle of 180-degree such that the final output is a surface, as shown in Figure 13-46.

c.   Create two extruded surfaces, as shown in Figure 13-48.

d.   Using the **Face Split** option, split the surfaces, as shown in Figure 13-49.

e. Using the **Delete Face** tool, delete the faces shown in Figure 13-52.
f. Define a new work plane at an offset distance of 45 mm and then create the sketch shown in Figure 13-53.
g. Using the last sketch, split the base surface and then delete the face, as shown in Figure 13-54.
h. Create a 3D sketch on the deleted face and then share the sketch that was used in splitting the base surface. Using the shared sketch and the 3D sketch, create a lofted surface, as shown in Figure 13-56.
i. Create a boundary patch to close the top face of the lofted surface, as shown in Figure 13-57.
j. Stitch all the surfaces together and fillet all the sharp edges, as shown in Figure 13-59.
k. Thicken the surface using the **Thicken/Offset** tool, as shown in Figure 13-60.

Creating the Base Surface

The base surface will be created using a sketch drawn on the XY plane. This sketch will be revolved through an angle of 180-degree.

1. Open a new metric standard part file and draw the sketch shown in Figure 13-45 on the XY plane. Note that a sketch point is placed at the origin and is fixed using the **Fix** constraint. The sketch is dimensioned using this point to make it a fully constrained sketch. Remember that a sketch is fully constrained only when all its entities turn blue in color.

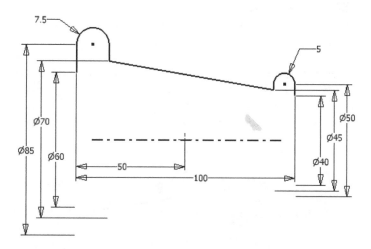

Figure 13-45 Fully constrained sketch for the base surface

2. Exit the sketching environment and then invoke the **Revolve** tool; the **Surface** button is automatically chosen in the **Output** area and you are prompted to select the profile.

3. Select the original sketch and then select the center line as the axis of revolution; the preview of the resultant surface is displayed.

4. Select **Angle** from the drop-down list in the **Extents** area and set the value of the angle to 180-degree and then Choose **OK**. The base surface is created, as shown in Figure 13-46.

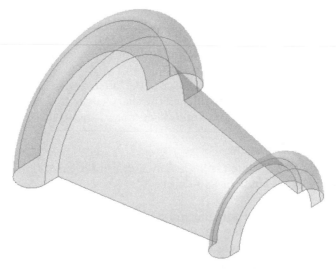

Figure 13-46 Base surface

Creating the Side Surfaces

The two side cuts in the base surface are created by splitting the base surface using the two surfaces at sides. Therefore, you first need to create the side surfaces.

1. Define a new sketch plane on the XY plane and then create two ellipses, as shown in Figure 13-47. Note that the center points of the two ellipses are made coincident with the edges of the base surface. Also, as the bottom ellipse is a mirror image of the upper ellipse, you need to dimension only one of the ellipses.

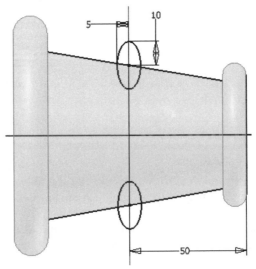

Figure 13-47 Fully dimensioned sketch for the side surfaces

Next, you need to extrude the two ellipses to create surfaces. However, when you extrude the sketches as surfaces, you cannot select more than one sketch. In this case, there are two separate ellipses, resulting in two sketches. Therefore, you need create one surface and then share the sketch to create the other.

Note

You cannot mirror surfaces and so you need to create both the side surfaces.

2. Exit the sketching environment and then extrude the lower ellipse as the surface through a distance of 30 mm.

3. Share the previous sketch using the browser and then extrude the upper ellipse as a surface through a distance of 30 mm. Turn off the visibility of the shared sketch using the browser. Figure 13-48 shows the model after creating the two side surfaces.

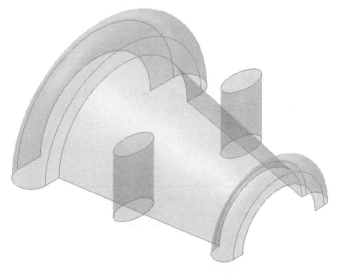

Figure 13-48 Model after creating the side surfaces

Creating Side Cuts Using the Side Surfaces

To create the side cuts, the two side surfaces will first be used to split the base surface. Next, the base surface will be used to split the side surfaces. Finally, all the unwanted surfaces will be deleted using the **Delete Face** tool.

1. Invoke the **Trim Surface** tool and select the lower extruded surface as the trim tool.

2. Now, select the portion common to the base surface and the extruded surface as the portion to be trimmed, as shown in Figure 13-49. Choose **OK** from the dialog box.

3. Similarly, using the upper extruded surface as the trimming tool, trim the base revolved surface.

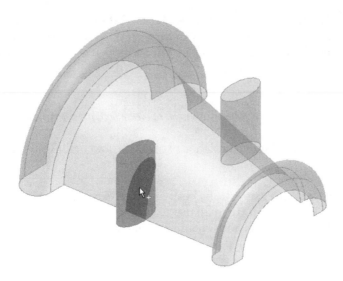

Figure 13-49 Trimming the base surface

4. Now, using the base surface as the trim tool, trim the lower extruded surface by clicking on its outer portion, as shown in Figure 13-50.

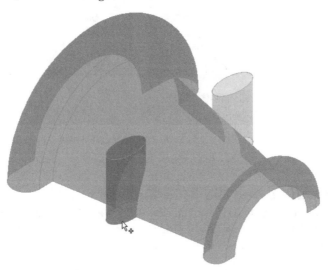

Figure 13-50 Trimming the lower extruded surface

5. Similarly, trim the upper extruded surface using the base surface as the trim tool. Remember that you need to select the outer portion of the surface to trim, as shown in Figure 13-51. The model, after deleting all the unwanted surfaces, is shown in Figure 13-52.

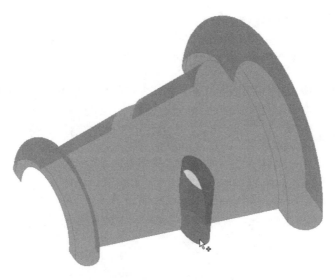

Figure 13-51 *Trimming the other extruded surface*

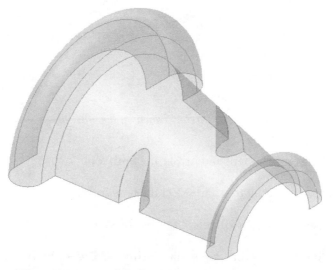

Figure 13-52 *Model after deleting the unwanted surfaces*

Creating the Lofted Surface

Next, you need to create the lofted surface. To create this surface, you first need to create a work plane at an offset distance of 45 mm from the XY plane.

1. Create a new work plane at an offset distance of 45 mm in the upward direction from the XY plane.

2. Select this plane as the sketching plane and draw the sketch, as shown in Figure 13-53.

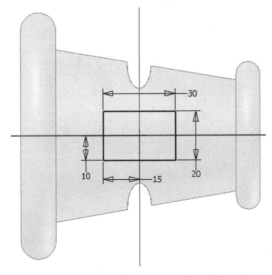

Figure 13-53 Sketch drawn on the offset plane

3. Exit the sketching environment and invoke the **Split** tool.

4. Select the sketch as the split tool and select the base surface as the face that will be split.

5. Choose **OK**; the base surface will be split using the sketch.

6. Delete the split surface on the base surface using the **Delete Face** tool. The model, after deleting the split surface, is shown in Figure 13-54.

    Next, you will create a 3D sketch using the edges of the surface that is removed from the base surface.

7. Invoke the 3D sketching environment and then choose **Include Geometry** from the **3D Sketch** panel bar.

8. Select the four edges that resulted from the split surface that was removed from the base surface, see Figure 13-55.

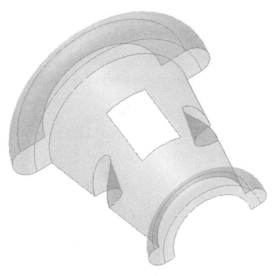

Figure 13-54 *Model after deleting the split surface*

Figure 13-55 *3D sketch created using the edges*

9. Exit the 3D sketching environment and then share the rectangular sketch (refer to Figure 13-53) that was used to split the base surface.

10. Create a lofted surface between the two sketches.

11. Turn off the visibility of the sketches. The model, after creating the lofted surface, is shown in Figure 13-56.

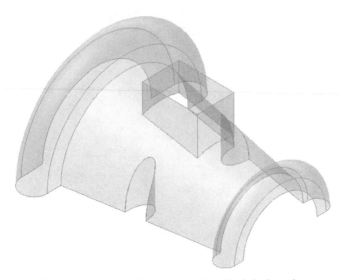

Figure 13-56 Model after creating the lofted surface

Next, you need to cover the top face of the lofted surface. This can be easily done using the boundary patch.

12. Choose **Boundary Patch** from the **Part Features** panel bar to invoke the **Boundary Patch** dialog box.

13. Select the edges on top of the lofted surface.

14. Choose **OK** from the dialog box. A boundary patch is created that covers the top of the lofted surface, see Figure 13-57.

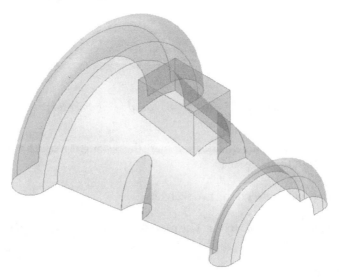

Figure 13-57 Model after covering the top face of the lofted surface

Stitching the Surfaces and Hiding the Original Surfaces

After creating all the surfaces, you need to stitch them together. The surfaces are stitched using the **Stitch Surface** tool.

1. Invoke the **Stitch Surface** tool. Select all the surfaces so that they are stitched together. Figure 13-58 shows the model after stitching the surfaces.

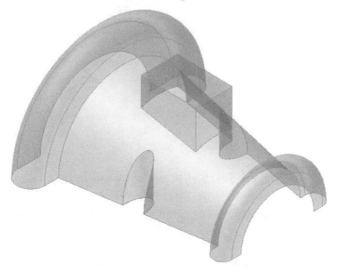

Figure 13-58 *Model after stitching the surfaces*

When you stitch the surfaces, the stitched surface is created above the original surfaces and the visibility of all the other surfaces is automatically turned off.

2. Fillet all the sharp edges of the stitched surface with a radius of 2 mm.

The surface, after creating the fillets, is shown in Figure 13-59.

Thickening the Surface

The final step in creating the hybrid surface-solid model is to thicken the complex surface created in the previous steps. By thickening, you can add material to the surface model so that it becomes a solid model. The model can be thickened using the **Thicken/Offset** tool.

1. Invoke the **Thicken/Offset** dialog box. Select the **Quilt** radio button.

2. Set the value of the **Distance** spinner to **1**, if it not already set. Select the stitched surface.

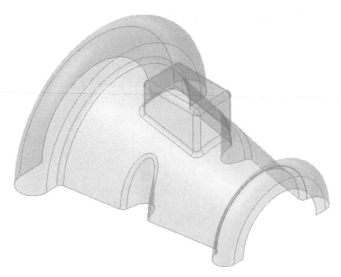

Figure 13-59 After filleting the surfaces

You will notice that because you have selected the **Quilt** option, the entire stitched surface is selected in a single click.

3.   Choose **OK** to exit the dialog box. Turn off the visibility of the stitched surface using the browser. The final model for Tutorial 1 is shown in Figure 13-60.

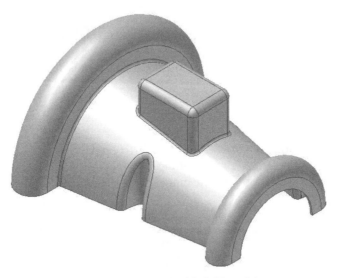

Figure 13-60 Final hybrid model

Figure 13-61 shows an alternate view of the same model.

Figure 13-61 *Alternate view of the hybrid model*

Self-Evaluation Test

Answer the following questions and then compare your answers with those given at the end of this chapter:

1. Autodesk Inventor allows you to create custom and standard iparts. (T/F)

2. You cannot turn off the display of surfaces. (T/F)

3. In Autodesk Inventor, hybrid surface-solid modeling is used to create complex surfaces. (T/F)

4. Autodesk Inventor does not allow you to display the dimensions as equations. (T/F)

5. The options in the _____ tab of the **iPart Author** dialog box are used to add the parameters related to the threads to the iPart factory.

6. _____ are mathematical expressions, in which the parameters are equated with the algebraic or the trigonometric functions.

7. _____ parts automatically change their dimensions based on the dimensions and functions of the other parts to which they are assembled.

8. Every dimension in Autodesk Inventor is assigned a unique name called _____.

9. _____ parameters are automatically created when you apply the dimensions to the entities or create a feature.

10. The _____ tool is used to manually create the bends at the corners of the 3D line.

Review Questions

Answer the following questions:

1. You can modify the dimensions while inserting custom iParts in the assembly. (T/F)

2. The profile that will be swept about a 3D path need not be normal to the start point of the path. (T/F)

3. Unlike the 2D sketching environment, you can save the file in the 3D sketching environment. (T/F)

4. The link parameters are created in a separate Microsoft Excel spreadsheet. (T/F)

5. User parameters are defined by the user for specifying the dimensions of entities and features. (T/F)

6. Using the options, in which tab of the **iPart Author** dialog box can you select the parameters and dimensions to be included in the iPart factory?

   (a) **Parameters**   (b) **Threads**
   (c) **Work Plane**   (d) None

7. Which one of the following is not a parameter?

   (a) Drawing   (b) Model
   (c) User   (d) Link

8. Using which one of the following tabs of the **Document Settings** dialog box can you display the dimensions as equations?

   (a) **Units**   (b) **Sketch**
   (c) **Modeling**   (d) None

9. Using which one of the following tabs of the **iPart Authors** dialog box can you specify whether the selected features will be computed or suppressed while creating a part using the iPart factory?

    (a) **Parameters**   (b) **Threads**
    (c) **Work Plane**   (d) **Suppression**

10. Which one of the following tools is used to merge a 2D sketch entity into a 3D sketch?

    (a) **Line**   (b) **Bend**
    (c) **Include Geometry**   (d) None

Exercise

Exercise 1

Create the following sketch with the help of parameters. After dimensioning the sketch, display the dimensions as equations, as shown in Figure 13-62.   **(Expected time: 30 min)**

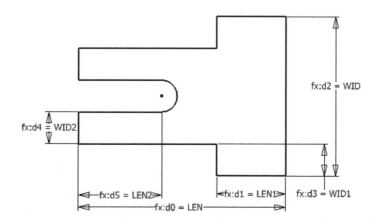

Figure 13-62 *Sketch with dimensions as equations*

The numeric values of the parameters are given below.
LEN = 60
LEN1 = LEN/3
LEN2 = LEN/2.5
WID = LEN*0.75
WID1 = WID/5
WID2 = WID1

After displaying the dimensions as expression, display them as names.

Note

*After selecting the option of displaying the dimensions as equations or names, sometimes the dimension display does not change on the graphics screen. In this case, double-click on any dimension and then press ENTER to close the **Edit Dimension** toolbar. The dimension display will automatically change.*

Answers to Self-Evaluation Test

1. T, **2.** F, **3.** T, **4.** F, **5. Threads**, **6.** Equations, **7.** Adaptive, **8.** parameter, **9.** Model, **10. Bend**

Chapter 14

Working with Sheet Metal Components

Learning Objectives

After completing this chapter, you will be able to:

- *Set the parameters for creating the sheet metal parts.*
- *Use the Face tool to create the base of the sheet metal component.*
- *Fold a part of the sheet metal part by using the Fold tool.*
- *Create a flange by using the Flange tool.*
- *Add a corner seam to the sheet metal parts by using the Corner Seam tool.*
- *Use the PunchTool tool.*
- *Add a hem to the sheet metal part by using the Hem tool.*
- *Create a cut feature in the sheet metal part by using the Cut tool.*
- *Fillet the corners of the sheet metal part by using the Corner Fillet tool.*
- *Chamfer the corners of the sheet metal part by using the Corner Chamfer tool.*
- *Create the flat pattern of the sheet metal component by using the Flat Pattern tool.*

THE SHEET METAL MODULE

A sheet metal component is created by bending, cutting, or deforming an existing sheet of metal of uniform thickness, see Figure 14-1.

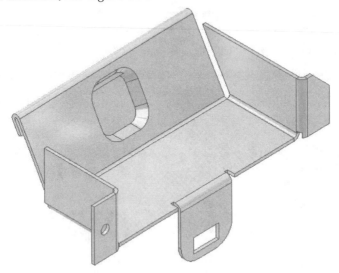

Figure 14-1 Sheet metal component

Because it is not possible to manufacture such a model, therefore, after creating the sheet metal component, you need to flatten it in order to manufacture it. Figure 14-2 shows the flattened view of the sheet metal component shown in Figure 14-1.

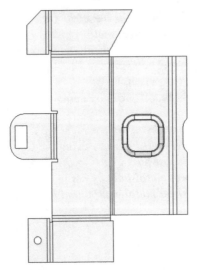

Figure 14-2 Flattened view of the sheet metal component

Autodesk Inventor allows you to create the sheet metal components in a special environment, called the **Sheet Metal** module, provided specially for the sheet metal components. This environment provides all the tools that are required for creating the sheet metal components. To invoke the **Sheet Metal** module, double-click on **Sheet Metal (mm).ipt** from the **Metric** tab of the **Open** dialog box, see Figure 14-3.

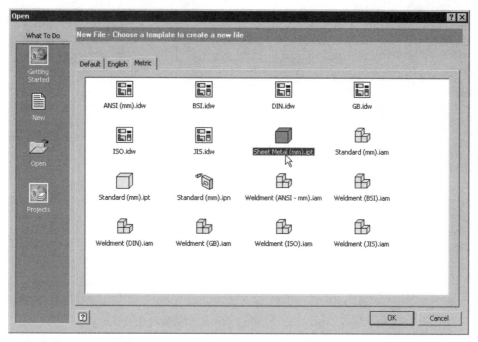

Figure 14-3 *Starting a new sheet metal file from the **Metric** tab of the **Open** dialog box*

When you select this file, you will proceed to the **Sheet Metal** module. Notice that when you open a new sheet metal file, by default the sketching environment is activated, as shown in Figure 14-4. This is because similar to the part modeling environment, you first need to create the sketch of the base feature of the sheet metal component. After creating it, the remaining tools will be available in the **Sheet Metal** module.

Note

Sheet metal files are also saved in the *.ipt format.

*To make sure you are in the sketching environment of the Sheet Metal module, choose **Convert** from the menu bar; the **Modeling** and **Sheet Metal** options will be available in the menu bar. Also, a check mark will be displayed on the left of the **Sheet Metal** option. This suggests that inside the sketching environment of the **Sheet Metal** module.*

*You can convert a sheet metal part into a solid part by choosing the **Convert > Modeling** from the menu bar; the **Sheet Metal Features** panel bar will be replaced by the **Part Features** panel bar and you can continue adding solid features to the part.*

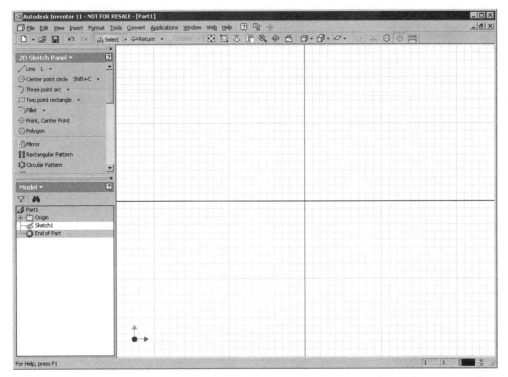

*Figure 14-4 Sketching environment of the **Sheet Metal** module*

After creating the sketch for the base of the sheet metal component, exit the sketching environment. You will notice that the **Sketch** panel bar is replaced by the **Sheet Metal** panel bar. Note that very few tools are available in this panel bar. More tools will be available when you create the base of the sheet metal part.

Before proceeding with converting the sketch into the sheet metal base, it is recommended that you set the options related to the sheet metal components by using the **Sheet Metal Styles** tool discussed next.

SETTING SHEET METAL COMPONENT OPTIONS

Toolbar:	Sheet Metal Features > Sheet Metal Styles
Panel bar:	Sheet Metal Features > Sheet Metal Styles

The **Sheet Metal Styles** tool is used to set the options related to the sheet metal component. When you invoke this tool, the **Sheet Metal Styles** dialog box will be displayed. The **Default** style is created by default. To create a new sheet metal style, choose the **New** button and enter the name of the style in the edit box in the **Style List** area. The **Sheet Metal Styles** dialog box provides three tabs for setting the parameters of the sheet metal components. The options in these three tabs are discussed next.

Sheet Tab

The options in the **Sheet** tab (Figure 14-5) are discussed next.

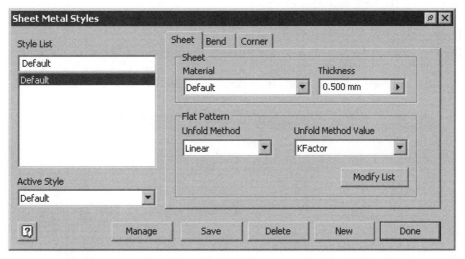

Figure 14-5 *The **Sheet** tab of the **Sheet Metal Styles** dialog box*

Sheet Area

The options in the **Sheet** area are used to specify the material and thickness of the sheet. These options are discussed next.

Material

The **Material** drop-down list is used to specify the material of the sheet. You can select the desired material from the predefined materials in this drop-down list.

Thickness

The **Thickness** edit box is used to specify the thickness of the sheet. You can enter the thickness of the sheet in this edit box or select from the predefined thicknesses by choosing the arrow on the right of this edit box.

Flat Pattern Area

The options in the **Flat Pattern** area are used to specify the parameters related to the unfolding of the sheet metal component for manufacturing. These options are discussed next.

Unfold Method

The **Unfold Method** drop-down list is used to specify the method that will be used while unfolding the sheet metal component. This drop-down list provides two methods for unfolding the sheet metal component. The first method is the **Linear** method and it uses a simple unfolding technique for flattening the component. The second method is the **Bend Table** method. When you select this method, the **Open** dialog box is displayed from which you can select the file in which the bend table is stored. The bend tables are stored in the *.txt* files.

Unfold Method Value
The **Unfold Method Value** drop-down list is used to specify the value of the unfold method. The options in this drop-down list will depend on the method selected from the **Unfold Method** drop-down list.

Modify List
When you choose the **Modify List** button, the **Unfold Method List** dialog box is displayed. This dialog box has the list of unfold methods, their type, and their values. If you have selected a bend table file, its path will also be displayed as shown in Figure 14-6.

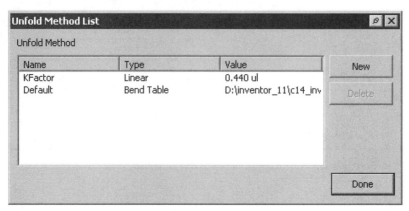

*Figure 14-6 The **Unfold Method List** dialog box*

Bend Tab
The options in the **Bend** tab (Figure 14-7) are used to set the parameters related to the bending of the sheet. These options are discussed next.

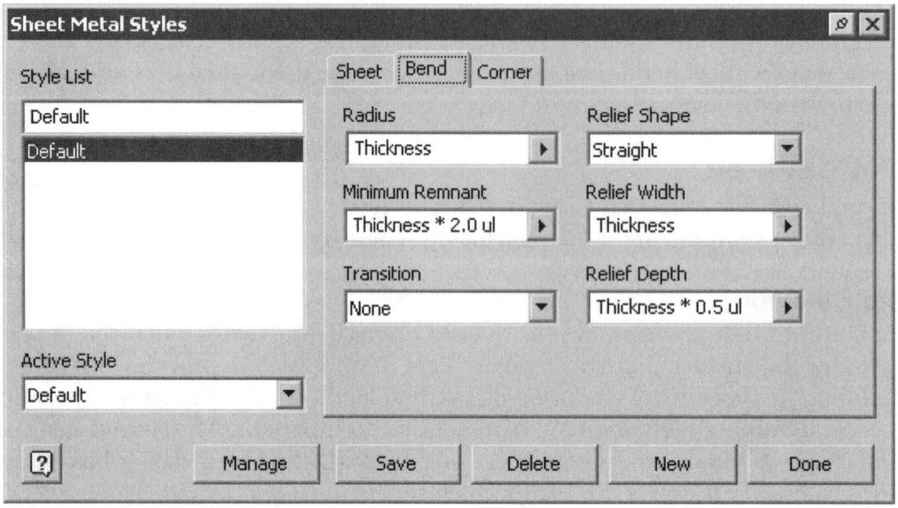

*Figure 14-7 The **Bend** tab of the **Sheet Metal Styles** dialog box*

Radius

The **Radius** edit box is used to set the radius of the bend or the fold. The default value of the radius of the bend is equal to the thickness of the sheet. You can enter a numeric value in this edit box to select it as the bend radius. Figure 14-8 shows a sheet folded with a radius of 1 mm and Figure 14-9 shows a sheet folded with a radius of 5 mm.

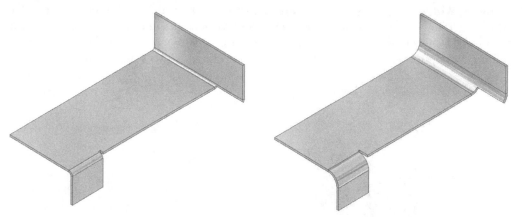

Figure 14-8 *Sheet with 1 mm bend radius*   *Figure 14-9* *Sheet with 5 mm bend radius*

 Tip. *If you modify the bend radius after bending or folding a sheet metal component, the model will be automatically updated and will acquire the new bend radius when you choose the **Save** button and exit the **Sheet Metal Styles** dialog box.*

Relief Shape

Whenever you bend or fold a sheet metal component such that the bend does not extend throughout the length of the edge, a groove is added at the end of the bend so that the walls of the sheet metal part do not intersect when folded or unfolded. This groove is known as relief. The **Relief Shape** drop-down list is used to select the shape of the relief. By default, a straight relief is added, as shown in Figure 14-10. You can also add a round relief by selecting **Round** from this drop-down list. Figure 14-11 shows a round relief.

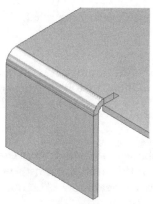   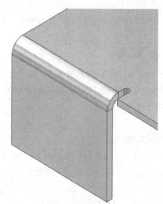

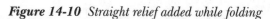

Figure 14-10 *Straight relief added while folding*   *Figure 14-11* *Round relief added while folding*

Minimum Remnant

The **Minimum Remnant** edit box is used to set the value of the material between the relief created by bending or folding and the edge of the sheet metal component.

Relief Width

The **Relief Width** edit box is used to enter the value of the width of the relief. The default value of the relief width is equal to the thickness of the sheet. You can enter the value of the relief width in this edit box. Figure 14-12 shows a sheet metal component with a relief width of 1 mm and Figure 14-13 shows a sheet metal component with a relief width of 4 mm.

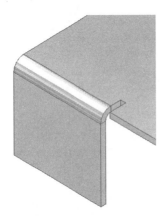   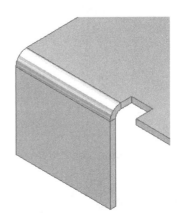

Figure 14-12 Relief width 1 mm   *Figure 14-13* Relief width 4 mm

Transition

The **Transition** drop-down list is used to specify the transition type in the unfolded view when no relief is specified. The default value of this drop-down list is **None**. You can select the **Intersection**, **Straight Line**, **Arc**, or **Trim to Bend** transition type from this drop-down list.

Relief Depth

The **Relief Depth** edit box is used to enter the value of the depth of the relief.

Corner Tab

The options in the **Corner** tab (Figure 14-14) are used to set the parameters related to the relief at the corners where the three faces of the sheet metal component are folded. These options are discussed next.

Relief Shape

The **Relief Shape** drop-down list is used to specify the shape of the relief at the corner where the three faces are folded. Remember that the options in this drop-down list will work only when one of the three faces is created by using the **Corner Seam** tool. The options in this drop-down list are discussed next.

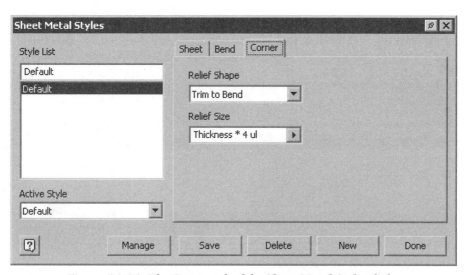

*Figure 14-14 The **Corner** tab of the **Sheet Metal Styles** dialog*

Note

*It is recommended that to view a better effect of various corner relief shapes, the sheet metal component should be flattened using the **Flat Pattern** tool.*

Trim to Bend

The **Trim to Bend** is the default option in this drop-down list and is used when you do not want any relief at the corner where the three faces are folded. Figure 14-15 shows an unfolded sheet metal part with no relief at the corner.

Linear Weld

This option is used to apply a linear weld type of relief at the corners.

Round

The **Round** option is used to create a round corner relief, as shown in Figure 14-16.

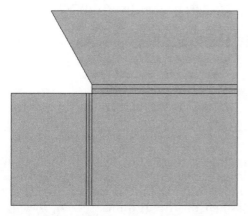

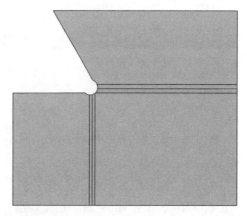

Figure 14-15 Flattened sheet metal part with no corner relief

Figure 14-16 Flattened sheet metal part with round corner relief

Square

The **Square** option is used to create a square corner relief, as shown in Figure 14-17.

Tear

The **Tear** option is used to create a corner relief that appears torn at the corners, as shown in Figure 14-18.

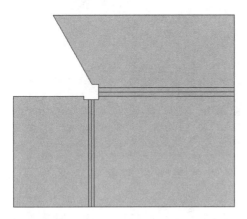
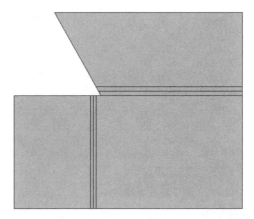

Figure 14-17 *Flattened sheet metal part with square corner relief*

Figure 14-18 *Flattened sheet metal part with torn corner relief*

Relief Size

The **Relief Size** edit box is used to specify the size of the corner relief. You can enter the value as an equation in terms of the thickness of the sheet or as a numeric value.

After making the necessary modifications, choose the **Save** button to save the changes and then choose the **Done** button to close the dialog box. As soon as you close the dialog box, the changes you made in the sheet metal style will be highlighted in the sheet metal component.

Once you have made the necessary initial settings, you are ready to create the sheet metal component. The tools required to create the sheet metal component are discussed next.

CREATING SHEET METAL COMPONENTS

Toolbar:	Sheet Metal Features > Face
Panel bar:	Sheet Metal Features > Face

The **Face** tool is used to create the base of the sheet metal component or for adding additional faces on the sheet metal component. As mentioned earlier, when you open a new sheet metal file, the sketching environment is activated. After creating the sketch for the base of the sheet metal component, exit the sketching environment and invoke this tool. When you invoke this tool, the **Face** dialog box will be displayed. This dialog box has three tabs. But because you are creating the base, the options in these tabs will not be required. Note that since there is only one sketch on the graphics screen, it will be automatically selected. The sheet thickness will be taken as the thickness defined in the **Sheet** tab of the **Sheet Metal Styles** dialog box. Figure 14-19 shows the sketch before converting it into a sheet metal component and Figure 14-20 shows the sheet metal component created using the given sketch.

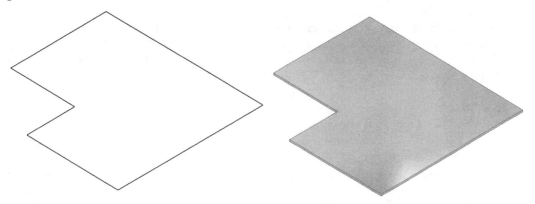

Figure 14-19 *Sketch before converting into sheet metal part*

Figure 14-20 *Sheet metal part created using the given sketch*

After creating the base of the sheet metal component, if you create a sketch and invoke the **Face** tool, the other options in the **Face** dialog box will be used. The options in the **Face** dialog box are discussed next.

Shape Tab

The options in the **Shape** tab (Figure 14-21) are used to specify the shape and bend options of the face. These options are discussed next.

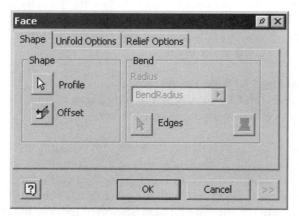

Figure 14-21 *The **Shape** tab of the **Face** dialog box*

Shape Area

The options in the **Shape** area are used to specify the shape of the face. These options are discussed next.

Select Profile

The **Select Profile** button is chosen to select the sketch of the face. If there is only one unconsumed sketch on the screen, it will be automatically selected. However, if there are more than one unconsumed sketches or the sketch consists of multiple closed loops, you will have to select them manually by using this button.

Flip Offset

The **Flip Offset** button is chosen to reverse the direction of the face creation.

Bend Area

Whenever you create a face on an existing sheet metal component, a bend is created at the edge where the new face joins the existing component. Also, a bend relief will be added to the new face. The options related to the bend and the bend relief are available in the **Bend** area. These options are discussed next.

Radius

The **Radius** edit box is used to specify the radius of the bend. By default, the bend radius value defined in the **Bend** tab of the **Sheet Metal Styles** dialog box is selected. You can also specify a new bend radius by entering a numeric value in this edit box.

Edges

The **Edges** button is chosen to select the edge that will be joined with the existing sheet metal component. If one of the edges of the sketch is coincident with an edge of the existing sheet metal part, the common edge will be automatically selected. However, if the edge of the sketch is not coincident with an edge of the sheet metal component, you will have to select the edge manually. You can also use this button to select additional faces that you want to be added in the bend.

Extend Bend Aligned to Side Faces

If you choose the **Extend Bend Aligned to Side Faces** button, the material is added on the sides of the edges along the faces and not normal to the axis of the bend.

Figure 14-22 shows the sketch that will be used for creating the face of the sheet metal component and Figure 14-23 shows the sheet metal component created after adding the face. Notice the bend and the bend relief created with the face. Figure 14-24 shows a sketch that has no edge coincident with the edge of the sheet metal part. Notice that in this figure the edge of the sheet metal base is selected for creating the bend. Figure 14-25 shows the sheet metal component created by using the given sketch.

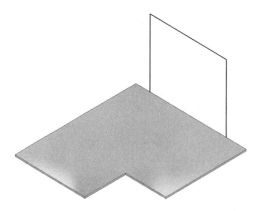

Figure 14-22 *Sketch before converting into a new face of the sheet metal part*

Figure 14-23 *Sheet metal part after creating the new face*

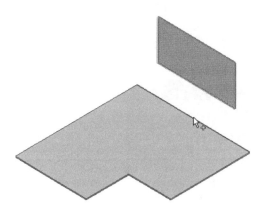

Figure 14-24 *Selecting the sketch and edge for creating the face of the sheet metal part*

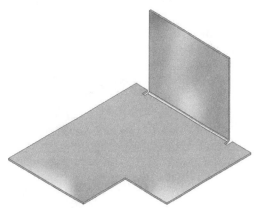

Figure 14-25 *Sheet metal part after creating the new face*

Unfold Options Tab

The options in the **Unfold Options** tab are used to specify the parameters related to unfolding of the face of the sheet metal component. By default, the options specified in the **Sheet** tab of the **Sheet Metal Styles** dialog box are used. This is the reason no option is available in this tab. However, if you want to override the options specified in the **Sheet Metal Styles** dialog box, select any option other than the **Default** option from the **Unfold Method** drop-down list. You will notice that the options in the **Unfold Options** tab are available, as shown in Figure 14-26. These options are similar to those discussed in the **Sheet Metal Styles** dialog box.

Relief Options Tab

The options in the **Relief Options** tab are used to specify the parameters related to bend relief.

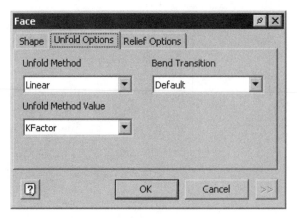

*Figure 14-26 The **Unfold Options** tab of the **Face** dialog box*

By default, the options specified in the **Bend** tab of the **Sheet Metal Styles** dialog box are used. If you want to override the options specified in the **Sheet Metal Styles** dialog box, select an option other than **Default** in the **Relief Shape** drop-down list. The options in the **Relief Options** tab are shown in Figure 14-27. These options are similar to the options discussed in the **Sheet Metal Styles** dialog box.

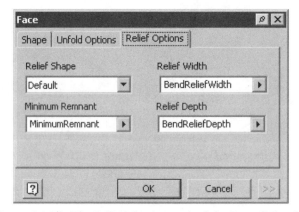

*Figure 14-27 The **Relief Options** tab of the **Face** dialog box*

FOLDING PARTS OF SHEET METAL COMPONENTS

Toolbar:	Sheet Metal Features > Fold
Panel bar:	Sheet Metal Features > Fold

Autodesk Inventor allows you to fold a part of the sheet metal component by using the **Fold** tool. Remember that the sheet metal part will be folded with the help of a sketched line. Note that the line that you want to use should not extend beyond the face that you want to fold. When you invoke the **Fold** tool, the **Fold** dialog box will be displayed. The options in the **Fold** dialog box are discussed next.

Shape Tab

The options in the **Shape** tab (Figure 14-28) are used to specify the shape of the fold. These options are discussed next.

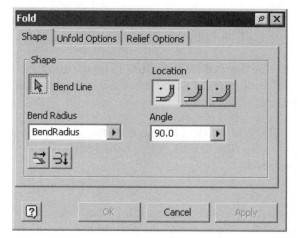

Figure 14-28 The **Shape** tab of the **Fold** dialog box

Shape Area

Bend Line

The **Bend Line** button is chosen to select the bend line that will be used to fold the component. When you invoke the **Fold** dialog box, this button is chosen by default. Note that only the line that has both its endpoints at the edges of the sheet metal component can be selected to bend the component. As soon as you select the bend line, two green arrows are displayed on it. The first arrow points in the direction of the portion of the sheet metal part that will be folded and the second arrow points in the direction of bending.

Bend Radius

The **Bend Radius** edit box is used to specify the radius of the bend. By default, the value specified in the **Bend** tab of the **Sheet Metal Styles** dialog box is taken as the bend radius. You can also enter any desired value in this edit box.

Flip Side

The **Flip Side** button is chosen to reverse the side of the sheet metal part that will be folded.

Flip Direction

The **Flip Direction** button is chosen to reverse the direction, in which the sheet metal component will be folded.

Location

The **Location** buttons are chosen to specify the location of the bend with respect to the sketch line selected as the bend line. There are three buttons that can be used to specify the location of the bend with respect to the bend line. These three buttons are discussed next.

Centerline of Bend. The **Centerline of Bend** is the first button below the **Location** heading. By default, this button is chosen for creating the bend. If you choose this button, the bend line will be considered as the centerline of the bend and the bend will be created equally in both the directions of the bend line.

Start of Bend. The **Start of Bend** button is on the right of the **Centerline of Bend** button. If this button is chosen, the bend will be created such that the bend line is located at the start of the bend.

End of Bend. The **End of Bend** button is on the right of the **Start of Bend** button. If this button is chosen, the bend will be created such that the bend line is located at the end of the bend.

Angle
The **Angle** edit box is used to specify the angle of the fold for the sheet metal component. The default value in this edit box is **90.0**. You can specify any desired value in this edit box.

Figure 14-29 shows a line that will be used to fold the sheet metal part and Figure 14-30 shows the sheet metal part folded through an angle of 60-degree by using the given line.

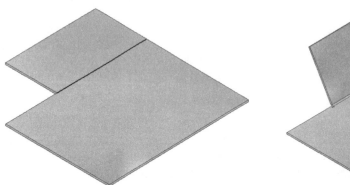

Figure 14-29 *Line that will be used to fold the sheet metal part*

Figure 14-30 *Sheet metal part after folding it through an angle of 60-degree by using the line*

Note
*The options in the **Unfold Options** and the **Relief Options** tabs are the same as those discussed in the previous sections of this chapter.*

ADDING FLANGES TO SHEET METAL COMPONENTS

Toolbar:	Sheet Metal Features > Flange
Panel bar:	Sheet Metal Features > Flange

 Autodesk Inventor allows you to directly add a folded face to the existing sheet metal component. This is done using the **Flange** tool. When you invoke this tool, the **Flange** dialog box will be displayed. The options in the **Flange** dialog box are discussed next.

Shape Tab

The options in the **Shape** tab (Figure 14-31) are used to set the parameters related to the shape and bend of the flange. These options are discussed next.

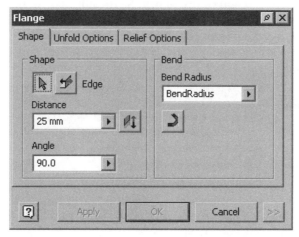

*Figure 14-31 The **Shape** tab of the **Flange** dialog box*

Shape Area

The options in the **Shape** area are used to set the parameters related to the shape of the flange. These options are discussed next.

Select Edge

The **Select Edge** button is the first button in the **Shape** area and is used to select the edge on which the flange will be created. When you invoke the **Flange** dialog box, the **Select Edge** button is chosen by default and you are prompted to select the edge. Note that if you select the edge on the upper face of the sheet metal component, by default the flange will be created in the upward direction. Similarly, if you select the edge on the lower face of the sheet metal component, by default the flange will be created in the downward direction.

Flip Offset

The **Flip Offset** button on the right of the **Select Edge** button is used to specify whether the inner edge or the outer edge of the flange will be aligned with the selected edge of the sheet metal component.

Distance

The **Distance** edit box is used to specify the height of the flange. The height will be calculated from the edge that was selected to create the flange.

Flip Direction

The **Flip Direction** button is chosen to reverse the direction of the flange creation. As mentioned earlier, if you select the edge on the top face of the sheet metal component, by default the flange will be created in the upward direction. But if you choose this button, the flange will be created in the downward direction. However, note that the selected edge will still be the starting edge of the flange.

Angle

The **Angle** edit box is used to specify the angle through which the flange will be bent with respect to the sheet metal component. The default value in this edit box is **90.0** and therefore, the flange will be bent through an angle of 90-degree The angle value of the flange can vary from 0-degree to 180-degree.

Tip. *If a flange is created through an angle of 180-degree, it will not be visible as it will be merged with the face of the sheet metal component. If a flange is created through an angle of 170-degree, it will create a face similar to a hem.*

Note
The hems will be discussed later in this chapter.

Bend Area

The options in the **Bend** area are used to set the parameters related to the bending of the flange. These options are discussed next.

Bend Radius

The **Bend Radius** edit box is used to enter the radius of the bend. By default, the value set in the **Sheet Metal Styles** dialog box is taken as the bend value. However, you can set any bend radius by entering its value in this edit box.

Bend Tangent To Side Face

The **Bend Tangent To Side Face** button is chosen to create a flange that is tangent to the side face of the sheet metal component.

Figure 14-32 shows the edge being selected for creating the flange and Figure 14-33 shows the sheet metal component after creating the flange.

More Button

The **More** button is the button with two arrows and is available on the lower right corner of the **Flange** dialog box. When you choose this button, the **Flange** dialog box expands and provides more options. These options are discussed next.

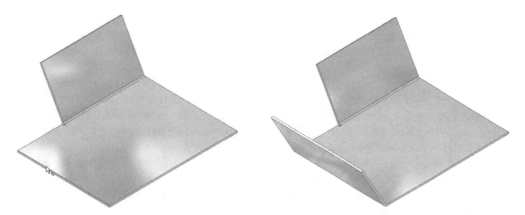

Figure 14-32 *Selecting the edge for creating the flange*

Figure 14-33 *Sheet metal component after creating the flange at an angle of 60-degree*

Extents Area

The options in the **Extents** area (Figure 14-34) are used to set the parameters related to the extents of the flange. These options are provided in the **Type** drop-down list and are discussed next.

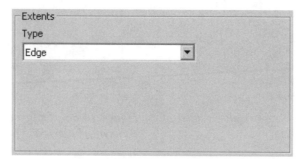

Figure 14-34 *The **Extents** area displayed by choosing the **More** button*

Edge

The **Edge** option is selected by default in this drop-down list. This option ensures that the flange is created through the edge selected from the sheet metal component.

Width

The **Width** option is used to create a flange through a specified width of the selected edge and at a specified offset distance. When you select this option, the **Select Start Point** button, **Offset** edit box, **Flip Direction** button, and **Width** edit box are displayed in the **Extents** area and you are prompted to select the start point of the flange. You can select a vertex, work point, or a work plane for defining the start point of the flange. The offset distance is specified in the **Offset** edit box and it is the distance by which the flange will be offset from the start point. You can reverse the direction of the offset by choosing the **Flip Direction** button. The width of the flange will be specified in the **Width** edit box. Figure 14-35 shows the flange created at an offset of 10 mm from the selected start point and with a width of 25 mm. Notice the bend relief that is automatically created on both the sides.

Offset

The **Offset** option is selected to define the width of the flange in terms of the offset from two points on the selected edge. When you invoke this option, the **Select Start Point** button, **Select End Point** button, **Offset1** edit box, and **Offset2** edit box are displayed in the **Extents** area and you are prompted to select the flange start point. Select the start point of the flange on the selected edge. Then you will be prompted to select the endpoint of the flange. Select the endpoint on the selected edge. After selecting the two points, you can define the offset from the first point and the second point in the **Offset1** and the **Offset2** edit boxes respectively. Based on the two offset values and the known length of the edge, the width of the flange is automatically calculated. Figure 14-36 shows a flange created with the offset 1 value as 20 mm and the offset 2 value as 10 mm.

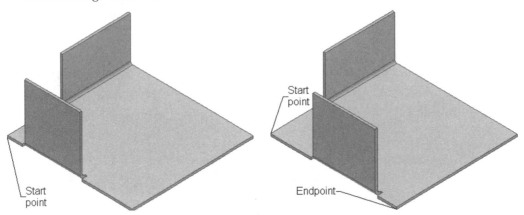

Figure 14-35 Flange created with an offset of 10 mm and width of 25 mm

Figure 14-36 Flange created with the offset 1 value as 20 mm and offset 2 value as 10 mm

Note
*The options in the **Unfold Options** and the **Relief Options** tabs of the **Flange** dialog box are similar to those discussed in the previous sections of this chapter.*

CREATING CUTS IN SHEET METAL COMPONENTS

Toolbar:	Sheet Metal Features > Cut
Panel bar:	Sheet Metal Features > Cut

You can create any type of cut in the sheet metal component by drawing its sketch and then cutting it by using the **Cut** tool. Note that if you invoke this tool without creating a sketch, you will be informed that there is no unconsumed sketch. When you invoke this tool, the **Cut** dialog box will be displayed, as shown in Figure 14-37. The options in this dialog box are discussed next.

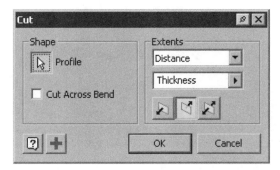

Figure 14-37 *The Cut dialog box*

Shape Area

The options in the **Shape** area are used to specify the shape of the cut. These options are discussed next.

Profile

The **Profile** button is chosen to select the profile of the cut. When you invoke the **Cut** dialog box, this button is chosen by default. If there is only one unconsumed sketch on the screen, it will be automatically selected for creating the cut. However, if there are more than one unconsumed sketches, you will be prompted to select the profile.

Cut Across Bend

The **Cut Across Bend** check box is selected to cut the material throughout the thickness of the sheet. If you select this check box, the options in the **Extents** area will not be available. This is because when you cut the material throughout the thickness of the sheet, you do not require to specify the extents of the cut.

Extents Area

The options in the **Extents** area are used to specify the extents of the cut. You can select the options for defining the extents of the cut from the drop-down list provided in this area. The options in this drop-down list are similar to those discussed for the solid model components.

Figure 14-38 shows two unconsumed sketches before creating the cut in the sheet metal component. Figure 14-39 shows the sheet metal component after creating the cut by using the two sketches.

CREATING SEAMS AT CORNERS OF SHEET METAL COMPONENTS

Toolbar:	Sheet Metal Features > Corner Seam
Panel bar:	Sheet Metal Features > Corner Seam

 Autodesk Inventor allows you to create the corner seams in a sheet metal component with the help of the **Corner Seam** tool. When you invoke this tool, the **Corner Seam**

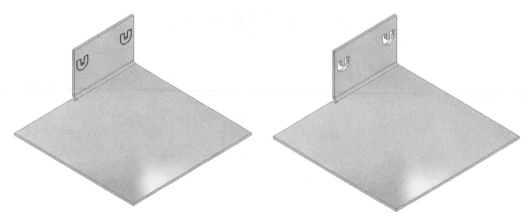

Figure 14-38 Unconsumed sketches before creating the cut

Figure 14-39 Sheet metal component after creating the cut

dialog box will be displayed. The options in this dialog box are discussed next.

Shape Tab

The options in the **Shape** tab (Figure 14-40) are used to set the parameters related to the shape of the seam. These options are discussed next.

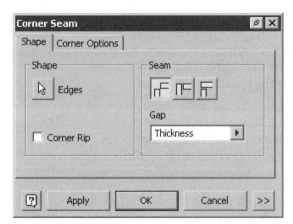

Figure 14-40 The **Shape** tab of the **Corner Seam** dialog box

Shape Area

Edge

The **Edge** button is chosen to select the edges for creating the corner seam. When you invoke this dialog box, the **Edge** button is chosen by default and no option is available in the **Seam** area. The options in the **Seam** area will be available only after you have selected the edges for creating the corner seam.

Corner Rip

The **Corner Rip** check box is selected when you want to rip a corner of a sheet metal component that has three faces meeting at a corner. This is generally used when you want to convert a shelled solid model into a sheet metal component and rip its corner in order to open it. To rip a corner of such a component, select the vertical edge at the corner. The corner will be automatically ripped and the solid model will be converted into a sheet metal component. Figure 14-41 shows a shelled solid model component before ripping the corners and Figure 14-42 shows the solid model component after its corners are ripped and it is converted into a sheet metal component.

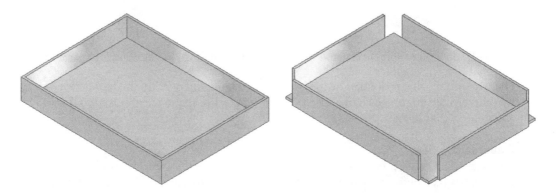

Figure 14-41 *Model before ripping the corners*   *Figure 14-42* *Model after ripping the corners*

 Tip. *To convert a solid model into a sheet metal component, you first need to shell it. Remember that the wall thickness in the shell should be equal to or less than the thickness of the sheet specified in the* ***Sheet Metal Styles*** *dialog box. If the wall thickness in the shell is more than the thickness of the sheet, you will not be able to rip the corners of the shelled model. After shelling the component, rip its corners by using the* ***Corner Seam*** *tool. By ripping the corners of a solid model component, you convert it into a sheet metal component. Once the solid model is converted into a sheet metal component, you can apply sheet metal operations on it.*

Seam Area

No Overlap

The **No Overlap** button is the first button in the **Seam** area. This button is chosen by default and it ensures that there is no overlapping of the faces whose edges are selected for creating the corner seam. Figure 14-43 shows the two faces that are selected to create the corner seam and Figure 14-44 shows the sheet metal component after creating the corner seam. Notice that there is no overlapping of the faces. Also, notice that the bend relief in both the faces is automatically adjusted with reference to the corner seam.

Overlap

The **Overlap** button is provided on the right of the **No Overlap** button. If this button is

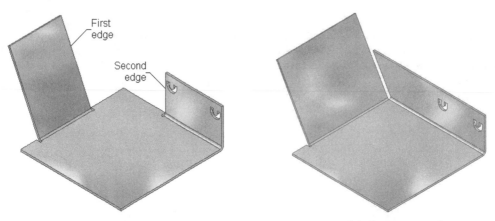

Figure 14-43 *Selecting the edges to create a seam* *Figure 14-44* *Model after creating the corner seam*

chosen, the face that is defined by the first selected edge will overlap the face defined by the second selected edge, see Figure 14-45. In this figure, the sequence of selecting the edges is the same as that in Figure 14-43.

Reverse Overlap

The **Reverse Overlap** button is on the right of the **Overlap** button, and if this button is chosen, the face defined by the second selected edge will overlap the face defined by the first selected edge, as shown in Figure 14-46. In this figure, also, the sequence of selecting the edges is the same as that in Figure 14-43.

Figure 14-45 *Overlapping of faces*   *Figure 14-46* *Reverse overlapping of faces*

Gap

The **Gap** edit box is used to define the gap between the two faces in the corner seam. By default, the value in this edit box is **Thickness**. This means that the thickness of the sheet will be taken as the gap between the faces. You can enter any desired value in this edit box.

Miter Area

The **Miter** area replaces the **Seam** area when the two edges selected for defining the corner seam are coplanar. Similar to the **Seam** area, this area also provides three buttons in addition to the **Gap** edit box. The function of the three buttons is discussed next.

45 Degrees

The **45 Degrees** button is the first button in the **Miter** area. This button is chosen to create a miter corner between the selected faces. Figure 14-47 shows the two edges selected to create a miter corner and Figure 14-48 shows a 45-degree miter corner.

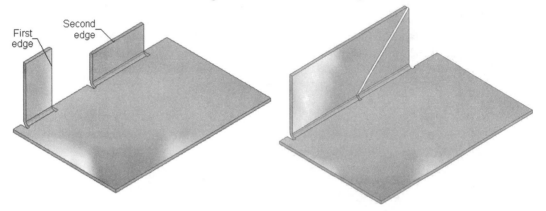

Figure 14-47 Selecting the edges to create a miter   *Figure 14-48 45-degree miter corner*

90 Degrees

The **90 Degrees** button is on the right of the **45 Degrees** button and it is chosen to create a 90-degree miter corner, as shown in Figure 14-49.

Reverse 90 Degrees

The **Reverse 90 Degrees** button is on the right of the **90 Degrees** button and it is chosen to create a reverse 90-degree miter corner, as shown in Figure 14-50.

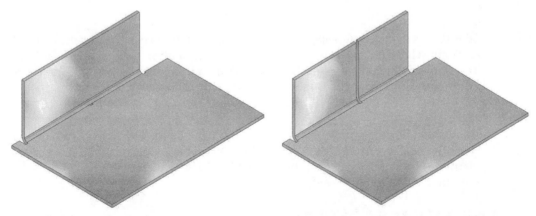

Figure 14-49 90-degree miter corner   *Figure 14-50 Reverse 90-degree miter corner*

BENDING SHEET METAL FACES

Toolbar:	Sheet Metal Features > Bend
Panel bar:	Sheet Metal Features > Bend

 Autodesk Inventor allows you to create a new face by adding a new bent face between the two existing faces. This is done by using the **Bend** tool. When you invoke this tool, the **Bend** dialog box will be displayed. The options in the **Bend** dialog box are discussed next.

Shape Tab

The options in the **Shape** tab (Figure 14-51) are used to set the parameters related to the shape of the bent face. These options are discussed next.

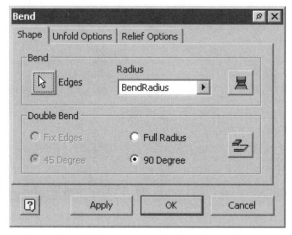

*Figure 14-51 The **Shape** tab of the **Bend** dialog box*

Bend Area

Edges

The **Edges** button is chosen to select the edges on the two faces between which the bent face will be added. When you invoke the **Bend** dialog box, this button is chosen by default and you are prompted to select the edge. Remember that until you select the edges for creating the bent face, the options in the **Double Bend** area will not be available.

Radius

The **Radius** edit box is used to specify the radius of the bend. The default value of this edit box is the bend radius specified in the **Sheet Metal Styles** dialog box. However, you can override the value specified in the **Sheet Metal Styles** dialog box and specify any desired value.

Extend Bend Aligned to Side Faces

If you choose the **Extend Bend Aligned to Side Faces** button, the material is added on the sides of the edges along the faces and not normal to the axis of the bend.

Double Bend Area

The options in the **Double Bend** area are used to create a bend between two noncoplanar parallel faces. These options are discussed next.

Fix Edges

The **Fix Edges** radio button is selected to create a bend of equal dimensions between the selected edges.

45 Degree

The **45 Degree** radio button is selected to create a 45-degree bend between the selected edges. Note that when you select the edges for defining the bend, the edge selected first is taken as the fixed edge. While creating the bent face, if the sizes of the two selected edges are different, the size of the fixed edge and the face defined by this edge remains constant by default. However, the size of the other edge and the face defined by it is either trimmed or extended in order to adjust the new face.

Full Radius

The **Full Radius** radio button is selected to create a half circle bent face between the two selected edges. Figure 14-52 shows the two edges selected for creating the bend and Figure 14-53 shows a full radius bend created between the selected faces. Notice that in Figure 14-53, the face defined by the second edge is modified to adjust the new bent face.

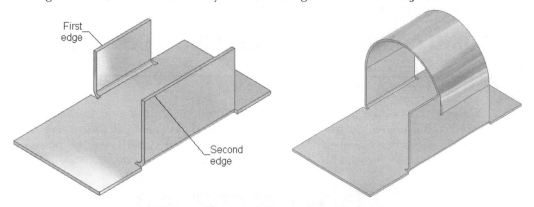

Figure 14-52 Selecting the edges   *Figure 14-53 Full radius bent face*

90 Degree

The **90 Degree** radio button is selected to create a 90-degree bend between the selected edges as shown in Figure 14-54. In this figure, the sequence of selecting the edges is the same as that in Figure 14-52.

Flip Fixed Edge

The **Flip Fixed Edge** check box is selected to change the fixed edge. As mentioned earlier, the edge selected first is taken as the fixed edge and the face defined by the other edge is modified in order to adjust the new bent face. However, if you choose this button, the edge selected second will be taken as the fixed edge and the face defined by the first edge will be modified in order to adjust the new bent face. Figure 14-55 shows a bent face that is added by selecting two edges in an order similar to that shown in Figure 14-52. Notice that the size of the face defined by the first edge is modified to adjust the new bent face.

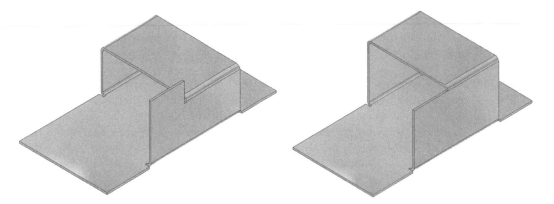

Figure 14-54 *90-degree bent*

Figure 14-55 *90-degree bent after flipping the fixed edge*

Note

*The options in the **Unfold Options** and the **Bend Relief Options** tabs are the same as those discussed in the previous sections of this chapter.*

ROUNDING CORNERS OF SHEET METAL COMPONENTS

Toolbar:	Sheet Metal Feature> Corner Round
Panel bar:	Sheet Metal Feature> Corner Round

The corners of a sheet metal component can be rounded by using the **Corner Round** tool. You can use this tool for rounding a single selected corner or all the corners of the selected face. When you invoke this tool, the **Corner Round** dialog box will be displayed, as shown in Figure 14-56. The options in this dialog box are discussed next.

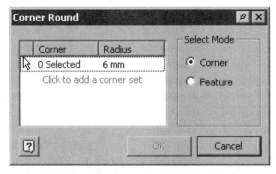

Figure 14-56 *The **Corner Round** dialog box*

Corner

The **Corner** column displays the corners that are selected to be rounded. When you invoke the **Corner Round** dialog box, you are prompted to select a corner to be rounded. By default, this column displays **0 Selected**. This is because no corner is selected for rounding. To round a corner, select the edge that defines the corner of the sheet metal plate. The selected corner will be rounded. When you select a corner, this column displays **1 Selected**. Similarly, if you select more corners, the **Corner** column displays the number of corners that you have selected. You can preview the corner round on the graphics screen.

Radius

The **Radius** column displays the radius of the corner round. To modify the radius, click on this column and enter the new value of the radius.

Select Mode

The options in the **Select Mode** area are used to select the mode for selecting the object to be filleted. The options in this area are discussed next.

Corner

The **Corner** radio button is selected by default in the **Select Mode** area and it allows you to individually select the corners that should be rounded.

Feature

The **Feature** radio button is selected to select a feature whose all corners will be rounded. On selecting this radio button, you will be prompted to select the feature to be rounded. As soon as you select a feature, you will notice that all its corners are selected to be rounded. Note that if a feature has some faces that are folded, even the corners at the folded faces are selected to be rounded. Figure 14-57 shows a feature being selected for rounding the corners. Notice that the dotted lines display the original feature before the face is folded. Figure 14-58 shows the sheet metal component after all the corners of the selected feature are rounded. Because the two flanges were not a part of the actual base feature, their corners are not rounded.

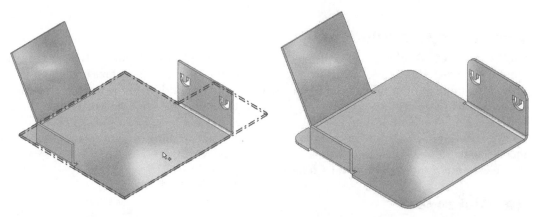

Figure 14-57 *Selecting the feature to be rounded*   *Figure 14-58* *After rounding the corners*

CHAMFERING CORNERS OF SHEET METAL COMPONENTS

Toolbar:	Sheet Metal Features > Corner Chamfer
Panel bar:	Sheet Metal Features > Corner Chamfer

 You can chamfer the corners of a sheet metal component by using the **Corner Chamfer** tool. When you invoke this tool, the **Corner Chamfer** dialog box will be displayed, as shown in Figure 14-59. The options in this dialog box are discussed next.

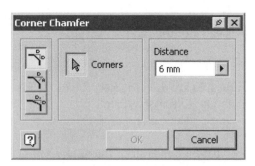

*Figure 14-59 The **Corner Chamfer** dialog box*

One Distance

The **One Distance** button, the first button in the area, is on the extreme left of the **Corner Chamfer** dialog box. This button is chosen to create a chamfer with an equal distance in both the directions of the chamfer corner. When you invoke the **Chamfer Corner** dialog box, the **One Distance** button is chosen by default and you are prompted to select a corner to be chamfered. This method creates a at a 45-degree angle. The chamfer distance can be specified in the **Distance** edit box that is available in the area that is on the extreme right of this dialog box. Because you have to specify only one distance value, only one edit box will be available in this area.

Distance and Angle

The **Distance and Angle** button is provided below the **One Distance** button. This button is chosen to define the chamfer by using one distance and one angle. When you choose this button, the **Edge** button is displayed in the area that is in the middle of the **Corner Chamfer** dialog box and you are prompted to select a face to be chamfered. This is the face along which the distance value will be calculated. On selecting the face, you will be prompted to select the corner to be chamfered. You can define the distance value in the **Distance** edit box and the angle value in the **Angle** edit box. These edit boxes are displayed in the area located on the extreme right of the **Corner Chamfer** dialog box.

Two Distances

The **Two Distances** button below the **Distance and Angle** button is used to create a chamfer by defining the two distances of the chamfer. The two distances can be entered in the **Distance1** and **Distance2** edit boxes. These edit boxes are displayed in the area located on the extreme right of the **Corner Chamfer** dialog box. Figure 14-60 shows a sheet metal component before chamfering the corners and Figure 14-61 shows the component after chamfering the corners.

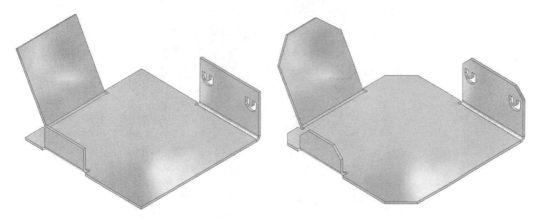

Figure 14-60 *Model before chamfering*   *Figure 14-61* *Model after chamfering*

PUNCHING 3D SHAPES INTO SHEET METAL COMPONENTS

Toolbar:	Sheet Metal Features > PunchTool
Panel bar:	Sheet Metal Features > PunchTool

You can punch a 3D shape into a sheet metal component with the help of the **PunchTool** tool. Note that a 3D shape can be punched only on a sketched point, endpoints of a line or an arc, or center points of arcs and circles. When you invoke this tool, the **PunchTool** dialog box is displayed. This dialog box has various pages that guide you through the process of punching a selected 3D shape into a sheet metal component.

Shape Page

The **Shape** page is the first page that is displayed when you invoke this dialog box, see Figure 14-62. This page allows you to select the shape that you want to punch on the sheet metal component. The options on this page are discussed next.

File Name

The **File Name** display box displays the name and path of the library file that is selected to punch the shape. To select a new punch shape library file, choose the **Browse** button. When you choose this button, the **Browse for Folder** dialog box is displayed. You can use this dialog box to select the library file that stores the punch shapes. The library file and its path will be displayed in the display box on the right of the **Browse** button.

List Box

The **List Box** displays the list of the punch shapes available in the selected library file. You

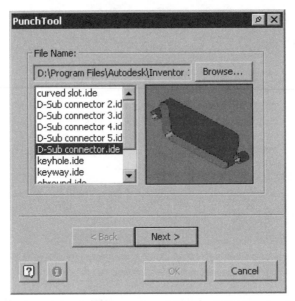

*Figure 14-62 The **Shape** page of the **PunchTool** dialog box*

can select the required punch shape from the list box. On doing so, its preview will be displayed in the preview window on the right of this list box.

Next

The **Next** button is chosen to proceed to the next page of the **Punch Tool** dialog box. Remember that if you choose the **Next** button, you cannot return to this page. Therefore, you need to be very careful in selecting the shape that you want to punch. If you have selected a wrong punch shape and chosen the **Next** button, you will have to exit the **PunchTool** dialog box and then invoke it again to select a different shape.

Geometry Page

The options in the **Geometry** page (Figure 14-63) are used to specify the location and orientation of the punch shape. If there is a sketched point on the sheet metal component, it will be automatically selected as the center of the punch shape. However, to use the endpoints of lines or arcs, or the center point of circle or ellipse, you will have to select them manually. As soon as you select the location of the punch shape, its preview will be displayed on the screen. You can change the orientation of the punch shape by entering its value in the **Angle** edit box. After setting these parameters, choose the **Next** button.

> **Note**
> *If you choose the **Next** button in the **Geometry** page to proceed to the next page, you can come back to the **Geometry** page by choosing the **Back** button in the next page.*

Size Page

The **Size** page of the **PunchTool** dialog box is used to set the size of the punch shape by modifying its dimensions. The name and the value of the dimension will be displayed in the

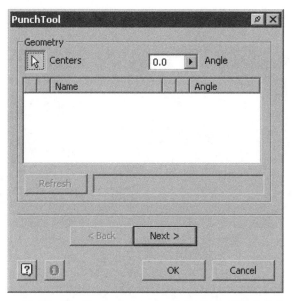

*Figure 14-63 The **Geometry** page of the **PunchTool** dialog box*

Name and the **Value** columns, respectively, as shown in Figure 14-64. To modify a dimension value, click on its field. The field will turn into an edit box or a drop-down list. If it turns into an edit box, you can enter the value in it. If the field turns into a drop-down list, you can select the value from the drop-down list. After setting the dimensions, choose the **OK** button to exit the dialog box and punch the shape on the sheet metal component.

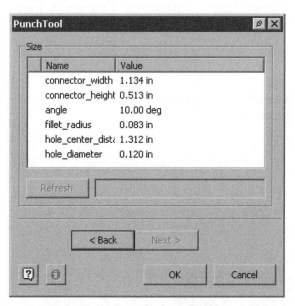

*Figure 14-64 The **Size** page of the **PunchTool** dialog box*

Figure 14-65 shows a sheet metal component after punching the keyway in the flange face.

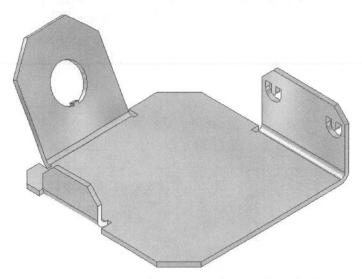

Figure 14-65 Sheet metal component after punching the keyway

CREATING HEMS

Toolbar: Sheet Metal Features > Hem
Panel bar: Sheet Metal Features > Hem

 Hems are defined as the rounded faces created on the sharp edges of a sheet metal component in order to reduce the area of the sharpness in a sheet metal component. This makes that sheet metal component easy to handle and assemble. You can create the hems by using the **Hem** dialog box. The options in the **Hem** dialog box are discussed next.

Shape Tab

The options in the **Shape** tab (Figure 14-66) are used to set the parameters related to the shape of the hem. These options are discussed next.

Type

The **Type** drop-down list provides the types of hems that you can create. These options are discussed next.

Single
The **Single** is the default hem type and it creates a single hem, as shown in Figure 14-67.

Teardrop
The **Teardrop** type creates a teardrop hem, as shown in Figure 14-68.

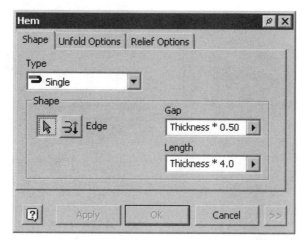

*Figure 14-66 The **Shape** tab of the **Hem** dialog box*

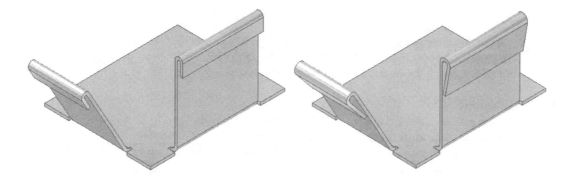

Figure 14-67 Single hem on flanges   *Figure 14-68 Teardrop hem on flanges*

Rolled

The **Rolled** type creates a rolled hem that does not have a face extending beyond the curve, as shown in Figure 14-69.

Double

The **Double** type creates a double hem by rotating the hem twice, as shown in Figure 14-70. This type of hem does not have any shared edge and so are very easy to handle.

Shape Area

Select Edge

When you invoke the **Hem** dialog box, this button is chosen by default and you are prompted to select the edge. The hem will be created on the selected edge. Note that you can select only one edge at a time for creating the hem. After selecting the edge, set the parameters and choose the **Apply** button to create the hem. Once the hem is created on one edge, this button will be chosen automatically and you are prompted to select the edge to create the hem.

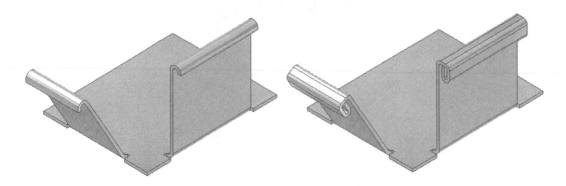

Figure 14-69 *Rolled hem on flanges*   **Figure 14-70** *Double hem on flanges*

Flip Direction

The **Flip Direction** button is chosen to reverse the direction of the hem creation.

Note

*If you do not want to create a relief while creating a bend, select the **None** option from the **Relief Shape** drop-down list of the **Relief Options** tab of the **Hem** dialog box. When you select this option, you will notice that no relief is created on the sides of the hem.*

Gap/Radius

The **Gap** edit box is used to set the value of the hem gap for single or double hem types. The default value in this edit box is **Thickness*0.5**. You can enter any desired value as the gap of the hem value in this edit box. This edit box will be replaced by the **Radius** edit box for teardrop and rolled hems to define the radius of the teardrop or rolled hem.

Length/Angle

The **Length** edit box is used to set the length of the hem for single or double hem types. The default value in this edit box is **Thickness*4.0**. You can enter any desired value as the length of the hem in this edit box. This edit box will be replaced by the **Angle** edit box for teardrop and rolled hems to define the angle of teardrop or rolled hem. The angle value can vary from 181-degree to 359-degree.

Note

*The options in the **More** area are the same as those discussed in the **Flange** dialog box.*

*The options in the **Unfold Options** tab and the **Relief Options** tab are the same as those discussed in the **Sheet Metal Styles** dialog box.*

CREATING CONTOUR FLANGES

Toolbar:	Sheet Metal Features > Contour Flange
Panel bar:	Sheet Metal Features > Contour Flange

Contour flanges are those that are created by using an open sketched shape. To create a contour flange, you need to first sketch an open shape. After sketching the shape, invoke the **Contour Flange** tool. Note that until you draw an open sketch, you cannot invoke this tool. When you invoke this tool, the **Contour Flange** dialog box will be displayed. The options in this dialog box are discussed next.

Shape Tab

The options in the **Shape** tab (Figure 14-71) are used to set the parameters related to the shape of the contour flange. These options are discussed next.

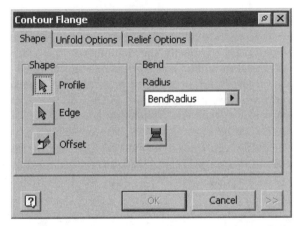

*Figure 14-71 The **Shape** tab of the **Contour Flange** dialog box*

Shape Area
Profile
The **Profile** button is chosen to select the profile that will be used to create the contour flange. When you invoke the **Contour Flange** dialog box, this button is chosen by default and you are prompted to select an open profile.

Edge
The **Edge** button is chosen to select the edge on which the flange will be created. As soon as you select the profile, this button is chosen automatically and you are prompted to select the edge.

Offset
The **Offset** button is chosen to reverse the direction of offset of the contour flange.

Bend Area
Radius
The **Radius** edit box is used to set the value of the radius of the bend in the contour flange. The default value is the value set in the **Sheet Metal Styles** dialog box. You can enter the required value in this edit box.

Extend Bend Aligned to Side Faces

If you choose the **Extend Bend Aligned to Side Faces** button, the material is added on the sides of the edges along the faces and not normal to the axis of the bend.

More

The **More** button is the button with two arrows and is available on the lower right corner of the **Contour Flange** dialog box. When you choose this button, the **Contour Flange** dialog box expands and displays the **Extents** area. This area has the **Type** drop-down list for specifying the extents of the flange. All the options in this drop-down list, except for the **Distance** option, are the same as those discussed in the previous sections of this chapter. The **Distance** option is discussed below.

Distance

The **Distance** option is used to specify the distance of the contour flange. When you select this option, the **Distance** edit box appears in the **Extents** area. You can define the distance of the contour flange in this edit box. You can reverse the direction of the flange creation by choosing the **Flip Direction** button on the right of the **Distance** edit box.

Figure 14-72 shows the profile and the edge selected for creating the contour flange and Figure 14-73 shows the contour flange created with some width and at an offset.

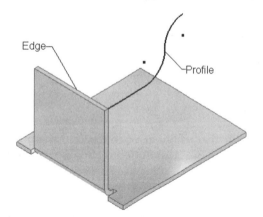
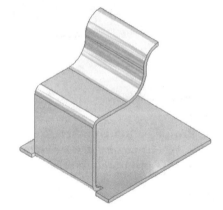

Figure 14-72 *Selecting the edge and the profile*   *Figure 14-73* *Contour flange*

Note
*The options in the **Unfold Options** and the **Relief Options** tabs are the same as those discussed in the previous sections of this chapter.*

CREATING FLAT PATTERNS OF SHEET METAL COMPONENTS

Toolbar:	Sheet Metal Features > Flat Pattern
Panel bar:	Sheet Metal Features > Flat Pattern

You can unfold the sheet metal components by using the **Flat Pattern** tool. When you invoke this tool, the sheet metal component is unfolded and is displayed in a separate graphics window. Note that you cannot make any modifications in the unfolded sheet metal component. However, if you make the changes in the sheet metal component, they are reflected in the flat pattern. When you create the flat pattern, it is added in the browser on top of the sheet metal component. Figure 14-74 shows a sheet metal component and Figure 14-75 shows the flat pattern of the same component.

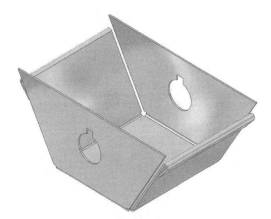

Figure 14-74 Sheet metal part

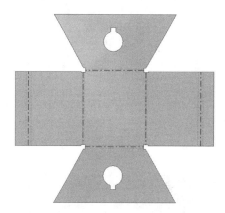

Figure 14-75 Flat pattern of the sheet metal part

 Tip. *To open a flat pattern window that was earlier closed by you, right-click on it in the browser and choose* **Open Window**; *the flat pattern window will be opened on the graphics screen.*

Note
The remaining tools in the **Sheet Metal** *module and their working is similar to the tools and their working in the* **Part** *module.*

TUTORIALS

Tutorial 1

In this tutorial, you will create the sheet metal component of the Holder Clip shown in Figure 14-76a. The flat pattern of the component is shown in Figure 14-76b. Its dimensions are shown in Figures 14-76c and 14-76d. The thickness of the sheet is 1 mm. After creating the sheet metal component, create its flat pattern. Save the component with the name given below.

\PersonalProject\c14\Tutorial1.ipt   **(Expected time: 45 min)**

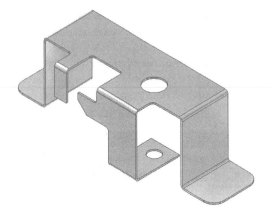

Figure 14-76a Sheet metal model of the Holder Clip

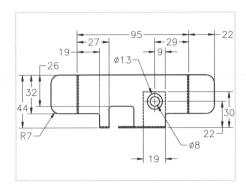

Figure 14-76c Top view of the Holder Clip

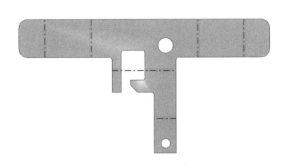

Figure 14-76b Flat pattern of the component

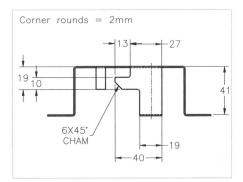

Figure 14-76d Front view of the Holder Clip

It is recommended that before creating the model, you should outline the steps that will be followed to complete the tutorial. The following steps are required to complete this tutorial:

a. Start a new metric sheet metal file and then draw the sketch of the top face of the sheet metal component.
b. Set the parameters in the **Sheet Metal Styles** dialog box and convert the sketch into the sheet metal face.
c. Add the contour flange on the right and the left faces of the top feature.
d. Add the contour flange on the front face of the feature.
e. Create a cut feature on the front face of the new flange and then add another face and chamfer to it.
f. Create the last flange and then create the two holes. Finally, create the flat pattern.

Opening a New Metric Sheet Metal File
1. Start Autodesk Inventor and then choose **New** in the **Open** dialog box.

2. Choose the **Metric** tab and then double-click on the **Sheet Metal (mm).ipt** option to start a new metric sheet metal file.

    The sketching environment, where you can draw the sketch for the top face of the sheet metal component, is activated.

3. Draw the sketch for the top face of the Holder Clip, as shown in Figure 14-77.

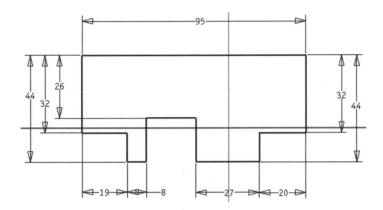

Figure 14-77 Sketch for the top face of the Holder Clip

 Note
In Figure 14-77, the grid lines are hidden for the clarity of the sketch.

4. Exit the sketching environment by choosing **Return** from the **Inventor Standard** toolbar.

Converting the Sketch into a Sheet Metal Face

Before converting the sketch into a sheet metal face, it is recommended that you set the parameters in the **Sheet Metal Styles** dialog box. These parameters will control the thickness of the sheet, radius of the bend, parameters of the relief, and so on.

1. Choose the **Sheet Metal Styles** button from the **Sheet Metal Features** panel bar to invoke the **Sheet Metal Styles** dialog box.

    When you invoke the **Sheet Metal Styles** dialog box, the **Sheet** tab is active by default. You can set the parameters related to the sheet thickness in this tab. Because all the other parameters are based on the thickness of the sheet, they will automatically change when you change the sheet thickness.

2. Enter **1** as the value in the **Thickness** edit box in the **Sheet** area.

    This will increase the sheet thickness to 1 mm.

3.   Choose **Save** and then choose **Done** to save the changes and exit the dialog box.

4.   Choose the **Face** button from the **Sheet Metal Features** panel bar to invoke the **Face** dialog box.

     Because there is only one unconsumed sketch, it is automatically selected and highlighted to create the sheet metal component face.

5.   Choose **OK** to create the face and exit the **Face** dialog box. Change the current view to the isometric view. The top of the Holder Clip is shown in Figure 14-78.

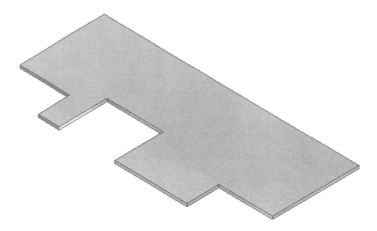

Figure 14-78 Top face of the Holder Clip

Creating the First Contour Flange

As mentioned earlier, the contour flange is created with the help of a sketched contour. Therefore, you first need to sketch the contour that will be used to create the flange.

1.   Define a new sketch plane on the face shown in Figure 14-79.

2.   Draw the sketch for the contour flange, as shown in Figure 14-80.

3.   Exit the sketching environment and then choose the **Contour Flange** button from the **Sheet Metal Features** panel bar to invoke the **Contour Flange** dialog box.

     The **Profile** button in the **Shape** area of the **Shape** tab is chosen by default and you are prompted to select the profile for creating the contour flange.

4.   Select one of the two sketched lines as the profile for creating the flange. Because the other line is a part of the same sketch, it is selected automatically and the sketch turns blue.

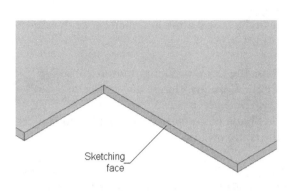

Figure 14-79 *Plane for sketching the profile*   *Figure 14-80* *Sketch for the contour flange*

As soon as you select the profile, the **Select Edge** button in the **Shape** area is chosen and you are prompted to select the edge on which the flange will be created.

5. Select the extreme right vertical edge on the top face to create the flange.

6. Accept the remaining default options and choose **OK** to create the flange. You will notice that a bend is automatically created between the base sheet and the flange. The dimensions and parameters of this bend will be taken as the parameters defined in the **Sheet Metal Styles** dialog box.

7. Similarly, create the flange on the other side of the top face. You may need to flip the direction by using the **Flip Offset** button in the **Shape** area of the **Shape** tab so that the front face of the flange is coplanar with the left face of the base sheet. The sheet metal model of the Holder Clip, after creating the two contour flanges, is shown in Figure 14-81.

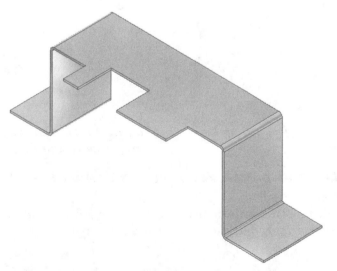

Figure 14-81 *Sheet metal component after creating the two contour flanges*

Creating the Second Contour Flange

1. Define a new sketch plane on the planar face of the base feature and then create the sketch for the contour flange, as shown in Figure 14-82.

2. Exit the sketching environment and then choose the **Contour Flange** button from the **Sheet Metal Features** panel bar to invoke the **Contour Flange** dialog box.

    The **Profile** button in the **Shape** area of the **Shape** tab is chosen by default and you are prompted to select the profile for creating the contour flange.

3. Select one of the two sketched lines as the contour for creating the flange. Because the other line is a part of the same sketch, it is also automatically selected and the sketch turns blue.

    As soon as you select the profile, the **Select Edge** button in the **Shape** area is chosen and you are prompted to select the edge on which the flange will be created.

4. Select the horizontal edge on the top face to create the flange.

5. Choose the **Flip Offset** button to reverse the direction, in which the flange face will be created.

6. Accept the remaining default options and choose **OK** to create the flange. The sheet metal component, after creating the third contour flange, is shown in Figure 14-83.

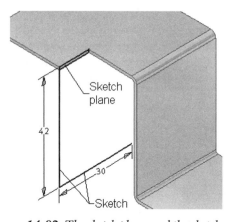
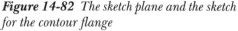

Figure 14-82 *The sketch plane and the sketch for the contour flange*

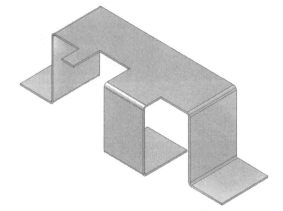

Figure 14-83 *Sheet metal component after creating the contour flange*

Creating a Cut and a New Face on the Front Face of the Previous Contour Flange

1. Define a new sketch plane on the front face of the previous flange and create a sketch for the cut feature. After creating the sketch, exit the sketching environment.

2.   Invoke the **Cut** tool and create the cut feature by using the **All** extents. The sheet metal component after creating the cut is shown in Figure 14-84.

3.   Similarly, define a sketch plane on the front face of the previous flange and create a new rectangular face by using the **Face** tool.

4.   Next, add the corner chamfer by using the **Corner Chamfer** tool, as shown in Figure 14-85.

Figure 14-84 *Sheet metal component after creating*   *Figure 14-85* *Sheet metal component after creating*
the cut feature   *the new face and corner chamfer*

Creating the Flange

1.   Choose the **Flange** button from the **Sheet Metal Features** panel bar to invoke the **Flange** dialog box. You are prompted to select the edge for creating the flange.

2.   Select the edge on the top face of the base feature, as shown in Figure 14-86.

3.   Enter **19** as the value in the **Distance** edit box. The size of the flange in the preview is modified.

4.   Choose the **Flip Direction** button.

5.   Accept the remaining default options and choose the **OK** button to create the flange and exit the dialog box.

     The sheet metal component after creating the flange is shown in Figure 14-87.

Creating the Rounds and Holes

1.   Create all the rounds by using the **Corner Round** tool.

2.   Create the two holes using the **Holes** dialog box.

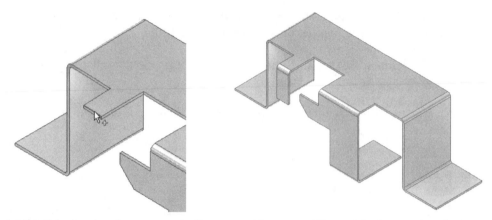

Figure 14-86 *Selecting the edge to create the flange*   *Figure 14-87* *Model after creating the flange*

This completes the sheet metal component for the Holder Clip. The final sheet metal component for the Holder Clip is shown in Figure 14-88.

3. Save the sheet metal component with the name *\PersonalProject\c14\Tutorial1.ipt* and then close the file.

Creating the Flat Pattern

The flattened view of a sheet metal component plays a very important role in process planning while designing the punch tools and dies for creating the sheet metal component. Therefore, the flattened view is a very important part of any sheet metal component. As mentioned earlier, you can unfold the sheet metal component and display its flattened view in a separate graphics window. This is done by using the **Flat Pattern** tool.

1. Choose the **Flat Pattern** button from the **Sheet Metal Features** panel bar.

The sheet metal component will be unfolded and displayed in a separate window, as shown in Figure 14-89.

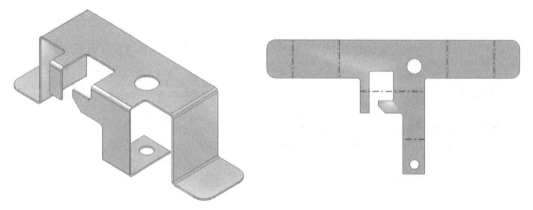

Figure 14-88 *Final model of the Holder Clip*   *Figure 14-89* *Flat Pattern of the sheet metal part*

Note
*If the orientation of the flat pattern is not similar to the one shown in Figure 14-89, close the flat pattern window and then right-click on **Flat Pattern** in the browser. Choose the **Select Base Face** option from the shortcut menu and then select the top face as the base face. Now, again right-click on **Flat Pattern** in the browser and choose **Open Window** to open the flat pattern window. You will notice that the orientation of the flat pattern is similar to the one shown in Figure 14-89.*

*You can also use the **Measure** tool to measure the distances in the flat pattern. To measure the distances, right-click in the flat pattern window and choose **Measure** from the shortcut menu.*

Tutorial 2

In this tutorial, you will create the sheet metal component shown in Figure 14-90a. Its dimensions are shown in Figures 14-90b through 14-90d. The flat pattern of the component is shown in Figure 14-91. The thickness of the sheet is 1 mm. The dimensions of the hems are not given. Select the default parameters as the dimensions for creating the hems on the two faces.

(Expected time: 45 min)

Figure 14-90a Sheet metal component

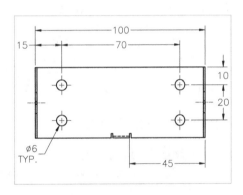

Figure 14-90b Top view of the model

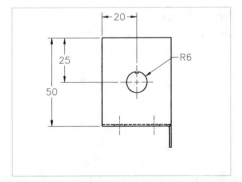

Figure 14-90c Left-side view of the model

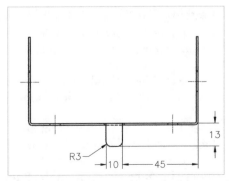

Figure 14-90d Front view of the model

Figure 14-91 *Flat pattern of the sheet metal component*

The following steps outline the procedure for creating the model:

a.   Start a new metric sheet metal file and create the sketch for the base of the sheet metal component on the XY plane.
b.   Exit the sketching environment and convert the sketch into a face by using the **Face** tool.
c.   Create one hole and then pattern it to create the remaining three instances.
d.   Create the flange on the left and right faces of the sheet metal base.
e.   Create hems on the two flanges and then create the two keyways using the **PunchTool** dialog box.
f.   Create the flange on the front face of the base.

Drawing the Sketch for the Base Feature

1.   Choose **New** from the **Inventor Standard** toolbar to invoke the **Open** dialog box.

2.   Choose the **Metric** tab and start a new metric sheet metal file.

3.   Draw the sketch for the base, as shown in Figure 14-92.

Converting the Sketch into a Sheet Metal Face

As mentioned earlier, you should first set the parameters in the **Sheet Metal Styles** dialog box and then convert the sketch into a face.

1.   Choose the **Sheet Metal Styles** button from the **Sheet Metal Features** panel bar to invoke the **Sheet Metal Styles** dialog box.

2.   Enter **1** as the value in the **Thickness** edit box in the **Sheet** area. This increases the sheet thickness to 1 mm. Choose **Save** and then choose **Done** to close the dialog box.

3.   Choose the **Face** button from the **Sheet Metal Features** panel bar to invoke the **Face** dialog box.

Because there is only one unconsumed sketch, it is automatically selected and highlighted to create the sheet metal component face.

4. Choose **OK** to create the face and exit the **Face** dialog box.

5. Invoke the **Holes** dialog box and create a hole at the lower left corner of the base using the **Linear** option.

6. Create the rectangular pattern of the hole. Change the current view to the isometric view. The base of the sheet metal component, after creating the hole pattern, is shown in Figure 14-93.

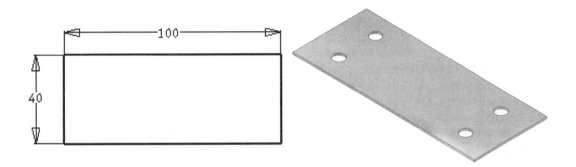

Figure 14-92 Sketch for the base feature   *Figure 14-93 Base after creating the hole pattern*

Creating the Two Flanges

1. Choose the **Flange** button from the **Sheet Metal Features** panel bar to invoke the **Flange** dialog box. You are prompted to select the edge for creating the flange.

2. Select the right vertical edge on the bottom face of the base. You will notice that the preview of the flange is shown in the downward direction.

3. Choose the **Flip Direction** button and enter **50** as the value in the **Distance** edit box.

4. Choose the **Apply** button.

   You will notice that the flange is created on the right edge and the **Flange** dialog box is still available. This is because you did not exit the dialog box after creating the flange.

5. Press and hold the F4 key down and rotate the model such that the bottom vertical edge on the other side of the base is visible.

6.   Release the F4 key and select the vertical edge on the bottom face of the base.

     You will notice that the flange is created in the upward direction. This is because the parameters are already set in the **Flange** dialog box.

7.   Choose the **OK** button from the **Flange** dialog box to create the flange and exit the dialog box. Change the current view to the isometric view. The sheet metal component, after creating the flanges, is shown in Figure 14-94.

Creating the Hems

1.   Choose the **Hem** button from the **Sheet Metal Features** panel bar to invoke the **Hem** dialog box. You are prompted to select an edge to create the hem.

2.   Select the outer edge on the top face of the right flange. You will notice that the preview of the hem is displayed on the graphics screen.

3.   Accept the default parameters in the **Hem** dialog box and choose **Apply** to create the hem.

4.   Now, select the outer edge on the left flange. The preview of the flange is displayed. Choose the **OK** button to create the flange and exit the dialog box. The sheet metal component, after creating the hems, is shown in Figure 14-95.

Figure 14-94 *Model after creating the flanges*   *Figure 14-95* *Model after creating the hems*

Creating the Cut Feature

Next, the cut feature with the keyway needs to be created. This feature will be created by punching the predefined shape on one of the flanges and will then be mirrored on the other side. As mentioned earlier, the shapes are punched by using a sketched point. Therefore, you first need to sketch a point in the middle of one of the flanges.

Before creating the cut feature, it is recommended that you suppress the hems. This is because after creating the hems, the actual dimensions of the face are reduced and you cannot get the proper dimensions of the face.

1. Using the browser, suppress the two hems. Now, define a new sketch plane on the outer face of the right flange.

2. Create a sketch point at the center of the face. The vertical dimension of the point from the top edge should be 25 mm.

3. Exit the sketching environment and then choose the **PunchTool** button from the **Sheet Metal Features** panel bar to invoke the **Shape** page of the **PunchTool** dialog box.

4. Select **keyway.ide** from the list box. The preview of the keyway is displayed in the preview window. Choose the **Next** button to proceed to the **Geometry** page.

   Because there is only one sketched point, it is selected as the center of the keyway and a preview of the keyway is displayed on the graphics screen. You will notice that in the preview, the keyway is toward the right of the circle. You need to rotate it in order to get the proper orientation.

5. Enter **90** as the value in the **Angle** edit box on the **Geometry** page. Choose the **Next** button to proceed to the next page. Accept the default dimension values and choose **OK** to create the keyway.

 Note
*The punched 3D shapes are displayed as **iFeature** in the browser.*

6. Similarly, define a new sketch plane on the outer face of the left flange and then project the last sketch point on this face. Using this projected point, create the keyway on the left flange. The model, after creating both the keyways, is shown in Figure 14-96.

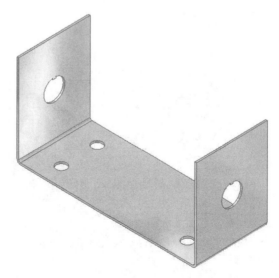

Figure 14-96 Sheet metal component after creating the punched features

Creating the Next Flange

1. Choose the **Flange** button from the **Sheet Metal Features** panel bar to invoke the **Flange** dialog box. You are prompted to select the edge for creating the flange.

2. Select the upper edge on the front face of the base of the sheet metal component. The preview of the flange is displayed on the graphics screen.

3. Enter **13** as the value in the **Distance** edit box and then choose the **Flip Direction** button to reverse the direction of the feature creation. Choose the **More** button on the lower right corner of the dialog box to expand it.

4. Select **Width** from the **Type** drop-down list in the **Extents** area. The **Offset** and **Width** edit boxes appear in the **Extents** area and you will be prompted to select the flange start point.

5. Select the right endpoint of the selected edge as the start point of the flange. Enter **43** as the flange offset value in the **Offset** edit box.

6. Enter **10** as the value of the width of the flange in the **Width** edit box. Choose **OK** to create the flange and exit the dialog box.

7. Create rounds on the two corners of the previous flange by using the **Corner Round** tool. The radius of the corner round is 3 mm.

   This completes the sheet metal component. Unsuppress all the suppressed features. The final sheet metal component is shown in Figure 14-97.

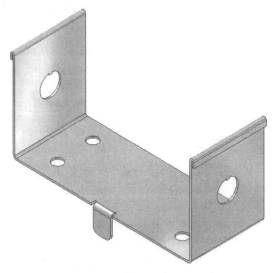

Figure 14-97 Completed sheet metal component for Tutorial 2

Creating the Flat Pattern

1. Choose the **Flat Pattern** button from the **Sheet Metal Features** panel bar. The flat pattern of the sheet metal component will be displayed in a separate window, as shown in Figure 14-98.

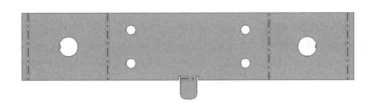

Figure 14-98 *Flat pattern of the component*

2. Save the model with the name given below and then close the file.

    \PersonalProject\c14\Tutorial2.ipt

Self-Evaluation Test

Answer the following questions and then compare your answers with those given at the end of this chapter:

1. The sheet metal files are saved as the *.ipt files. (T/F)

2. When you invoke a new sheet metal file, you are by default in the sketching environment. (T/F)

3. The contour flange will be created only with the help of a sketched contour. (T/F)

4. A sketched point will automatically be selected as the center of the punched 3D shape. (T/F)

5. You can unfold a sheet metal component by using the _____ tool.

6. By default, the value of the bend radius is equal to the _____ of the sheet.

7. In Autodesk Inventor you can fold a sheet metal face only by using a _____ line that acts as the _____ line.

8. Autodesk Inventor allows you to create the corner seams in a sheet metal component with the help of the _____ tool.

9. If a flange is created through an angle of _____, it will not be visible as it will be merged with the face of the sheet metal component.

10. To convert a solid model into a sheet metal component, you first need to _____ it.

Review Questions

Answer the following questions:

1. If you modify a value in the **Sheet Metal Styles** dialog box, after creating the sheet metal component, the changes will be reflected in the sheet metal component when you exit the dialog box after saving the changes. (T/F)

2. The flat pattern is displayed in a separate window. (T/F)

3. You can set the material for the sheet metal component from the **Sheet Metal Styles** dialog box. (T/F)

4. The value of the bend and unfold parameters that are set in the **Sheet Metal Styles** dialog box cannot be overridden from the dialog boxes of any tool. (T/F)

5. You can set the value of an edit box as an equation in terms of the thickness of the sheet. (T/F)

6. A punched 3D shape cannot be mirrored. (T/F)

7. The flange that follows a sketched shape in a sheet metal component can be created using which one of the following tools?

    (a) **Flange**   (b) **Contour Flange**
    (c) **Face**   (d) **Hem**

8. Which one of the following is not a type of hem?

    (a) **Single**   (b) **Double**
    (c) **Tripple**   (d) **Teardrop**

9. The base of the sheet metal component can be created by using which one of the following tools?

    (a) **Flange**   (b) **Contour Flange**
    (c) **Face**   (d) **Hem**

10. You can fillet all the corners of the base feature by using which one of the following tools?

    (a) **Round**   (b) **Corner Round**

    (c) **Face**   (d) **Hem**

Exercise

Exercise 1

Create the sheet metal component shown in Figure 14-99a. The flat pattern of the component is shown in Figure 14-99b. The dimensions of the model are shown in Figures 14-99c and 14-99d. Assume the missing dimensions. **(Expected time: 30 min)**

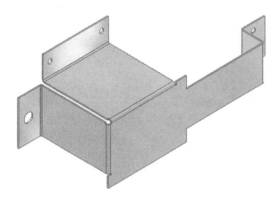

Figure 14-99a Sheet metal part for Exercise 1

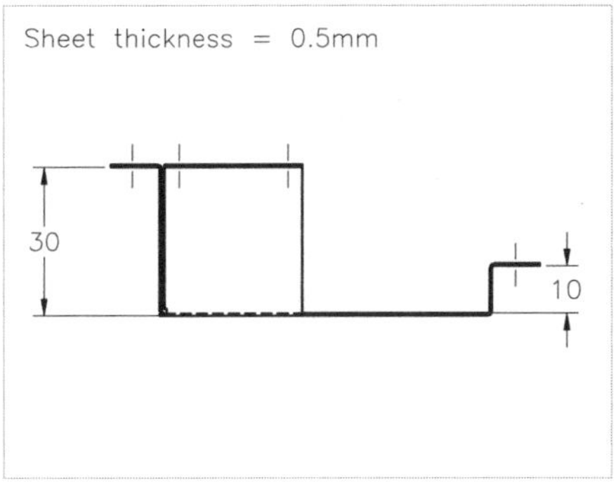

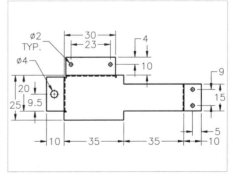

Figure 14-99c Top view of the component

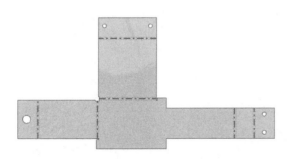

Figure 14-99b Flat pattern of the component

Figure 14-99d Front view of the component

Hint
*The flanges on the top face and the left face can be created to some width and then by using the **Corner Seam** tool, you can force them to close together. This way the corner relief will also be created.*

Answers to Self-Evaluation Test

1. T, **2.** T, **3.** T, **4.** T, **5. Flat Pattern**, **6.** thickness, **7.** sketched, folding, **8. Corner Seam**, **9.** 180-degree, **10.** shell

Chapter 15

Introduction to Weldments

Learning Objectives

After completing this chapter, you will be able to:

- *Understand weldment assemblies.*
- *Understand the weldment environment.*
- *Understand fillet and cosmetic welds.*
- *Create weldments with fillet and cosmetic welds.*

UNDERSTANDING WELDMENT ASSEMBLIES

The weldment assemblies are those in which you can weld a component with another component using various types of welds and then provide details about the welds. These assemblies are also called weldments. Autodesk Inventor provides you with a special type of environment for creating weldments. This environment is called the weldment environment. This environment is similar to the assembly modeling environment. In addition to the tools to assemble the components, this environment also provides the tools to weld the components. In this environment, you can also make some initial preparations to weld the components. The initial preparations include creating cut features using the assembly features.

Similar to various types of drawing files, you are also provided with various weldment files to invoke the weldment assembly environment. To invoke the weldment assembly environment, double-click on any of the weldment assembly files from the **Open** dialog box, see Figure 15-1.

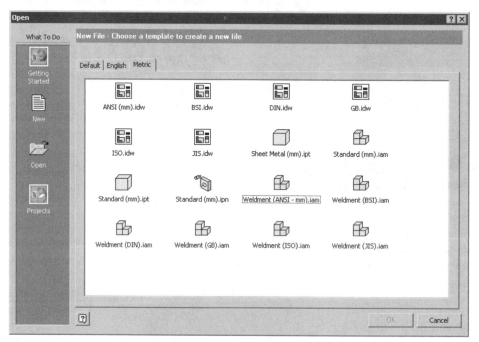

Figure 15-1 *Various types of weldment files to invoke the weldment environment*

Figure 15-2 shows the weldment assembly environment invoked using the **Weldment (ANSI - mm).iam** file.

Note
*You can convert an assembly created in the assembly modeling environment to a weldment assembly by choosing **Convert > Weldment** from the menu bar. However, remember that an assembly once converted into a weldment cannot be converted back into a simple assembly.*

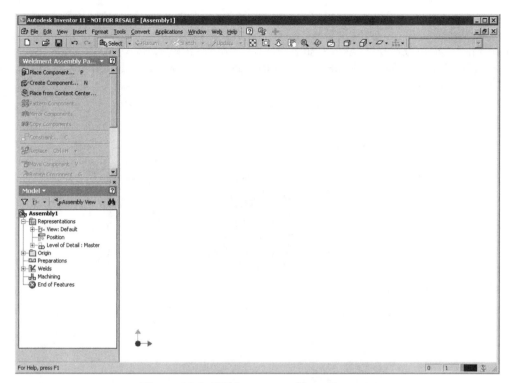

Figure 15-2 Weldment assembly environment

MAJOR TYPES OF WELDS IN AUTODESK INVENTOR

Autodesk Inventor allows you to create three major types of welds. These are cosmetic welds, fillet welds, and groove welds. There are other types of welds also that can be used to create weldments. However, they are not discussed in this book. The three main types of welds are discussed next.

Cosmetic Welds

Cosmetic welds are artificial welds added to the selected edge. These type of welds are not actual welds and as a result no weld bead is added to the model. To create a cosmetic weld, you just need to select the edge that requires welding.

Note

Adding cosmetic welds does not modify the physical properties of the assembly. This is because adding cosmetic welds does not physically add any material to the model. It only adds a convention that gives an impression of a welding.

Figure 15-3 shows a part of the Shock assembly in which the cylinder is assembled with the bracket. Note that because there is no physical bonding between these two components, they could not be held together. As a result, you need to weld these two components together. Figure 15-4 shows the same assembly after adding a cosmetic weld. The cosmetic weld symbol is also shown in the assembly.

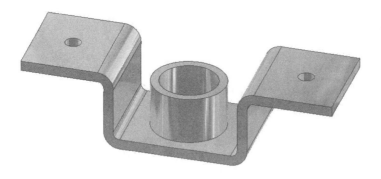

Figure 15-3 *Assembly before welding*

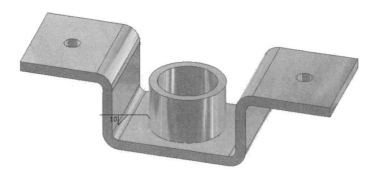

Figure 15-4 *Assembly after creating the cosmetic weld and placing the symbol*

Fillet Welds

Fillet welds are actual welds and are represented with a solid feature in the assembly. When you add fillet welds, a solid feature is added, which represents the weld bead in the assembly. Also, the physical properties of the assembly are modified when you add the fillet welds. To create a fillet weld, you need to select two surfaces that will be weld together. Figure 15-5 shows the Shock assembly after adding a fillet weld to the bracket and cylinder. Figure 15-6 shows a butt-joint with a fillet weld.

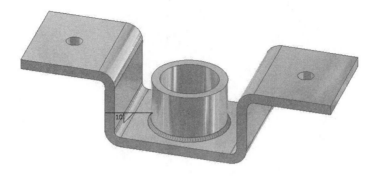

Figure 15-5 *Assembly with the fillet weld*

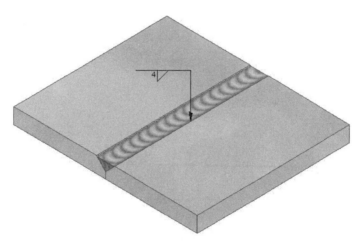

Figure 15-6 *Butt-joint with the fillet weld*

Groove Welds

Groove welds are used to weld parts that are placed at a certain offset from each other or have some grooves in between. These are also the actual welds and are represented with a solid feature in the assembly. Figure 15-7 shows a partial three-quarter section view of the Shock assembly after adding a groove weld to the bracket and cylinder. Note that in this case, the cylinder is assembled at some offset from the bracket. As evident in the figure, the groove weld bead is filled between this offset space. Figure 15-8 shows a butt-joint with a groove weld. As evident in this figure also, some offset is maintained between the two mating faces of the plates between which the groove weld bead is filled.

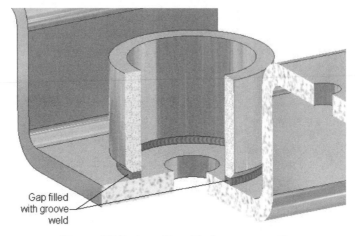

Figure 15-7 *Assembly with the groove weld*

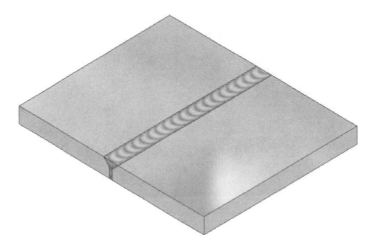

Figure 15-8 *Butt-joint with groove weld*

ADDING WELDS TO ASSEMBLIES

The process of creating weldment assemblies is completed in three steps: assembling the components, preparing components for welding, and creating welds. These three steps are discussed next.

Assembling Components of Weldment Assemblies

As mentioned earlier, you can create the weldment assemblies in the weldment environment. Alternatively, you can assemble the components in the assembly modeling environment and then switch to the weldment environment to add welds to the components. Remember that once you shift from the assembly modeling environment to the weldment environment, you cannot switch back.

Preparing Assemblies for Weldments

Once you have assembled components of the weldment assemblies, you need to prepare them for welding by removing material from the components to accommodate the weld beads. You can create cut features, holes, fillets, and chamfers to remove the material. For example, to create a butt-joint, you need to chamfer the two edges of the plates between which the weld bead will be added. This step is not required if the components were chamfered during their creation. Note that similar to the assembly features, these features are also limited to the assembly and are not made on the individual part files.

To prepare weldments, double-click on the **Preparations** option in the browser; the **Weldment Features Panel** panel bar will be invoked. This panel bar provides various material removal tools that you can use to create cuts in weldments for accommodating the weld bead. After preparing weldments, choose the **Return** button to return to the **Weldment** environment.

 Note
*While preparing the weldments, the **Extrude** and **Revolve** tools provide only the **Cut** operations.*

Adding Welds

The final step in creating weldments is to add welds. To do so, double-click on the **Welds** option in the browser; the **Weldment Assembly Panel** panel bar will be replaced by the **Weldment Features Panel** panel bar. The tools to create all three types of welds are available in this panel bar. You can add the fillet symbol while adding welds or separately using the **Weld Symbol** tool.

The tools to create all three types of welds are discussed next.

CREATING FILLET WELDS

Panel Bar:	Weldment Features Panel > Fillet Weld
Toolbar:	Weldment Features Panel > Fillet Weld

 Choose the **Fillet Weld** button from the **Weldment Features Panel** panel bar; the **Fillet Weld** dialog box will be displayed, as shown in Figure 15-9.

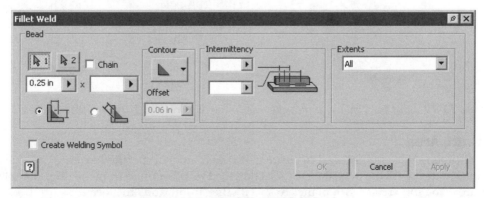

*Figure 15-9 The **Fillet Weld** dialog box*

Bead Area

To create a fillet weld, you need to select two surfaces that will be welded together. This is the reason the **1** button in the **Bead** area will be automatically chosen when you invoke the **Fillet Weld** dialog box and you will be prompted to select the face for the weld. After selecting the first face to weld, choose the **2** button; you will again be prompted to select the face to weld. Select the second face. The second face will turn green and the preview of the fillet weld will appear. Selecting the **Chain** check box ensures all the chained tangent faces are also selected.

You can specify the dimension of the weld in terms of leg length or in terms of throat measurement by selecting their radio buttons from this area. The value of the weld leg or the throat measurement can be entered in the edit boxes below the **1** and **2** buttons.

Contour Area

The options in this area are used to specify the contour of the resulting weld bead. By default, the **Flat** option is chosen. To specify any other option, choose the down arrow on the right of the **Flat** button in this area; a flyout appears. Choose the **Convex** or **Concave** button to specify the type of weld bead. Specify the offset value of the convex or concave surface in the **Offset** edit box in this area.

Figure 15-10 shows a fillet weld with a convex contour.

Intermittency Area

The options in this area are used to create an intermittent fillet weld. You can specify the length of the intermittent fillet in the **Length** edit box and the pitch in the **Pitch** edit box. Figure 15-11 shows an intermittent fillet weld in a butt joint. In this case, the length is 10 mm and the pitch value is 20 mm.

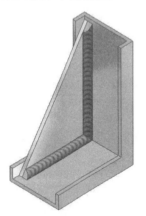

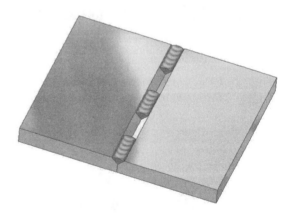

Figure 15-10 *Fillet weld with a convex contour*   *Figure 15-11* *Intermittent fillet weld*

Extents Area

The options in this area are used to create a fillet weld up to a specified extent. The extent of the intermittent weld can be defined by selecting the **From-To** option from the drop-down list in this area. You can create work planes to specify the "from" and "to" faces.

Create Weld Symbol

When you select this check box, the dialog box expands and provides the option to add the weld symbols.

> **Tip**. *You can define the contour finish for the welded surfaces by choosing it from the **Other Side Symbol** and **Arrow Side Symbol** buttons from the area that is displayed when you expand the **Fillet Weld** dialog box.*

CREATING COSMETIC WELDS

Panel Bar:	Weldment Features Panel > Cosmetic Weld
Toolbar:	Weldment Features Panel > Cosmetic Weld

 Choose the **Cosmetic Weld** button from the **Weldment Features Panel** panel bar; the **Cosmetic Weld** dialog box will be displayed, as shown in Figure 15-12.

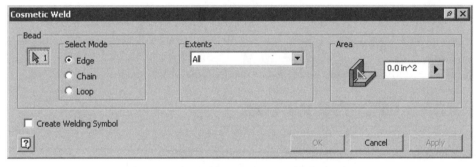

*Figure 15-12 The **Cosmetic Weld** dialog box*

Bead Area

When you invoke the **Cosmetic Weld** dialog box, the **1** button in will be chosen and you will be prompted to select an edge or loop for the weld. You can set the selection mode using the options in the **Select Mode** area on the right of the **1** button. The selected edge turns blue.

Extents Area

The options in this area are used to create a fillet weld up to a specified extent. The extent of the weld can be specified by selecting the **From-To** option from drop-down list in this area. You can create work planes to specify the "from" and "to" faces.

Area

The edit box in this area is used to specify the cross-sectional area of the fillet weld. Note that even when you increase this value, there will be no change in the display of the fillet weld in the model. This is because this value is used only for calculating the physical properties of the model after welding.

Figure 15-13 shows two components welded together using the cosmetic weld.

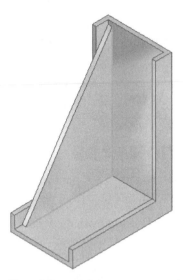

Figure 15-13 *Two side welding of the components using the cosmetic weld*

Note

*The welds are listed in the **Beads** folder under **Welds** in the browser.*

CREATING GROOVE WELDS

Panel Bar:	Weldment Features Panel > Groove Weld
Toolbar:	Weldment Features Panel > Groove Weld

As mentioned earlier, the groove welds are created between the components assembled at some offset or have some grooves between them. After assembling the components and invoking the weld environment, choose the **Groove Weld** button from the **Weldment Features Panel** panel bar; the **Groove Weld** dialog box will be displayed, as shown in Figure 15-14.

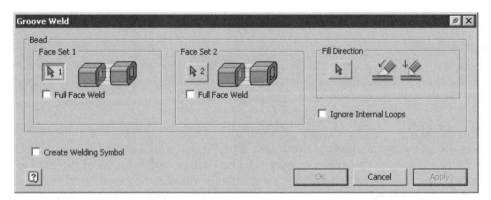

Figure 15-14 *The **Groove Weld** dialog box*

Bead Area

The options in this area are used to specify the faces and fill the direction of the groove weld. These options are discussed next.

Face Set 1 Area

The options in this area are used to select the first face for applying the groove weld. When you invoke the **Groove Weld** dialog box, the **1** button in the **Face Set 1** area will be chosen and you will be prompted to select face for the weld. The face selected as face set 1 turns blue. You can select the **Full Face Weld** button to add the weld bead to the entire face.

Face Set 2 Area

The options in this area are used to select the second face for applying the groove weld. The face selected as face set 2 turns blue. You can select the **Full Face Weld** button to add the weld bead to the entire face.

Fill Direction Area

If you are not creating a full face weld, you need to specify the direction of the groove weld. You can specify the direction using a linear edge, cylindrical face, planar face, or by using two vertices.

Figure 15-15 shows the quarter section view of a full face groove weld. Note that in this case, the cylinder is assembled at an offset from the bracket.

Ignore Internal Loops

This check box is selected to create a groove weld by ignoring the internal loop. Figure 15-16 shows the quarter section view of a groove weld created by ignoring the internal loop, which is the hole in the bracket.

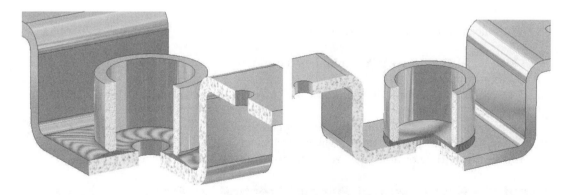

Figure 15-15 *Full face groove weld*   *Figure 15-16* *Internal loops ignored in the groove weld*

TUTORIALS

Tutorial 1

In this tutorial, you will create the welded Butt-joint shown in Figure 15-17. To create this weldment, you will use the **Weldment (ANSI - mm).iam** file and use the top-down approach for assembling the Plates. You will prepare the Plate for welding in the weldment environment by creating the chamfer for welding. The Plate that will be used to create the butt-joint is 30 mm long and 50 mm wide. The thickness of the Plate is 5 mm. The chamfer is a 3 mm equal distance chamfer.   **(Expected time: 30 min)**

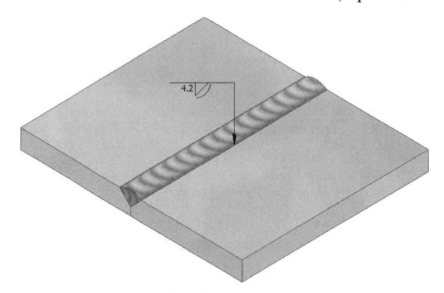

Figure 15-17 *Welded Butt-joint for Tutorial 1*

The following steps are required to complete this tutorial:

a. Open a new **Weldment (ANSI - mm).iam** file and then create the plate using the top-down assembly options.
b. Exit the part modeling environment and insert another instance of the Plate in the weldment environment.
c. Prepare the Plates for welding by creating chamfers.
d. Assemble the two plates using the assembly constraints.
e. Invoke the welding options and create the butt-joint using the fillet weld.

Opening a New Weldment File and Creating the Plate

As mentioned in the tutorial description, you need to use the **Weldment (ANSI - mm).iam** file for creating the butt-joint. As a result, you need to select this file from the **Open** dialog box.

1. Start Autodesk Inventor and then double-click on the **Weldment (ANSI - mm).iam** file to invoke the weldment environment.

2. Using the **Create Component** tool, create the Plate. The weldment assembly, after creating the Plate, is shown in Figure 15-18.

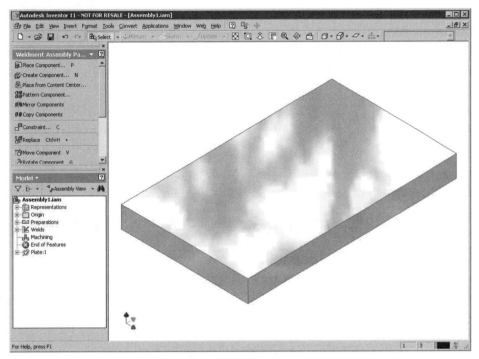

Figure 15-18 *Weldment after creating the Plate*

Placing Another Instance of the Plate

Next, you need to place another instance of the Plate. Note that you will not assemble the two plates at this stage. You first need to prepare them for the welding by chamfering the edges.

1. Choose **Place Component** from the **Weldment Assembly Panel** panel bar to invoke the **Open** dialog box.

2. Double-click on **Plate.ipt** to select this file; the **Open** dialog box is closed and you are prompted to place the component.

3. Specify a point on the screen at a location where it does not interfere with the previous instance. Right-click and choose **Done** from the shortcut menu.

4. Choose **Zoom All** from the **Inventor Standard** toolbar to modify the drawing display area.

Preparing the Two Plates for Welding

Next, you need to prepare the two Plates for welding by chamfering them. To chamfer the edges, you need to invoke the **Preparations** environment.

1. Double-click on **Preparations** in the browser to invoke the **Weldment Features Panel** panel bar.

2. Choose the **Chamfer** button to invoke the **Chamfer** dialog box. Enter **3** as the value in the **Distance** edit box and then select the edge on the top face of one of the Plates. Choose **OK** to create the chamfer and exit the dialog box.

3. Similarly, chamfer the edge on the top face of the other plate.

   You will notice that **Chamfer 1** and **Chamfer 2** are added under **Preparations** in the browser. This is because you created both the chamfers in the two Plates as two different features.

4. Choose **Return** to restore the weldment environment. The weldment assembly, after chamfering the edges of the two Plates, is shown in Figure 15-19.

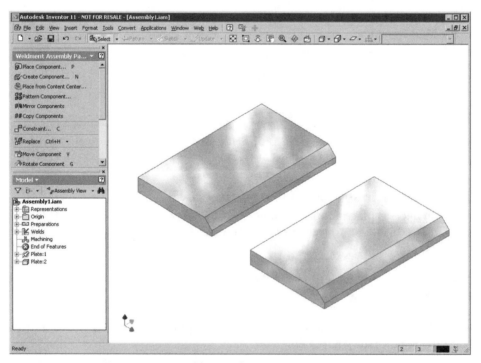

Figure 15-19 *Weldment after preparing the two plates*

Assembling the Two Plates

1. Apply multiple instances of the **Mate** constraints to the two instances of the Plate and assemble them together. The assembly of the two plates is shown in Figure 15-20.

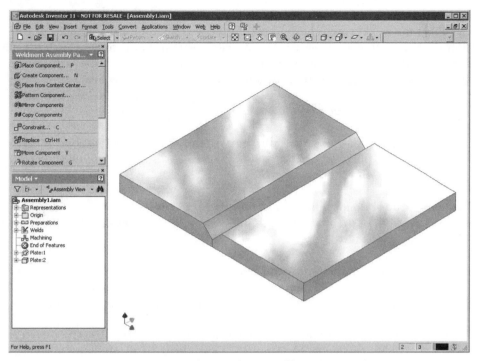

Figure 15-20 Weldment after assembling the two Plates

Creating the Fillet Weld

Next, you need to create the fillet weld. To weld the components, you need to invoke the **Weldment Features Panel** panel bar.

1. Double-click on **Welds** in the browser; the **Weldment Features Panel** panel bar appears in place of the **Weldment Assembly Panel** panel bar.

    Remember that when you invoke the **Weldment Features Panel** panel bar by double-clicking on **Preparations**, the welding tools in this panel bar are not enabled. However, when you invoke this panel bar using **Welds** in the browser, these tool are enabled.

2. Choose **Fillet Weld** from the **Weldment Features Panel** panel bar to invoke the **Fillet Weld** dialog box; the **Fillet Weld** dialog box is displayed and you are prompted to select the face to weld.

3. Select the chamfered face on one of the Plates; the selected face turns blue.

4. Now choose the **2** button to select the second face; you are again prompted to select the face to weld.

5. Rotate the model using the **Rotate** tool and select the chamfered face on the other Plate.

The second face turns green. Also, the preview of the weld appears on the plates. You will notice that the weld extends beyond the V groove created in the two plates. If you try to apply the weld at this stage, a warning box will appear and you are informed that the face selected for the leg of the bead is smaller than the leg size. The leg size is the thickness of the weld bead. As a result, you need to reduce the leg size of the bead.

6. Enter **4.2 mm** as the value in the **Leg 1** edit box below the **1** button.

   The welding shown in the preview does not extend beyond the V groove. As evident in Figure 15-17, the fillet weld has a convex contour. As a result, you need to select this option from the **Contour** drop-down list.

7. Choose the **Convex** button from the flyout that is displayed when you choose the down arrow on the right of the **Flat** button in the **Contour** area. You will notice that the **Offset** edit box is enabled.

8. Enter **1** as the value in the **Offset** edit box.

   With this, all the welding options are defined and you can now apply the weld.

9. Choose the **Apply** button and then **Cancel** to exit the dialog box. Choose **Return** to invoke the weldment assembly environment. The welded Plates are shown in Figure 15-21.

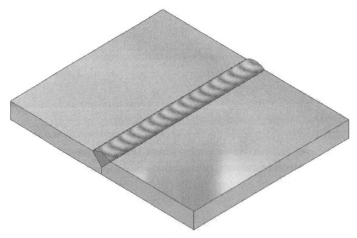

Figure 15-21 *Final weldment assembly after creating the fillet weld*

10. Save the assembly with the name *\Butt Joint\Butt Joint.iam*.

Tutorial 2

In this tutorial, you will create the Bracket and Cylinder assembly in the assembly modeling environment. Next, you will switch to the weldment environment and weld the components, as shown in Figure 15-22. The dimensions of the two components are given in Figures 15-23 and 15-24. **(Expected time: 45 min)**

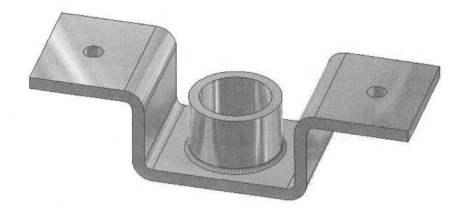

Figure 15-22 Weldment assembly of the Bracket and the Cylinder

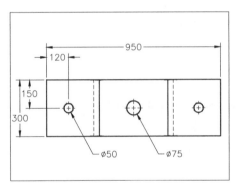

Figure 15-23a Top view of the Bracket

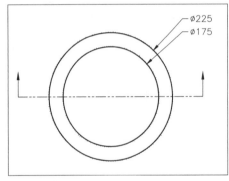

Figure 15-24a Top view of the Cylinder

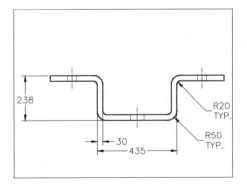

Figure 15-23b Front view of the Bracket

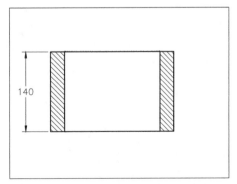

Figure 15-24b Sectioned front view of the Cylinder

The steps required to complete this tutorial are listed below.

a. Create the Bracket and Cylinder as separate part files.
b. Start a new assembly file and then place the Bracket and Cylinder in the assembly file.
c. Assemble the two components using the assembly constraints.
d. Switch to the weldment environment.
e. Weld the components using the fillet weld.

Creating the Components

1. Create the two components in separate part files and save them in the *c15**Shock Assembly* folder.

Assembling the Components

As mentioned in the tutorial description, you need to assemble the components in the assembly modeling environment and then switch to the weldment environment. So you will start a new assembly file using the **Open** dialog box to assemble the components.

1. Start a new assembly file using the **Open** dialog box. Place one instance each of the Bracket and the Cylinder in the current assembly file.

2. Assemble the Cylinder with the Bracket using the assembly constraints. The assembly file, after assembling the components, is shown in Figure 15-25.

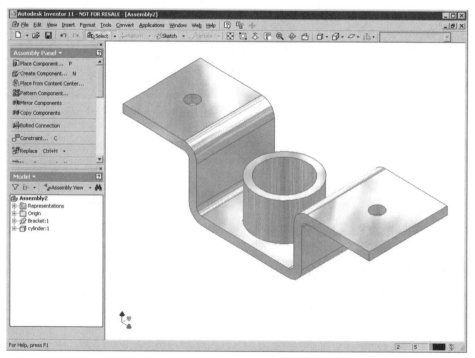

Figure 15-25 *Assembly file after assembling the Bracket and Cylinder*

Welding the Two Components

The components can be welded in the weldment assembly environment. This is the reason you need to switch to the weldment assembly environment. As mentioned earlier, you can switch from the assembly modeling environment to the weldment assembly environment.

1. Choose **Convert > Weldment** from the menu bar.

   The Autodesk Inventor warning box is displayed and you are informed that once an assembly is converted into a weldment, you cannot convert it back to an assembly.

2. Choose **Yes** from the warning box; the **Convert to Weldment** dialog box is displayed, as shown in Figure 15-26.

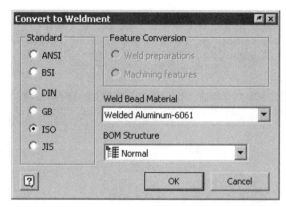

Figure 15-26 The **Convert to Weldment** *dialog box*

This dialog box allows you to convert the assembly into a weldment of the specified standard. You can also change the color of the weldment using this dialog box.

3. Select the **ANSI** radio button from the **Standard** area of this dialog box. Accept the remaining default options and choose **OK** to close this dialog box and proceed to the weldment environment.

   The weldment environment is invoked and the **Assembly Panel** panel bar is replaced by the **Weldment Assembly Panel** panel bar. As you do not need to make any preparations of the components, you can directly proceed to weld the components.

4. Double-click on **Welds** in the browser to invoke the **Weldment Features Panel** panel bar.

5. Choose **Fillet Weld** from this panel bar; the **Fillet Weld** dialog box is invoked and you are prompted to select the face to weld.

6. Select the outer face of the Cylinder as the first face to be welded; the selected face turns blue.

7. Choose the **2** button; you are again prompted to select the face to weld.

8. Select the upper face of the Bracket with which the Cylinder is assembled.

    The preview of the weld appears on the assembly.

9. Enter **10 mm** as the value in the **Leg 1** edit box below the **1** button.

    Because the fillet contour in Figure 15-22 is concave, you need to select it from the **Contour** drop-down list.

10. Choose the down arrow on the right of the **Flat** button in the **Contour** area and choose the **Concave** button.

11. Enter **2 mm** as the value in the **Offset** edit box. Choose **Apply** and then choose **Cancel** to exit the dialog box. Choose the **Return** button from the **Inventor Standard** toolbar. The final weldment assembly is shown in Figure 15-27.

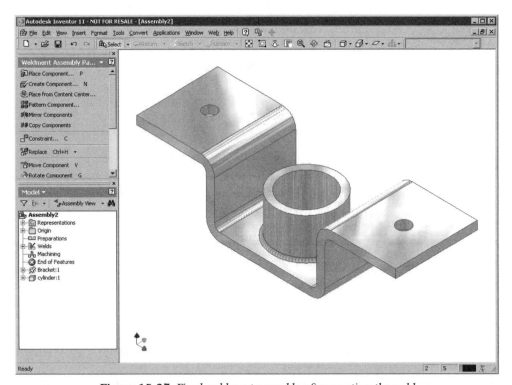

Figure 15-27 Final weldment assembly after creating the weld

12. Save the assembly with the name *Shock Assembly**Shock Assembly.iam*.

Student Projects

Student Project 1

Create different components of the Shaper's Tool Head Slide assembly and then assemble them as shown in Figure 1. Figure 2 shows the exploded view of the assembly. The dimensions of various components are given in Figure 2 to Figure 6.

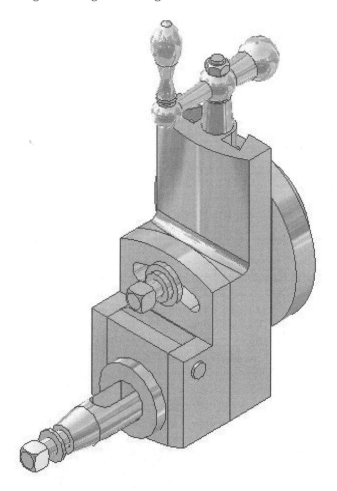

Figure 1 *Shaper's Tool Head Slide assembly*

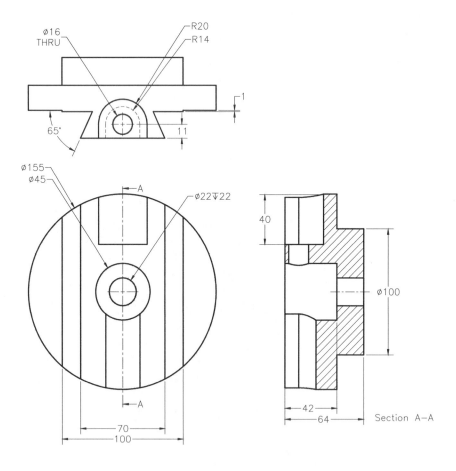

Figure 2 *Views and dimensions of the Back Plate*

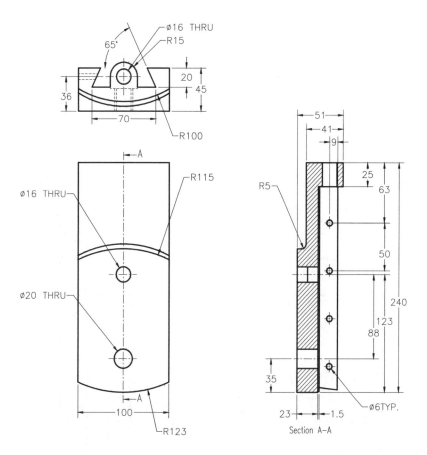

Figure 3 *Views and dimensions of the Vertical Slide*

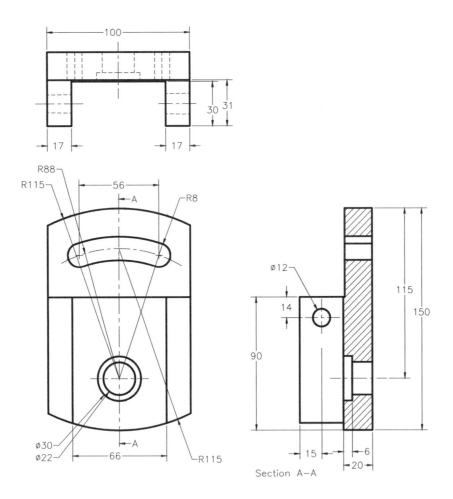

Figure 4 *Views and dimensions of the Swivel Plate*

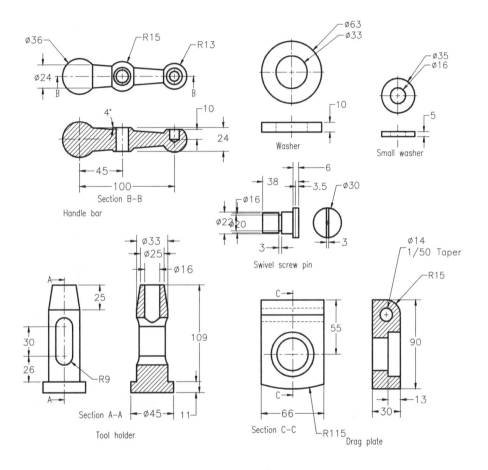

Figure 5 *Views and dimensions of the components*

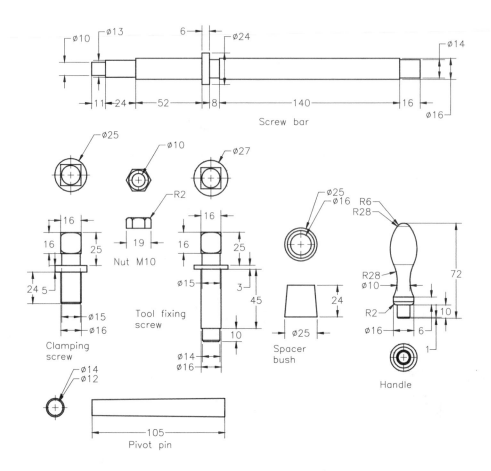

Figure 6 *Views and dimensions of the components*

Student Project 2

Create the Stock Bracket assembly shown in Figure 7. The dimensions of the components of the assembly are shown in Figures 8 through 14.

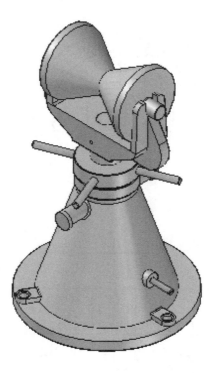

Figure 7 *The Stock Bracket assembly*

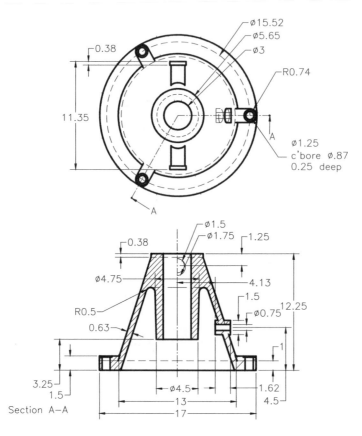

Figure 8 *Top and front views of the Stock Support Base*

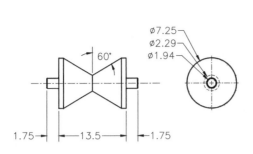

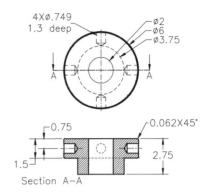

Figure 9 *Front and right-side views of the Stock Support Roller*

Figure 10 *Top and front views of the Adjusting Screw Nut*

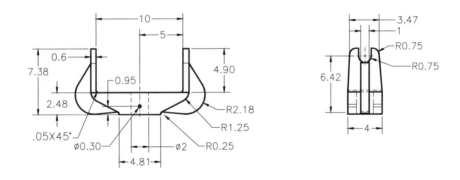

Figure 11 *Front and right-side views of the Support Roller Bracket*

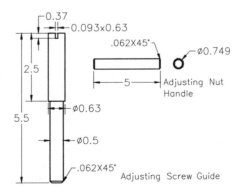

Figure 12 *Views of the Adjusting Nut Handle and Adjusting Screw Guide*

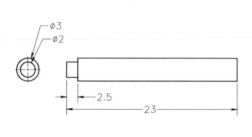

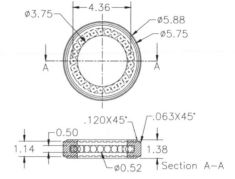

Figure 13 *Views of the Support Adjusting Screw*

Figure 14 *Top and front views of the Thrust Bearing*

Index

Rendered Image of the Stock Bracket Assembly

Other Publications by CADCIM Technologies

The following is the list of the other publications by Prof. Sham Tickoo and the CADD Engineers of CADCIM Technologies.

Autodesk Inventor Textbooks
- Autodesk Inventor for Designers, Release 10
  CADCIM Technologies, USA
- Autodesk Inventor for Designers, Release 9
  CADCIM Technologies, USA
- Autodesk Inventor for Designers Release 6 with Release 7 Update Guide
  CADCIM Technologies, USA
- Autodesk Inventor for Designers, Release 6
  CADCIM Technologies, USA
- Autodesk Inventor for Designers: Update Guide Release 6
  CADCIM Technologies, USA
- Autodesk Inventor for Engineers and Designers, Release 6
  Dreamtech Press, India
- Autodesk Inventor for Designers, Release 5
  CADCIM Technologies, USA

Solid Edge Textbooks
- Solid Edge V18 for Designers
  CADCIM Technologies, USA
- Solid Edge V18 for Engineers & Designers
  Dreamtech Press, India
- Solid Edge for Designers, Version 16
  CADCIM Technologies, USA
- Solid Edge for Designers, Version 15
  CADCIM Technologies, USA
- Solid Edge for Engineers and Designers, Version 15
  Dreamtech Press, India

NX Textbooks
- NX 3 for Designers
  CADCIM Technologies, USA
- NX 3 for Engineers & Designers
  Dreamtech Press, India

CATIA Textbooks

- CATIA V5R15 for Designers
  CADCIM Technologies, USA
- CATIA V5R15 for Engineers and Designers
  Dreamtech Press, India
- CATIA for Designers, V5R14
  CADCIM Technologies, USA
- CATIA for Engineers and Designers, V5R14
  Dreamtech Press, India
- CATIA for Designers, V5R13
  CADCIM Technologies, USA
- CATIA for Engineers and Designers, V5R13
  Dreamtech Press, India

SolidWorks Textbooks

- SolidWorks 2006 for Designers
  CADCIM Technologies, USA
- SolidWorks 2006 for Engineers & Designers
  Dreamtech Press, India
- SolidWorks for Designers, Release 2005
  CADCIM Technologies, USA
- SolidWorks for Designers, Release 2005
  Piter Publishing Press, Russia
- SolidWorks for Designers, Release 2004
  CADCIM Technologies, USA
- SolidWorks for Designers, Release 2004
  Piter Publishing Press, Russia
- SolidWorks for Designers, Release 2003
  CADCIM Technologies, USA
- SolidWorks for Engineers and Designers, Release 2003
  Dreamtech Press, India

Pro/ENGINEER Textbooks

- Pro/ENGINEER Wildfire for Designers Release 2.0
  CADCIM Technologies, USA
- Pro/ENGINEER Wildfire for Engineers & Designers Release 2.0
  Dreamtech Press, India
- Pro/ENGINEER Wildfire for Designers
  CADCIM Technologies, USA
- Pro/ENGINEER for Designers, Release 2001
  CADCIM Technologies, USA
- Pro/ENGINEER Wildfire for Engineers and Designers
  Dreamtech Press, India

- Pro/ENGINEER for Engineers and Designers, Release 2001
  Dreamtech Press, India
- Designing with Pro/ENGINEER, Release 2001
  Dreamtech Press, India

Autodesk Revit Building Textbooks

- Autodesk Revit Building 8 for Designers & Architects
  CADCIM Technologies, USA
- Autodesk Revit for Building Designers & Architects, Release 7.0
  CADCIM Technologies, USA

AutoCAD LT Textbook

- AutoCAD LT 2006 for Designers
  CADCIM Technologies, USA

Mechanical Desktop Textbook

- Mechanical Desktop Instructor, Release 5
  McGraw Hill Publishing Company, USA

AutoCAD Textbooks (US Edition)

- AutoCAD 2006: A Problem-Solving Approach
  Autodesk Press
- Customizing AutoCAD 2006
  Autodesk Press
- AutoCAD 2005: A Problem-Solving Approach
  Autodesk Press
- AutoCAD LT 2004: A Problem-Solving Approach with Update Guide AutoCAD LT 2005
  Autodesk Press
- Customizing AutoCAD 2004 and 2005
  Autodesk Press
- AutoCAD 2004: A Problem-Solving Approach
  Autodesk Press
- AutoCAD LT 2004: A Problem-Solving Approach
  Autodesk Press
- Customizing AutoCAD 2004
  Autodesk Press
- AutoCAD 2002: A Problem-Solving Approach
  Autodesk Press
- AutoCAD LT 2002: A Problem-Solving Approach
  Autodesk Press
- Customizing AutoCAD 2002
  Autodesk Press
- AutoCAD 2000: A Problem Solving Approach
  Autodesk Press

- Customizing AutoCAD 2000
  Autodesk Press
- AutoCAD LT 2000: A Problem-Solving Approach
  Autodesk Press

AutoCAD Textbooks (Russian Edition)

- AutoCAD 2005
  Piter Publishing Press, Russia
- AutoCAD 2004
  Piter Publishing Press, Russia
- AutoCAD 2002
  Piter Publishing Press, Russia
- AutoCAD 2000
  Piter Publishing Press, Russia

AutoCAD Textbooks (Italian Edition)

- AutoCAD 2000 Fondamenti
- AutoCAD 2000 Tecniche Avanzate

AutoCAD Textbook (Chinese Edition)

- AutoCAD 2000

AutoCAD Textbooks (Indian Edition)

- AutoCAD 2006 for Engineers and Designers
  Dreamtech Press, India
- Understanding AutoCAD 2006: A Beginner's Guide
  Dreamtech Press, India
- AutoCAD 2005 for Engineers and Designers
  Dreamtech Press, India
- AutoCAD 2004 for Engineers and Designers
  Dreamtech Press, India
- Understanding AutoCAD 2004: A Beginner's Guide
  Dreamtech Press, India
- Customizing AutoCAD 200
  Dreamtech Press, India
- AutoCAD 2002 with Applications
  Tata McGraw Hill Publishers
- Understanding AutoCAD 2002
  Tata McGraw Hill Publishers
- Advanced Techniques in AutoCAD 2002
  Tata McGraw Hill Publishers

- AutoCAD 2000 with Applications
  Galgotia Publishers
- Understanding AutoCAD 2000
  Galgotia Publishers
- Advanced Techniques in AutoCAD 2000
  Galgotia Publishers

3D Studio MAX and VIZ Textbooks

- Leaning 3ds max5: A Tutorial Approach
  (Complete manuscript available for free download on *www.cadcim.com*)
- Learning 3DS Max: A Tutorial Approach, Release 4
  Goodheart-Wilcox Publishers (USA)
- Learning 3D Studio VIZ: A Tutorial Approach
  Goodheart-Wilcox Publishers (USA)
- Learning 3D Studio R4: A Tutorial Approach
  Goodheart-Wilcox Publishers (USA)
- Learning 3D Studio MAX/VIZ 3.0: A Tutorial Approach
  BPB Publishers (India)

Paper Craft Book

- Constructing 3-Dimensional Models: A Paper-Craft Workbook
  CADCIM Technologies

Coming Soon: New Textbooks from CADCIM Technologies

- CATIA V5R16 for Designers
- Pro/ENGINEER Wildfire 3.0 for Designers
- NX 4 for Designers
- EdgeCAM for Manufacturers

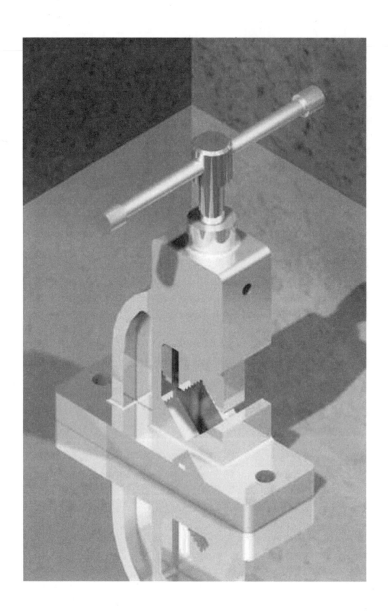

Rendered Image of the Pipe Vice Assembly